VOLUME

IMDG CODE

INTERNATIONAL MARITIME DANGEROUS GOODS CODE

2016 EDITION

AMENDMENT 38-16

IMO · INTERNATIONAL MARITIME ORGANIZATION

London, 2016

Published in 2016
by the INTERNATIONAL MARITIME ORGANIZATION
4 Albert Embankment, London SE1 7SR
www.imo.org

Printed by Wheatons Exeter Ltd, Exeter, EX2 8RP

ISBN: 978-92-801-1636-6

IMO PUBLICATION
Sales number: IK200E

This publication has been prepared from official documents of IMO, and every effort
has been made to eliminate errors and reproduce the original text(s) faithfully. Readers
should be aware that, in case of inconsistency, the official IMO text will prevail.

081309

Contents

Page

APPENDICES

INDEX

Foreword

The International Convention for the Safety of Life at Sea, 1974 (SOLAS), as amended, deals with various aspects of maritime safety and contains in chapter VII the mandatory provisions governing the carriage of dangerous goods in packaged form or in solid form in bulk. The carriage of dangerous goods is prohibited except in accordance with the relevant provisions of chapter VII, which are amplified by the International Maritime Dangerous Goods (IMDG) Code.

Regulation II-2/19 of the SOLAS Convention, as amended, specifies the special requirements for a ship intended to carry dangerous goods, the keel of which was laid or which was at a similar stage of construction on or after 1 July 2002.

The International Convention for the Prevention of Pollution from Ships, 1973, as modified by the Protocol of 1978 relating thereto (MARPOL), deals with various aspects of prevention of marine pollution, and contains in its Annex III the mandatory provisions for the prevention of pollution by harmful substances carried by sea in packaged form. Regulation 1(2) prohibits the carriage of harmful substances in ships except in accordance with the provisions of Annex III, which are also amplified by the IMDG Code.

In accordance with the Provisions concerning Reports on Incidents Involving Harmful Substances (Protocol I to MARPOL), incidents involving losses of such substances from ships must be reported by the master or other person having charge of the ship concerned.

The IMDG Code that was adopted by resolution A.716(17) and amended by amendments 27 to 30 was recommended to Governments for adoption or for use as the basis for national regulations in pursuance of their obligations under regulation VII/1.4 of the 1974 SOLAS Convention, as amended, and regulation 1(3) of Annex III of MARPOL. The IMDG Code, as amended, attained mandatory status from 1 January 2004 under the umbrella of SOLAS; however, some parts of the Code continue to be recommendatory. Observance of the Code harmonizes the practices and procedures followed in the carriage of dangerous goods by sea and ensures compliance with the mandatory provisions of the SOLAS Convention and of Annex III of MARPOL.

The Code, which sets out in detail the requirements applicable to each individual substance, material or article, has undergone many changes, in both layout and content, in order to keep pace with the expansion and progress of industry. IMO's Maritime Safety Committee (MSC) is authorized by the Organization's Assembly to adopt amendments to the Code, thus enabling IMO to respond promptly to developments in transport.

The MSC at its ninety-sixth session agreed that, in order to facilitate the multimodal transport of dangerous goods, the provisions of the IMDG Code, 2016 edition, may be applied from 1 January 2017 on a voluntary basis, pending their official entry into force on 1 January 2018 without any transitional period. This is described in resolution MSC.406(96) and the Preamble to this Code. It needs to be emphasized that, in the context of the language of the Code, the words "shall", "should" and "may", when used in the Code, mean that the relevant provisions are "mandatory", "recommendatory" and "optional", respectively.

Reference marks
The following symbols placed against an item indicate changes from the previous edition, in accordance with amendment 38-16 to the IMDG Code:

- ■   Insertion of an item
- ⊗   Deletion of an item
- △   Change to an item

For detailed information on changes, please visit **http://gisis.imo.org** and navigate to the IMDG Code module (free, instant registration required). Please inform IMO of any apparent discrepancies or errors in the texts of the different versions of the IMDG Code (IMO documents, the printed publication and CD/download and Internet versions of the Code) by means of the same link.

The IMDG Code is also available as a fully searchable database on CD or as a download (including the items within its Supplement). Intranet and Internet (subscription) versions are also available. For more information, please visit the IMO Publishing Service website at www.imo.org to see a live demonstration of the CD/download versions and obtain details of how online subscription to the IMDG Code works. If and when required, the IMO website will also include any files that show errata or corrigenda to this edition of the IMDG Code.

Preamble

1   Carriage of dangerous goods by sea is regulated in order to reasonably prevent injury to persons or damage to ships and their cargoes. Carriage of marine pollutants is primarily regulated to prevent harm to the marine environment. The objective of the IMDG Code is to enhance the safe carriage of dangerous goods while facilitating the free unrestricted movement of such goods and prevent pollution to the environment.

2   Over the years, many maritime countries have taken measures to regulate the transport of dangerous goods by sea. The various regulations, codes and practices, however, differed in their framework and, in particular, in the identification and labelling of such goods. Both the terminology used and the provisions for packaging and stowage varied from country to country and created difficulties for all directly or indirectly concerned with the transport of dangerous goods by sea.

3   The need for international regulation of the transport of dangerous goods by sea was recognized by the 1929 International Conference on Safety of Life at Sea (SOLAS), which recommended that rules on the subject have international effect. The classification of dangerous goods and certain general provisions concerning their transport in ships were adopted by the 1948 SOLAS Conference. This Conference also recommended further study with the object of developing international regulations.

4   Meanwhile, the Economic and Social Council of the United Nations had appointed an ad hoc Committee of Experts on the Transport of Dangerous Goods (UN Committee of Experts), which had been actively considering the international aspect of the transport of dangerous goods by all modes of transport. This committee completed a report in 1956 dealing with classification, listing and labelling of dangerous goods and with the transport documents required for such goods. This report, with subsequent modifications, offered a general framework to which existing regulations could be harmonized and within which they could be further developed. The primary goal being world-wide uniformity for regulations concerning the transport of dangerous goods by sea as well as other modes of transport.

5   As a further step towards meeting the need for international rules governing the transport of dangerous goods in ships, the 1960 SOLAS Conference, in addition to laying down a general framework of provisions in chapter VII of the SOLAS Convention, invited IMO (Recommendation 56) to undertake a study with a view to establishing a unified international code for the transport of dangerous goods by sea. This study would be pursued in cooperation with the UN Committee of Experts and should take account of existing maritime practices and procedures. The Conference further recommended that the unified code be prepared by IMO and that it be adopted by the Governments that were Parties to the 1960 Convention.

6   To implement Recommendation 56, IMO's Maritime Safety Committee (MSC) appointed a working group drawn from those countries having considerable experience in the transport of dangerous goods by sea. Preliminary drafts for each class of substances, materials and articles were subsequently brought under close scrutiny by the working group to take into account throughout the practices and procedures of a number of maritime countries in order to make the Code as widely acceptable as possible. This new International Maritime Dangerous Goods (IMDG) Code was approved by the MSC and recommended to Governments by the Assembly of IMO in 1965.

7   During another SOLAS Conference held in 1974, chapter VII of the Convention remained essentially unchanged. Since that date, several amendments to chapter VII adopted by the MSC have entered into force. Although invoked by a footnote reference in regulation 1 of chapter VII, the IMDG Code itself had only recommendatory status until 31 December 2003.

8   At the International Conference on Marine Pollution, 1973, the need was recognized to preserve the marine environment. It was further recognized that negligent or accidental release of marine pollutants transported by sea in packaged form should be minimized. Consequently, provisions were established and adopted by the Conference, and are contained in Annex III of the International Convention for the Prevention of Pollution from Ships, 1973, as modified by the Protocol of 1978 relating thereto (MARPOL). The Marine Environment Protection Committee (MEPC) decided in 1985 that Annex III should be implemented through the IMDG Code. This decision was also endorsed by the MSC in 1985. Since that date, several amendments to Annex III to MARPOL have entered into force.

9   The UN Committee of Experts has continued to meet until the present day and its published *Recommendations on the Transport of Dangerous Goods* are updated biennially. In 1996, the MSC agreed that the IMDG Code should be reformatted consistent with the format of the UN *Recommendations on the Transport of Dangerous Goods*. The consistency in format of the UN Recommendations, the IMDG Code and other dangerous goods transport regulations is intended to enhance user-friendliness, compliance with the regulations, and the safe transport of dangerous goods.

10   In 2002, the MSC adopted amendments to SOLAS chapter VII to make the IMDG Code mandatory, which came into force on 1 January 2004. Since then, further amendments were adopted to facilitate user friendliness and promote uniform implementation of the Code. In addition, at its ninety-sixth session in May 2016, the MSC adopted amendment 38-16 to the mandatory IMDG Code, which is a complete consolidated and updated version of its text and which will enter into force on 1 January 2018 without any transitional period. However, in accordance with resolution MSC.406(96), Governments were encouraged to apply this amendment in whole or on part on a voluntary basis from 1 January 2017.

11   In order to keep the Code up to date from the maritime transport operational aspect, the MSC will continue to take into account technological developments, as well as changes to chemical classifications and the related consignment provisions that primarily concern the shipper/consignor. The two-year periodicity of amendments to the UN Recommendations on Transport of Dangerous Goods will also provide the source of most future updating of the IMDG Code.

12   The MSC will also have regard to future implications for the carriage of dangerous goods by sea, in particular, arising from any acceptance by the UN Conference on Environmental Development (UNCED) of common criteria for the classification of chemicals on the basis of a Global Harmonization System (GHS).

13   Attention is drawn to IMO document FAL.6/Circ.14, a list of existing publications relevant to areas and topics relating to ship/port interface matters.

14   Advice on emergency procedures and for initial management of chemical poisoning and diagnosis that may be used in conjunction with the IMDG Code is published separately in The EmS Guide: Emergency Response Procedures for Ships Carrying Dangerous Goods (MSC.1/Circ.1025 as amended by MSC.1/Circ.1025/Add.1, MSC.1/Circ.1262, MSC.1/Circ.1360, MSC.1/Circ.1438, MSC.1/Circ.1476 and MSC.1/Circ.1522) and in the Medical First Aid Guide for Use in Accidents Involving Dangerous Goods (see MSC/Circ.857 and DSC 3/15/Add.2), respectively.

15   In addition, referring to part D of chapter VII of the SOLAS Convention, a ship transporting INF cargo, as defined in regulation VII/14.2, shall comply with the requirements of the International Code for the Safe Carriage of Packaged Irradiated Nuclear Fuel, Plutonium and High-Level Radioactive Wastes on board Ships (INF Code).

PART 1

GENERAL PROVISIONS, DEFINITIONS AND TRAINING

Chapter 1.1

General provisions

1.1.0 Introductory note

It should be noted that other international and national modal regulations exist and that those regulations may recognize all or part of the provisions of this Code. In addition, port authorities and other bodies and organizations should recognize the Code and may use it as a basis for their storage and handling bye-laws within loading and discharge areas.

1.1.1 Application and implementation of the Code

1.1.1.1 The provisions contained in this Code are applicable to all ships to which the International Convention for the Safety of Life at Sea, 1974 (SOLAS), as amended, applies and which are carrying dangerous goods as defined in regulation 1 of part A of chapter VII of that Convention.

1.1.1.2 The provisions of regulation II-2/19 of that Convention apply to passenger ships and to cargo ships constructed on or after 1 July 2002.

For:

.1 a passenger ship constructed on or after 1 September 1984 but before 1 July 2002; or

.2 a cargo ship of 500 gross tons or over constructed on or after 1 September 1984 but before 1 July 2002; or

.3 a cargo ship of less than 500 gross tons constructed on or after 1 February 1992 but before 1 July 2002,

the requirements of regulation II-2/54 of SOLAS, as amended by resolutions MSC.1(XLV), MSC.6(48), MSC.13(57), MSC.22(59), MSC.24(60), MSC.27(61), MSC.31(63) and MSC.57(67), apply (see II-2/1.2).

For cargo ships of less than 500 gross tons constructed on or after 1 September 1984 and before 1 February 1992, it is recommended that Contracting Governments extend such application to these cargo ships as far as possible.

1.1.1.3 All ships, irrespective of type and size, carrying substances, materials or articles identified in this Code as marine pollutants are subject to the provisions of this Code.

1.1.1.4 In certain parts of this Code, a particular action is prescribed, but the responsibility for carrying out the action is not specifically assigned to any particular person. Such responsibility may vary according to the laws and customs of different countries and the international conventions into which these countries have entered. For the purpose of this Code, it is not necessary to make this assignment, but only to identify the action itself. It remains the prerogative of each Government to assign this responsibility.

1.1.1.5 Although this Code is legally treated as a mandatory instrument under chapter VII of SOLAS, as amended, the following provisions of the Code remain recommendatory:

.1 paragraph 1.1.1.8 (Notification of infringements);

.2 paragraphs 1.3.1.4 to 1.3.1.7 (Training);

.3 chapter 1.4 (Security provisions) except 1.4.1.1, which is mandatory;

.4 section 2.1.0 of chapter 2.1 (Class 1 – Explosives, Introductory notes);

.5 section 2.3.3 of chapter 2.3 (Determination of flashpoint);

.6 columns 15 and 17 of the Dangerous Goods List in chapter 3.2;

.7 the segregation flow chart and example in the annex to chapter 7.2;

.8 section 5.4.5 of chapter 5.4 (Multimodal Dangerous Goods Form), insofar as the layout of the form is concerned;

.9   chapter 7.8 (Special requirements in the event of an incident and fire precautions involving dangerous goods);

.10   section 7.9.3 (Contact information for the main designated national competent authorities); and

.11   appendix B.

△ **1.1.1.6   Application of standards**

Where the application of a standard is required and there is any conflict between the standard and the provisions of this Code, the provisions of this Code take precedence. The requirements of the standard that do not conflict with the provisions of this Code shall be applied as specified, including the requirements of any other standard, or part of a standard, referenced within that standard as normative.

1.1.1.7   Transport of dangerous goods used as a coolant or conditioner

Dangerous goods, that are only asphyxiant (which dilute or replace the oxygen normally in the atmosphere), when used in cargo transport units for cooling or conditioning purposes are only subject to the provisions of section 5.5.3.

Note: When carried on board as ship's stores or equipment, these coolants and conditioners are not subject to the provisions of this Code.

1.1.1.8   Notification of infringements

When a competent authority has reasons to believe that the safety of the transport of dangerous goods is compromised as a result of serious or repeated infringements of this Code by an enterprise which has its headquarters on the territory of another competent authority, it should if necessary notify that competent authority of such infringements.

1.1.1.9   Lamps containing dangerous goods

The following lamps are not subject to this Code provided that they do not contain radioactive material and do not contain mercury in quantities above those specified in special provision 366 of chapter 3.3:

.1   lamps that are collected directly from individuals and households when transported to a collection or recycling facility;

.2   lamps each containing not more than 1 g of dangerous goods and packaged so that there is not more than 30 g of dangerous goods per package, provided that:

(i)   the lamps are manufactured according to a certified quality management system;

Note: The application of ISO 9001:2008 may be considered acceptable for this purpose.

and

(ii)   each lamp is either individually packed in inner packagings, separated by dividers, or surrounded with cushioning material to protect the lamps and packed into strong outer packagings meeting the general provisions of 4.1.1.1 and capable of passing a 1.2 m drop test.

.3   used, damaged or defective lamps each containing not more than 1 g of dangerous goods with not more than 30 g of dangerous goods per package when transported from a collection or recycling facility. The lamps shall be packed in strong outer packagings sufficient for preventing release of the contents under normal conditions of transport meeting the general provisions of 4.1.1.1 and that are capable of passing a drop test of not less than 1.2 m.

Note: Lamps containing radioactive material are addressed in 2.7.2.2.2.2.

.4   lamps containing only gases of class 2.2 (according to 2.2.2.2) provided they are packaged so that the projectile effects of any rupture of the bulb will be contained within the package.

1.1.2   Conventions

1.1.2.1   International Convention for the Safety of Life at Sea, 1974

Part A of chapter VII of the International Convention for the Safety of Life at Sea, 1974 (SOLAS), as amended, deals with the carriage of dangerous goods in packaged form, and is reproduced in full:

Chapter VII
Carriage of dangerous goods

Part A
Carriage of dangerous goods in packaged form

Regulation 1
Definitions

For the purpose of this chapter, unless expressly provided otherwise:

1   *IMDG Code* means the International Maritime Dangerous Goods (IMDG) Code adopted by the Maritime Safety Committee of the Organization by resolution MSC.122(75), as may be amended by the Organization, provided that such amendments are adopted, brought into force and take effect in accordance with the provisions of article VIII of the present Convention concerning the amendment procedures applicable to the annex other than chapter I.

2   *Dangerous goods* mean the substances, materials and articles covered by the IMDG Code.

3   *Packaged form* means the form of containment specified in the IMDG Code.

Regulation 2
*Application**[*]

1   Unless expressly provided otherwise, this part applies to the carriage of dangerous goods in packaged form in all ships to which the present regulations apply and in cargo ships of less than 500 gross tonnage.

2   The provisions of this part do not apply to ships' stores and equipment.

3   The carriage of dangerous goods in packaged form is prohibited except in accordance with the provisions of this chapter.

4   To supplement the provisions of this part, each Contracting Government shall issue, or cause to be issued, detailed instructions on emergency response and medical first aid relevant to incidents involving dangerous goods in packaged form, taking into account the guidelines developed by the Organization.[†]

Regulation 3
Requirements for the carriage of dangerous goods

The carriage of dangerous goods in packaged form shall be in compliance with the relevant provisions of the IMDG Code.

Regulation 4
Documents

1   Transport information relating to the carriage of dangerous goods in packaged form and the container/ vehicle packing certificate shall be in accordance with the relevant provisions of the IMDG Code and shall be made available to the person or organization designated by the port State authority.

2   Each ship carrying dangerous goods in packaged form shall have a special list, manifest or stowage plan setting forth, in accordance with the relevant provisions of the IMDG Code, the dangerous goods on board and the location thereof. A copy of one of these documents shall be made available before departure to the person or organization designated by the port State authority.

---

[*] Refer to:
   .1   part D which contains special requirements for the carriage of INF cargo; and
   .2   regulation II-2/19, which contains special requirements for ships carrying dangerous goods.

[†] Refer to:
   .1   the Emergency Response Procedures for Ships Carrying Dangerous Goods (EmS Guide) (MSC/Circ.1025, as amended); and
   .2   the Medical First Aid Guide for Use in Accidents Involving Dangerous Goods (MFAG) which is reproduced in the Supplement to the IMDG Code published by the Organization.

Regulation 5
Cargo Securing Manual

Cargo, cargo units[*] and cargo transport units shall be loaded, stowed and secured throughout the voyage in accordance with the Cargo Securing Manual approved by the Administration. The Cargo Securing Manual shall be drawn up to a standard at least equivalent to the guidelines developed by the Organization.[†]

Regulation 6
Reporting of incidents involving dangerous goods

1   When an incident takes place involving the loss or likely loss overboard of dangerous goods in packaged form into the sea, the master, or other person having charge of the ship, shall report the particulars of such an incident without delay and to the fullest extent possible to the nearest coastal State. The report shall be drawn up based on general principles and guidelines developed by the Organization.[‡]

2   In the event of the ship referred to in paragraph 1 being abandoned, or in the event of a report from such a ship being incomplete or unobtainable, the company, as defined in regulation IX/1.2, shall, to the fullest extent possible, assume the obligations placed upon the master by this regulation.

1.1.2.2   International Convention for the Prevention of Pollution from Ships (MARPOL)

1.1.2.2.1   Annex III of the International Convention for the Prevention of Pollution from Ships, 1973, as modified by the Protocol of 1978 relating thereto (MARPOL), deals with the prevention of pollution by harmful substances carried by sea in packaged form and is reproduced in full, as revised by the Marine Environment Protection Committee.[§]

Annex III
Regulations for the prevention of pollution by harmful substances carried by sea in packaged form

Regulation 1
Application

1   Unless expressly provided otherwise, the regulations of this Annex apply to all ships carrying harmful substances in packaged form.

> **.1**   For the purpose of this Annex, "harmful substances" are those substances which are identified as marine pollutants in the International Maritime Dangerous Goods Code (IMDG Code)[¶] or which meet the criteria in the Appendix of this Annex.

> **.2**   For the purposes of this Annex, "packaged form" is defined as the forms of containment specified for harmful substances in the IMDG Code.

2   The carriage of harmful substances is prohibited, except in accordance with the provisions of this Annex.

3   To supplement the provisions of this Annex, the Government of each Party to the Convention shall issue, or cause to be issued, detailed requirements on packing, marking, labelling, documentation, stowage, quantity limitations and exceptions for preventing or minimizing pollution of the marine environment by harmful substances.[*]

4   For the purposes of this Annex, empty packagings which have been used previously for the carriage of harmful substances shall themselves be treated as harmful substances unless adequate precautions have been taken to ensure that they contain no residue that is harmful to the marine environment.

5   The requirements of this Annex do not apply to ship's stores and equipment.

---

[*] As defined in the Code of Safe Practice for Cargo Stowage and Securing (resolution A.714(17), as amended).

[†] Refer to Revised Guidelines for the preparation of the Cargo Securing Manual (MSC/Circ.1353).

[‡] Refer to the General principles for ship reporting systems and ship reporting requirements, including Guidelines for reporting incidents involving dangerous goods, harmful substances and/or marine pollutants (resolution A.851(20), as amended.

[§] The revised text of Annex III was adopted by resolution MEPC.193(61), which will enter into force on 1 January 2014, which is the mandatory entry into force date of amendment 36-12 to the IMDG Code.

[¶] Refer to the IMDG Code adopted by the Organization by resolution MSC.122(75), as amended by the Maritime Safety Committee.

Regulation 2
Packing

Packages shall be adequate to minimize the hazard to the marine environment, having regard to their specific contents.

Regulation 3
Marking and labelling

1   Packages containing a harmful substance shall be durably marked or labelled to indicate that the substance is a harmful substance in accordance with the relevant provisions of the IMDG Code.

2   The method of affixing marks or labels on packages containing a harmful substance shall be in accordance with the relevant provisions of the IMDG Code.

Regulation 4[*]
Documentation

1   Transport information relating to the carriage of harmful substances shall be in accordance with the relevant provisions of the IMDG Code and shall be made available to the person or organization designated by the port State authority.

2   Each ship carrying harmful substances shall have a special list, manifest or stowage plan setting forth, in accordance with the relevant provisions of the IMDG Code, the harmful substances on board and the location thereof. A copy of one of these documents shall be made available before departure to the person or organization designated by the port State authority.

Regulation 5
Stowage

Harmful substances shall be properly stowed and secured so as to minimize the hazards to the marine environment without impairing the safety of the ship and persons on board.

Regulation 6
Quantity limitations

Certain harmful substances may, for sound scientific and technical reasons, need to be prohibited for carriage or be limited as to the quantity which may be carried aboard any one ship. In limiting the quantity, due consideration shall be given to size, construction and equipment of the ship, as well as the packaging and the inherent nature of the substances.

Regulation 7
Exceptions

1   Jettisoning of harmful substances carried in packaged form shall be prohibited, except where necessary for the purpose of securing the safety of the ship or saving life at sea.

2   Subject to the provisions of the present Convention, appropriate measures based on the physical, chemical and biological properties of harmful substances shall be taken to regulate the washing of leakages overboard, provided that compliance with such measures would not impair the safety of the ship and persons on board.

Regulation 8
Port State control on operational requirements[†]

1   A ship when in a port or an offshore terminal of another Party is subject to inspection by officers duly authorized by such Party concerning operational requirements under this Annex.

2   Where there are clear grounds for believing that the master or crew are not familiar with essential shipboard procedures relating to the prevention of pollution by harmful substances, the Party shall take such steps, including carrying out detailed inspection and, if required, will ensure that the ship shall not sail until the situation has been brought to order in accordance with the requirements of this Annex.

3   Procedures relating to the port State control prescribed in article 5 of the present Convention shall apply to this regulation.

4   Nothing in this regulation shall be construed to limit the rights and obligations of a Party carrying out control over operational requirements specifically provided for in the present Convention.

---

[*] Reference to "documents" in this regulation does not preclude the use of electronic data processing (EDP) and electronic data interchange (EDI) transmission techniques as an aid to paper documentation.

[†] Refer to the Procedures for port State control adopted by the Organization by resolution A.1052(27).

Appendix to Annex III
Criteria for the identification of harmful substances in packaged form

For the purposes of this Annex, substances identified by any one of the following criteria are harmful substances:[*]

(a) Acute (short-term) aquatic hazard

Category: Acute 1	
96 hr LC_{50} (for fish)	≤ 1 mg/ℓ and/or
48 hr EC_{50} (for crustacea)	≤ 1 mg/ℓ and/or
72 or 96 hr ErC_{50} (for algae or other aquatic plants)	≤ 1 mg/ℓ

(b) Long-term aquatic hazard

(i) Non-rapidly degradable substances for which there are adequate chronic toxicity data available

Category: Chronic 1	
Chronic NOEC or EC_x (for fish)	≤ 0.1 mg/ℓ and/or
Chronic NOEC or EC_x (for crustacea)	≤ 0.1 mg/ℓ and/or
Chronic NOEC or EC_x (for algae or other aquatic plants)	≤ 0.1 mg/ℓ

Category: Chronic 2	
Chronic NOEC or EC_x (for fish)	≤ 1 mg/ℓ and/or
Chronic NOEC or EC_x (for crustacea)	≤ 1 mg/ℓ and/or
Chronic NOEC or EC_x (for algae or other aquatic plants)	≤ 1 mg/ℓ

(ii) Rapidly degradable substances for which there are adequate chronic toxicity data available

Category: Chronic 1	
Chronic NOEC or EC_x (for fish)	≤ 0.01 mg/ℓ and/or
Chronic NOEC or EC_x (for crustacea)	≤ 0.01 mg/ℓ and/or
Chronic NOEC or EC_x (for algae or other aquatic plants)	≤ 0.01 mg/ℓ

Category: Chronic 2	
Chronic NOEC or EC_x (for fish)	≤ 0.1 mg/ℓ and/or
Chronic NOEC or EC_x (for crustacea)	≤ 0.1 mg/ℓ and/or
Chronic NOEC or EC_x (for algae or other aquatic plants)	≤ 0.1 mg/ℓ

---

[*] The criteria are based on those developed by the United Nations Globally Harmonized System of Classification and Labelling of Chemicals (GHS), as amended. For definitions of acronyms or terms used in this appendix, refer to the relevant paragraphs of the IMDG Code.

(iii) Substances for which adequate chronic toxicity data are not available

Category: Chronic 1	
96 hr LC$_{50}$ (for fish)	$\leq$ 1 mg/ℓ and/or
48 hr EC$_{50}$ (for crustacea)	$\leq$ 1 mg/ℓ and/or
72 or 96 hr ErC$_{50}$ (for algae or other aquatic plants)	$\leq$ 1 mg/ℓ
and the substance is not rapidly degradable and/or the experimentally determined BCF is $\geq$ 500 (or, if absent, the log K$_{ow}$ $\geq$ 4).	

Category: Chronic 2	
96 hr LC$_{50}$ (for fish)	> 1 mg/ℓ but $\leq$ 10 mg/ℓ and/or
48 hr EC$_{50}$ (for crustacea)	> 1 mg/ℓ but $\leq$ 10 mg/ℓ and/or
72 or 96 hr ErC$_{50}$ (for algae or other aquatic plants)	> 1 mg/ℓ but $\leq$ 10 mg/ℓ
and the substance is not rapidly degradable and/or the experimentally determined BCF is $\geq$ 500 (or, if absent, the log K$_{ow}$ $\geq$ 4).	

Additional guidance on the classification process for substances and mixtures is included in the IMDG Code.

1.1.2.3   **International Convention for Safe Containers, 1972, as amended**

1.1.2.3.1   Regulations 1 and 2 of annex I to the International Convention for Safe Containers (CSC), 1972, as amended, deal with safety approval plates and maintenance and examination of containers, and are reproduced in full.

Annex I
Regulations for the testing, inspection, approval and maintenance of containers

Chapter I
Regulations common to all systems of approval

General provisions

The following definitions shall be applied for the purpose of this annex:

The letter *g* means the standard acceleration of gravity; *g* equals 9.8 m/s^2.

The word *load*, when used to describe a physical quantity to which units may be ascribed, signifies mass.

Maximum operating gross mass or *Rating* or *R* means the maximum allowable sum of the mass of the container and its cargo. The letter *R* is expressed in units of mass. Where the annexes are based on gravitational forces derived from this value, that force, which is an inertial force, is indicated as *Rg*.

Maximum permissible payload or *P* means the difference between maximum operating gross mass or rating and tare. The letter *P* is expressed in units of mass. Where the annexes are based on the gravitational forces derived from this value, that force, which is an inertial force, is indicated as *Pg*.

Tare means the mass of the empty container, including permanently affixed ancillary equipment.

Regulation 1
Safety Approval Plate

1   **(a)**   A Safety Approval Plate conforming to the specifications set out in the appendix to this annex shall be permanently affixed to every approved container at a readily visible place, adjacent to any other approval plate issued for official purposes, where it would not be easily damaged.

        (b)   On each container, all maximum operating gross mass markings shall be consistent with the maximum operating gross mass information on the Safety Approval Plate.

(c) The owner of the container shall remove the Safety Approval Plate on the container if:

(i) the container has been modified in a manner which would void the original approval and the information found on the Safety Approval Plate, or

(ii) the container is removed from service and is not being maintained in accordance with the Convention, or

(iii) the approval has been withdrawn by the Administration.

2 **(a)** The plate shall contain the following information in at least the English or French language:

CSC SAFETY APPROVAL

Country of approval and approval reference

Date (month and year) of manufacture

Manufacturer's identification number of the container or, in the case of existing containers for which that number is unknown, the number allotted by the Administration

Maximum operating gross mass (kg and lb)

Allowable stacking load for 1.8g (kg and lb)

Transverse racking test force (newtons).

(b) A blank space should be reserved on the plate for insertion of end-wall and/or side-wall strength values (factors) in accordance with paragraph 3 of this regulation and annex II, tests 6 and 7. A blank space should also be reserved on the plate for the first and subsequent maintenance examination dates (month and year) when used.

3 Where the Administration considers that a new container satisfies the requirements of the present Convention in respect of safety and if, for such container, the end-wall and/or side-wall strength values (factors) are designed to be greater or less than those stipulated in annex II, such values shall be indicated on the Safety Approval Plate. Where the stacking or racking values are less than 192,000 kg or 150 kN, respectively, the container shall be considered as having limited stacking or racking capacity and shall be conspicuously marked, as required under the relevant standards,[*] at or before their next scheduled examination or before any other date approved by the Administration, provided this is not later than 1 July 2015.

4 The presence of the Safety Approval Plate does not remove the necessity of displaying such labels or other information as may be required by other regulations which may be in force.

5 A container, the construction of which was completed prior to 1 July 2014, may retain the Safety Approval Plate as permitted by the Convention prior to that date as long as no structural modifications occur to that container.

Regulation 2
Maintenance and examination

1 The owner of the container shall be responsible for maintaining it in safe condition.

2 **(a)** The owner of an approved container shall examine the container or have it examined in accordance with the procedure either prescribed or approved by the Contracting Party concerned, at intervals appropriate to operating conditions.

(b) The date (month and year) before which a new container shall undergo its first examination shall be marked on the Safety Approval Plate.

(c) The date (month and year) before which the container shall be re-examined shall be clearly marked on the container on or as close as practicable to the Safety Approval Plate and in a manner acceptable to that Contracting Party which prescribed or approved the particular examination procedure involved.

(d) The interval from the date of manufacture to the date of the first examination shall not exceed five years. Subsequent examination of new containers and re-examination of existing containers shall be at intervals of not more than 30 months. All examinations shall determine whether the container has any defects which could place any person in danger.

3 **(a)** As an alternative to paragraph 2, the Contracting Party concerned may approve a continuous examination programme if satisfied, on evidence submitted by the owner, that such a programme provides a standard of safety not inferior to the one set out in paragraph 2 above.

(b) To indicate that the container is operated under an approved continuous examination programme, a mark showing the letters **ACEP** and the identification of the Contracting Party which has granted approval of the programme shall be displayed on the container on or as close as practicable to the Safety Approval Plate.

---

[*] Refer to current standard ISO 6346, *Freight containers – Coding, identification and marking.*

(c)   All examinations performed under such a programme shall determine whether a container has any defects which could place any person in danger. They shall be performed in connection with a major repair, refurbishment, or on-hire/off-hire interchange and in no case less than once every 30 months.

4   As a minimum, approved programmes should be reviewed once every 10 years to ensure their continued viability. In order to ensure uniformity by all involved in the inspection of containers and their ongoing operational safety, the Contracting Party concerned shall ensure the following elements are covered in each prescribed periodic or approved continuous examination programme:

(a)   methods, scope and criteria to be used during examinations;

(b)   frequency of examinations;

(c)   qualifications of personnel to carry out examinations;

(d)   system of keeping records and documents that will capture:

(i)   the owner's unique serial number of the container;

(ii)   the date on which the examination was carried out;

(iii)   identification of the competent person who carried out the examination;

(iv)   the name and location of the organization where the examination was carried out;

(v)   the results of the examination; and

(vi)   in the case of a periodic examination scheme (PES), the next examination date (NED);

(e)   a system for recording and updating the identification numbers of all containers covered by the appropriate examination scheme;

(f)   methods and systems for maintenance criteria that addresses the design characteristics of the specific containers;

(g)   provisions for maintaining leased containers if different than those used for owned containers; and

(h)   conditions and procedures for adding containers into an already approved programme.

5   The Contracting Party shall carry out periodic audits of approved programmes to ensure compliance with the provisions approved by the Contracting Party. The Contracting Party shall withdraw any approval when the conditions of approval are no longer complied with.

6   For the purpose of this regulation, *the Contracting Party concerned* is the Contracting Party of the territory in which the owner is domiciled or has his head office. However, in the event that the owner is domiciled or has his head office in a country the government of which has not yet made arrangements for prescribing or approving an examination scheme and until such time as the arrangements have been made, the owner may use the procedure prescribed or approved by the Administration of a Contracting Party which is prepared to act as the Contracting Party concerned. The owner shall comply with the conditions for the use of such procedures set by the Administration in question.

7   Administrations shall make information on approved continuous examination programmes publicly available.

1.1.3   Dangerous goods forbidden from transport

1.1.3.1   Unless provided otherwise by this Code, the following are forbidden from transport:

Any substance or article which, as presented for transport, is liable to explode, dangerously react, produce a flame or dangerous evolution of heat or dangerous emission of toxic, corrosive or flammable gases or vapours under normal conditions of transport.

In chapter 3.3, special provisions 349, 350, 351, 352, 353 and 900 list certain substances, which are forbidden for transport.

Chapter 1.2

Definitions, units of measurement and abbreviations

1.2.1   Definitions

The following is a list of definitions of general applicability that are used throughout this Code. Additional definitions of a highly specific nature are presented in the relevant chapters.

For the purposes of this Code:

△ *Aerosols* or *aerosol dispensers* means an article consisting of non-refillable receptacles meeting the provisions of 6.2.4, made of metal, glass or plastics and containing a gas compressed, liquefied or dissolved under pressure, with or without a liquid, paste or powder, and fitted with a release device allowing the contents to be ejected as solid or liquid particles in suspension in a gas, as a foam, paste or powder or in a liquid state or in a gaseous state.

Alternative arrangement means an approval granted by the competent authority for a portable tank or MEGC that has been designed, constructed or tested to technical requirements or testing methods other than those specified in this Code (see, for instance, 6.7.5.11.1).

Animal material means animal carcasses, animal body parts, or animal foodstuffs.

Approval

Multilateral approval, for the transport of radioactive material, means approval by the relevant competent authority of the country of origin of the design or shipment, as applicable, and also, where the consignment is to be transported through or into any other country, approval by the competent authority of that country.

Unilateral approval, for the transport of radioactive material, means an approval of a design which is required to be given by the competent authority of the country of origin of the design only.

Bags means flexible packagings made of paper, plastic film, textiles, woven material, or other suitable materials.

Barge-carrying ship means a ship specially designed and equipped to transport shipborne barges.

Barge feeder vessel means a vessel specially designed and equipped to transport shipborne barges to or from a barge-carrying ship.

Boxes means packagings with complete rectangular or polygonal faces, made of metal, wood, plywood, reconstituted wood, fibreboard, plastics, or other suitable material. Small holes for purposes such as ease of the handling or opening of the box or to meet classification provisions are permitted as long as they do not compromise the integrity of the packaging during transport.

Bulk containers are containment systems (including any liner or coating) intended for the transport of solid substances which are in direct contact with the containment system. Packagings, intermediate bulk containers (IBCs), large packagings and portable tanks are not included.

Bulk containers:

–   are of a permanent character and accordingly strong enough to be suitable for repeated use;

–   are specially designed to facilitate the transport of goods by one or more means of transport without intermediate reloading;

–   are fitted with devices permitting ready handling; and

–   have a capacity of not less than 1 cubic metre.

Examples of bulk containers are freight containers, offshore bulk containers, skips, bulk bins, swap bodies, trough-shaped containers, roller containers, load compartments of vehicles or flexible bulk containers.

Bundles of cylinders are assemblies of cylinders that are fastened together and which are interconnected by a manifold and transported as a unit. The total water capacity shall not exceed 3,000 litres except that bundles intended for the transport of gases of class 2.3 shall be limited to 1,000 litres water capacity.

Cargo transport unit means a road transport tank or freight vehicle, a railway transport tank or freight wagon, a multimodal freight container or portable tank, or an MEGC.

Carrier means any person, organization or Government undertaking the transport of dangerous goods by any means of transport. The term includes both carriers for hire or reward (known as *common* or *contract carriers* in some countries) and carriers on own account (known as *private carriers* in some countries).

Cellular ship means a ship in which containers are loaded under deck into specially designed slots giving a permanent stowage of the container during sea transport. Containers loaded on deck in such a ship are specially stacked and secured on fittings.

Closed cargo transport unit, with the exception of class 1, means a cargo transport unit which totally encloses the contents by permanent structures with complete and rigid surfaces. Cargo transport units with fabric sides or tops are not considered closed cargo transport units; for definition of closed cargo transport unit for class 1, see 7.1.2.

Closed ro-ro cargo space means a ro-ro cargo space which is neither an open ro-ro cargo space nor a weather deck.

Closure means a device which closes an opening in a receptacle.

Combination packagings means a combination of packagings for transport purposes, consisting of one or more inner packagings secured in an outer packaging in accordance with 4.1.1.5.

Competent authority means any body or authority designated or otherwise recognized as such for any purpose in connection with this Code.

Compliance assurance means a systematic programme of measures applied by a competent authority which is aimed at ensuring that the provisions of this Code are met in practice.

Composite packagings means packagings consisting of an outer packaging and an inner receptacle so constructed that the inner receptacle and the outer packaging form an integral packaging. Once assembled, it remains thereafter an integrated single unit; it is filled, stored, transported and emptied as such.

Confinement system, for the transport of radioactive material, means the assembly of fissile material and packaging components specified by the designer and agreed to by the competent authority as intended to preserve criticality safety.

Consignee means any person, organization or Government which is entitled to take delivery of a consignment.

Consignment means any package or packages, or load of dangerous goods, presented by a consignor for transport.

Consignor means any person, organization or Government which prepares a consignment for transport.

Containment system, for the transport of radioactive material, means the assembly of components of the packaging specified by the designer as intended to retain the radioactive material during transport.

Control temperature means the maximum temperature at which certain substances (such as organic peroxides and self-reactive and related substances) can be safely transported during a prolonged period of time.

Conveyance means:

.1 for transport by road or rail: any vehicle,

.2 for transport by water: any ship, or any cargo space or defined deck area of a ship,

.3 for transport by air: any aircraft.

Crates are outer packagings with incomplete surfaces.

Criticality safety index (CSI) assigned to a package, overpack or freight container containing fissile material, for the transport of radioactive material, means a number which is used to provide control over the accumulation of packages, overpacks or freight containers containing fissile material.

Critical temperature is the temperature above which the substance cannot exist in the liquid state.

Cryogenic receptacles are transportable thermally insulated receptacles for refrigerated liquefied gases, of a water capacity of not more than 1,000 litres.

■ *CTU Code* means the IMO/ILO/UNECE Code of Practice for Packing of Cargo Transport Units (MSC.1/Circ.1497).[*]

---

[*] Further practical guidance and background information related to the CTU Code are available as informative material (MSC.1/Circ.1498). The CTU Code and the Informative Material may be found at www.unece.org/trans/wp24/guidelinespackingctus/intro.html.

Cylinders are transportable pressure receptacles of a water capacity not exceeding 150 litres.

Defined deck area means the area, of the weather deck of a ship, or of a vehicle deck of a roll-on/roll-off ship, which is allocated for the stowage of dangerous goods.

Design, for the transport of radioactive material, means the description of fissile material excepted under 2.7.2.3.5.6, special form radioactive material, low dispersible radioactive material, package or packaging which enables such an item to be fully identified. The description may include specifications, engineering drawings, reports demonstrating compliance with regulatory requirements, and other relevant documentation.

■ *Design life*, for composite cylinders and tubes, means the maximum life (in number of years) to which the cylinder or tube is designed and approved in accordance with the applicable standard.

Drums means flat-ended or convex-ended cylindrical packagings made of metal, fibreboard, plastics, plywood or other suitable materials. This definition also includes packagings of other shapes, such as round taper-necked packagings, or pail-shaped packagings. Wooden barrels and jerricans are not covered by this definition.

Elevated temperature substance means a substance which is transported or offered for transport:
- in the liquid state at a temperature at or above 100°C
- in the liquid state with a flashpoint above 60°C that is intentionally heated to a temperature above its flashpoint; or
- in the solid state at a temperature at or above 240°C.

Emergency temperature means the temperature at which emergency procedures shall be implemented.

Exclusive use, for the transport of radioactive material, means the sole use, by a single consignor, of a conveyance or of a large freight container, in respect of which all initial, intermediate and final loading and unloading and shipment are carried out in accordance with the directions of the consignor or consignee, where so required by the provisions of this Code.

Filling ratio means the ratio of the mass of gas to the mass of water at 15°C that would fill completely a pressure receptacle fitted ready for use.

Flashpoint means the lowest temperature of a liquid at which its vapour forms an ignitable mixture with air.

Foodstuff includes foodstuffs, feeds or other edible substances intended for consumption by humans or animals.

Freight container means an article of transport equipment that is of a permanent character and accordingly strong enough to be suitable for repeated use; specially designed to facilitate the transport of goods, by one or more modes of transport, without intermediate reloading; designed to be secured and/or readily handled, having fittings for these purposes, and approved in accordance with the International Convention for Safe Containers (CSC), 1972, as amended. In addition: *Small freight container* means a freight container that has an internal volume of not more than 3 m³. *Large freight container* means a freight container that has an internal volume of more than 3 m³.

For freight containers for the transport of radioactive material, a freight container may be used as a packaging. A small freight container is that which has either any overall outer dimension less than 1.5 m, or an internal volume of not more than 3 m³. Any other freight container is considered to be a large freight container.

Fuel cell means an electrochemical device that converts the chemical energy of a fuel to electrical energy, heat and reaction products.

Fuel cell engine means a device used to power equipment and which consists of a fuel cell and its fuel supply, whether integrated with or separate from the fuel cell, and includes all appurtenances necessary to fulfil its function.

△ *GHS* means the sixth revised edition of the *Globally Harmonized System of Classification and Labelling of Chemicals*, published by the United Nations as document ST/SG/AC.10/30/Rev.6.

IMO type 4 tank means a road tank vehicle for the transport of dangerous goods of classes 3 to 9 and includes a semi-trailer with a permanently attached tank or a tank attached to a chassis, with at least four twist locks that take account of ISO standards (e.g. ISO 1161:1984).

IMO type 6 tank means a road tank vehicle for the transport of non-refrigerated liquefied gases of class 2 and includes a semi-trailer with a permanently attached tank or a tank attached to a chassis which is fitted with items of service equipment and structural equipment necessary for the transport of gases.

IMO type 8 tank means a road tank vehicle for the transport of refrigerated liquefied gases of class 2 and includes a semi-trailer with a permanently attached thermally insulated tank fitted with items of service equipment and structural equipment necessary for the transport of refrigerated liquefied gases.

Inner packagings means packagings for which an outer packaging is required for transport.

Inner receptacles means receptacles which require an outer packaging in order to perform their containment function.

Inspection body means an independent inspection and testing body approved by the competent authority.

Intermediate bulk containers (IBCs) means rigid or flexible portable packagings, other than specified in chapter 6.1, that:

.1   have a capacity of:

    .1   not more than 3.0 m^3 (3,000 litres) for solids and liquids of packing groups II and III;

    .2   not more than 1.5 m^3 for solids of packing group I when packed in flexible, rigid plastics, composite, fibreboard or wooden IBCs;

    .3   not more than 3.0 m^3 for solids of packing group I when packed in metal IBCs;

    .4   not more than 3.0 m^3 for radioactive material of class 7;

.2   are designed for mechanical handling; and

.3   are resistant to the stresses produced in handling and transport, as determined by tests.

Remanufactured IBCs are metal, rigid plastics or composite IBCs that:

.1   are produced as a UN type from a non-UN type; or

.2   are converted from one UN design type to another UN design type.

Remanufactured IBCs are subject to the same provisions of this Code that apply to new IBCs of the same type (see also design type definition in 6.5.6.1.1).

Repaired IBCs are metal, rigid plastics or composite IBCs that, as a result of impact or for any other cause (e.g. corrosion, embrittlement or other evidence of reduced strength as compared to the design type) are restored so as to conform to the design type and to be able to withstand the design type tests. For the purposes of this Code, the replacement of the rigid inner receptacle of a composite IBC with a receptacle conforming to the original design type from the same manufacturer is considered repair. However, routine maintenance of rigid IBCs (see definition below) is not considered repair. The bodies of rigid plastics IBCs and the inner receptacles of composite IBCs are not repairable. Flexible IBCs are not repairable, unless approved by the competent authority.

Routine maintenance of flexible IBCs is the routine performance on plastics or textile flexible IBCs of operations, such as:

.1   cleaning; or

.2   replacement of non-integral components, such as non-integral liners and closure ties, with components conforming to the original manufacturer's specification;

provided that these operations do not adversely affect the containment function of the flexible IBC or alter the design type.

Note: For rigid IBCs, see "Routine maintenance of rigid IBCs".

Routine maintenance of rigid IBCs is the routine performance on metal, rigid plastics or composite IBCs of operations such as:

.1   cleaning;

.2   removal and reinstallation or replacement of body closures (including associated gaskets), or of service equipment, conforming to the original manufacturer's specifications, provided that the leaktightness of the IBC is verified; or

.3   restoration of structural equipment not directly performing a dangerous goods containment or discharge pressure retention function so as to conform to the design type (e.g. the straightening of legs or lifting attachments) provided that the containment function of the IBC is not affected.

Note: For flexible IBCs, see "Routine maintenance of flexible IBCs".

Intermediate packagings means packagings placed between inner packagings, or articles, and an outer packaging.

Jerricans means metal or plastics packagings of rectangular or polygonal cross-section.

Large packagings means packagings consisting of an outer packaging which contains articles or inner packagings and which:

.1   are designed for mechanical handling; and

.2   exceed 400 kg net mass or 450 litre capacity but have a volume of not more than 3 m^3.

△ *Large salvage packaging* means a special packaging which:

.1 is designed for mechanical handling; and

.2 exceeds 400 kg net mass or 450 litre capacity but has a volume of not more than 3 m³;

into which damaged, defective, leaking or non-conforming dangerous goods packages, or dangerous goods that have spilled or leaked are placed for purposes of transport for recovery or disposal.

Liner means a separate tube or bag inserted into a packaging (including IBCs and large packagings) but not forming an integral part of it, including the closures of its openings.

△ *Liquids* are dangerous goods which at 50°C have a vapour pressure of not more than 300 kPa (3 bar), which are not completely gaseous at 20°C and at a pressure of 101.3 kPa, and which have a melting point or initial melting point of 20°C or less at a pressure of 101.3 kPa. A viscous substance for which a specific melting point cannot be determined shall be subjected to the ASTM D 4359-90 test; or to the test for determining fluidity (penetrometer test) prescribed in section 2.3.4 of Annex A of the European Agreement concerning the International Carriage of Dangerous Goods by Road (ADR).[*]

Long international voyage means an international voyage that is not a short international voyage.

Management system, for the transport of radioactive material, means a set of interrelated or interacting elements (system) for establishing policies and objectives and enabling the objectives to be achieved in an efficient and effective manner.

△ *Manual of Tests and Criteria* means the sixth revised edition of the United Nations publication entitled *Recommendations on the Transport of Dangerous Goods, Manual of Tests and Criteria* (ST/SG/AC.10/11/Rev.6).

Maximum capacity as used in 6.1.4 means the maximum inner volume of receptacles or packagings expressed in litres.

Maximum net mass as used in 6.1.4 means the maximum net mass of contents in a single packaging or maximum combined mass of inner packagings and the contents thereof and is expressed in kilograms.

Maximum normal operating pressure, for the transport of radioactive material, means the maximum pressure above atmospheric pressure at mean sea-level that would develop in the containment system in a period of one year under the conditions of temperature and solar radiation corresponding to environmental conditions in the absence of venting, external cooling by an ancillary system, or operational controls during transport.

Metal hydride storage system means a single complete hydrogen storage system, including a receptacle, metal hydride, pressure relief device, shut-off valve, service equipment and internal components used for the transport of hydrogen only.

Multiple-element gas containers (MEGCs) are multimodal assemblies of cylinders, tubes or bundles of cylinders which are interconnected by a manifold and which are assembled within a framework. The MEGC includes service equipment and structural equipment necessary for the transport of gases.

Net explosive mass (NEM) means the total mass of the explosive substances, without the packagings, casings, etc. (*Net explosive quantity (NEQ)*, *net explosive contents (NEC)*, or *net explosive weight (NEW)* are often used to convey the same meaning.)

Neutron radiation detector is a device that detects neutron radiation. In such a device, a gas may be contained in a hermetically-sealed electron tube transducer that converts neutron radiation into a measureable electric signal.

Offshore bulk container means a bulk container specially designed for repeated use for the transport of dangerous goods to, from and between offshore facilities. An offshore bulk container is designed and constructed in accordance with Guidelines for the approval of offshore containers handled in open seas (MSC/Circ.860).

Open cargo transport unit means a unit which is not a closed cargo transport unit.

Open cryogenic receptacle means a transportable thermally insulated receptacle for refrigerated liquefied gases maintained at atmospheric pressure by continuous venting of the refrigerated liquefied gas.

Open ro-ro cargo space means a ro-ro cargo space either open at both ends, or open at one end and provided with adequate natural ventilation effective over its entire length through permanent openings in the side plating or deckhead to the satisfaction of the Administration.

---

[*] United Nations Publication: ECE/TRANS/225 (Sales No. E.14.VIII.1).

Outer packaging means the outer protection of a composite or combination packaging together with any absorbent materials, cushioning and any other components necessary to contain and protect inner receptacles or inner packagings.

Overpack means an enclosure used by a single consignor to contain one or more packages and to form one unit for the convenience of handling and stowage during transport. Examples of overpacks are a number of packages either:

.1 placed or stacked on to a load board, such as a pallet, and secured by strapping, shrink-wrapping, stretch-wrapping, or other suitable means; or

.2 placed in a protective outer packaging such as a box or crate.

Overstowed means that a package or container is directly stowed on top of another.

Package means the complete product of the packing operation, consisting of the packaging and its contents prepared for transport.

Packaging means one or more receptacles and any other components or materials necessary for the receptacles to perform their containment and other safety functions.

Pressure drums are welded transportable pressure receptacles of a water capacity exceeding 150 litres and of not more than 1,000 litres (e.g. cylindrical receptacles equipped with rolling hoops, spheres on skids).

Pressure receptacles is a collective term that includes cylinders, tubes, pressure drums, closed cryogenic receptacles, metal hydride storage systems, bundles of cylinders and salvage pressure receptacles.

Quality assurance means a systematic programme of controls and inspections applied by any organization or body which is aimed at providing adequate confidence that the standard of safety prescribed in this Code is achieved in practice.

Radiation detection system is an apparatus that contains radiation detectors as components.

Radiation level, for the transport of radioactive material, means the corresponding dose rate expressed in millisieverts per hour or microsieverts per hour.

Radioactive contents, for the transport of radioactive material, mean the radioactive material together with any contaminated or activated solids, liquids, and gases within the packaging.

Receptacles means containment vessels for receiving and holding substances or articles, including any means of closing.

Reconditioned packagings include:

.1 metal drums that:

    .1 are cleaned to original materials of construction, with all former contents, internal and external corrosion, and external coatings and labels removed;

    .2 are restored to original shape and contour, with chimes (if any) straightened and sealed, and all non-integral gaskets replaced; and

    .3 are inspected after cleaning, but before painting, with rejection of packagings with visible pitting, significant reduction in material thickness, metal fatigue, damaged threads or closures, or other significant defects;

.2 plastic drums and jerricans that:

    .1 are cleaned to original materials of construction, with all former contents, external coatings and labels removed;

    .2 have all non-integral gaskets replaced; and

    .3 are inspected after cleaning, with rejection of packagings with visible damage such as tears, creases or cracks, or damaged threads or closures, or other significant defects.

Recycled plastics material means material recovered from used industrial packagings that has been cleaned and prepared for processing into new packagings. The specific properties of the recycled material used for production of new packagings shall be assured and documented regularly as part of a quality assurance programme recognized by the competent authority. The quality assurance programme shall include a record of proper pre-sorting and verification that each batch of recycled plastics material has the proper melt flow rate, density, and tensile yield strength, consistent with that of the design type manufactured from such recycled material. This necessarily includes knowledge about the packaging material from which the recycled plastics have been derived, as well as awareness of the prior contents of those packagings if those prior contents might reduce the capability of new packagings produced using that material. In addition, the packaging manufacturer's quality assurance programme under 6.1.1.3 shall include performance of the mechanical design type test in 6.1.5 on packagings manufactured from each batch of recycled plastics material. In this testing, stacking performance may be verified by appropriate dynamic compression testing rather than static load testing.

Note: ISO 16103:2005, *Packaging – Transport packages for dangerous goods – Recycled plastics material*, provides additional guidance on procedures to be followed in approving the use of recycled plastics material.

Remanufactured IBCs (see *Intermediate bulk containers (IBCs)*).

Remanufactured large packaging means a metal or rigid plastics large packaging that:

.1 is produced as a UN type from a non-UN type; or

.2 is converted from one UN design type to another UN design type.

Remanufactured large packagings are subject to the same provisions of this Code that apply to new large packagings of the same type (see also design type definition in 6.6.5.1.2).

Remanufactured packagings include:

.1 metal drums that:

    .1 are produced as a UN type from a non-UN type;

    .2 are converted from one UN type to another UN type; or

    .3 undergo the replacement of integral structural components (such as non-removable heads); or

.2 plastic drums that:

    .1 are converted from one UN type to another UN type (such as 1H1 to 1H2); or

    .2 undergo the replacement of integral structural components.

Remanufactured drums are subject to the same provisions of this Code that apply to a new drum of the same type.

Repaired IBCs (see *Intermediate bulk containers (IBCs)*).

Re-used large packaging means a large packaging to be refilled which has been examined and found free of defects affecting the ability to withstand the performance tests: the term includes those which are refilled with the same or similar compatible contents and are transported within distribution chains controlled by the consignor of the product.

Re-used packagings means packagings to be refilled which have been examined and found free of defects affecting the ability to withstand the performance tests; the term includes those which are refilled with the same or similar compatible contents and are transported within distribution chains controlled by the consignor of the product.

Road tank vehicle means a vehicle equipped with a tank with a capacity of more than 450 litres, fitted with pressure-relief devices.

Ro-ro cargo space means spaces not normally subdivided in any way and extending to either a substantial length or the entire length of the ship in which goods (packaged or in bulk, in or on rail or road cars, vehicles (including road or rail tankers), trailers, containers, pallets, demountable tanks or in or on similar stowage units or other receptacles) can be loaded and unloaded normally in a horizontal direction.

Ro-ro ship (roll-on/roll-off ship) means a ship which has one or more decks, either closed or open, not normally subdivided in any way and generally running the entire length of the ship, carrying goods which are normally loaded and unloaded in a horizontal direction.

Routine maintenance of IBCs (see *Intermediate bulk containers (IBCs)*).

Salvage packagings are special packagings into which damaged, defective, leaking or non-conforming dangerous goods packages, or dangerous goods that have spilled or leaked, are placed for purposes of transport for recovery or disposal.

△ *Salvage pressure receptacle* means a pressure receptacle with a water capacity not exceeding 3,000 litres into which are placed damaged, defective, leaking or non-conforming pressure receptacle(s) for the purpose of transport, e.g. for recovery or disposal.

Self-accelerating decomposition temperature (SADT) means the lowest temperature at which self-accelerating decomposition may occur for a substance in the packaging as used in transport. The self-accelerating decomposition temperature (SADT) shall be determined in accordance with the latest version of the Manual of Tests and Criteria.

■ *Self-accelerating polymerization temperature (SAPT)* means the lowest temperature at which polymerization may occur with a substance in the packaging, IBC or portable tank as offered for transport. The SAPT shall be determined in accordance with the test procedures established for the self-accelerating decomposition temperature for self-reactive substances in accordance with Part II, Section 28 of the Manual of Tests and Criteria.

Semi-trailer means any trailer designed to be coupled to a motor vehicle in such a way that part of it rests on the motor vehicle and a substantial part of its mass and of the mass of its load is borne by the motor vehicle.

■ *Service life*, for composite cylinders and tubes, means the number of years the cylinder or tube is permitted to be in service.

Settled pressure means the pressure of the contents of a pressure receptacle in thermal and diffusive equilibrium.

Shipborne barge or *barge* means an independent, non-self-propelled vessel, specially designed and equipped to be lifted in a loaded condition and stowed aboard a barge-carrying ship or barge feeder vessel.

Shipment means the specific movement of a consignment from origin to destination.

Shipper, for the purpose of this Code, has the same meaning as *consignor.*

Short international voyage means an international voyage in the course of which a ship is not more than 200 miles from a port or place in which the passengers and crew could be placed in safety. Neither the distance between the last port of call in the country in which the voyage begins and the final port of destination nor the return voyage shall exceed 600 miles. The final port of destination is the last port of call in the scheduled voyage at which the ship commences its return voyage to the country in which the voyage began.

Sift-proof packagings are packagings impermeable to dry contents, including fine solid material produced during transport.

Solid bulk cargo means any material, other than liquid or gas, consisting of a combination of particles, granules or any larger pieces of material, generally uniform in composition, which is loaded directly into the cargo spaces of a ship without any intermediate form of containment (this includes a material loaded in a barge on a barge-carrying ship).

Solids are dangerous goods, other than gases, that do not meet the definition of *liquids* in this chapter.

Special category space means an enclosed space, above or below deck, intended for the transport of motor vehicles with fuel in their tanks for their own propulsion, into and from which such vehicles can be driven and to which passengers have access.

Tank means a portable tank (including a tank-container), a road tank-vehicle, a rail tank-wagon or a receptacle to contain solids, liquids, or liquefied gases and has a capacity of not less than 450 litres when used for the transport of gases as defined in 2.2.1.1.

Test pressure means the required pressure applied during a pressure test for qualification or requalification (for portable tanks, see 6.7.2.1).

Through or into means through or into the countries in which a consignment is transported but specifically excludes countries "over" which a consignment is carried by air, provided that there are no scheduled stops in those countries.

Transboundary movement of wastes means any shipment of wastes from an area under the national jurisdiction of one country to or through an area under the national jurisdiction of another country, or to or through an area not under the national jurisdiction of any country, provided at least two countries are concerned by the movement.

Transport index (TI) assigned to a package, overpack or freight container, or to unpackaged LSA-I or SCO-I, for the transport of radioactive material, means a number which is used to provide control over radiation exposure.

△ *Tube* means a transportable pressure receptacle of seamless or composite construction having a water capacity exceeding 150 litres and of not more than 3,000 litres.

Unit load means that a number of packages are either:

.1 placed or stacked on and secured by strapping, shrink-wrapping, or other suitable means to a load board, such as a pallet;

.2 placed in a protective outer enclosure, such as a pallet box;

.3 permanently secured together in a sling.

Vehicle means a road vehicle (including an articulated vehicle, i.e. a tractor and semi-trailer combination) or railroad car or railway wagon. Each trailer shall be considered as a separate vehicle.

Wastes means substances, solutions, mixtures, or articles containing or contaminated with one or more constituents which are subject to the provisions of this Code and for which no direct use is envisaged but which are transported for dumping, incineration, or other methods of disposal.

Water-reactive means a substance which, in contact with water, emits flammable gas.

Weather deck means a deck which is completely exposed to the weather from above and from at least two sides.

Wooden barrels means packagings made of natural wood, of round cross-section, having convex walls, consisting of staves and heads and fitted with hoops.

Working pressure means the settled pressure of a compressed gas at a reference temperature of 15°C in a full pressure receptacle.

1.2.1.1 Clarifying examples for certain defined terms

The following explanations and examples are meant to assist in clarifying the use of some of the packaging terms defined in this chapter.

The definitions in this chapter are consistent with the use of the defined terms throughout the Code. However, some of the defined terms are commonly used in other ways. This is particularly evident in respect of the term "inner receptacle" which has often been used to describe the "inners" of a combination packaging.

The "inners" of "combination packagings" are always termed "inner packagings", not "inner receptacles". A glass bottle is an example of such an "inner packaging".

The "inners" of "composite packagings" are normally termed "inner receptacles". For example, the "inner" of a 6HA1 composite packaging (plastics material) is such an "inner receptacle" since it is normally not designed to perform a containment function without its "outer packaging" and is not, therefore, an "inner packaging".

1.2.2 Units of measurement

1.2.2.1 The following units of measurement[*] are applicable in this Code:

Measurement of:	SI unit[a]		Acceptable alternative unit		Relationship between units
Length	m	(metre)	–		–
Area	m^2	(square metre)	–		–
Volume	m^3	(cubic metre)	L[b]	(litre)	$1\,L = 10^{-3}\,m^3$
Time	s	(second)	min	(minute)	$1\,min = 60\,s$
			h	(hour)	$1\,h = 3{,}600\,s$
			d	(day)	$1\,d = 86{,}400\,s$
Mass	kg	(kilogram)	g	(gram)	$1\,g = 10^{-3}\,kg$
			t	(ton)	$1\,t = 10^3\,kg$
Mass density	kg/m^3		kg/L		$1\,kg/L = 10^3\,kg/m^3$
Temperature	K	(kelvin)	°C	(degree Celsius)	$0°C = 273.15\,K$
Difference of temperature	K	(kelvin)	°C	(degree Celsius)	$1°C = 1\,K$
Force	N	(newton)	–		$1\,N = 1\,kg{\cdot}m/s^2$
Pressure	Pa	(pascal)	bar	(bar)	$1\,bar = 10^5\,Pa$
					$1\,Pa = 1\,N/m^2$
Stress	N/m^2		N/mm^2		$1\,N/mm^2 = 1\,MPa$
Work, Energy, Quantity of heat	J	(joule)	kWh	(kilowatt hour)	$1\,kWh = 3.6\,MJ$
					$1\,J = 1\,N{\cdot}m = 1\,W{\cdot}s$
			eV	(electronvolt)	$1\,eV = 0.1602 \times 10^{-18}\,J$
Power	W	(watt)	–		$1\,W = 1\,J/s = 1\,N{\cdot}m/s$
Kinematic viscosity	m^2/s		mm^2/s		$1\,mm^2/s = 10^{-6}\,m^2/s$
Dynamic viscosity	Pa·s		mPa·s		$1\,mPa{\cdot}s = 10^{-3}\,Pa{\cdot}s$

---

[*] The following round figures are applicable for the conversion of the units hitherto used into SI units.

Measurement of:	SI unit[a]		Acceptable alternative unit	Relationship between units
Activity	Bq	(becquerel)	–	–
Dose equivalent	Sv	(sievert)	–	–
Conductivity	S/m	(siemens/metre)	–	–

[a] The International System of Units (SI) is the result of decisions taken at the General Conference on Weights and Measures (Address: Pavillon de Breteuil, Parc de St-Cloud, F-92312 Sèvres).

[b] The abbreviation "ℓ" for litre may also be used in place of the abbreviation "L".

Force
$1 \text{ kg} = 9.807 \text{ N}$
$1 \text{ N} = 0.102 \text{ kg}$

Stress
$1 \text{ kg/mm}^2 = 9.807 \text{ N/mm}^2$
$1 \text{ N/mm}^2 = 0.102 \text{ kg/mm}^2$

Pressure
$1 \text{ Pa} = 1 \text{ N/m}^2 = 10^{-5} \text{ bar} \quad = 1.02 \times 10^{-5} \text{ kg/cm}^2 \quad = 0.75 \times 10^{-2} \text{ torr}$
$1 \text{ bar} = 10^5 \text{ Pa} \quad = 1.02 \text{ kg/cm}^2 \quad = 750 \text{ torr}$
$1 \text{ kg/cm}^2 = 9.807 \times 10^4 \text{ Pa} \quad = 0.9807 \text{ bar} \quad = 736 \text{ torr}$
$1 \text{ torr} = 1.33 \times 10^2 \text{ Pa} \quad = 1.33 \times 10^{-3} \text{ bar} \quad = 1.36 \times 10^{-3} \text{ kg/cm}^2$

Energy, work, quantity of heat
$1 \text{ J} = 1 \text{ N·m} \quad = 0.278 \times 10^{-6} \text{ kWh} \quad = 0.102 \text{ kg·m} \quad = 0.239 \times 10^{-3} \text{ kcal}$
$1 \text{ kWh} = 3.6 \times 10^6 \text{ J} \quad = 367 \times 10^3 \text{ kg·m} \quad = 860 \text{ kcal}$
$1 \text{ kg·m} = 9.807 \text{ J} \quad = 2.72 \times 10^{-6} \text{ kWh} \quad = 2.34 \times 10^{-3} \text{ kcal}$
$1 \text{ kcal} = 4.19 \times 10^3 \text{ J} \quad = 1.16 \times 10^{-3} \text{ kWh} \quad = 427 \text{ kg·m}$

Power
$1 \text{ W} = 0.102 \text{ kg·m/s} \quad = 0.86 \text{ kcal/h}$
$1 \text{ kg·m/s} = 9.807 \text{ W} \quad = 8.43 \text{ kcal/h}$
$1 \text{ kcal/h} = 1.16 \text{ W} \quad = 0.119 \text{ kg·m/s}$

Kinematic viscosity
$1 \text{ m}^2\text{/s} = 10^4 \text{ St (stokes)}$
$1 \text{ St} = 10^{-4} \text{ m}^2\text{/s}$

Dynamic viscosity
$1 \text{ Pa·s} = 1 \text{ N·s/m}^2 \quad = 10 \text{ P (poise)} \quad = 0.102 \text{ kg·s/m}^2$
$1 \text{ P} = 0.1 \text{ Pa·s} \quad = 0.1 \text{ N·s/m}^2 \quad = 1.02 \times 10^{-2} \text{ kg·s/m}^2$
$1 \text{ kg·s/m}^2 = 9.807 \text{ Pa·s} \quad = 9.807 \text{ N·s/m}^2 \quad = 98.07 \text{ P}$

The decimal multiples and sub-multiples of a unit may be formed by prefixes or symbols, having the following meanings, placed before the name or symbol of the unit:

Multiplying factor			Prefix	Symbol
1 000 000 000 000 000 000	=	10^{18}	quintillion	exa	E
1 000 000 000 000 000	=	10^{15}	quadrillion	peta	P
1 000 000 000 000	=	10^{12}	trillion	tera	T
1 000 000 000	=	10^{9}	billion	giga	G
1 000 000	=	10^{6}	million	mega	M
1 000	=	10^{3}	thousand	kilo	k
100	=	10^{2}	hundred	hecto	h
10	=	10^{1}	ten	deca	da
0.1	=	10^{-1}	tenth	deci	d
0.01	=	10^{-2}	hundredth	centi	c
0.001	=	10^{-3}	thousandth	milli	m
0.000 001	=	10^{-6}	millionth	micro	μ
0.000 000 001	=	10^{-9}	billionth	nano	n
0.000 000 000 001	=	10^{-12}	trillionth	pico	p
0.000 000 000 000 001	=	10^{-15}	quadrillionth	femto	f
0.000 000 000 000 000 001	=	10^{-18}	quintillionth	atto	a

Note: $10^9 = 1$ billion is United Nations usage in English. By analogy, so is $10^{-9} = 1$ billionth.

1.2.2.2   [Reserved]

1.2.2.3   Whenever the mass of a package is mentioned, the gross mass is meant unless otherwise stated. The mass of containers or tanks used for the transport of goods is not included in the gross mass.

1.2.2.4   Unless expressly stated otherwise, the sign "%" represents:

.1   in the case of mixtures of solids or of liquids, and also in the case of solutions and of solids wetted by a liquid: a percentage mass based on the total mass of the mixture, the solution or the wetted solid;

.2   in the case of mixtures of compressed gases: when filled by pressure, the proportion of the volume indicated as a percentage of the total volume of the gaseous mixture, or, when filled by mass, the proportion of the mass indicated as a percentage of the total mass of the mixture;

.3   in the case of mixtures of liquefied gases and gases dissolved under pressure: the proportion of the mass indicated as a percentage of the total mass of the mixture.

1.2.2.5   Pressures of all kinds relating to receptacles (such as test pressure, internal pressure, safety-valve opening pressure) are always indicated in gauge pressure (pressure in excess of atmospheric pressure); however, the vapour pressure of substances is always expressed in absolute pressure.

1.2.2.6   **Tables of equivalence**

1.2.2.6.1   *Mass conversion tables*

1.2.2.6.1.1   *Conversion factors*

Multiply	by	to obtain
Grams	0.03527	Ounces
Grams	0.002205	Pounds
Kilograms	35.2736	Ounces
Kilograms	2.2046	Pounds
Ounces	28.3495	Grams
Pounds	16	Ounces
Pounds	453.59	Grams
Pounds	0.45359	Kilograms
Hundredweight	112	Pounds
Hundredweight	50.802	Kilograms

1.2.2.6.1.2   *Pounds to kilograms and vice versa*

When the central value in any row of these mass conversion tables is taken to be in pounds, its equivalent value in kilograms is shown on the left; when the central value is in kilograms, its equivalent in pounds is shown on the right.

kg	← lb → kg	lb	kg	← lb → kg	lb	kg	← lb → kg	lb
0.227	0.5	1.10	22.7	50	110	90.7	200	441
0.454	1	2.20	24.9	55	121	95.3	210	463
0.907	2	4.41	27.2	60	132	99.8	220	485
1.36	3	6.61	29.5	65	143	102	225	496
1.81	4	8.82	31.8	70	154	104	230	507
2.27	5	11.0	34.0	75	165	109	240	529
2.72	6	13.2	36.3	80	176	113	250	551
3.18	7	15.4	38.6	85	187	118	260	573
3.63	8	17.6	40.8	90	198	122	270	595
4.08	9	19.8	43.1	95	209	125	275	606
4.54	10	22.0	45.4	100	220	127	280	617
4.99	11	24.3	47.6	105	231	132	290	639
5.44	12	26.5	49.9	110	243	136	300	661
5.90	13	28.7	52.2	115	254	159	350	772
6.35	14	30.9	54.4	120	265	181	400	882
6.80	15	33.1	56.7	125	276	204	450	992
7.26	16	35.3	59.0	130	287	227	500	1,102
7.71	17	37.5	61.2	135	298	247	545	1,202
8.16	18	39.7	63.5	140	309	249	550	1,213
8.62	19	41.9	65.8	145	320	272	600	1,323
9.07	20	44.1	68.0	150	331	318	700	1,543
11.3	25	55.1	72.6	160	353	363	800	1,764
13.6	30	66.1	77.1	170	375	408	900	1,984
15.9	35	77.2	79.4	175	386	454	1,000	2,205
18.1	40	88.2	81.6	180	397			
20.4	45	99.2	86.2	190	419			

1.2.2.6.2 *Liquid measure conversion tables*

1.2.2.6.2.1 *Conversion factors*

Multiply	by	to obtain
Litres	0.2199	Imperial gallons
Litres	1.759	Imperial pints
Litres	0.2643	US gallons
Litres	2.113	US pints
Gallons	8	Pints
Imperial gallons	4.546	Litres
Imperial gallons Imperial pints	1.20095	US gallons US pints
Imperial pints	0.568	Litres
US gallons	3.7853	Litres
US gallons US pints	0.83268	Imperial gallons Imperial pints
US pints	0.473	Litres

1.2.2.6.2.2 *Imperial pints to litres and vice versa*

When the central value in any row of these liquid measure conversion tables is taken to be in pints, its equivalent value in litres is shown on the left; when the central value is in litres, its equivalent in pints is shown on the right.

	←	→	
L	pt	L	pt
0.28	0.5		0.88
0.57	1		1.76
0.85	1.5		2.64
1.14	2		3.52
1.42	2.5		4.40
1.70	3		5.28
1.99	3.5		6.16
2.27	4		7.04
2.56	4.5		7.92
2.84	5		8.80
3.12	5.5		9.68
3.41	6		10.56
3.69	6.5		11.44
3.98	7		12.32
4.26	7.5		13.20
4.55	8		14.08

1.2.2.6.2.3 *Imperial gallons to litres and vice versa*

When the central value in any row of these liquid measure conversion tables is taken to be in gallons, its equivalent value in litres is shown on the left; when the central value is in litres, its equivalent in gallons is shown on the right.

L	gal ← → L	gal	L	gal ← → L	gal
2.27	0.5	0.11	159.11	35	7.70
4.55	1	0.22	163.65	36	7.92
9.09	2	0.44	168.20	37	8.14
13.64	3	0.66	172.75	38	8.36
18.18	4	0.88	177.29	39	8.58
22.73	5	1.10	181.84	40	8.80
27.28	6	1.32	186.38	41	9.02
31.82	7	1.54	190.93	42	9.24
36.37	8	1.76	195.48	43	9.46
40.91	9	1.98	200.02	44	9.68
45.46	10	2.20	204.57	45	9.90
50.01	11	2.42	209.11	46	10.12
54.55	12	2.64	213.66	47	10.34
59.10	13	2.86	218.21	48	10.56
63.64	14	3.08	222.75	49	10.78
68.19	15	3.30	227.30	50	11.00
72.74	16	3.52	250.03	55	12.09
77.28	17	3.74	272.76	60	13.20
81.83	18	3.96	295.49	65	14.29
86.37	19	4.18	318.22	70	15.40
90.92	20	4.40	340.95	75	16.49
95.47	21	4.62	363.68	80	17.60
100.01	22	4.84	386.41	85	18.69
104.56	23	5.06	409.14	90	19.80
109.10	24	5.28	431.87	95	20.89
113.65	25	5.50	454.60	100	22.00
118.19	26	5.72	613.71	135	29.69
122.74	27	5.94	681.90	150	32.98
127.29	28	6.16	909.20	200	43.99
131.83	29	6.38	1,022.85	225	49.48
136.38	30	6.60	1,136.50	250	54.97
140.92	31	6.82	1,363.80	300	65.99
145.47	32	7.04	1,591.10	350	76.96
150.02	33	7.26	1,818.40	400	87.99
154.56	34	7.48	2,045.70	450	98.95

1.2.2.6.3 Temperature conversion tables

Degrees Fahrenheit to degrees Celsius and vice versa

When the central value in any row of these temperature conversion tables is taken to be in °F, its equivalent value in °C is shown on the left; when the central value is in °C, its equivalent value in °F is shown on the right.

General formula: $°F = (°C \times \frac{9}{5}) + 32;$ $°C = (°F - 32) \times \frac{5}{9}$

°C	← °F → °C	°F	°C	← °F → °C	°F	°C	← °F → °C	°F
−73.3	−100	−148	−21.1	−6	21.2	1.1	34	93.2
−67.8	−90	−130	−20.6	−5	23.0	1.7	35	95
−62.2	−80	−112	−20.0	−4	24.8	2.2	36	96.8
−56.7	−70	−94	−19.4	−3	26.6	2.8	37	98.6
−51.1	−60	−76	−18.9	−2	28.4	3.3	38	100.4
−45.6	−50	−58	−18.3	−1	30.2	3.9	39	102.2
−40	−40	−40	−17.8	0	32.0	4.4	40	104
−39.4	−39	−38.2	−17.2	1	33.8	5	41	105.8
−38.9	−38	−36.4	−16.7	2	35.6	5.6	42	107.6
−38.3	−37	−34.6	−16.1	3	37.4	6.1	43	109.4
−37.8	−36	−32.8	−15.6	4	39.2	6.7	44	111.2
−37.2	−35	−31	−15.0	5	41.0	7.2	45	113
−36.7	−34	−29.2	−14.4	6	42.8	7.8	46	114.8
−36.1	−33	−27.4	−13.9	7	44.6	8.3	47	116.6
−35.6	−32	−25.6	−13.3	8	46.4	8.9	48	118.4
−35	−31	−23.8	−12.8	9	48.2	9.4	49	120.2
−34.4	−30	−22	−12.2	10	50.0	10.0	50	122.0
−33.9	−29	−20.2	−11.7	11	51.8	10.6	51	123.8
−33.3	−28	−18.4	−11.1	12	53.6	11.1	52	125.6
−32.8	−27	−16.6	−10.6	13	55.4	11.7	53	127.4
−32.2	−26	−14.8	−10.0	14	57.2	12.2	54	129.2
−31.7	−25	−13	−9.4	15	59.0	12.8	55	131.0
−31.1	−24	−11.2	−8.9	16	60.8	13.3	56	132.8
−30.6	−23	−9.4	−8.3	17	62.6	13.9	57	134.6
−30	−22	−7.6	−7.8	18	64.4	14.4	58	136.4
−29.4	−21	−5.8	−7.2	19	66.2	15.0	59	138.2
−28.9	−20	−4	−6.7	20	68	15.6	60	140.0
−28.3	−19	−2.2	−6.1	21	69.8	16.1	61	141.8
−27.8	−18	−0.4	−5.6	22	71.6	16.7	62	143.6
−27.2	−17	1.4	−5	23	73.4	17.2	63	145.4
−26.7	−16	3.2	−4.4	24	75.2	17.8	64	147.2
−26.1	−15	5	−3.9	25	77	18.3	65	149.0
−25.6	−14	6.8	−3.3	26	78.8	18.9	66	150.8
−25.0	−13	8.6	−2.8	27	80.6	19.4	67	152.6
−24.4	−12	10.4	−2.2	28	82.4	20.0	68	154.4
−23.9	−11	12.2	−1.7	29	84.2	20.6	69	156.2
−23.3	−10	14.0	−1.1	30	86	21.1	70	158.0
−22.8	−9	15.8	−0.6	31	87.8	21.7	71	159.8
−22.2	−8	17.6	0	32	89.6	22.2	72	161.6
−21.7	−7	19.4	0.6	33	91.4	22.8	73	163.4

°C	←°F	→°C	°F	°C	←°F	→°C	°F	°C	←°F	→°C	°F
23.3	74		165.2	37.8	100		212	52.2	126		258.8
23.9	75		167.0	38.3	101		213.8	52.8	127		260.6
24.4	76		168.8	38.9	102		215.6	53.3	128		262.4
25.0	77		170.6	39.4	103		217.4	53.9	129		264.2
25.6	78		172.4	40	104		219.2	54.4	130		266.0
26.1	79		174.2	40.6	105		221	55.0	131		267.8
26.7	80		176.0	41.1	106		222.8	55.6	132		269.6
27.2	81		177.8	41.7	107		224.6	56.1	133		271.4
27.8	82		179.6	42.2	108		226.4	56.7	134		273.2
28.3	83		181.4	42.8	109		228.2	57.2	135		275.0
28.9	84		183.2	43.3	110		230	57.8	136		276.8
29.4	85		185	43.9	111		231.8	58.3	137		278.6
30	86		186.8	44.4	112		233.6	58.9	138		280.4
30.6	87		188.6	45	113		235.4	59.4	139		282.2
31.1	88		190.4	45.6	114		237.2	60.0	140		284.0
31.7	89		192.2	46.1	115		239.0	65.6	150		302.0
32.2	90		194	46.7	116		240.8	71.1	160		320.0
32.8	91		195.8	47.2	117		242.6	76.7	170		338.0
33.3	92		197.6	47.8	118		244.4	82.2	180		356.0
33.9	93		199.4	48.3	119		246.2	87.8	190		374.0
34.4	94		201.2	48.9	120		248.0	93.3	200		392.0
35	95		203	49.4	121		249.8	98.9	210		410.0
35.6	96		204.8	50.0	122		251.6	104.4	220		428.0
36.1	97		206.6	50.6	123		253.4	110.0	230		446.0
36.7	98		208.4	51.1	124		255.2	115.6	240		464.0
37.2	99		210.2	51.7	125		257.0	121.1	250		482.0

1.2.3 List of abbreviations

ASTM	American Society for Testing and Materials (ASTM International, 100 Barr Harbor Drive, P.O. Box C700, West Conshohocken, PA, 19428-2959, United States of America)
CGA	Compressed Gas Association (CGA, 14501 George Carter Way, Suite 103, Chantilly, VA 20151, United States of America)
△ CCC	IMO Sub-Committee on Carriage of Cargoes and Containers
CSC	International Convention for Safe Containers, 1972, as amended
DSC	IMO Sub-Committee on Dangerous Goods, Solid Cargoes and Containers
ECOSOC	Economic and Social Council (UN)
EmS	The EmS Guide: Emergency Response Procedures for Ships Carrying Dangerous Goods
EN (standard)	European standard published by the European Committee for Standardization (CEN) (CEN, 36 rue de Stassart, B-1050 Brussels, Belgium)
FAO	Food and Agriculture Organization (FAO, Viale delle Terme di Caracalla, 00100 Rome, Italy)
HNS Convention	International Convention on Liability and Compensation for Damage in Connection with the Transport of Hazardous and Noxious Substances (IMO)
IAEA	International Atomic Energy Agency (IAEA, P.O. Box 100, A – 1400 Vienna, Austria)
ICAO	International Civil Aviation Organization (ICAO, 999 University Street, Montreal, Quebec H3C 5H7, Canada)
IEC	International Electrotechnical Commission (IEC, 3 rue de Varembé, P.O. Box 131, CH-1211 Geneva 20, Switzerland)

	ILO	International Labour Organization/Office (ILO, 4 route des Morillons, CH-1211 Geneva 22, Switzerland)
	IMGS	International Medical Guide for Ships
	IMO	International Maritime Organization (IMO, 4 Albert Embankment, London SE1 7SR, United Kingdom)
	IMDG Code	International Maritime Dangerous Goods Code
	IMSBC Code	International Maritime Solid Bulk Cargoes Code
	INF Code	International Code for the Safe Carriage of Packaged Irradiated Nuclear Fuel, Plutonium and High-Level Radioactive Wastes on board Ships
	ISO (standard)	An international standard published by the International Organization for Standardization (ISO, 1, ch. de la Voie-Creuse, CH-1211 Geneva 20, Switzerland)
	MARPOL	International Convention for the Prevention of Pollution from Ships, 1973, as amended by the 1978 and 1997 Protocols relating thereto
	MAWP	Maximum allowable working pressure
	MEPC	Marine Environment Protection Committee (IMO)
	MFAG	Medical First Aid Guide for use in Accidents Involving Dangerous Goods
	MSC	Maritime Safety Committee (IMO)
	N.O.S.	not otherwise specified
	SADT	Self-accelerating decomposition temperature
△	SAPT	Self-accelerating polymerization temperature
	SOLAS	International Convention for the Safety of Life at Sea, 1974, as amended
	UNECE	United Nations Economic Commission for Europe (UNECE, Palais des Nations, 8–14 avenue de la Paix, CH-1211 Geneva 10, Switzerland)
	UN number	Four-digit United Nations number is assigned to dangerous, hazardous and harmful substances, materials and articles most commonly transported
	UNEP	United Nations Environment Programme (United Nations Avenue, Gigiri, PO Box 30552, 00100, Nairobi, Kenya)
	UNESCO/IOC	UN Educational, Scientific and Cultural Organization/Intergovernmental Oceanographic Commission (UNESCO/IOC, 1 rue Miollis, 75732 Paris Cedex 15, France)
	WHO	World Health Organization (Avenue Appia 20, CH-1211 Geneva 27, Switzerland)
	WMO	World Meteorological Organization (WMO, 7bis, avenue de la Paix, Case postale No. 2300, CH-1211 Geneva 2, Switzerland)

Chapter 1.3

Training

1.3.0 Introductory note

The successful application of regulations concerning the transport of dangerous goods and the achievement of their objectives are greatly dependent on the appreciation by all persons concerned of the risks involved and on a detailed understanding of the regulations. This can only be achieved by properly planned and maintained initial and retraining programmes for all persons concerned with the transport of dangerous goods. The provisions of paragraphs 1.3.1.4 to 1.3.1.7 remain recommendatory (see 1.1.1.5).

1.3.1 Training of shore-side personnel

1.3.1.1 Shore-based personnel* engaged in the transport of dangerous goods intended to be transported by sea shall be trained in the contents of dangerous goods provisions commensurate with their responsibilities. Employees shall be trained in accordance with the provisions of 1.3.1 before assuming responsibilities and shall only perform functions, for which required training has not yet been provided, under the direct supervision of a trained person. Training requirements specific to security of dangerous goods in chapter 1.4 shall also be addressed.

Entities engaging shore-based personnel in such activities shall determine which staff will be trained, what levels of training they require and the training methods used to enable them to comply with the provisions of the IMDG Code. This training shall be provided or verified upon employment in a position involving dangerous goods transport. For personnel who have not yet received the required training, the entities shall ensure that those personnel may only perform functions under the direct supervision of a trained person. The training shall be periodically supplemented with refresher training to take account of changes in regulations and practice. The competent authority, or its authorized body, may audit the entity to verify the effectiveness of the system in place, in providing training of staff commensurate with their role and responsibilities in the transport chain.

1.3.1.2 Shore-based personnel such as those who:

– classify dangerous goods and identify proper shipping names of dangerous goods;

– pack dangerous goods;

– mark, label or placard dangerous goods;

– load/unload Cargo Transport Units;

– prepare transport documents for dangerous goods;

– offer dangerous goods for transport;

– accept dangerous goods for transport;

– handle dangerous goods in transport;

– prepare dangerous goods loading/stowage plans;

– load/unload dangerous goods into/from ships;

– carry dangerous goods in transport;

– enforce or survey or inspect for compliance with applicable rules and regulations; or

– are otherwise involved in the transport of dangerous goods as determined by the competent authority

shall be trained in the following:

1.3.1.2.1 *General awareness/familiarization training:*

.1 each person shall be trained in order to be familiar with the general provisions of dangerous goods transport provisions;

---

* For the training of officers and ratings responsible for cargo handling on ships carrying dangerous and hazardous substances in solid form in bulk, or in packaged form, see the STCW Code, as amended.

.2   such training shall include a description of the classes of dangerous goods; labelling, marking, placarding, packing, stowage, segregation and compatibility provisions; a description of the purpose and content of the dangerous goods transport documents (such as the Multimodal Dangerous Goods Form and the Container/Vehicle Packing Certificate); and a description of available emergency response documents.

1.3.1.2.2   *Function-specific training:* Each person shall be trained in specific dangerous goods transport provisions which are applicable to the function that person performs. An indicative list, for guidance purposes only, of some of the functions typically found in dangerous goods transport operations by sea and training requirements is given in paragraph 1.3.1.6.

1.3.1.3   Records of training received according to this chapter shall be kept by the employer and made available to the employee or competent authority, upon request. Records shall be kept by the employer for a period of time established by the competent authority.

1.3.1.4   *Safety training*: Commensurate with the risk of exposure in the event of a release and the functions performed, each person should be trained in:

.1   methods and procedures for accident avoidance, such as proper use of package-handling equipment and appropriate methods of stowage of dangerous goods;

.2   available emergency response information and how to use it;

.3   general dangers presented by the various classes of dangerous goods and how to prevent exposure to those hazards, including, if appropriate, the use of personal protective clothing and equipment; and

.4   immediate procedures to be followed in the event of an unintentional release of dangerous goods, including any emergency response procedures for which the person is responsible and personal protection procedures to be followed.

1.3.1.5   Recommended training needs for shore-side personnel involved in the transport of dangerous goods under the IMDG Code

The following indicative table is for information purposes only as every entity is arranged differently and may have varied roles and responsibilities within that entity.

Function	Specific training requirements	Numbers in this column refer to the list of related codes and publications in 1.3.1.7
1 Classify dangerous goods and identify proper shipping name	Classification requirements, in particular – the structure of the description of substances – the classes of dangerous goods and the principles of their classification – the nature of the dangerous substances and articles transported (their physical, chemical and toxicological properties) – the procedure for classifying solutions and mixtures – identification by proper shipping name – use of Dangerous Goods List	.1, .4, .5 and .12
2 Pack dangerous goods	Classes Packaging requirements – type of packages (IBC, large packaging, tank container and bulk container) – UN marking for approved packagings – segregation requirements – limited quantities and excepted quantities Marking and labelling First aid measures Emergency response procedures Safe handling procedures	.1 and .4
3 Mark, label or placard dangerous goods	Classes Marking, labelling and placarding requirements – primary and subsidiary risk labels – marine pollutants – limited quantities and excepted quantities	.1

	Function	Specific training requirements	Numbers in this column refer to the list of related codes and publications in 1.3.1.7
△ 4	Load/unload cargo transport units	Documentation Classes Marking, labelling and placarding Stowage requirements, where applicable Segregation requirements Cargo securing requirements (as contained in the CTU Code) Emergency response procedures First aid measures CSC requirements Safe handling procedures	.1, .6, .7 and .8

5	Prepare transport documents for dangerous goods	Documentation requirements
		  – transport document
		  – container/vehicle packing certificate
		  – competent authorities' approval
		  – waste transport documentation
		  – special documentation, where appropriate
			.1

6	Offer dangerous goods for transport	Thorough knowledge of the IMDG Code
		Local requirements at loading and discharge ports
		  – port byelaws
		  – national transport regulations
			.1 to .10 and .12

7	Accept dangerous goods for transport	Thorough knowledge of the IMDG Code
		Local requirements at loading, transiting and discharge ports
		  – port byelaws, in particular quantity limitations
		  – national transport regulations
			.1 to .12

8	Handle dangerous goods in transport	Classes and their hazards
		Marking, labelling and placarding
		Emergency response procedures
		First aid measures
		Safe handling procedures such as
		  – use of equipment
		  – appropriate tools
		  – safe working loads
		CSC requirements, local requirements at loading, transit and discharge ports
		Port byelaws, in particular, quantity limitation
		National transport regulations
			.1, .2, .3, .6, .7, .8 and .10

9	Prepare dangerous goods loading/ stowage plans	Documentation Classes Stowage requirements Segregation requirements Document of compliance Relevant IMDG Code parts, local requirements at loading, transit and discharge ports Port byelaws, in particular, quantity limitations	.1, .10, .11 and .12

10	Load/unload dangerous goods into/ from ships	Classes and their hazards
		Marking, labelling and placarding
		Emergency response procedures
		First aid measures
		Safe handling procedures such as
		  – use of equipment
		  – appropriate tools
		  – safe working loads
		Cargo securing requirements
		CSC requirements, local requirements at loading, transit and discharge ports
		Port byelaws, in particular, quantity limitation
		National transport regulations
			.1, .2, .3, .7, .9, .10 and .12

Function	Specific training requirements	Numbers in this column refer to the list of related codes and publications in 1.3.1.7

△ 11 Carry dangerous goods	Documentation
	Classes
	Marking, labelling and placarding
	Stowage requirements, where applicable
	Segregation requirements
	Local requirements at loading, transit and discharge ports
	   – port byelaws, in particular, quantity limitations
	   – national transport regulations
	Cargo securing requirements (as contained in the CTU Code)
	Emergency response procedures
	First aid measures
	CSC requirements
	Safe handling procedures
		.1, .2, .3, .6, .7, .10, .11 and .12

12 Enforce or survey or inspect for compliance with applicable rules and regulations	Knowledge of IMDG Code and relevant guidelines and safety procedures	.1 to .13
13 Are otherwise involved in the transport of dangerous goods, as determined by the competent authority	As required by the competent authority commensurate with the task assigned	–

1.3.1.6 Indicative table describing sections of the IMDG Code or other relevant instruments that may be appropriate to be considered in any training for the transport of dangerous goods

	Function	1	2	2.0	3	4	5	6	6*	7.1	7.2	7.3	7.4	7.5	7.6	7.7	7.8	7.9	SOLAS chapter II-2/19	Port byelaws	National transport regulations	CSC	Guidelines for packing of cargo transport units	Emergency response procedures	First aid measures	Safe handling procedures
												IMDG Code part/section														
1	Classify	X	X		X		X											X								
2	Pack	X		X	X	X	X	X			X	X						X						X	X	X
3	Mark, label, placard			X	X		X																			
4	Load/unload cargo transport units	X		X	X	X	X		X		X	X											X	X	X	X
5	Prepare transport documents	X		X	X		X											X						X	X	
6	Offer for transport	X	X		X	X	X	X		X	X	X	X	X	X	X	X	X		X	X	X	X	X	X	
7	Accept for transport	X	X		X	X	X	X		X	X	X	X	X	X	X	X	X	X	X	X	X	X	X	X	
8	Handle in transport	X		X	X		X		X		X									X	X	X		X	X	X
9	Prepare loading/ stowage plans	X		X	X	X	X			X	X	X	X	X	X	X	X	X	X					X		
10	Load/unload from ships	X	X		X		X				X		X				X		X		X		X	X	X	X
11	Carry	X		X	X	X	X		X	X	X	X	X	X	X	X	X	X	X	X	X	X	X	X	X	X

*Only sections 6.1.2, 6.1.3, 6.5.2, 6.6.3, 6.7.2.20, 6.7.3.16 and 6.7.4.15 apply

1.3.1.7 Related Codes and publications which may be appropriate for function-specific training

.1 International Maritime Dangerous Goods (IMDG) Code, as amended

.2 The EmS Guide: Emergency Response Procedures for Ships Carrying Dangerous Goods (EmS), as amended

.3 Medical First Aid Guide for Use in Accidents Involving Dangerous Goods (MFAG), as amended

.4 United Nations Recommendations on the Transport of Dangerous Goods – Model Regulations, as amended

.5 United Nations Recommendations on the Transport of Dangerous Goods – Manual of Tests and Criteria, as amended

△ .6 CTU Code

.7 Recommendations on the Safe Transport of Dangerous Cargoes and Related Activities in Port Areas

.8 International Convention for Safe Containers (CSC), 1972, as amended

.9 Code of Safe Practice for Cargo Stowage and Securing (CSS Code), as amended

.10 Recommendations on the safe use of pesticides in ships applicable to the fumigation of cargo transport units (MSC.1/Circ.1265)[*]

.11 International Convention for the Safety of Life at Sea (SOLAS), 1974, as amended

.12 International Convention for the Prevention of Pollution from Ships 1973 as modified by the Protocol of 1978 (MARPOL), as amended.

.13 Inspection programmes for cargo transport units carrying dangerous goods (MSC.1/Circ.1442).

---

[*] At its eighty-seventh session, in May 2010, the Maritime Safety Committee of the IMO approved Revised Recommendations on the safe use of pesticides in ships applicable to the fumigation of cargo transport units (MSC.1/Circ.1361), which supersedes MSC.1/Circ.1265.

IMDG Code (amendment 38-16)

Chapter 1.4

Security provisions

1.4.0 Scope

1.4.0.1 The provisions of this chapter address the security of dangerous goods in transport by sea. National competent authorities may apply additional security provisions, which should be considered when offering or transporting dangerous goods. The provisions of this chapter remain recommendatory except 1.4.1.1 (see 1.1.1.5).

1.4.0.2 The provisions of 1.4.2 and 1.4.3 do not apply to:

.1 UN 2908 and UN 2909 excepted packages;

.2 UN 2910 and UN 2911 excepted packages with an activity level not exceeding the A_2 value; and

.3 UN 2912 LSA-I and UN 2913 SCO-I.

1.4.1 General provisions for companies, ships and port facilities[*]

1.4.1.1 The relevant provisions of chapter XI-2 of SOLAS, as amended, and of part A of the International Ship and Port Facility Security (ISPS) Code apply to companies, ships and port facilities engaged in the transport of dangerous goods and to which regulation XI-2 of SOLAS, as amended, apply taking into account the guidance given in part B of the ISPS Code.

1.4.1.2 For cargo ships of less than 500 gross tons engaged in the transport of dangerous goods, it is recommended that Contracting Governments to SOLAS, as amended, consider security provisions for these cargo ships.

1.4.1.3 Any shore-based company personnel, ship-based personnel and port facility personnel engaged in the transport of dangerous goods should be aware of the security requirements for such goods, in addition to those specified in the ISPS Code, and commensurate with their responsibilities.

1.4.1.4 The training of the company security officer, shore-based company personnel having specific security duties, port facility security officer and port facility personnel having specific duties, engaged in the transport of dangerous goods, should also include elements of security awareness related to those goods.

1.4.1.5 All shipboard personnel and port facility personnel who are not mentioned in 1.4.1.4 and are engaged in the transport of dangerous goods should be familiar with the provisions of the relevant security plans related to those goods, commensurate with their responsibilities.

1.4.2 General provisions for shore-side personnel

1.4.2.1 For the purpose of this subsection, shore-side personnel covers individuals mentioned in 1.3.1.2. However, the provisions of 1.4.2 do not apply to:

– the company security officer and appropriate shore-based company personnel mentioned in 13.1 of part A of the ISPS Code,

– the ship security officer and the shipboard personnel mentioned in 13.2 and 13.3 of part A of the ISPS Code,

– the port facility security officer, the appropriate port facility security personnel and the port facility personnel having specific security duties mentioned in 18.1 and 18.2 of part A of the ISPS Code.

For the training of those officers and personnel, refer to the International Ship and Port Facility Security (ISPS) Code.

---

[*] Refer to MSC.1/Circ.1341 on Guidelines on security-related training and familiarization for port facility personnel and to MSC.1/Circ.1188 on Guidelines on training and certification for port facility security officers.

1.4.2.2 Shore-side personnel engaged in transport by sea of dangerous goods should consider security provisions for the transport of dangerous goods commensurate with their responsibilities.

1.4.2.3 Security training

1.4.2.3.1 The training of shore-side personnel, as specified in chapter 1.3, shall also include elements of security awareness.

1.4.2.3.2 Security awareness training should address the nature of security risks, recognizing security risks, methods to address and reduce risks and actions to be taken in the event of a security breach. It should include awareness of security plans (if appropriate, refer to 1.4.3) commensurate with the responsibilities of individuals and their part in implementing security plans.

1.4.2.3.3 Such training should be provided or verified upon employment in a position involving dangerous goods transport and should be periodically supplemented with retraining.

1.4.2.3.4 Records of all security training received should be kept by the employer and made available to the employee or competent authority, upon request. Records should be kept by the employer for a period of time established by the competent authority.

1.4.3 Provisions for high consequence dangerous goods

1.4.3.1 Definition of high consequence dangerous goods

1.4.3.1.1 High consequence dangerous goods are those which have the potential for misuse in a terrorist event and which may, as a result, produce serious consequences such as mass casualties, mass destruction or, particularly for class 7, mass socio-economic disruption.

1.4.3.1.2 An indicative list of high consequence dangerous goods in classes and divisions other than class 7 is given in table 1.4.1 below.

Table 1.4.1 – Indicative list of high consequence dangerous goods

Class 1, Division 1.1	explosives
Class 1, Division 1.2	explosives
Class 1, Division 1.3	compatibility group C explosives
Class 1, Division 1.4	UN Nos. 0104, 0237, 0255, 0267, 0289, 0361, 0365, 0366, 0440, 0441, 0455, 0456 and 0500
Class 1, Division 1.5	explosives
Class 2.1	flammable gases in quantities greater than 3,000 L in a road tank vehicle, a railway tank wagon or a portable tank
Class 2.3	toxic gases
Class 3	flammable liquids of packing groups I and II in quantities greater than 3,000 L in a road tank vehicle, a railway tank wagon or a portable tank
Class 3	liquid desensitized explosives
Class 4.1	solid desensitized explosives
Class 4.2	goods of packing group I in quantities greater than 3,000 kg or 3,000 L in a road tank vehicle, a railway tank wagon, a portable tank or a bulk container
Class 4.3	goods of packing group I in quantities greater than 3,000 kg or 3,000 L in a road tank vehicle, a railway tank wagon, a portable tank or a bulk container
Class 5.1	oxidizing liquids of packing group I in quantities greater than 3,000 L in a road tank vehicle, a railway tank wagon or a portable tank
Class 5.1	perchlorates, ammonium nitrate, ammonium nitrate fertilizers and ammonium nitrate emulsions or suspensions or gels in quantities greater than 3,000 kg or 3,000 L in a road tank vehicle, a railway tank wagon, a portable tank or a bulk container
Class 6.1	toxic substances of packing group I
Class 6.2	infectious substances of category A (UN Nos. 2814 and 2900)

Class 8 corrosive substances of packing group I in quantities greater than 3,000 kg or 3,000 L in a road tank vehicle, a railway tank wagon, a portable tank or a bulk container

1.4.3.1.3 For dangerous goods of class 7, high consequence radioactive material is that with an activity equal to or greater than a transport security threshold of 3,000 A_2 per single package (see also 2.7.2.2.1) except for the following radionuclides where the transport security threshold is given in table 1.4.2 below.

Table 1.4.2 – Transport security thresholds for specific radionuclides

Element	Radionuclide	Transport security threshold (TBq)
Americium	Am-241	0.6
Gold	Au-198	2
Cadmium	Cd-109	200
Californium	Cf-252	0.2
Curium	Cm-244	0.5
Cobalt	Co-57	7
Cobalt	Co-60	0.3
Caesium	Cs-137	1
Iron	Fe-55	8,000
Germanium	Ge-68	7
Gadolinium	Gd-153	10
Iridium	Ir-192	0.8
Nickel	Ni-63	600
Palladium	Pd-103	900
Promethium	Pm-147	400
Polonium	Po-210	0.6
Plutonium	Pu-238	0.6
Plutonium	Pu-239	0.6
Radium	Ra-226	0.4
Ruthenium	Ru-106	3
Selenium	Se-75	2
Strontium	Sr-90	10
Thallium	Tl-204	200
Thulium	Tm-170	200
Ytterbium	Yb-169	3

1.4.3.1.4 For mixtures of radionuclides, determination of whether or not the transport security threshold has been met or exceeded can be calculated by summing the ratios of activity present for each radionuclide divided by the transport security threshold for that radionuclide. If the sum of the fractions is less than 1, then the radioactivity threshold for the mixture has not been met nor exceeded.

This calculation can be made with the formula:

$$\sum_i \frac{A_i}{T_i} < 1$$

where:

A_i = activity of radionuclide *i* that is present in a package (TBq)

T_i = transport security threshold for radionuclide *i* (TBq).

1.4.3.1.5 When radioactive materials possess subsidiary risks of other classes or divisions, the criteria of table 1.4.1 should also be taken into account (see also 1.5.5.1).

1.4.3.2 Specific security provisions for high consequence dangerous goods

1.4.3.2.1 The provisions of this section do not apply to ships and to port facilities (see the ISPS Code for ship security plan and for port facility security plan).

1.4.3.2.2 *Security plans*

1.4.3.2.2.1 Consignors and others engaged in the transport of high consequence dangerous goods (see 1.4.3.1) should adopt, implement and comply with a security plan that addresses at least the elements specified in 1.4.3.2.2.2.

1.4.3.2.2.2 The security plan should comprise at least the following elements:

.1 specific allocation of responsibilities for security to competent and qualified persons with appropriate authority to carry out their responsibilities;

.2 records of dangerous goods or types of dangerous goods transported;

.3 review of current operations and assessment of vulnerabilities, including intermodal transfer, temporary transit storage, handling and distribution, as appropriate;

.4 clear statements of measures, including training, policies (including response to higher threat conditions, new employee/employment verification, etc.), operating practices (e.g. choice/use of routes where known, access to dangerous goods in temporary storage, proximity to vulnerable infrastructure, etc.), equipment and resources that are to be used to reduce security risks;

.5 effective and up-to-date procedures for reporting and dealing with security threats, breaches of security or security-related incidents;

.6 procedures for the evaluation and testing of security plans and procedures for periodic review and update of the plans;

.7 measures to ensure the security of transport information contained in the plan; and

.8 measures to ensure that the distribution of transport information is limited as far as possible. (Such measures shall not preclude provision of transport documentation required by chapter 5.4 of this Code.)

1.4.3.2.3 For radioactive material, the provisions of this chapter are deemed to be complied with when the provisions of the Convention on Physical Protection of Nuclear Material[*] and the IAEA circular on The Physical Protection of Nuclear Material and Nuclear Facilities[†] are applied.

---

[*] INFCIRC/274/Rev.1, IAEA, Vienna (1980).

[†] INFCIRC/225/Rev.4 (Corrected), IAEA, Vienna (1999).

Chapter 1.5

General provisions concerning radioactive material

1.5.1 Scope and application

1.5.1.1 The provisions of this Code establish standards of safety which provide an acceptable level of control of the radiation, criticality and thermal hazards to persons, property and the environment that are associated with the transport of radioactive material. These provisions are based on the IAEA *Regulations for the Safe Transport of Radioactive Material*, 2012 Edition, *IAEA Safety Standards Series No. SSR-6, IAEA, Vienna (2012)*. Explanatory material can be found in *Advisory Material for the IAEA Regulations for the Safe Transport of Radioactive Material* (2012 Edition), *IAEA Safety Standards Series No. SSG-26, IAEA, Vienna (2014)*.

1.5.1.2 The objective of this Code is to establish provisions that shall be satisfied to ensure safety and to protect persons, property and the environment from the effects of radiation in the transport of radioactive material. This protection is achieved by requiring:

.1 containment of the radioactive contents;

.2 control of external radiation levels;

.3 prevention of criticality; and

.4 prevention of damage caused by heat.

These provisions are satisfied firstly by applying a graded approach to contents limits for packages and conveyances and to performance standards applied to package designs depending upon the hazard of the radioactive contents. Secondly, they are satisfied by imposing conditions on the design and operation of packages and on the maintenance of packagings, including a consideration of the nature of the radioactive contents. Finally, they are satisfied by requiring administrative controls including, where appropriate, approval by competent authorities.

1.5.1.3 The provisions of this Code apply to the transport of radioactive material by sea, including transport which is incidental to the use of the radioactive material. Transport comprises all operations and conditions associated with and involved in the movement of radioactive material; these include the design, manufacture, maintenance and repair of packaging, and the preparation, consigning, loading, transport including in-transit storage, unloading and receipt at the final destination of loads of radioactive material and packages. A graded approach is applied to the performance standards in the provisions of this Code that are characterized by three general severity levels:

.1 routine conditions of transport (incident-free);

.2 normal conditions of transport (minor mishaps); and

.3 accident conditions of transport.

1.5.1.4 The provisions of this Code do not apply to any of the following:

.1 radioactive material that is an integral part of the means of transport;

.2 radioactive material moved within an establishment which is subject to appropriate safety regulations in force in the establishment and where the movement does not involve public roads or railways;

.3 radioactive material implanted or incorporated into a person or live animal for diagnosis or treatment;

.4 radioactive material in or on a person who is to be transported for medical treatment because the person has been subject to accidental or deliberate intake of radioactive material or to contamination;

.5 radioactive material in consumer products which have received regulatory approval, following their sale to the end user;

.6 natural material and ores containing naturally occurring radionuclides (which may have been processed), provided the activity concentration of the material does not exceed 10 times the values specified in table 2.7.2.2.1, or calculated in accordance with 2.7.2.2.1 and 2.7.2.2.3 to 2.7.2.2.6. For natural materials and ores containing naturally occurring radionuclides that are not in secular equilibrium the calculation of the activity concentration shall be performed in accordance with 2.7.2.2.4; and

.7 non-radioactive solid objects with radioactive substances present on any surfaces in quantities not in excess of the limit set out in the definition for "contamination" in 2.7.1.2.

1.5.1.5 Specific provisions for the transport of excepted packages

1.5.1.5.1 Excepted packages which may contain radioactive material in limited quantities, instruments, manufactured articles or empty packagings as specified in 2.7.2.4.1 shall be subject only to the following provisions of parts 5 to 7:

.1 the applicable provisions specified in 5.1.1.2, 5.1.2, 5.1.3.2, 5.1.5.2.2, 5.1.5.2.3, 5.1.5.4, 5.2.1.7, 7.1.4.5.9, 7.1.4.5.10, 7.1.4.5.12, 7.8.4.1 to 7.8.4.6 and 7.8.9.1; and

.2 the requirements for excepted packages specified in 6.4.4,

except when the radioactive material possesses other hazardous properties and has to be classified in a class other than class 7 in accordance with special provision 290 or 369 of chapter 3.3, where the provisions listed in .1 and .2 above apply only as relevant and in addition to those relating to the main class or division.

1.5.1.5.2 Excepted packages shall be subject to the relevant provisions of all other parts of this Code. If the excepted package contains fissile material, one of the fissile exceptions provided by 2.7.2.3.5 shall apply and the requirements of 5.1.5.5 shall be met.

1.5.2 Radiation protection programme

1.5.2.1 The transport of radioactive material shall be subject to a radiation protection programme which shall consist of systematic arrangements aimed at providing adequate consideration of radiation protection measures.

1.5.2.2 Doses to persons shall be below the relevant dose limits. Protection and safety shall be optimized in order that the magnitude of individual doses, the number of persons exposed, and the likelihood of incurring exposure shall be kept as low as reasonably achievable, economic and social factors being taken into account, within the restrictions that the doses to individuals be subject to dose constraints. A structured and systematic approach shall be adopted and shall include consideration of the interfaces between transport and other activities.

1.5.2.3 The nature and extent of the measures to be employed in the programme shall be related to the magnitude and likelihood of radiation exposures. The programme shall incorporate the provisions in 1.5.2.2, 1.5.2.4 and 7.1.4.5.13 to 7.1.4.5.18. Programme documents shall be available, on request, for inspection by the relevant competent authority.

1.5.2.4 For occupational exposures arising from transport activities, where it is assessed that the effective dose either:

.1 is likely to be between 1 and 6 mSv in a year, a dose assessment programme via workplace monitoring or individual monitoring shall be conducted; or

.2 is likely to exceed 6 mSv in a year, individual monitoring shall be conducted.

When individual monitoring or workplace monitoring is conducted, appropriate records shall be kept.

Note: For occupational exposures arising from transport activities, where it is assessed that the effective dose is most unlikely to exceed 1 mSv in a year, no special work patterns, detailed monitoring, dose assessment programmes or individual record keeping need be required.

1.5.3 Management system

1.5.3.1 A management system based on international, national or other standards acceptable to the competent authority shall be established and implemented for all activities within the scope of this Code, as identified in 1.5.1.3, to ensure compliance with the relevant provisions of this Code. Certification that the design specification has been fully implemented shall be available to the competent authority. The manufacturer, consignor or user shall be prepared:

.1 to provide facilities for inspection during manufacture and use; and

.2 to demonstrate compliance with this Code to the competent authority.

Where competent authority approval is required, such approval shall take into account and be contingent upon the adequacy of the management system.

1.5.4 Special arrangement

1.5.4.1 *Special arrangement* shall mean those provisions, approved by the competent authority, under which consignments which do not satisfy all the provisions of this Code applicable to radioactive material may be transported.

1.5.4.2 Consignments for which conformity with any provision applicable to radioactive material is impracticable shall not be transported except under special arrangement. Provided the competent authority is satisfied that conformity with the radioactive material provisions of this Code is impracticable and that the requisite standards of safety established by this Code have been demonstrated through alternative means, the competent authority may approve special arrangement transport operations for single or a planned series of multiple consignments. The overall level of safety in transport shall be at least equivalent to that which would be provided if all the applicable provisions had been met. For international consignments of this type, multilateral approval shall be required.

1.5.5 Radioactive material possessing other dangerous properties

1.5.5.1 In addition to the radioactive and fissile properties, any subsidiary risk of the contents of a package, such as explosiveness, flammability, pyrophoricity, chemical toxicity and corrosiveness, shall also be taken into account in the documentation, packing, labelling, marking, placarding, stowage, segregation and transport, in order to be in compliance with all relevant provisions for dangerous goods. (See also special provision 172 and, for excepted packages, special provision 290.)

1.5.6 Non-compliance

1.5.6.1 In the event of non-compliance with any limit in the provisions of this Code applicable to radiation level or contamination,

.1 the consignor, consignee, carrier and any organization involved during transport who may be affected, as appropriate, shall be informed of the non-compliance:

.1 by the carrier if the non-compliance is identified during transport; or

.2 by the consignee if the non-compliance is identified at receipt;

.2 the carrier, consignor or consignee, as appropriate, shall:

.1 take immediate steps to mitigate the consequences of the non-compliance;

.2 investigate the non-compliance and its causes, circumstances and consequences;

.3 take appropriate action to remedy the causes and circumstances that led to the non-compliance and to prevent a recurrence of similar circumstances that led to the non-compliance; and

.4 communicate to the relevant competent authority(ies) on the causes of the non-compliance and on corrective or preventive actions taken or to be taken;

.3 The communication of the non-compliance to the consignor and relevant competent authority(ies), respectively, shall be made as soon as practicable and it shall be immediate whenever an emergency exposure situation has developed or is developing.

PART 2

CLASSIFICATION

2

Chapter 2.0

Introduction

2

Note: For the purposes of this Code, it has been necessary to classify dangerous goods in different classes, to subdivide a number of these classes and to define and describe characteristics and properties of the substances, materials and articles which would fall within each class or division. Moreover, in accordance with the criteria for the selection of marine pollutants for the purposes of Annex III of the International Convention for the Prevention of Pollution from Ships, 1973, as modified by the Protocol of 1978 relating thereto (MARPOL), a number of dangerous substances in the various classes have also been identified as substances harmful to the marine environment (MARINE POLLUTANTS).

2.0.0 Responsibilities

△ **2.0.0.1** The classification shall be made by the shipper/consignor or by the appropriate competent authority where specified in this Code.

■ **2.0.0.2** A consignor who has identified, on the basis of test data, that a substance listed by name in column 2 of the Dangerous Goods List in chapter 3.2 meets classification criteria for a hazard class or division that is not identified in the list, may, with the approval of the competent authority, consign the substance:

– under the most appropriate "generic" or "not otherwise specified" (N.O.S.) entry reflecting all hazards; or

– under the same UN number and name but with additional hazard communication information as appropriate to reflect the additional subsidiary risk(s) (documentation, label, placard) provided that the primary hazard class remains unchanged and that any other transport conditions (e.g. limited quantity, packaging and tank provisions) that would normally apply to substances possessing such a combination of hazards are the same as those applicable to the substance listed.

Note: When a competent authority grants such approvals, it should inform the United Nations Sub-Committee of Experts on the Transport of Dangerous Goods[*] accordingly and submit a relevant proposal of amendment to the Dangerous Goods List. Should the proposed amendment be rejected, the competent authority should withdraw its approval.

2.0.1 Classes, divisions, packing groups

2.0.1.1 Definitions

Substances (including mixtures and solutions) and articles subject to the provisions of this Code are assigned to one of the classes 1–9 according to the hazard or the most predominant of the hazards they present. Some of these classes are subdivided into divisions. These classes or divisions are as listed below:

Class 1: Explosives

Division 1.1: substances and articles which have a mass explosion hazard

Division 1.2: substances and articles which have a projection hazard but not a mass explosion hazard

Division 1.3: substances and articles which have a fire hazard and either a minor blast hazard or a minor projection hazard or both, but not a mass explosion hazard

Division 1.4: substances and articles which present no significant hazard

Division 1.5: very insensitive substances which have a mass explosion hazard

Division 1.6: extremely insensitive articles which do not have a mass explosion hazard

Class 2: Gases

Class 2.1: flammable gases

Class 2.2: non-flammable, non-toxic gases

Class 2.3: toxic gases

---

[*] UNECE United Nations Economic Commission for Europe, Dangerous Goods and Special Cargoes Section, Transport Division. Palais des Nations, Bureau 418, CH-1211 Geneva 10, Switzerland. Tel: +41 22 917 24 56, Fax: +41 22 917 00 39. www.unece.org/trans/danger/danger.html.

Class 3:   Flammable liquids

Class 4:   Flammable solids; substances liable to spontaneous combustion; substances which, in contact with water, emit flammable gases

△ Class 4.1:   flammable solids, self-reactive substances, solid desensitized explosives and polymerizing substances

Class 4.2:   substances liable to spontaneous combustion

Class 4.3:   substances which, in contact with water, emit flammable gases

Class 5:   Oxidizing substances and organic peroxides

Class 5.1:   oxidizing substances

Class 5.2:   organic peroxides

Class 6:   Toxic and infectious substances

Class 6.1:   toxic substances

Class 6.2:   infectious substances

Class 7:   Radioactive material

Class 8:   Corrosive substances

Class 9:   Miscellaneous dangerous substances and articles

The numerical order of the classes and divisions is not that of the degree of danger.

2.0.1.2   Marine pollutants

2.0.1.2.1 Many of the substances assigned to classes 1 to 6.2, 8 and 9 are deemed as being *marine pollutants* (see chapter 2.10).

2.0.1.2.2 Known marine pollutants are noted in the Dangerous Goods List and are indicated in the Index.

2.0.1.3 For packing purposes, substances other than those of classes 1, 2, 5.2, 6.2 and 7, and other than self-reactive substances of class 4.1, are assigned to three packing groups in accordance with the degree of danger they present:

Packing group I: substances presenting high danger;

Packing group II: substances presenting medium danger; and

Packing group III: substances presenting low danger.

The packing group to which a substance is assigned is indicated in the Dangerous Goods List in chapter 3.2.

Articles are not assigned to packing groups. For packing purposes, any requirement for a specific packaging performance level is set out in the applicable packing instruction.

2.0.1.4 Dangerous goods are determined to present one or more of the dangers represented by classes 1 to 9, marine pollutants and, if applicable, the degree of danger (packing group) on the basis of the provisions in chapters 2.1 to 2.10.

2.0.1.5 Dangerous goods presenting a danger of a single class or division are assigned to that class or division and the packing group, if applicable, determined. When an article or substance is specifically listed by name in the Dangerous Goods List in chapter 3.2, its class or division, its subsidiary risk(s) and, when applicable, its packing group are taken from this list.

2.0.1.6 Dangerous goods meeting the defining criteria of more than one hazard class or division and which are not listed by name in the Dangerous Goods List are assigned to a class or division and subsidiary risk(s) on the basis of the precedence of hazard provisions prescribed in 2.0.3.

2.0.2   UN numbers and proper shipping names

2.0.2.1 Dangerous goods are assigned to UN numbers and proper shipping names according to their hazard classification and their composition.

△ **2.0.2.2** Dangerous goods commonly transported are listed in the Dangerous Goods List in chapter 3.2. Where an article or substance is specifically listed by name, it shall be identified in transport by the proper shipping name in the Dangerous Goods List. Such substances may contain technical impurities (for example those deriving from the production process) or additives for stability or other purposes that do not affect their classification. However, a substance listed by name containing technical impurities or additives for stability or other purposes affecting its classification shall be considered a mixture or solution (see 2.0.2.5). For dangerous goods not specifically listed by name, "generic" or "not otherwise specified" entries are provided (see 2.0.2.7) to identify the article or substance in transport. The substances listed by name in column (2) of the Dangerous Goods List of chapter 3.2 shall be transported according to their classification in the list or under the conditions specified in 2.0.0.2.

Each entry in the Dangerous Goods List is assigned a UN number. This list also contains relevant information for each entry, such as hazard class, subsidiary risk(s) (if any), packing group (where assigned), packing and tank transport provisions, EmS, segregation and stowage, properties and observations, etc.

Entries in the Dangerous Goods List are of the following four types:

.1   single entries for well-defined substances or articles:

    e.g. UN 1090   acetone

        UN 1194   ethyl nitrite solution

.2   generic entries for well-defined groups of substances or articles:

    e.g. UN 1133   adhesives

        UN 1266   perfumery product

        UN 2757   carbamate pesticide, solid, toxic

        UN 3101   organic peroxide type B, liquid

.3   specific N.O.S. entries covering a group of substances or articles of a particular chemical or technical nature:

    e.g. UN 1477   nitrates, inorganic, N.O.S.

        UN 1987   alcohols, N.O.S.

.4   general N.O.S. entries covering a group of substances or articles meeting the criteria of one or more classes:

    e.g. UN 1325   flammable solid, organic, N.O.S.

        UN 1993   flammable liquid, N.O.S.

2.0.2.3   All self-reactive substances of class 4.1 are assigned to one of 20 generic entries in accordance with the classification principles described in 2.4.2.3.3.

2.0.2.4   All organic peroxides of class 5.2 are assigned to one of 20 generic entries in accordance with the classification principles described in 2.5.3.3.

2.0.2.5   A mixture or solution meeting the classification criteria of this Code composed of a single predominant substance identified by name in the Dangerous Goods List and one or more substances not subject to the provisions of this Code and/or traces of one or more substances identified by name in the Dangerous Goods List, shall be assigned the UN number and proper shipping name of the predominant substance named in the Dangerous Goods List unless:

.1   the mixture or solution is identified by name in the Dangerous Goods List;

.2   the name and description of the substance named in the Dangerous Goods List specifically indicate that they apply only to the pure substance;

.3   the hazard class or division, subsidiary risk(s), packing group, or physical state of the mixture or solution is different from that of the substance named in the Dangerous Goods List; or

.4   the hazard characteristics and properties of the mixture or solution necessitate emergency response measures that are different from those required for the substance identified by name in the Dangerous Goods List.

In those other cases, except the one described in .1, the mixture or solution shall be treated as a dangerous substance not specifically listed by name in the Dangerous Goods List.

2.0.2.6   When the class, physical state or packing group has changed in comparison with the pure substance, the solution or mixture shall be shipped in accordance with the provisions for the changed hazard under an appropriate N.O.S. entry.

2.0.2.7   Substances or articles which are not specifically listed by name in the Dangerous Goods List shall be classified under a "generic" or "not otherwise specified" (N.O.S.) proper shipping name. The substance or article shall be classified according to the class definitions and test criteria in this part, and the article or substance classified under the generic or "N.O.S." proper shipping name in the Dangerous Goods List which most appropriately describes the article or substance. This means that a substance is only to be assigned to an entry of type .3, as defined in 2.0.2.2, if it cannot be assigned to an entry of type .2, and to an entry of type .4 if it cannot be assigned to an entry of type .2 or .3.[*]

2.0.2.8   When considering a solution or mixture in accordance with 2.0.2.5, due account shall be given to whether the dangerous constituent comprising the solution or mixture has been identified as a marine pollutant. If this is the case, the provisions of chapter 2.10 are also applicable.

---

[*] See also the generic or N.O.S. proper shipping name in appendix A.

2.0.2.9   A mixture or solution, containing one or more substances identified by name in this Code or classified under an N.O.S. or generic entry and one or more substances not subject to the provisions of this Code, is not subject to the provisions of this Code if the hazard characteristics of the mixture or solution are such that they do not meet the criteria (including human experience criteria) for any class.

2.0.2.10   A mixture or solution meeting the classification criteria of this Code that is not identified by name in the Dangerous Goods List and that is composed of two or more dangerous goods shall be assigned to an entry that has the proper shipping name, description, hazard class or division, subsidiary risk(s) and packing group that most precisely describe the mixture or solution.

2.0.3   Classification of substances, mixtures and solutions with multiple hazards (precedence of hazard characteristics)

2.0.3.1   The table of precedence of hazard characteristics in 2.0.3.6 shall be used to determine the class of a substance, mixture or solution having more than one hazard when it is not specifically listed by name in this Code. For substances, mixtures or solutions having multiple hazards which are not specifically listed by name, the most stringent packing group of those assigned to the respective hazards of the goods takes precedence over other packing groups, irrespective of the precedence of hazard table in 2.0.3.6.

2.0.3.2   The precedence of hazard table indicates which of the hazards shall be regarded as the primary hazard. The class which appears at the intersection of the horizontal line and the vertical column is the primary hazard and the remaining class is the subsidiary hazard. The packing groups for each of the hazards associated with the substance, mixture or solution shall be determined by reference to the appropriate criteria. The most stringent of the groups so indicated shall then become the packing group of the substance, mixture or solution.

2.0.3.3   The proper shipping name (see 3.1.2) of a substance, mixture or solution when classified in accordance with 2.0.3.1 and 2.0.3.2 shall be the most appropriate N.O.S. ("not otherwise specified") entry in this Code for the class shown as the primary hazard.

2.0.3.4   The precedence of hazard characteristics of the following substances, materials and articles have not been dealt with in the precedence of hazard table, as these primary hazards always take precedence:

     .1   substances and articles of class 1;

     .2   gases of class 2;

     .3   liquid desensitized explosives of class 3;

     .4   self-reactive substances and solid desensitized explosives of class 4.1;

     .5   pyrophoric substances of class 4.2;

     .6   substances of class 5.2;

     .7   substances of class 6.1 with a packing group I vapour inhalation toxicity;

     .8   substances of class 6.2; and

     .9   materials of class 7.

2.0.3.5   Apart from excepted radioactive material (where the other hazardous properties take precedence), radioactive material having other hazardous properties shall always be classified in class 7, with the greatest of the additional hazards being identified. For radioactive material in excepted packages, except for UN 3507, URANIUM HEXAFLUORIDE, RADIOACTIVE MATERIAL, EXCEPTED PACKAGE, special provision 290 of chapter 3.3 applies.

2.0.3.6   **Precedence of hazards**

Class and Packing Group	4.2	4.3	5.1 I	5.1 II	5.1 III	6.1, I Dermal	6.1, I Oral	6.1 II	6.1 III	8, I Liquid	8, I Solid	8, II Liquid	8, II Solid	8, III Liquid	8, III Solid
3 I*		4.3				3	3	3	3	3	–	3	–	3	–
3 II*		4.3				3	3	3	3	8	–	3	–	3	–
3 III*		4.3				6.1	6.1	6.1	3†	8	–	8	–	3	–
4.1 II*	4.2	4.3	5.1	4.1	4.1	6.1	6.1	4.1	4.1	–	8	–	4.1	–	4.1
4.1 III*	4.2	4.3	5.1	4.1	4.1	6.1	6.1	6.1	4.1	–	8	–	8	–	4.1
4.2 II		4.3	5.1	4.2	4.2	6.1	6.1	4.2	4.2	8	8	4.2	4.2	4.2	4.2
4.2 III		4.3	5.1	5.1	4.2	6.1	6.1	6.1	4.2	8	8	8	8	4.2	4.2
4.3 I			5.1	4.3	4.3	6.1	4.3	4.3	4.3	4.3	4.3	4.3	4.3	4.3	4.3
4.3 II			5.1	4.3	4.3	6.1	4.3	4.3	4.3	8	8	4.3	4.3	4.3	4.3
4.3 III			5.1	5.1	4.3	6.1	6.1	6.1	4.3	8	8	8	8	4.3	4.3

Class and Packing Group	4.2	4.3	5.1 I	5.1 II	5.1 III	6.1, I Dermal	6.1, I Oral	6.1 II	6.1 III	8, I Liquid	8, I Solid	8, II Liquid	8, II Solid	8, III Liquid	8, III Solid
5.1 I						5.1	5.1	5.1	5.1	5.1	5.1	5.1	5.1	5.1	5.1
5.1 II						6.1	5.1	5.1	5.1	8	8	5.1	5.1	5.1	5.1
5.1 III						6.1	6.1	6.1	5.1	8	8	8	8	5.1	5.1
6.1 I, Dermal										8	6.1	6.1	6.1	6.1	6.1
6.1 I, Oral										8	6.1	6.1	6.1	6.1	6.1
6.1 II, Inhalation										8	6.1	6.1	6.1	6.1	6.1
6.1 II, Dermal										8	6.1	8	6.1	6.1	6.1
6.1 II, Oral										8	8	8	6.1	6.1	6.1
6.1 III										8	8	8	8	8	8

* Substances of class 4.1 other than self-reactive substances and solid desensitized explosives and substances of class 3 other than liquid desensitized explosives.

† 6.1 for pesticides.

– Denotes an impossible combination.

For hazards not shown in this table, see 2.0.3.4 and 2.0.3.5.

2.0.4   Transport of samples

2.0.4.1   When the hazard class of a substance is uncertain and it is being transported for further testing, a tentative hazard class, proper shipping name and identification number shall be assigned on the basis of the consignor's knowledge of the substances and application of:

.1   the classification criteria of this Code; and

.2   the precedence of hazards given in 2.0.3.

The most severe packing group possible for the proper shipping name chosen shall be used.

Where this provision is used, the proper shipping name shall be supplemented with the word "SAMPLE" (such as FLAMMABLE LIQUID, N.O.S., SAMPLE). In certain instances, where a specific proper shipping name is provided for a sample of a substance considered to meet certain classification criteria (such as UN 3167, GAS SAMPLE, NON-PRESSURIZED, FLAMMABLE), that proper shipping name shall be used. When an N.O.S. entry is used to transport the sample, the proper shipping name need not be supplemented with the technical name as required by special provision 274.

2.0.4.2   Samples of the substance shall be transported in accordance with the provisions applicable to the tentative assigned proper shipping name provided:

.1   the substance is not considered to be a substance prohibited for transport by 1.1.3;

.2   the substance is not considered to meet the criteria for class 1 or considered to be an infectious substance or a radioactive material;

.3   the substance is in compliance with 2.4.2.3.2.4.2 or 2.5.3.2.5.1 if it is a self-reactive substance or an organic peroxide, respectively;

.4   the sample is transported in a combination packaging with a net mass per package not exceeding 2.5 kg; and

.5   the sample is not packed together with other goods.

2.0.5   Transport of wastes

2.0.5.1   Preamble

Wastes, which are dangerous goods, shall be transported in accordance with the relevant international recommendations and conventions and, in particular, where it concerns transport by sea, with the provisions of this Code.

2.0.5.2   Applicability

2.0.5.2.1   The provisions of this chapter are applicable to the transport of wastes by ships and shall be considered in conjunction with all other provisions of this Code.

2.0.5.2.2 Substances, solutions, mixtures or articles containing or contaminated with radioactive material are subject to the applicable provisions for radioactive material in class 7, and are not to be considered as wastes for the purposes of this chapter.

2.0.5.3 Transboundary movements under the Basel Convention[*]

2.0.5.3.1 Transboundary movement of wastes is permitted to commence only when:

.1 notification has been sent by the competent authority of the country of origin, or by the generator or exporter through the channel of the competent authority of the country of origin, to the country of final destination; and

.2 the competent authority of the country of origin, having received the written consent of the country of final destination stating that the wastes will be safely incinerated or treated by other methods of disposal, has given authorization to the movement.

2.0.5.3.2 In addition to the transport document required in chapter 5.4, all transboundary movements of wastes shall be accompanied by a waste movement document from the point at which a transboundary movement commences to the point of disposal. This document shall be available at all times to the competent authorities and to all persons involved in the management of waste transport operations.

2.0.5.3.3 The transport of solid wastes in bulk in cargo transport units and road vehicles is only permitted with the approval of the competent authority of the country of origin.

2.0.5.3.4 In the event that packages and cargo transport units containing wastes are suffering from leakage or spillage, the competent authorities of the countries of origin and destination shall be immediately informed and advice on the action to be taken obtained from them.

2.0.5.4 Classification of wastes

2.0.5.4.1 A waste containing only one constituent which is a dangerous substance subject to the provisions of this Code shall be regarded as being that particular substance. If the concentration of the constituent is such that the waste continues to present a hazard inherent in the constituent itself, it shall be classified according to the criteria of the applicable classes.

2.0.5.4.2 A waste containing two or more constituents which are dangerous substances subject to the provisions of this Code shall be classified under the applicable class in accordance with their dangerous characteristics and properties as described in 2.0.5.4.3 and 2.0.5.4.4.

2.0.5.4.3 The classification according to the dangerous characteristics and properties shall be carried out as follows:

.1 determination of the physical and chemical characteristics and physiological properties by measurement or calculation followed by classification according to the criteria of the applicable class(es); or

.2 if the determination is not practicable, the waste shall be classified according to the constituent presenting the predominant hazard.

2.0.5.4.4 In determining the predominant hazard, the following criteria shall be taken into account:

.1 if one or more constituents fall within a certain class and the waste presents a hazard inherent in these constituents, the waste shall be included in that class; or

.2 if there are constituents falling under two or more classes, the classification of the waste shall take into account the order of precedence applicable to dangerous substances with multiple hazards set out in 2.0.3.

2.0.5.4.5 Wastes harmful to the marine environment only shall be transported under the class 9 entries for ENVIRONMENTALLY HAZARDOUS SUBSTANCE, LIQUID, N.O.S., UN 3082, or ENVIRONMENTALLY HAZARDOUS SUBSTANCE, SOLID, N.O.S., UN 3077, with the addition of the word "WASTE". However, this is not applicable to substances which are covered by individual entries in this Code.

2.0.5.4.6 Wastes not otherwise subject to the provisions of this Code but covered under the Basel Convention may be transported under the class 9 entries for ENVIRONMENTALLY HAZARDOUS SUBSTANCE, LIQUID, N.O.S., UN 3082 or ENVIRONMENTALLY HAZARDOUS SUBSTANCE, SOLID, N.O.S., UN 3077 with the addition of the word WASTE.

---

[*] Basel Convention on the Control of Transboundary Movements of Hazardous Wastes and their Disposal (1989).

Chapter 2.1

Class 1 – Explosives

2.1.0 Introductory notes (these notes are not mandatory)

Note 1: Class 1 is a restricted class, that is, only those explosive substances and articles that are listed in the Dangerous Goods List in chapter 3.2 may be accepted for transport. However, the competent authorities retain the right by mutual agreement to approve transport of explosive substances and articles for special purposes under special conditions. Therefore entries have been included in the Dangerous Goods List for "Substances, explosive, not otherwise specified" and "Articles, explosive, not otherwise specified". It is intended that these entries should only be used when no other method of operation is possible.

Note 2: General entries such as "Explosive, blasting, type A" are used to allow for the transport of new substances. In preparing these provisions, military ammunition and explosives have been taken into consideration to the extent that they are likely to be transported by commercial carriers.

Note 3: A number of substances and articles in class 1 are described in appendix B. These descriptions are given because a term may not be well-known or may be at variance with its usage for regulatory purposes.

Note 4: Class 1 is unique in that the type of packaging frequently has a decisive effect on the hazard and therefore on the assignment to a particular division. The correct division is determined by use of the procedures provided in this chapter.

2.1.1 Definitions and general provisions

2.1.1.1 Class 1 comprises:

.1 explosive substances (a substance which is not itself an explosive but which can form an explosive atmosphere of gas, vapour or dust is not included in class 1), except those which are too dangerous to transport or those where the predominant hazard is one appropriate to another class;

.2 explosive articles, except devices containing explosive substances in such quantity or of such a character that their inadvertent or accidental ignition or initiation during transport shall not cause any effect external to the device either by projection, fire, smoke, heat or loud noise (see 2.1.3.4); and

.3 substances and articles not mentioned under .1 and .2 which are manufactured with a view to producing a practical, explosive or pyrotechnic effect.

2.1.1.2 Transport of explosive substances which are unduly sensitive, or so reactive as to be subject to spontaneous reaction, is prohibited.

2.1.1.3 Definitions

For the purposes of this Code, the following definitions apply:

.1 *Explosive substance* means a solid or liquid substance (or a mixture of substances) which is in itself capable by chemical reaction of producing gas at such a temperature and pressure and at such a speed as to cause damage to the surroundings. Pyrotechnic substances are included even when they do not evolve gases.

.2 *Pyrotechnic substance* means a substance or a mixture of substances designed to produce an effect by heat, light, sound, gas or smoke or a combination of these as the result of non-detonative self-sustaining exothermic chemical reactions.

.3 *Explosive article* means an article containing one or more explosive substances.

.4 *Mass explosion* means one which affects almost the entire load virtually instantaneously.

.5 *Phlegmatized* means that a substance (or "phlegmatizer") has been added to an explosive to enhance its safety in handling and transport. The phlegmatizer renders the explosive insensitive, or less sensitive, to the following actions: heat, shock, impact, percussion or friction. Typical phlegmatizing agents include, but are not limited to: wax, paper, water, polymers (such as chlorofluoropolymers), alcohol and oils (such as petroleum jelly and paraffin).

2.1.1.4   Hazard divisions

The six hazard divisions of class 1 are:

Division 1.1   Substances and articles which have a mass explosion hazard

Division 1.2   Substances and articles which have a projection hazard but not a mass explosion hazard

Division 1.3   Substances and articles which have a fire hazard and either a minor blast hazard or a minor projection hazard or both, but not a mass explosion hazard

This division comprises substances and articles:
.1 which give rise to considerable radiant heat; or
.2 which burn one after another, producing minor blast or projection effects or both.

Division 1.4   Substances and articles which present no significant hazard

This division comprises substances and articles which present only a small hazard in the event of ignition or initiation during transport. The effects are largely confined to the package and no projection of fragments of appreciable size or range is to be expected. An external fire must not cause virtually instantaneous explosion of almost the entire contents of the package.

Note: Substances and articles in this division are in compatibility group S if they are so packaged or designed that any hazardous effects arising from the accidental functioning are confined within the package unless the package has been degraded by fire, in which case all blast or projection effects are limited to the extent that they do not significantly hinder fire fighting or other emergency response efforts in the immediate vicinity of the package.

Division 1.5   Very insensitive substances which have a mass explosion hazard

This division comprises substances which have a mass explosion hazard but are so insensitive that there is very little probability of initiation or of transition from burning to detonation under normal conditions of transport.

Note: The probability of transition from burning to detonation is greater when large quantities are transported in a ship. As a consequence, the stowage provisions for explosive substances in division 1.1 and for those in division 1.5 are identical.

△ Division 1.6   Extremely insensitive articles which do not have a mass explosion hazard

This division comprises articles which predominantly contain extremely insensitive substances and which demonstrate a negligible probability of accidental initiation or propagation.

Note: The risk from articles of division 1.6 is limited to the explosion of a single article.

2.1.1.5   Any substance or article having or suspected of having explosive characteristics shall first be considered for classification in class 1 in accordance with the procedures in 2.1.3. Goods are not classified in class 1 when:

.1   unless specially authorized, the transport of an explosive substance is prohibited because sensitivity of the substance is excessive;

.2   the substance or article comes within the scope of those explosive substances and articles which are specifically excluded from class 1 by the definition of this class; or

.3   the substance or article has no explosive properties.

2.1.2   Compatibility groups and classification codes

2.1.2.1   Goods of class 1 are considered to be "compatible" if they can be safely stowed or transported together without significantly increasing either the probability of an accident or, for a given quantity, the magnitude of the effects of such an accident. By this criterion, goods listed in this class have been divided into a number of compatibility groups, each denoted by a letter from A to L (excluding I), N and S. These are described in 2.1.2.2 and 2.1.2.3.

2.1.2.2 Compatibility groups and classification codes

Description of substance or articles to be classified	Compatibility group	Classification code
Primary explosive substance	A	1.1A
Article containing a primary explosive substance and not containing two or more effective protective features. Some articles, such as detonators for blasting, detonator assemblies for blasting and primers, cap-type, are included even though they do not contain primary explosives	B	1.1B 1.2B 1.4B
Propellant explosive substance or other deflagrating explosive substance or article containing such explosive substance	C	1.1C 1.2C 1.3C 1.4C
Secondary detonating explosive substance or black powder or article containing a secondary detonating explosive substance, in each case without means of initiation and without a propelling charge, or article containing a primary explosive substance and containing two or more effective protective features	D	1.1D 1.2D 1.4D 1.5D
Article containing a secondary detonating explosive substance, without means of initiation, with a propelling charge (other than one containing a flammable liquid or gel or hypergolic liquids)	E	1.1E 1.2E 1.4E
Article containing a secondary detonating explosive substance with its own means of initiation, with a propelling charge (other than one containing a flammable liquid or gel or hypergolic liquids) or without a propelling charge	F	1.1F 1.2F 1.3F 1.4F
Pyrotechnic substance, or article containing a pyrotechnic substance, or article containing both an explosive substance and an illuminating, incendiary, tear- or smoke-producing substance (other than a water-activated article or one containing white phosphorus, phosphides, a pyrophoric substance, a flammable liquid or gel, or hypergolic liquids)	G	1.1G 1.2G 1.3G 1.4G
Article containing both an explosive substance and white phosphorus	H	1.2H 1.3H
Article containing both an explosive substance and a flammable liquid or gel	J	1.1J 1.2J 1.3J
Article containing both an explosive substance and a toxic chemical agent	K	1.2K 1.3K
Explosive substance or article containing an explosive substance and presenting a special risk (such as due to water-activation or presence of hypergolic liquids, phosphides or a pyrophoric substance) and needing isolation of each type (see 7.2.7.1.4, note 2)	L	1.1L 1.2L 1.3L
△ Articles predominantly containing extremely insensitive substances	N	1.6N
Substance or article so packaged or designed that any hazardous effects arising from accidental functioning are confined within the package unless the package has been degraded by fire, in which case all blast or projection effects are limited to the extent that they do not significantly hinder or prohibit fire fighting or other emergency response efforts in the immediate vicinity of the package	S	1.4S

Note 1: Articles of compatibility groups D and E may be fitted or packed together with their own means of initiation provided that such means have at least two effective protective features designed to prevent an explosion in the event of accidental functioning of the means of initiation. Such articles and packages shall be assigned to compatibility groups D or E.

Note 2: Articles of compatibility groups D and E may be packed together with their own means of initiation, which do not have two effective protective features when, in the opinion of the competent authority of the country of origin, the accidental functioning of the means of initiation does not cause the explosion of an article under normal conditions of transport. Such packages shall be assigned to compatibility groups D or E.

2.1.2.3   Scheme of classification of explosives, combination of hazard division with compatibility group

Hazard division	Compatibility group													$\sum$ A–S
	A	B	C	D	E	F	G	H	J	K	L	N	S	
1.1	1.1A	1.1B	1.1C	1.1D	1.1E	1.1F	1.1G		1.1J		1.1L			9
1.2		1.2B	1.2C	1.2D	1.2E	1.2F	1.2G	1.2H	1.2J	1.2K	1.2L			10
1.3			1.3C			1.3F	1.3G	1.3H	1.3J	1.3K	1.3L			7
1.4		1.4B	1.4C	1.4D	1.4E	1.4F	1.4G						1.4S	7
1.5				1.5D										1
1.6												1.6N		1
$\sum$ 1.1–1.6	1	3	4	4	3	4	4	2	3	2	3	1	1	35

2.1.2.4   The definitions of compatibility groups in 2.1.2.2 are intended to be mutually exclusive, except for a substance or article which qualifies for compatibility group S. Since the criterion of compatibility group S is an empirical one, assignment to this group is necessarily linked to the tests for assignment to division 1.4.

2.1.3   Classification procedure

2.1.3.1   Any substance or article having or suspected of having explosive characteristics shall be considered for classification in class 1. Substances and articles classified in class 1 shall be assigned to the appropriate division and compatibility group. Goods of class 1 shall be classified in accordance with the latest version of the Manual of Tests and Criteria.

2.1.3.2   Prior to transport, the classification of all explosive substances and articles, together with the compatibility group assignment and the proper shipping name under which the substance or article is to be transported, shall have been approved by the competent authority of the country of manufacture. A new approval would be required for:

.1   a new explosive substance; or

.2   a new combination or mixture of explosive substances which is significantly different from other combinations or mixtures previously manufactured and approved; or

.3   a new design of an explosive article, an article containing a new explosive substance, or an article containing a new combination or mixture of explosive substances; or

.4   an explosive substance or article with a new design or type of packaging, including a new type of inner packaging.

2.1.3.3   Assessment of the hazard division is usually made on the basis of test results. A substance or article shall be assigned to the hazard division which corresponds to the results of the tests to which the substance or article, as offered for transport, has been subjected. Other test results, and data assembled from accidents which have occurred, may also be taken into account.

2.1.3.4   Exclusion from class 1

2.1.3.4.1   The competent authority may exclude an article or substance from class 1 by virtue of test results and the class 1 definition.

2.1.3.4.2   An article may be excluded from class 1 by the competent authority when three unpackaged articles, each individually activated by its own means of initiation or ignition or external means to function in the designed mode, meet the following test criteria:

.1   no external surface shall have a temperature of more than 65°C. A momentary spike in temperature up to 200°C is acceptable;

.2   no rupture or fragmentation of the external casing or movement of the article or detached parts thereof of more than one metre in any direction;

Note: Where the integrity of the article may be affected in the event of an external fire these criteria shall be examined by a fire test, such as described in ISO 12097-3.

.3   no audible report exceeding 135 dB(C) peak at a distance of one metre;

.4   no flash or flame capable of igniting a material such as a sheet of 80 $\pm$ 10 g/m² paper in contact with the article; and

.5 no production of smoke, fumes or dust in such quantities that the visibility in a one cubic metre chamber equipped with appropriately sized blow out panels is reduced more than 50% as measured by a calibrated light (lux) meter or radiometer located one metre from a constant light source located at the midpoint on opposite walls. The general guidance on Optical Density Testing in ISO 5659-1 and the general guidance on the Photometric System described in Section 7.5 in ISO 5659-2 may be used or similar optical density measurement methods designed to accomplish the same purpose may also be employed. A suitable hood cover surrounding the back and sides of the light meter shall be used to minimize effects of scattered or leaking light not emitted directly from the source.

Note 1: If during the tests addressing criteria .1, .2, .3 and .4 no or very little smoke is observed the test described in .5 may be waived.

Note 2: The competent authority may require testing in packaged form if it is determined that, as packaged for transport, the article may pose a greater risk.

2.1.3.5 Assignment of fireworks to hazard divisions

△ **2.1.3.5.1** Fireworks shall normally be assigned to hazard divisions 1.1, 1.2, 1.3, and 1.4 on the basis of test data derived from Test Series 6 of the Manual of Tests and Criteria. However:

.1 waterfalls giving a positive result when tested in the HSL Flash composition test in appendix 7 of the Manual of Tests and Criteria shall be classified as 1.1G regardless of the results of Test Series 6;

.2 since the range of fireworks is very extensive and the availability of test facilities may be limited, assignment to hazard divisions may also be made in accordance with the procedure in 2.1.3.5.2.

2.1.3.5.2 Assignment of fireworks to UN Nos. 0333, 0334, 0335 or 0336 may be made on the basis of analogy, without the need for Test Series 6 testing, in accordance with the default fireworks classification table in 2.1.3.5.5. Such assignment shall be made with the agreement of the competent authority. Items not specified in the table shall be classified on the basis of test data derived from Test Series 6 of the Manual of Tests and Criteria.

Note: The addition of other types of fireworks to column 1 of the table in 2.1.3.5.5 shall only be made on the basis of full test data submitted to the UN Sub-Committee of Experts on the Transport of Dangerous Goods for consideration.

2.1.3.5.3 Where fireworks of more than one hazard division are packed in the same package they shall be classified on the basis of the highest hazard division unless test data derived from Test Series 6 of the Manual of Tests and Criteria indicate otherwise.

2.1.3.5.4 The classification shown in the table in 2.1.3.5.5 applies only for articles packed in fibreboard boxes (4G).

2.1.3.5.5   Default fireworks classification table*

Note 1: References to percentages in the table, unless otherwise stated, are to the mass of all pyrotechnic substances (e.g. rocket motors, lifting charge, bursting charge and effect charge).

Note 2: "Flash composition" in this table refers to pyrotechnic substances in powder form or as pyrotechnic units as presented in the fireworks that are used to produce an aural effect or used as a bursting charge, or propellant charge unless the time taken for the pressure rise is demonstrated to be more than 6 ms for 0.5 g of pyrotechnic substance in the HSL Flash Composition Test in appendix 7 of the Manual of Tests and Criteria.

Note 3: Dimensions in mm refers to:

– for spherical and peanut shells, the diameter of the sphere of the shell;

– for cylinder shells, the length of the shell;

– for a shell in mortar, Roman candle, shot tube firework or mine, the inside diameter of the tube comprising or containing the firework;

– for a bag mine or cylinder mine, the inside diameter of the mortar intended to contain the mine.

*This table contains a list of firework classifications that may be used in the absence of Test Series 6, of the Manual of Tests and Criteria, data (see 2.1.3.5.2).

Type	Includes: / Synonym:	Definition	Specification	Classification
Shell, spherical or cylindrical	Spherical display shell: aerial shell, colour shell, dye shell, multi-break shell, multi-effect shell, nautical shell, parachute shell, smoke shell, star shell; report shell: maroon, salute, sound shell, thunderclap, aerial shell kit	Device with or without propellant charge, with delay fuse and bursting charge, pyrotechnic unit(s) or loose pyrotechnic substance and designed to be projected from a mortar	All report shells	1.1G
			Colour shell: $\geq$ 180 mm	1.1G
			Colour shell: $<$ 180 mm with $>$ 25% flash composition, as loose powder and/or report effects	1.1G
			Colour shell: $<$ 180 mm with $\leq$ 25% flash composition, as loose powder and/or report effects	1.3G
			Colour shell: $\leq$ 50 mm, or $\leq$ 60 g pyrotechnic substance, with $\leq$ 2% flash composition as loose powder and/or report effects	1.4G
	Peanut shell	Device with two or more spherical aerial shells in a common wrapper propelled by the same propellant charge with separate external delay fuses	The most hazardous spherical aerial shell determines the classification	
	Preloaded mortar, shell in mortar	Assembly comprising a spherical or cylindrical shell inside a mortar from which the shell is designed to be projected	All report shells	1.1G
			Colour shell: $\geq$ 180 mm	1.1G
			Colour shell: $>$ 25% flash composition as loose powder and/or report effects	1.1G
			Colour shell: $>$ 50 mm and $<$ 180 mm	1.2G
			Colour shell: $\leq$ 50 mm, or $<$ 60 g pyrotechnic substance, with $\leq$ 25% flash composition as loose powder and/or report effects	1.3G

2

Type	Includes: / Synonym:	Definition	Specification	Classification
	Shell of shells (spherical) (Reference to percentages for shell of shells are to the gross mass of the fireworks article)	Device without propellant charge, with delay fuse and bursting charge, containing report shells and inert materials and designed to be projected from a mortar	> 120 mm	1.1G
		Device without propellant charge, with delay fuse and bursting charge, containing report shells ≤ 25 g flash composition per report unit, with ≤ 33% flash composition and ≥ 60% inert materials and designed to be projected from a mortar	≤ 120 mm	1.3G
		Device without propellant charge, with delay fuse and bursting charge, containing colour shells and/or pyrotechnic units and designed to be projected from a mortar	> 300 mm	1.1G
		Device without propellant charge, with delay fuse and bursting charge, containing colour shells ≤ 70 mm and/or pyrotechnic units, with ≤ 25% flash composition and ≤ 60% pyrotechnic substance and designed to be projected from a mortar	> 200 mm and ≤ 300 mm	1.3G
		Device with propellant charge, with delay fuse and bursting charge, containing colour shells ≤ 70 mm and/or pyrotechnic units, with ≤ 25% flash composition and ≤ 60% pyrotechnic substance and designed to be projected from a mortar	≤ 200 mm	1.3G
Battery/ combination	Barrage, bombardos, cakes, finale box, flowerbed, hybrid, multiple tubes, shell cakes, banger batteries, flash banger batteries	Assembly including several elements either containing the same type or several types each corresponding to one of the types of fireworks listed in this table, with one or two points of ignition	The most hazardous firework type determines the classification	
Roman candle	Exhibition candle, candle, bombettes	Tube containing a series of pyrotechnic units consisting of alternate pyrotechnic substance, propellant charge, and transmitting fuse	≥ 50 mm inner diameter, containing flash composition, or < 50 mm with > 25% flash composition	1.1G
			≥ 50 mm inner diameter, containing no flash composition	1.2G
			< 50 mm inner diameter and ≤ 25% flash composition	1.3G
			≤ 30 mm inner diameter, each pyrotechnic unit ≤ 25 g and ≤ 5% flash composition	1.4G
Shot tube	Single shot Roman candle, small preloaded mortar	Tube containing a pyrotechnic unit consisting of pyrotechnic substance, propellant charge with or without transmitting fuse	≤ 30 mm inner diameter and pyrotechnic unit > 25 g, or > 5% and ≤ 25% flash composition	1.3G
			≤ 30 mm inner diameter, pyrotechnic unit ≤ 25 g and ≤ 5% flash composition	1.4G

Type	Includes: / Synonym:	Definition	Specification	Classification
Rocket	Avalanche rocket, signal rocket, whistling rocket, bottle rocket, sky rocket, missile type rocket, table rocket	Tube containing pyrotechnic substance and/or pyrotechnic units, equipped with stick(s) or other means for stabilization of flight, and designed to be propelled into the air	Flash composition effects only	1.1G
			Flash composition > 25% of the pyrotechnic substance	1.1G
			> 20 g pyrotechnic substance and flash composition ≤ 25 %	1.3G
			≤ 20 g pyrotechnic substance, black powder bursting charge and ≤ 0.13 g flash composition per report and ≤ 1 g in total	1.4G
Mine	Pot-a-feu, ground mine, bag mine, cylinder mine	Tube containing propellant charge and pyrotechnic units and designed to be placed on the ground or to be fixed in the ground. The principal effect is ejection of all the pyrotechnic units in a single burst producing a widely dispersed visual and/or aural effect in the air or: Cloth or paper bag or cloth or paper cylinder containing propellant charge and pyrotechnic units, designed to be placed in a mortar and to function as a mine	> 25% flash composition, as loose powder and/or report effects	1.1G
			≥ 180 mm and ≤ 25% flash composition, as loose powder and/or report effects	1.1G
			< 180 mm and ≤ 25% flash composition, as loose powder and/or report effects	1.3G
			≤ 150 g pyrotechnic substance, containing ≤ 5% flash composition as loose powder and/or report effects. Each pyrotechnic unit ≤ 25 g, each report effect < 2 g; each whistle, if any, ≤ 3 g	1.4G
Fountain	Volcanos, gerbs, lances, Bengal fire, flitter sparkle, cylindrical fountains, cone fountains, illuminating torch	Non-metallic case containing pressed or consolidated pyrotechnic substance producing sparks and flame **Note:** Fountains intended to produce a vertical cascade or curtain of sparks are considered to be waterfalls (see row below).	≥ 1 kg pyrotechnic substance	1.3G
			< 1 kg pyrotechnic substance	1.4G
Waterfall	Cascades, showers	Pyrotechnic fountain intended to produce a vertical cascade or curtain of sparks	Containing a pyrotechnic substance which gives a positive result when tested in the HSL Flash composition test in appendix 7 of the Manual of Tests and Criteria regardless of the results of Test Series 6 (see 2.1.3.5.1)	1.1G
			Containing a pyrotechnic substance which gives a negative result when tested in the HSL Flash composition test in appendix 7 of the Manual of Tests and Criteria	1.3G
Sparkler	Handheld sparklers, non-handheld sparklers, wire sparklers	Rigid wire partially coated (along one end) with slow-burning pyrotechnic substance with or without an ignition tip	Perchlorate based sparklers: > 5 g per item or > 10 items per pack	1.3G
			Perchlorate based sparklers: ≤ 5 g per item and ≤ 10 items per pack Nitrate based sparklers: ≤ 30 g per item	1.4G

2

Type	Includes: / Synonym:	Definition	Specification	Classification
Bengal stick	Dipped stick	Non-metallic stick partially coated (along one end) with slow-burning pyrotechnic substance and designed to be held in the hand	Perchlorate based items: > 5 g per item or > 10 items per pack	1.3G
			Perchlorate based items: ≤ 5 g per item and ≤ 10 items per pack; nitrate based items: ≤ 30 g per item	1.4G
Low hazard fireworks and novelties	Table bombs, throwdowns, crackling granules, smokes, fog, snakes, glow worm, serpents, snaps, party poppers	Device designed to produce very limited visible and/or audible effect which contains small amounts of pyrotechnic and/or explosive substance	Throwdowns and snaps may contain up to 1.6 mg of silver fulminate; snaps and party poppers may contain up to 16 mg of potassium chlorate/red phosphorus mixture; other articles may contain up to 5 g of pyrotechnic substance, but no flash composition	1.4G
Spinner	Aerial spinner, helicopter, chaser, ground spinner	Non-metallic tube or tubes containing gas- or spark-producing pyrotechnic substance, with or without noise-producing substance, with or without aerofoils attached	Pyrotechnic substance per item > 20 g, containing ≤ 3% flash composition as report effects, or whistle composition ≤ 5 g	1.3G
			Pyrotechnic substance per item ≤ 20 g, containing ≤ 3% flash composition as report effects, or whistle composition ≤ 5 g	1.4G
Wheels	Catherine wheels, Saxon	Assembly including drivers containing pyrotechnic substance and provided with a means of attaching it to a support so that it can rotate	≥ 1 kg total pyrotechnic substance, no report effect, each whistle (if any) ≤ 25 g and ≤ 50 g whistle composition per wheel	1.3G
			< 1 kg total pyrotechnic substance, no report effect, each whistle (if any) ≤ 5 g and ≤ 10 g whistle composition per wheel	1.4G
Aerial wheel	Flying Saxon, UFOs, rising crown	Tubes containing propellant charges and sparks-, flame- and/or noise-producing pyrotechnic substances, the tubes being fixed to a supporting ring	> 200 g total pyrotechnic substance or > 60 g pyrotechnic substance per driver, ≤ 3% flash composition as report effects, each whistle (if any) ≤ 25 g and ≤ 50 g whistle composition per wheel	1.3G
			≤ 200 g total pyrotechnic substance and ≤ 60 g pyrotechnic substance per driver, ≤ 3% flash composition as report effects, each whistle (if any) ≤ 5 g and ≤ 10 g whistle composition per wheel	1.4G
Selection pack	Display selection box, display selection pack, garden selection box, indoor selection box; assortment	A pack of more than one type each corresponding to one of the types of fireworks listed in this table	The most hazardous firework type determines the classification	
Firecracker	Celebration cracker, celebration roll, string cracker	Assembly of tubes (paper or cardboard) linked by a pyrotechnic fuse, each tube intended to produce an aural effect	Each tube ≤ 140 mg of flash composition or ≤ 1 g black powder	1.4G

Type	Includes: / Synonym:	Definition	Specification	Classification
Banger	Salute, flash banger, lady cracker	Non-metallic tube containing report composition intended to produce an aural effect	> 2 g flash composition per item	1.1G
			≤ 2 g flash composition per item and ≤ 10 g per inner packaging	1.3G
			≤ 1 g flash composition per item and ≤ 10 g per inner packaging or ≤ 10 g black powder per item	1.4G

■ **2.1.3.6**   **Classification documentation**

2.1.3.6.1   A competent authority assigning an article or substance into class 1 should confirm with the applicant that classification in writing.

2.1.3.6.2   A competent authority classification document may be in any form and may consist of more than one page, provided pages are numbered consecutively. The document should have a unique reference.

2.1.3.6.3   The information provided shall be easy to identify, legible and durable.

2.1.3.6.4   Examples of the information that may be provided in the classification documents are as follows:

.1   the name of the competent authority and the provisions in national legislation under which it is granted its authority;

.2   the modal or national regulations for which the classification document is applicable;

.3   confirmation that the classification has been approved, made or agreed in accordance with the United Nations Recommendations on the Transport of Dangerous Goods or the relevant modal regulations;

.4   the name and address of the person in law to which the classification has been assigned and any company registration which uniquely identifies a company or other body corporate under national legislation;

.5   the name under which the explosives will be placed on the market or otherwise supplied for transport;

.6   the Proper Shipping Name, UN number, Class, Hazard Division and corresponding compatibility group of the explosives;

.7   where appropriate, the maximum net explosive mass of the package or article;

.8   the name, signature, stamp, seal or other identification of the person authorized by the competent authority to issue the classification document is clearly visible;

.9   where safety in transport or the hazard division is assessed as being dependent upon the packaging, the packaging mark or a description of the permitted:

–   inner packagings

–   intermediate packagings

–   outer packagings

.10   the classification document states the part number, stock number or other identifying reference under which the explosives will be placed onto the market or otherwise supplied for transport;

.11   the name and address of the person in law who manufactured the explosives and any company registration which uniquely identifies a company or other body corporate under national legislation;

.12   any additional information regarding the applicable packing instruction and special packing provisions where appropriate;

.13   the basis for assigning the classification, i.e. whether on the basis of test results, default for fireworks, analogy with classified explosive, by definition from the Dangerous Goods List etc.;

.14   any special conditions or limitations that the competent authority has identified as relevant to the safety for transport of the explosives, the communication of the hazard and international transport; and

.15   the expiry date of the classification document is given where the competent authority considers one to be appropriate.

Chapter 2.2

Class 2 – Gases

2

2.2.0 Introductory note

"Toxic" has the same meaning as "poisonous".

2.2.1 Definitions and general provisions

2.2.1.1   A gas is a substance which:

    .1   at 50°C has a vapour pressure greater than 300 kPa; or

    .2   is completely gaseous at 20°C at a standard pressure of 101.3 kPa.

2.2.1.2   The transport condition of a gas is described according to its physical state as:

    .1   *compressed gas:* a gas which when packaged under pressure for transport is entirely gaseous at −50°C; this category includes all gases with a critical temperature less than or equal to −50°C;

    .2   *liquefied gas:* a gas which when packaged under pressure for transport is partially liquid at temperatures above −50 °C. A distinction is made between:

         high pressure liquefied gas: a gas with a critical temperature between −50°C and +65°C, and

         low pressure liquefied gas: a gas with a critical temperature above +65°C;

    .3   *refrigerated liquefied gas*: a gas which when packaged for transport is made partially liquid because of its low temperature; or

    .4   *dissolved gas:* a gas which when packaged under pressure for transport is dissolved in a liquid phase solvent;

    .5   *adsorbed gas:* a gas which when packaged for transport is adsorbed onto a solid porous material resulting in an internal receptacle pressure of less than 101.3 kPa at 20°C and less than 300 kPa at 50°C.

2.2.1.3   The class comprises compressed gases, liquefied gases, dissolved gases, refrigerated liquefied gases, adsorbed gases, mixtures of one or more gases with one or more vapours of substances of other classes, articles charged with a gas and aerosols.

2.2.1.4   Gases are normally transported under pressure varying from high pressure in the case of compressed gases to low pressure in the case of refrigerated gases.

2.2.1.5   According to their chemical properties or physiological effects, which may vary widely, gases may be: flammable; non-flammable; non-toxic; toxic; supporters of combustion; corrosive; or may possess two or more of these properties simultaneously.

2.2.1.5.1   Some gases are chemically and physiologically inert. Such gases as well as other gases, normally accepted as non-toxic, will nevertheless be suffocating in high concentrations.

2.2.1.5.2   Many gases of this class have narcotic effects which may occur at comparatively low concentrations or may evolve highly toxic gases when involved in a fire.

2.2.1.5.3   All gases which are heavier than air will present a potential danger if allowed to accumulate in the bottom of cargo spaces.

2.2.2 Class subdivisions

Class 2 is subdivided further according to the primary hazard of the gas during transport:

Note: For UN 1950 AEROSOLS, see also the criteria in special provision 63 and for UN 2037 RECEPTACLES, SMALL, CONTAINING GAS (GAS CARTRIDGES) see also special provision 303.

2.2.2.1   **Class 2.1   Flammable gases**

Gases which at 20°C and a standard pressure of 101.3 kPa:

.1   are ignitable when in a mixture of 13% or less by volume with air; or

.2   have a flammable range with air of at least 12 percentage points regardless of the lower flammable limit. Flammability shall be determined by tests or calculation in accordance with methods adopted by the International Organization for Standardization (see ISO 10156:2010). Where insufficient data are available to use these methods, tests by a comparable method recognized by a national competent authority may be used.

2.2.2.2   **Class 2.2   Non-flammable, non-toxic gases**

Gases which:

.1   are asphyxiant – gases which dilute or replace the oxygen normally in the atmosphere; or

.2   are oxidizing – gases which may, generally by providing oxygen, cause or contribute to the combustion of other material more than air does; or

.3   do not come under the other classes.

Note: In 2.2.2.2.2, "gases which cause or contribute to the combustion of other material more than air does" means pure gases or gas mixtures with an oxidizing power greater than 23.5% as determined by a method specified in ISO 10156:2010.

2.2.2.3   **Class 2.3   Toxic gases**

Gases which:

.1   are known to be so toxic or corrosive to humans as to pose a hazard to health; or

.2   are presumed to be toxic or corrosive to humans because they have a LC_{50} value (as defined in 2.6.2.1) equal to or less than 5,000 mL/m^3 (ppm).

Note: Gases meeting the above criteria owing to their corrosivity are to be classified as toxic with a subsidiary corrosive risk.

2.2.2.4   Gases and gas mixtures with hazards associated with more than one division take the following precedence:

.1   class 2.3 takes precedence over all other classes;

.2   class 2.1 takes precedence over class 2.2.

2.2.2.5   Gases of class 2.2 are not subject to the provisions of this Code if they are transported at a pressure of less than 200 kPa at 20°C and are not liquefied or refrigerated liquefied gases.

2.2.2.6   Gases of class 2.2 are not subject to the provisions of this Code when contained in the following:

.1   foodstuffs (except UN 1950), including carbonated beverages;

.2   balls intended for use in sports; or

.3   tyres (except for air transport).

Note: This exemption does not apply to lamps. For lamps see 1.1.1.9.

2.2.3   Mixtures of gases

For the classification of gas mixtures (including vapours of substances from other classes), the following principles shall be used:

.1   Flammability shall be determined by tests or calculation in accordance with methods adopted by the International Organization for Standardization (see ISO 10156:2010). Where insufficient data are available to use these methods, tests by a comparable method recognized by a national competent authority may be used.

.2   The level of toxicity is determined either by tests to measure the LC_{50} value (as defined in 2.6.2.1) or by a calculation method using the following formula:

$$LC_{50} \quad \text{Toxic (mixture)} = \frac{1}{\displaystyle\sum_{i=1}^{n} \frac{f_i}{T_i}}$$

where: f_i =   mole fraction of the ith component substance of the mixture;

T_i =   toxicity index of the ith component substance of the mixture (the T_i equals the LC_{50} value when available).

When LC_{50} values are unknown, the toxicity index is determined by using the lowest LC_{50} value of substances of similar physiological and chemical effects, or through testing if this is the only practical possibility.

.3 A gas mixture has a subsidiary risk of corrosivity when the mixture is known by human experience to be destructive to the skin, eyes or mucous membranes or when the LC_{50} value of the corrosive components of the mixture is equal to or less than 5,000 mL/m^3 (ppm) when the LC_{50} is calculated by the formula:

$$LC_{50} \quad \text{Corrosive (mixture)} = \frac{1}{\displaystyle\sum_{i=1}^{n} \frac{f_{ci}}{T_{ci}}}$$

where: $f_{ci} =$ mole fraction of the ith corrosive component substance of the mixture;

   $T_{ci} =$ toxicity index of the ith corrosive component substance of the mixture (the T_{ci} equals the LC_{50} value when available).

.4 Oxidizing ability is determined either by tests or by calculation methods adopted by the International Organization for Standardization (see note in 2.2.2.2).

■ 2.2.4   Gases not accepted for transport

Chemically unstable gases of class 2 shall not be accepted for transport unless the necessary precautions have been taken to prevent the possibility of a dangerous decomposition or polymerization under normal conditions of transport or unless transported in accordance with special packing provision (r) of packing instruction P200 (5) of 4.1.4.1, as applicable. For the precautions necessary to prevent polymerization, see special provision 386 of chapter 3.3. To this end particular care shall be taken to ensure that receptacles and tanks do not contain any substances liable to promote these reactions.

Chapter 2.3

Class 3 – Flammable liquids

2

2.3.0 Introductory note

The flashpoint of a flammable liquid may be altered by the presence of an impurity. The substances listed in class 3 in the Dangerous Goods List in chapter 3.2 shall generally be regarded as chemically pure. Since commercial products may contain added substances or impurities, flashpoints may vary, and this may have an effect on classification or determination of the packing group for the product. In the event of doubt regarding the classification or packing group of a substance, the flashpoint of the substance shall be determined experimentally.

2.3.1 Definitions and general provisions

2.3.1.1 Class 3 includes the following substances:

    .1 flammable liquids (see 2.3.1.2 and 2.3.1.3);

    .2 liquid desensitized explosives (see 2.3.1.4).

2.3.1.2 *Flammable liquids* are liquids, or mixtures of liquids, or liquids containing solids in solution or suspension (such as paints, varnishes, lacquers, etc., but not including substances which, on account of their other dangerous characteristics, have been included in other classes) which give off a flammable vapour at or below 60°C closed-cup test (corresponding to 65.6°C open-cup test), normally referred to as the "flashpoint". This also includes:

    .1 liquids offered for transport at temperatures at or above their flashpoint; and

    .2 substances transported or offered for transport at elevated temperatures in a liquid state, which give off a flammable vapour at temperatures equal to or below the maximum transport temperature.

2.3.1.3 However, the provisions of this Code need not apply to such liquids with a flashpoint of more than 35°C which do not sustain combustion. Liquids are considered to be unable to sustain combustion for the purposes of the Code if:

    .1 they have passed the suitable combustibility test (see the Sustained Combustibility Test prescribed in part III, 32.5.2 of the Manual of Tests and Criteria); or

    .2 their fire point according to ISO 2592:1973 is greater than 100°C; or

    .3 they are water-miscible solutions with a water content of more than 90%, by mass.

2.3.1.4 *Liquid desensitized explosives* are explosive substances which are dissolved or suspended in water or other liquid substances, to form a homogeneous liquid mixture to suppress their explosive properties. Entries in the Dangerous Goods List for liquid desensitized explosives are UN 1204, UN 2059, UN 3064, UN 3343, UN 3357 and UN 3379.

2.3.2 Assignment of packing group

2.3.2.1 The criteria in 2.3.2.6 are used to determine the hazard grouping of a liquid that presents a risk due to flammability.

2.3.2.1.1 For liquids whose only risk is flammability, the packing group for the substance is the hazard grouping shown in 2.3.2.6.

2.3.2.1.2 For a liquid with additional risk(s), the hazard group determined from 2.3.2.6 and the hazard group based on the severity of the additional risk(s) shall be considered, and the classification and packing group determined in accordance with the provisions in chapter 2.0.

2.3.2.2 Viscous flammable liquids such as paints, enamels, lacquers, varnishes, adhesives and polishes having a flashpoint of less than 23°C may be placed in packing group III in conformity with the procedures prescribed in the Manual of Tests and Criteria, part III, subsection 32.3, provided that:

△ .1 The viscosity* and flashpoint are in accordance with the following table:

Kinematic viscosity (extrapolated) v (at near-zero shear rate) mm²/s at 23°C	Flow-time t in seconds	Jet diameter (mm)	Flashpoint (closed-cup) in °C
$20 < v \leq 80$	$20 < t \leq 60$	4	above 17
$80 < v \leq 135$	$60 < t \leq 100$	4	above 10
$135 < v \leq 220$	$20 < t \leq 32$	6	above 5
$220 < v \leq 300$	$32 < t \leq 44$	6	above −1
$300 < v \leq 700$	$44 < t \leq 100$	6	above −5
$700 < t$	$100 < t$	6	no limit

.2 less than 3% of the clear solvent layer separates in the solvent separation test;

.3 the mixture or any separated solvent does not meet the criteria for class 6.1 or class 8;

.4 the substances are packed in receptacles of not more than 30-litre capacity.

2.3.2.3 [Reserved]

2.3.2.4 Substances classified as flammable liquids due to their being transported or offered for transport at elevated temperatures are included in packing group III.

2.3.2.5 Viscous liquids which:

– have a flashpoint of 23°C or above and less than or equal to 60°C;

■ – are not toxic or corrosive;

■ – are not environmentally hazardous or are environmentally hazardous transported in single or combination packagings containing a net quantity per single or inner packaging of 5 litres or less, provided the packagings meet the general provisions of 4.1.1.1, 4.1.1.2 and 4.1.1.4 to 4.1.1.8;

– contain not more than 20% nitrocellulose, provided the nitrocellulose contains not more than 12.6% nitrogen by dry mass; and

– are packed in receptacles of not more than 30-litre capacity

are not subject to the provisions for the marking, labelling and testing of packages in chapters 4.1, 5.2 and 6.1, if:

.1 in the solvent separation test (see part III, 32.5.1 of the Manual of Tests and Criteria) the height of the separated layer of solvent is less than 3% of the total height; and

.2 the flowtime in the viscosity test (see part III, 32.4.3 of the Manual of Tests and Criteria) with a jet diameter of 6 mm is equal to or greater than:

.1 60 s; or

.2 40 s if the viscous liquids contains not more than 60% of class 3 substances.

The following statement shall be included in the transport document: "Transport in accordance with 2.3.2.5 of the IMDG Code." (see 5.4.1.5.10).

2.3.2.6 Hazard grouping based on flammability

Flammable liquids are grouped for packing purposes according to their flashpoint, their boiling point, and their viscosity. This table shows the relationship between two of these characteristics.

Packing group	Flashpoint (closed-cup) in °C	Initial boiling point in °C
I	–	≤ 35
II	< 23	> 35
III	≥ 23 to ≤ 60	> 35

---

* *Viscosity determination:* Where the substance concerned is non-Newtonian, or where a flow cup method of viscosity determination is otherwise unsuitable, a variable shear-rate viscometer shall be used to determine the dynamic viscosity coefficient of the substance, at 23 °C, at a number of shear rates. The values obtained are plotted against shear rate and then extrapolated to zero shear rate. The dynamic viscosity thus obtained, divided by the density, gives the apparent kinematic viscosity at near-zero shear rate.

2.3.3 Determination of flashpoint

Note: The provisions of this section are not mandatory.

2.3.3.1 The flashpoint of a flammable liquid is the lowest temperature of the liquid at which its vapour forms an ignitable mixture with air. It gives a measure of the risk of formation of explosive or ignitable mixtures when the liquid escapes from its packing. A flammable liquid cannot be ignited so long as its temperature remains below the flashpoint.

Note: Do not confuse the flashpoint with the ignition temperature, which is the temperature to which an explosive vapour–air mixture must be heated to cause actual explosion. There is no relationship between the flashpoint and the ignition temperature.

2.3.3.2 The flashpoint is not an exact physical constant for a given liquid. It depends to some extent on the construction of the test apparatus used and on the testing procedure. Therefore, when providing flashpoint data, specify the name of the test apparatus.

2.3.3.3 Several standard apparatuses are in current use. They all operate on the same principle: a specified quantity of the liquid is introduced into a receptacle at a temperature well below the flashpoint to be expected, then slowly heated; periodically, a small flame is brought near to the surface of the liquid. The flashpoint is the lowest temperature at which a "flash" is observed.

2.3.3.4 The test methods can be divided into two groups, depending on the use in an apparatus of an open receptacle (open-cup methods) or a closed one which is only opened to admit the flame (closed-cup methods). As a rule, the flashpoints found in an open-cup test are a few degrees higher than in a closed-cup test.

2.3.3.5 In general, reproducibility in closed-cup apparatus is better than in open-cup.

2.3.3.5.1 It is therefore recommended that flashpoints, especially in the range around 23°C, shall be determined by means of closed-cup (c.c) methods.

2.3.3.5.2 Flashpoint data in this Code are generally based on closed-cup methods. In countries where it is customary to determine flashpoints by the open-cup method, the temperatures given by that method would need to be reduced to correspond with those in this Code.

2.3.3.6 Determination of flashpoint

The following methods for determining the flashpoint of flammable liquids may be used:

International standards:

ISO 1516
ISO 1523
ISO 2719
ISO 13736
ISO 3679
ISO 3680

National standards:

American Society for Testing Materials International, 100 Barr Harbor Drive, PO Box C700, West Conshohocken, Pennsylvania, USA 19428-2959:

ASTM D3828-07a, Standard Test Methods for Flash Point by Small Scale Closed Cup Tester
ASTM D56-05, Standard Test Method for Flash Point by Tag Closed Cup Tester
ASTM D3278-96(2004)e, Standard Test Methods for Flash Point of Liquids by Small Scale Closed-Cup Apparatus
ASTM D93-08, Standard Test Methods for Flash Point by Pensky-Martens Closed Cup Tester

Association française de normalisation, AFNOR, 11, rue Francis de Pressensé, 93571 La Plaine Saint-Denis Cedex:

French Standard NF M 07-019
French Standards NF M 07-011/NF T 30-050/NF T 66-009
French Standard NF M 07-036

Deutsches Institut für Normung, Burggrafenstr. 6, D-10787 Berlin:

Standard DIN 51755 (flashpoints below 65°C)

State Committee of the Council of Ministers for Standardization, 113813, GSP, Moscow, M-49 Leninsky Prospect, 9:

GOST 12.1.044-84

2

2.3.4   Determination of initial boiling point

The following methods for determining the initial boiling point of flammable liquids may be used:

International standards:

ISO 3924
ISO 4626
ISO 3405

National standards:

American Society for Testing Materials International, 100 Barr Harbor Drive, PO Box C700,
West Conshohocken, Pennsylvania, USA 19428-2959:

ASTM D86-07a, Standard Test Method for Distillation of Petroleum Products at Atmospheric Pressure
ASTM D1078-05, Standard Test Method for Distillation Range of Volatile Organic Liquids

Further acceptable methods:

Method A.2 as described in Part A of the Annex to Commission Regulation (EC) No 440/2008.[*]

■ 2.3.5   Substances not accepted for transport

Chemically unstable substances of class 3 shall not be accepted for transport unless the necessary precautions have been taken to prevent the possibility of a dangerous decomposition or polymerization under normal conditions of transport. For the precautions necessary to prevent polymerization, see special provision 386 of chapter 3.3. To this end particular care shall be taken to ensure that receptacles and tanks do not contain any substances liable to promote these reactions.

---

[*] Commission Regulation (EC) No 440/2008 of 30 May 2008 laying down test methods pursuant to Regulation (EC) No 1907/2006 of the European Parliament and of the Council on the Registration, Evaluation, Authorisation and Restriction of Chemicals (REACH) (Official Journal of the European Union, No L 142 of 31.05.2008, pages 1–739 and No L 143 of 03.06.2008, page 55).

Chapter 2.4

Class 4 – Flammable solids; substances liable to spontaneous combustion; substances which, in contact with water, emit flammable gases

2

2.4.0 Introductory note

Since organometallic substances can be classified in classes 4.2 or 4.3 with additional subsidiary risks, depending on their properties, a specific classification flowchart for these substances is given in 2.4.5.

2.4.1 Definition and general provisions

2.4.1.1 In this Code, class 4 deals with substances, other than those classified as explosives, which, under conditions of transport, are readily combustible or may cause or contribute to a fire. Class 4 is subdivided as follows:

△ Class 4.1 – Flammable solids
Solids which, under conditions encountered in transport, are readily combustible or may cause or contribute to fire through friction; self-reactive substances (solids and liquids) and polymerizing substances which are liable to undergo a strongly exothermic reaction; solid desensitized explosives which may explode if not diluted sufficiently;

Class 4.2 – Substances liable to spontaneous combustion
Substances (solids and liquids) which are liable to spontaneous heating under normal conditions encountered in transport, or to heating up in contact with air, and being then liable to catch fire;

Class 4.3 – Substances which, in contact with water, emit flammable gases
Substances (solids and liquids) which, by interaction with water, are liable to become spontaneously flammable or to give off flammable gases in dangerous quantities.

2.4.1.2 As referenced in this chapter, test methods and criteria, with advice on application of the tests, are given in the Manual of Tests and Criteria for the classification of following types of substances of class 4:

    .1   flammable solids (class 4.1);

    .2   self-reactive substances (class 4.1);

■ .3   polymerizing substances (class 4.1);

△ .4   pyrophoric solids (class 4.2);

△ .5   pyrophoric liquids (class 4.2);

△ .6   self-heating substances (class 4.2); and

△ .7   substances which, in contact with water, emit flammable gases (class 4.3).

△ Test methods and criteria for self-reactive substances and polymerizing substances are given in part II of the Manual of Tests and Criteria, and test methods and criteria for the other types of substances of class 4 are given in the Manual of Tests and Criteria, part III, chapter 33.

△ 2.4.2 Class 4.1 – Flammable solids, self-reactive substances, solid desensitized explosives and polymerizing substances

2.4.2.1 General

Class 4.1 includes the following types of substances:

    .1   flammable solids (see 2.4.2.2);

△ .2   self-reactive substances (see 2.4.2.3);

.3   solid desensitized explosives (see 2.4.2.4); and

■ .4   polymerizing substances (see 2.4.2.5).

Some substances (such as celluloid) may evolve toxic and flammable gases when heated or if involved in a fire.

2.4.2.2   Class 4.1 Flammable solids

2.4.2.2.1   *Definitions and properties*

2.4.2.2.1.1   For the purpose of this Code, *flammable solids* means readily combustible solids and solids which may cause fire through friction.

2.4.2.2.1.2   *Readily combustible solids* means fibres, powdered, granular, or pasty substances which are dangerous if they can be easily ignited by brief contact with an ignition source such as a burning match, and if the flame spreads rapidly. The danger may come not only from the fire but also from toxic combustion products. Metal powders are especially dangerous because of the difficulty of extinguishing a fire, since normal extinguishing agents such as carbon dioxide or water can increase the hazard.

2.4.2.2.2   *Classification of flammable solids*

2.4.2.2.2.1   Powdered, granular or pasty substances shall be classified as readily combustible solids of class 4.1 when the time of burning of one or more of the test runs, performed in accordance with the test method described in the Manual of Tests and Criteria, part III, 33.2.1, is less than 45 s or the rate of burning is more than 2.2 mm/s. Powders of metals or metal alloys shall be classified in class 4.1 when they can be ignited and the reaction spreads over the whole length of the sample in 10 min or less.

2.4.2.2.2.2   Solids which may cause fire through friction shall be classified in class 4.1 by analogy with existing entries (such as matches) until definitive criteria are established.

2.4.2.2.3   *Assignment of packing groups*

2.4.2.2.3.1   Packing groups are assigned on the basis of the test methods referred to in 2.4.2.2.2.1. For readily combustible solids (other than metal powders), packing group II shall be assigned if the burning time is less than 45 s and the flame passes the wetted zone. Packing group II shall be assigned to powders of metal or metal alloys if the zone of reaction spreads over the whole length of the sample in five minutes or less.

2.4.2.2.3.2   Packing groups are assigned on the basis of the test methods referred to in 2.4.2.2.2.1. For readily combustible solids (other than metal powders), packing group III shall be assigned if the burning time is less than 45 s and the wetted zone stops the flame propagation for at least four minutes. Packing group III shall be assigned to metal powders if the reaction spreads over the whole length of the sample in more than five minutes but not more than 10 min.

2.4.2.2.3.3   For solids which may cause fire through friction, the packing group shall be assigned by analogy with existing entries or in accordance with any appropriate special provision.

2.4.2.2.4   Pyrophoric metal powders, if wetted with sufficient water to suppress their pyrophoric properties, may be classified as class 4.1.

2.4.2.3   Class 4.1 Self-reactive substances

2.4.2.3.1   *Definitions and properties*

2.4.2.3.1.1   For the purposes of this Code:

Self-reactive substances are thermally unstable substances liable to undergo a strongly exothermic decomposition even without participation of oxygen (air). Substances are not considered to be self-reactive substances of class 4.1, if:

.1   they are explosives according to the criteria of class 1;

.2   they are oxidizing substances according to the classification procedure for class 5.1 (see 2.5.2) except that mixtures of oxidizing substances which contain 5.0% or more of combustible organic substances shall be subjected to the classification procedure defined in note 3;

.3   they are organic peroxides according to the criteria of class 5.2;

.4   their heat of decomposition is less than 300 J/g; or

.5   their self-accelerating decomposition temperature (SADT) (see 2.4.2.3.4) is greater than 75°C for a 50 kg package.

Note 1: The heat of decomposition may be determined using any internationally recognized method such as differential scanning calorimetry and adiabatic calorimetry.

Note 2: Any substance which shows the properties of a self-reactive substance shall be classified as such, even if this substance gives a positive test result according to 2.4.3.2 for inclusion in class 4.2.

Note 3: Mixtures of oxidizing substances meeting the criteria of class 5.1 which contain 5.0% or more of combustible organic substances, which do not meet the criteria mentioned in .1, .3, .4 or .5 above, shall be subjected to the self-reactive substance classification procedure.

A mixture showing the properties of a self-reactive substance, types B to F, shall be classified as a self-reactive substance of class 4.1.

A mixture showing the properties of a self-reactive substance, type G, according to the principle of 2.4.2.3.3.2.7 shall be considered for classification as a substance of class 5.1 (see 2.5.2).

2.4.2.3.1.2   The decomposition of self-reactive substances can be initiated by heat, contact with catalytic impurities (such as acids, heavy-metal compounds, bases), friction or impact. The rate of decomposition increases with temperature and varies with the substance. Decomposition, particularly if no ignition occurs, may result in the evolution of toxic gases or vapours. For certain self-reactive substances, the temperature shall be controlled. Some self-reactive substances may decompose explosively, particularly if confined. This characteristic may be modified by the addition of diluents or by the use of appropriate packagings. Some self-reactive substances burn vigorously. Self-reactive substances are, for example, some compounds of the types listed below:

.1   aliphatic azo compounds (–C–N=N–C–);

.2   organic azides (–C–N$_3$);

.3   diazonium salts (–CN$_2^+$ Z$^-$);

.4   *N*-nitroso compounds (–N–N=O); and

.5   aromatic sulphohydrazides (–SO$_2$–NH–NH$_2$).

This list is not exhaustive and substances with other reactive groups and some mixtures of substances may have similar properties.

2.4.2.3.2   *Classification of self-reactive substances*

2.4.2.3.2.1   Self-reactive substances are classified into seven types according to the degree of danger they present. The types of self-reactive substance range from type A, which may not be accepted for transport in the packaging in which it is tested, to type G, which is not subject to the provisions for self-reactive substances of class 4.1. The classification of types B to F is directly related to the maximum quantity allowed in one packaging.

2.4.2.3.2.2   Self-reactive substances permitted for transport in packagings are listed in 2.4.2.3.2.3, those permitted for transport in IBCs are listed in packing instruction IBC520 and those permitted for transport in portable tanks are listed in portable tank instruction T23. For each permitted substance listed, the appropriate generic entry of the Dangerous Goods List (UN 3221 to UN 3240) is assigned, and appropriate subsidiary risks and remarks providing relevant transport information are given. The generic entries specify:

.1   self-reactive substance type (B to F);

.2   physical state (liquid or solid); and

.3   temperature control, when required (2.4.2.3.4).

2.4.2.3.2.3   *List of currently assigned self-reactive substances in packagings*

In the column "Packing Method" codes "OP1" to "OP8" refer to packing methods in packing instruction P520. Self-reactive substances to be transported shall fulfil the classification and the control and emergency temperatures (derived from the SADT) as listed. For substances permitted in IBCs, see packing instruction IBC520, and for those permitted in tanks, see portable tank instruction T23.

Note: The classification given in this table is based on the technically pure substance (except where a concentration of less than 100% is specified). For other concentrations, the substances may be classified differently following the procedures in 2.4.2.3.3 and 2.4.2.3.4.

UN generic entry	Self-reactive substance	Concentration (%)	Packing method	Control temperature (°C)	Emergency temperature (°C)	Remarks
3222	2-DIAZO-1-NAPHTHOL-4-SULPHONYL CHLORIDE	100	OP5			(2)
	2-DIAZO-1-NAPHTHOL-5-SULPHONYL CHLORIDE	100	OP5			(2)
3223	SELF-REACTIVE LIQUID, SAMPLE		OP2			(8)

UN generic entry	Self-reactive substance	Concentration (%)	Packing method	Control temperature (°C)	Emergency temperature (°C)	Remarks
3224	AZODICARBONAMIDE FORMULATION TYPE C	< 100	OP6			(3)
	2,2'-AZODI(ISOBUTYRONITRILE) as a water-based paste	≤ 50	OP6			
	N,N'-DINITROSO-N,N'-DIMETHYL-TEREPHTHALAMIDE, as a paste	72	OP6			
	N,N'-DINITROSOPENTAMETHYLENETETRAMINE	82	OP6			(7)
	SELF-REACTIVE SOLID, SAMPLE		OP2			(8)
3226	AZODICARBONAMIDE FORMULATION TYPE D	< 100	OP7			(5)
	1,1'-AZODI(HEXAHYDROBENZONITRILE)	100	OP7			
	BENZENE-1,3-DISULPHONYL HYDRAZIDE as a paste	52	OP7			
	BENZENESULPHONYL HYDRAZIDE	100	OP7			
	4-(BENZYL(ETHYL)AMINO)-3-ETHOXY-BENZENEDIAZONIUM ZINC CHLORIDE	100	OP7			
	3-CHLORO-4-DIETHYLAMINOBENZENE-DIAZONIUM ZINC CHLORIDE	100	OP7			
	2-DIAZO-1-NAPHTHOLSULPHONIC ACID ESTER MIXTURE TYPE D	< 100	OP7			(9)
	2,5-DIETHOXY-4-(4-MORPHOLINYL)-BENZENEDIAZONIUM SULPHATE	100	OP7			
	DIPHENYLOXIDE-4,4'-DISULPHONYL HYDRAZIDE	100	OP7			
	4-DIPROPYLAMINOBENZENEDIAZONIUM ZINC CHLORIDE	100	OP7			
	4-METHYLBENZENESULPHONYLHYDRAZIDE	100	OP7			
	SODIUM 2-DIAZO-1-NAPHTHOL-4-SULPHONATE	100	OP7			
	SODIUM 2-DIAZO-1-NAPHTHOL-5-SULPHONATE	100	OP7			
3228	ACETONE–PYROGALLOL COPOLYMER 2-DIAZO-1-NAPHTHOL-5-SULPHONATE	100	OP8			
	4-(DIMETHYLAMINO)BENZENEDIAZONIUM TRICHLOROZINCATE(–1)	100	OP8			
	2,5-DIBUTOXY-4-(4-MORPHOLINYL)-BENZENEDIAZONIUM TETRACHLOROZINCATE(2:1)	100	OP8			
3232	AZODICARBONAMIDE FORMULATION TYPE B, TEMPERATURE CONTROLLED	< 100	OP5			(1) (2)
3233	SELF-REACTIVE LIQUID, SAMPLE, TEMPERATURE CONTROLLED		OP2			(8)
3234	AZODICARBONAMIDE FORMULATION TYPE C, TEMPERATURE CONTROLLED	< 100	OP6			(4)
	2,2'-AZODI(ISOBUTYRONITRILE)	100	OP6	+40	+45	
	3-METHYL-4-(PYRROLIDIN-1-YL)BENZENE-DIAZONIUM TETRAFLUOROBORATE	95	OP6	+45	+50	
	SELF-REACTIVE SOLID, SAMPLE, TEMPERATURE CONTROLLED		OP2			(8)
	TETRAMINEPALLADIUM(II) NITRATE	100	OP6	+30	+35	
3235	2,2'-AZODI(ETHYL-2-METHYLPROPIONATE)	100	OP7	+20	+25	

UN generic entry	Self-reactive substance	Concen- tration (%)	Packing method	Control temper- ature (°C)	Emergency temper- ature (°C)	Remarks
3236	AZODICARBONAMIDE FORMULATION TYPE D, TEMPERATURE CONTROLLED	< 100	OP7			(6)
	2,2'-AZODI(2,4-DIMETHYL-4-METHOXY-VALERONITRILE)	100	OP7	−5	+5	
	2,2'-AZODI(2,4-DIMETHYLVALERONITRILE)	100	OP7	+10	+15	
	2,2'-AZODI(2-METHYLBUTYRONITRILE)	100	OP7	+35	+40	
	4-(BENZYL(METHYL)AMINO)-3-ETHOXY-BENZENEDIAZONIUM ZINC CHLORIDE	100	OP7	+40	+45	
	2,5-DIETHOXY-4-MORPHOLINO-BENZENEDIAZONIUM ZINC CHLORIDE	67–100	OP7	+35	+40	
	2,5-DIETHOXY-4-MORPHOLINO-BENZENEDIAZONIUM ZINC CHLORIDE	66	OP7	+40	+45	
	2,5-DIETHOXY-4-MORPHOLINOBENZENE-DIAZONIUM TETRAFLUOROBORATE	100	OP7	+30	+35	
	2,5-DIETHOXY-4-(PHENYLSULPHONYL)-BENZENEDIAZONIUM ZINC CHLORIDE	67	OP7	+40	+45	
	2,5-DIMETHOXY-4-(4-METHYLPHENYL-SULPHONYL)BENZENEDIAZONIUM ZINC CHLORIDE	79	OP7	+40	+45	
	4-DIMETHYLAMINO-6-(2-DIMETHYLAMINO-ETHOXY)TOLUENE-2-DIAZONIUM ZINC CHLORIDE	100	OP7	+40	+45	
	2-(N,N-ETHOXYCARBONYLPHENYLAMINO)-3-METHOXY-4-(N-METHYL-N-CYCLOHEXYLAMINO)-BENZENEDIAZONIUM ZINC CHLORIDE	63–92	OP7	+40	+45	
	2-(N,N-ETHOXYCARBONYLPHENYLAMINO)-3-METHOXY-4-(N-METHYL-N-CYCLOHEXYLAMINO)-BENZENEDIAZONIUM ZINC CHLORIDE	62	OP7	+35	+40	
	N-FORMYL-2-(NITROMETHYLENE)-1,3-PERHYDROTHIAZINE	100	OP7	+45	+50	
	2-(2-HYDROXYETHOXY)-1-(PYRROLIDIN-1-YL)-BENZENE-4-DIAZONIUM ZINC CHLORIDE	100	OP7	+45	+50	
	3-(2-HYDROXYETHOXY)-4-(PYRROLIDIN-1-YL)-BENZENEDIAZONIUM ZINC CHLORIDE	100	OP7	+40	+45	
	2-(N,N-METHYLAMINOETHYLCARBONYL)-4-(3,4-DIMETHYLPHENYLSULPHONYL)-BENZENEDIAZONIUM HYDROGEN SULPHATE	96	OP7	+45	+50	
	4-NITROSOPHENOL	100	OP7	+35	+40	
3237	DIETHYLENEGLYCOL BIS(ALLYLCARBONATE) + DI-ISOPROPYL PEROXYDICARBONATE	≥ 88 + ≤ 12	OP8	−10	0	

Remarks

(1)   Azodicarbonamide formulations which fulfil the criteria of 2.4.2.3.3.2.2. The control and emergency temperatures shall be determined by the procedure given in 7.3.7.2.

(2)   "EXPLOSIVE" subsidiary risk label (Model No 1, see 5.2.2.2.2) required.

(3)   Azodicarbonamide formulations which fulfil the criteria of 2.4.2.3.3.2.3.

(4)   Azodicarbonamide formulations which fulfil the criteria of 2.4.2.3.3.2.3. The control and emergency temperatures shall be determined by the procedure given in 7.3.7.2.

(5)   Azodicarbonamide formulations which fulfil the criteria of 2.4.2.3.3.2.4.

(6)   Azodicarbonamide formulations which fulfil the criteria of 2.4.2.3.3.2.4. The control and emergency temperatures shall be determined by the procedure given in 7.3.7.2.

(7)   With a compatible diluent having a boiling point of not less than 150°C.

(8)   See 2.4.2.3.2.4.2.

(9)   This entry applies to mixtures of esters of 2-diazo-1-naphthol-4-sulphonic acid and 2-diazo-1-naphthol-5-sulphonic acid meeting the criteria of 2.4.2.3.3.2.4.

2.4.2.3.2.4 Classification of self-reactive substances not listed in 2.4.2.3.2.3, packing instruction IBC520 or portable tank instruction T23 and assignment to a generic entry shall be made by the competent authority of the country of origin on the basis of a test report. Principles applying to the classification of such substances are provided in 2.4.2.3.3. The applicable classification procedures, test methods and criteria, and an example of a suitable test report, are given in the Manual of Tests and Criteria, part II. The statement of approval shall contain the classification and the relevant transport conditions.

.1 Activators, such as zinc compounds, may be added to some self-reactive substances to change their reactivity. Depending on both the type and the concentration of the activator, this may result in a decrease in thermal stability and a change in explosive properties. If either of these properties is altered, the new formulation shall be assessed in accordance with this classification procedure.

.2 Samples of self-reactive substances or formulations of self-reactive substances not listed in 2.4.2.3.2.3, for which a complete set of test results is not available and which are to be transported for further testing or evaluation, may be assigned to one of the appropriate entries for self-reactive substances type C provided the following conditions are met:

.1 the available data indicate that the sample would be no more dangerous than self-reactive substances type B;

.2 the sample is packaged in accordance with packing method OP2 (see applicable packing instruction) and the quantity per cargo transport unit is limited to 10 kg; and

.3 the available data indicate that the control temperature, if any, is sufficiently low to prevent any dangerous decomposition and sufficiently high to prevent any dangerous phase separation.

2.4.2.3.3 *Principles for classification of self-reactive substances*

Note: This section refers only to those properties of self-reactive substances which are decisive for their classification. A flow chart, presenting the classification principles in the form of a graphically arranged scheme of questions concerning the decisive properties together with the possible answers, is given in Figure 2.4.1 in chapter 2.4 of the United Nations *Recommendations on the Transport of Dangerous Goods*. These properties shall be determined experimentally. Suitable test methods with pertinent evaluation criteria are given in the Manual of Tests and Criteria, part II.

2.4.2.3.3.1 A self-reactive substance is regarded as possessing explosive properties when, in laboratory testing, the formulation is liable to detonate, to deflagrate rapidly or to show a violent effect when heated under confinement.

2.4.2.3.3.2 The following principles apply to the classification of self-reactive substances not listed in 2.4.2.3.2.3:

.1 Any substance which can detonate or deflagrate rapidly, as packaged for transport, is prohibited from transport under the provisions for self-reactive substances of class 4.1 in that packaging (defined as SELF-REACTIVE SUBSTANCE TYPE A);

.2 Any substance possessing explosive properties and which, as packaged for transport, neither detonates nor deflagrates rapidly, but is liable to undergo a thermal explosion in that package, shall also bear an "EXPLOSIVE" subsidiary risk label (Model No. 1, see 5.2.2.2.2). Such a substance may be packaged in amounts of up to 25 kg unless the maximum quantity has to be limited to a lower amount to preclude detonation or rapid deflagration in the package (defined as SELF-REACTIVE SUBSTANCE TYPE B);

.3 Any substance possessing explosive properties may be transported without an "EXPLOSIVE" subsidiary risk label when the substance as packaged (maximum 50 kg) for transport cannot detonate or deflagrate rapidly or undergo a thermal explosion (defined as SELF-REACTIVE SUBSTANCE TYPE C);

.4 Any substance which, in laboratory testing:

.1 detonates partially, does not deflagrate rapidly and shows no violent effect when heated under confinement; or

.2 does not detonate at all, deflagrates slowly and shows no violent effect when heated under confinement; or

.3 does not detonate or deflagrate at all and shows a medium effect when heated under confinement

may be accepted for transport in packages of not more than 50 kg net mass (defined as SELF-REACTIVE SUBSTANCE TYPE D);

.5 Any substance which, in laboratory testing, neither detonates nor deflagrates at all and shows low or no effect when heated under confinement may be accepted for transport in packages of not more than 400 kg/450 L (defined as SELF-REACTIVE SUBSTANCE TYPE E);

.6   Any substance which, in laboratory testing, neither detonates in the cavitated state nor deflagrates at all and shows only a low or no effect when heated under confinement as well as low or no explosive power may be considered for transport in IBCs (defined as SELF-REACTIVE SUBSTANCE TYPE F); (for additional provisions see 4.1.7.2.2);

.7   Any substance which, in laboratory testing, neither detonates in the cavitated state nor deflagrates at all and shows no effect when heated under confinement nor any explosive power shall be exempted from classification as a self-reactive substance of class 4.1 provided that the formulation is thermally stable (self-accelerating decomposition temperature 60°C to 75°C for a 50 kg package) and any diluent meets the provisions of 2.4.2.3.5 (defined as SELF-REACTIVE SUBSTANCE TYPE G). If the formulation is not thermally stable or a compatible diluent having a boiling point less than 150°C is used for desensitization, the formulation shall be defined as SELF-REACTIVE LIQUID/SOLID TYPE F.

2.4.2.3.4   *Temperature control provisions*

2.4.2.3.4.1   Self-reactive substances are subject to temperature control in transport if their self-accelerating decomposition temperature (SADT) is less than or equal to 55°C. For currently assigned self-reactive substances, the control and emergency temperatures are shown in 2.4.2.3.2.3. Test methods for determining the SADT are given in the Manual of Tests and Criteria, part II, chapter 28. The test selected shall be conducted in a manner which is representative, both in size and material, of the package to be transported. The temperature control provisions are given in 7.3.7.

2.4.2.3.5   *Desensitization of self-reactive substances*

2.4.2.3.5.1   In order to ensure safety during transport, self-reactive substances may be desensitized through the use of a diluent. If a diluent is used, the self-reactive substance shall be tested with the diluent present in the concentration and form used in transport.

2.4.2.3.5.2   Diluents which may allow a self-reactive substance to concentrate to a dangerous extent in the event of leakage from a package shall not be used.

2.4.2.3.5.3   The diluent shall be compatible with the self-reactive substance. In this regard, compatible diluents are those solids or liquids which have no detrimental influence on the thermal stability and hazard type of the self-reactive substance.

2.4.2.3.5.4   Liquid diluents in liquid formulations requiring temperature control shall have a boiling point of at least 60°C and a flashpoint not less than 5°C. The boiling point of the liquid shall be at least 50°C higher than the control temperature of the self-reactive substance (see 7.3.7.2).

2.4.2.4   **Class 4.1 Solid desensitized explosives**

2.4.2.4.1   *Definitions and properties*

2.4.2.4.1.1   Solid desensitized explosives are explosive substances which are wetted with water or alcohols or are diluted with other substances to form a homogeneous solid mixture to suppress their explosive properties. The desensitizing agent shall be distributed uniformly throughout the substance in the state in which it is to be transported. Where transport under conditions of low temperature is anticipated for substances containing or wetted with water, a suitable and compatible solvent, such as alcohol, may have to be added to lower the freezing point of the liquid. Some of these substances, when in a dry state, are classified as explosives. Where reference is made to a substance which is wetted with water, or some other liquid, it shall be permitted for transport as a class 4.1 substance only when in the wetted condition specified. Entries in the Dangerous Goods List in chapter 3.2 for solid desensitized explosives are UN 1310, UN 1320, UN 1321, UN 1322, UN 1336, UN 1337, UN 1344, UN 1347, UN 1348, UN 1349, UN 1354, UN 1355, UN 1356, UN 1357, UN 1517, UN 1571, UN 2555, UN 2556, UN 2557, UN 2852, UN 2907, UN 3317, UN 3319, UN 3344, UN 3364, UN 3365, UN 3366, UN 3367, UN 3368, UN 3369, UN 3370, UN 3376, UN 3380 and UN 3474.

2.4.2.4.2   Substances that:

.1   have been provisionally accepted into class 1 according to Test Series 1 and 2 but exempted from class 1 by Test Series 6;

.2   are not self-reactive substances of class 4.1;

.3   are not substances of class 5

are also assigned to class 4.1. UN 2956, UN 3241, UN 3242 and UN 3251 are such entries.

■ **2.4.2.5** **Class 4.1 Polymerizing substances and mixtures (stabilized)**

2.4.2.5.1 *Definitions and properties*

Polymerizing substances are substances which, without stabilization, are liable to undergo a strongly exothermic reaction resulting in the formation of larger molecules or resulting in the formation of polymers under conditions normally encountered in transport. Such substances are considered to be polymerizing substances of class 4.1 when:

.1 their self-accelerating polymerization temperature (SAPT) is 75°C or less under the conditions (with or without chemical stabilization as offered for transport) and in the packaging, IBC or portable tank in which the substance or mixture is to be transported;

.2 they exhibit a heat of reaction of more than 300 J/g; and

.3 they do not meet any other criteria for inclusion in classes 1 to 8.

A mixture meeting the criteria of a polymerizing substance shall be classified as a polymerizing substance of Class 4.1.

2.4.2.5.2 Polymerizing substances are subject to temperature control in transport if their self-accelerating polymerization temperature (SAPT) is:

.1 when offered for transport in a packaging or IBC, 50°C or less in the packaging or IBC in which the substance is to be transported; or

.2 when offered for transport in a portable tank, 45°C or less in the portable tank in which the substance is to be transported.

2.4.3 Class 4.2 – Substances liable to spontaneous combustion

2.4.3.1 Definitions and properties

2.4.3.1.1 Class 4.2 comprises:

.1 *Pyrophoric substances*, which are substances, including mixtures and solutions (liquid or solid), which, even in small quantities, ignite within 5 minutes of coming into contact with air. These substances are the most liable to spontaneous combustion; and

.2 *Self-heating substances*, which are substances, other than pyrophoric substances, which, in contact with air without energy supply, are liable to self-heating. These substances will ignite only when in large amounts (kilograms) and after long periods of time (hours or days).

2.4.3.1.2 Self-heating of a substance is a process where the gradual reaction of that substance with oxygen (in air) generates heat. If the rate of heat production exceeds the rate of heat loss, then the temperature of the substance will rise which, after an induction time, may lead to self-ignition and combustion.

2.4.3.1.3 Some substances may also give off toxic gases if involved in a fire.

2.4.3.2 Classification of class 4.2 substances

2.4.3.2.1 Solids are considered pyrophoric solids which shall be classified in class 4.2 if, in tests performed in accordance with the test method given in the Manual of Tests and Criteria, part III, 33.3.1.4, the sample ignites in one of the tests.

2.4.3.2.2 Liquids are considered pyrophoric liquids which shall be classified in class 4.2 if, in tests performed in accordance with the test method given in the Manual of Tests and Criteria, part III, 33.3.1.5, the liquid ignites in the first part of the test, or if it ignites or chars the filter paper.

2.4.3.2.3 *Self-heating substances*

2.4.3.2.3.1 A substance shall be classified as a self-heating substance of class 4.2 if, in tests performed in accordance with the test method given in the Manual of Tests and Criteria, part III, 33.3.1.6:

.1 a positive result is obtained using a 25 mm cube sample at 140°C;

.2 a positive result is obtained in a test using a 100 mm cube sample at 140°C and a negative result is obtained in a test using a 100 mm cube sample at 120°C <u>and</u> the substance is to be transported in packages with a volume of more than 3 m^3;

.3 a positive result is obtained in a test using a 100 mm cube sample at 140°C and a negative result is obtained in a test using a 100 mm cube sample at 100°C <u>and</u> the substance is to be transported in packages with a volume of more than 450 L;

.4 a positive result is obtained in a test using a 100 mm cube sample at 140°C <u>and</u> a positive result is obtained using a 100 mm cube sample at 100°C.

Note: Self-reactive substances, except for type G, giving also a positive result with this test method shall not be classified in class 4.2 but in class 4.1 (see 2.4.2.3.1.1).

2.4.3.2.3.2 A substance shall not be classified in class 4.2 if:

.1 a negative result is obtained in a test using a 100 mm cube sample at 140°C;

.2 a positive result is obtained in a test using a 100 mm cube sample at 140°C and a negative result is obtained in a test using a 25 mm cube sample at 140°C, a negative result is obtained in a test using a 100 mm cube sample at 120°C <u>and</u> the substance is to be transported in packages with a volume not more than 3 m^3;

.3 a positive result is obtained in a test using a 100 mm cube sample at 140°C and a negative result is obtained in a test using a 25 mm cube sample at 140°C, a negative result is obtained in a test using a 100 mm cube sample at 100°C <u>and</u> the substance is to be transported in packages with a volume not more than 450 L.

2.4.3.3 Assignment of packing groups

2.4.3.3.1 Packing group I shall be assigned to all pyrophoric solids and liquids.

2.4.3.3.2 Packing group II shall be assigned to self-heating substances which give a positive result in a test using a 25 mm cube sample at 140°C.

2.4.3.3.3 Packing group III shall be assigned to self-heating substances if:

.1 a positive result is obtained in a test using a 100 mm cube sample at 140°C and a negative result is obtained in a test using a 25 mm cube sample at 140°C <u>and</u> the substance is to be transported in packages with a volume of more than 3 m^3;

.2 a positive result is obtained in a test using a 100 mm cube sample at 140°C and a negative result is obtained in a test using a 25 mm cube sample at 140°C, a positive result is obtained in a test using a 100 mm cube sample at 120°C <u>and</u> the substance is to be transported in packages with a volume of more than 450 L;

.3 a positive result is obtained in a test using a 100 mm cube sample at 140°C and a negative result is obtained in a test using a 25 mm cube sample at 140°C <u>and</u> a positive result is obtained in a test using a 100 mm cube sample at 100°C.

2.4.4 Class 4.3 – Substances which, in contact with water, emit flammable gases

2.4.4.1 Definitions and properties

2.4.4.1.1 For the purpose of this Code, the substances in this class are either liquids or solids which, by interaction with water, are liable to become spontaneously flammable or to give off flammable gases in dangerous quantities.

2.4.4.1.2 Certain substances, in contact with water, may emit flammable gases that can form explosive mixtures with air. Such mixtures are easily ignited by all ordinary sources of ignition, for example naked lights, sparking handtools or unprotected lamps. The resulting blast wave and flames may endanger people and the environment. The test method referred to in 2.4.4.2 is used to determine whether the reaction of a substance with water leads to the development of a dangerous amount of gases which may be flammable. This test method shall not be applied to pyrophoric substances.

2.4.4.2 Classification of class 4.3 substances

2.4.4.2.1 Substances which, in contact with water, emit flammable gases shall be classified in class 4.3 if, in tests performed in accordance with the test method given in the Manual of Tests and Criteria, part III, 33.4.1:

.1 spontaneous ignition takes place in any step of the test procedure; or

.2 there is an evolution of a flammable gas at a rate greater than 1 litre per kilogram of the substance per hour.

2.4.4.3   Assignment of packing groups

2.4.4.3.1   Packing group I shall be assigned to any substance which reacts vigorously with water at ambient temperatures and demonstrates generally a tendency for the gas produced to ignite spontaneously, or which reacts readily with water at ambient temperatures such that the rate of evolution of flammable gas is equal to or greater than 10 litres per kilogram of substance over any one minute.

2.4.4.3.2   Packing group II shall be assigned to any substance which reacts readily with water at ambient temperatures such that the maximum rate of evolution of flammable gas is equal to or greater than 20 litres per kilogram of substance per hour, and which does not meet the criteria for packing group I.

△ **2.4.4.3.3**   Packing group III shall be assigned to any substance which reacts slowly with water at ambient temperatures such that the maximum rate of evolution of flammable gas is greater than 1 litre per kilogram of substance per hour, and which does not meet the criteria for packing groups I or II.

2.4.5   Classification of organometallic substances

Depending on their properties, organometallic substances may be classified in classes 4.2 or 4.3, as appropriate, in accordance with the following flowchart:

Flowchart scheme for organometallic substances[1,2]

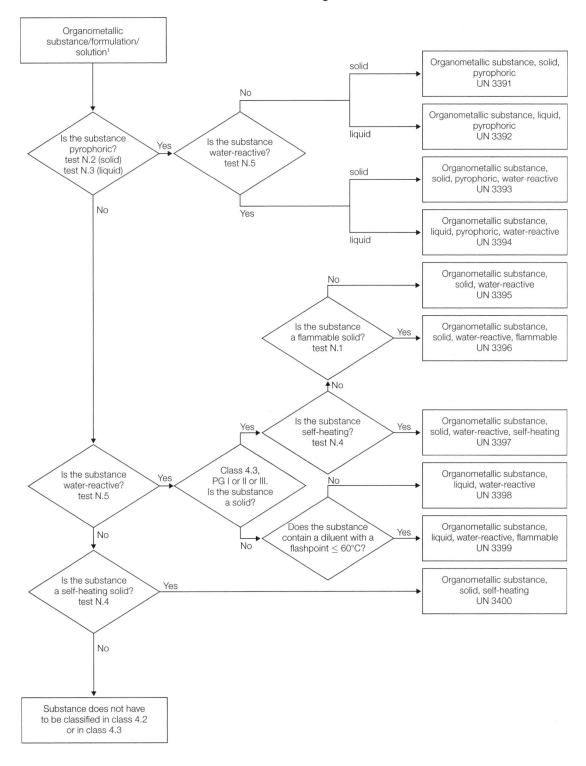

---

[1] If applicable and testing is relevant, taking into account reactivity properties, class 6.1 and class 8 properties shall be considered according to the Precedence of hazards table 2.0.3.6.

[2] Test methods N.1 to N.5 can be found in the Manual of Tests and Criteria, part III, section 33.

Chapter 2.5

Class 5 – Oxidizing substances and organic peroxides

2.5.0 Introductory note

Because of the differing properties exhibited by dangerous goods within classes 5.1 and 5.2, it is impracticable to establish a single criterion for classification in either class. Tests and criteria for assignment to the two classes are addressed in this chapter.

2.5.1 Definitions and general provisions

In this Code, class 5 is divided into two classes as follows:

Class 5.1 – Oxidizing substances

Substances which, while in themselves not necessarily combustible, may, generally by yielding oxygen, cause, or contribute to, the combustion of other material. Such substances may be contained in an article;

Class 5.2 – Organic peroxides

Organic substances which contain the bivalent –O–O– structure and may be considered derivatives of hydrogen peroxide, where one or both of the hydrogen atoms have been replaced by organic radicals. Organic peroxides are thermally unstable substances which may undergo exothermic self-accelerating decomposition. In addition, they may have one or more of the following properties:

– be liable to explosive decomposition;

– burn rapidly;

– be sensitive to impact or friction;

– react dangerously with other substances;

– cause damage to the eyes.

2.5.2 Class 5.1 – Oxidizing substances

Note: For the classification of oxidizing substances to class 5.1, in the event of divergence between test results and known experience, judgement based on known experience shall take precedence over test results.

2.5.2.1 Properties

2.5.2.1.1 Substances of class 5.1 in certain circumstances directly or indirectly evolve oxygen. For this reason, oxidizing substances increase the risk and intensity of fire in combustible material with which they come into contact.

2.5.2.1.2 Mixtures of oxidizing substances with combustible material and even with material such as sugar, flour, edible oils, mineral oils, etc., are dangerous. These mixtures are readily ignited, in some cases by friction or impact. They may burn violently and may lead to explosion.

2.5.2.1.3 There will be a violent reaction between most oxidizing substances and liquid acids, evolving toxic gases. Toxic gases may also be evolved when certain oxidizing substances are involved in a fire.

2.5.2.1.4 The above-mentioned properties are, in general, common to all substances in this class. Additionally, some substances possess specific properties, which shall be taken into account in transport. These properties are shown in the Dangerous Goods List in chapter 3.2.

2.5.2.2   Oxidizing solids

2.5.2.2.1   *Classification of solid substances of class 5.1*

2.5.2.2.1.1   Tests are performed to measure the potential for the solid substance to increase the burning rate or burning intensity of a combustible substance when the two are thoroughly mixed. The procedure is given in the Manual of Tests and Criteria, part III, subsection 34.4.1 (test O.1) or alternatively, in subsection 34.4.3 (test O.3). Tests are conducted on the substance to be evaluated mixed with dry fibrous cellulose in mixing ratios of 1:1 and 4:1, by mass, of sample to cellulose. The burning characteristics of the mixtures are compared:

.1   in the test O.1, with the standard 3:7 mixture, by mass, of potassium bromate to cellulose. If the burning time is equal to or less than this standard mixture, the burning times shall be compared with those from the packing group I or II reference standards, 3:2 and 2:3 ratios, by mass, of potassium bromate to cellulose, respectively; or

.2   in the test O.3, with the standard 1:2 mixture, by mass, of calcium peroxide to cellulose. If the burning rate is equal to or greater than this standard mixture, the burning rates shall be compared with those from the packing group I or II reference standards, 3:1 and 1:1 ratios, by mass, of calcium peroxide to cellulose, respectively.

2.5.2.2.1.2   The classification test results are assessed on the basis of:

.1   the comparison of the mean burning time (for the test O.1) or burning rate (for the test O.3) with those of the reference mixtures; and

.2   whether the mixture of substance and cellulose ignites and burns.

2.5.2.2.1.3   A solid substance is classified in class 5.1 if the 4:1 or 1:1 sample-to-cellulose ratio (by mass) tested, exhibits:

.1   in the test O.1, a mean burning time equal to or less than the mean burning time of a 3:7 mixture (by mass) of potassium bromate and cellulose; or

.2   in the test O.3, a mean burning rate equal to or greater than the mean burning rate of a 1:2 mixture (by mass) of calcium peroxide and cellulose.

2.5.2.2.2   *Assignment of packing groups*

Solid oxidizing substances are assigned to a packing group according to one of the test procedures in the Manual of Tests and Criteria, part III, subsection 34.4.1 (test O.1) or subsection 34.4.3 (test O.3), in accordance with the following criteria:

.1   Test O.1:

.1   Packing group I: any substance which, in the 4:1 or 1:1 sample-to-cellulose ratio (by mass) tested, exhibits a mean burning time less than the mean burning time of a 3:2 mixture, by mass, of potassium bromate and cellulose;

.2   Packing group II: any substance which, in the 4:1 or 1:1 sample-to-cellulose ratio (by mass) tested, exhibits a mean burning time equal to or less than the mean burning time of a 2:3 mixture (by mass) of potassium bromate and cellulose, and the criteria for packing group I are not met;

.3   Packing group III: any substance which, in the 4:1 or 1:1 sample-to-cellulose ratio (by mass) tested, exhibits a mean burning time equal to or less than the mean burning time of a 3:7 mixture (by mass) of potassium bromate and cellulose, and the criteria for packing groups I and II are not met;

.4   Not class 5.1: any substance which, in both the 4:1 and 1:1 sample-to-cellulose ratio (by mass) tested, does not ignite and burn, or exhibits mean burning times greater than that of a 3:7 mixture (by mass) of potassium bromate and cellulose.

.2   Test O.3:

.1   Packing group I: any substance which, in the 4:1 or 1:1 sample-to-cellulose ratio (by mass) tested, exhibits a mean burning rate greater than the mean burning rate of a 3:1 mixture (by mass) of calcium peroxide and cellulose;

.2   Packing group II: any substance which, in the 4:1 or 1:1 sample-to-cellulose ratio (by mass) tested, exhibits a mean burning rate equal to or greater than the mean burning rate of a 1:1 mixture (by mass) of calcium peroxide and cellulose, and the criteria for packing group I are not met;

.3   Packing group III: any substance which, in the 4:1 or 1:1 sample-to-cellulose ratio (by mass) tested, exhibits a mean burning rate equal to or greater than the mean burning rate of a 1:2 mixture (by mass) of calcium peroxide and cellulose, and the criteria for packing groups I and II are not met;

.4   Not class 5.1: any substance which, in both the 4:1 and 1:1 sample-to-cellulose ratio (by mass) tested, does not ignite and burn, or exhibits a mean burning rate less than the mean burning rate of a 1:2 mixture (by mass) of calcium peroxide and cellulose.

2.5.2.3   Oxidizing liquids

2.5.2.3.1   *Classification of liquid substances of class 5.1*

2.5.2.3.1.1   A test is performed to determine the potential for a liquid substance to increase the burning rate or burning intensity of a combustible substance or for spontaneous ignition to occur when the two are thoroughly mixed. The procedure is given in the Manual of Tests and Criteria, part III, 34.4.2 (test O.2). It measures the pressure rise time during combustion. Whether a liquid is an oxidizing substance of class 5.1 and, if so, whether packing group I, II or III shall be assigned, is decided on the basis of the test result (see also Precedence of hazard characteristics in 2.0.3).

2.5.2.3.1.2   The classification test results are assessed on the basis of:

.1   whether the mixture of substance and cellulose spontaneously ignites;

.2   the comparison of the mean time taken for the pressure to rise from 690 kPa to 2070 kPa gauge with those of the reference substances.

2.5.2.3.1.3   A liquid substance is classified in class 5.1 if the 1:1 mixture, by mass, of substance and cellulose tested exhibits a mean pressure rise time less than or equal to the mean pressure rise time of a 1:1 mixture, by mass, of 65% aqueous nitric acid and cellulose.

2.5.2.3.2   *Assignment of packing groups*

2.5.2.3.2.1   Liquid oxidizing substances are assigned to a packing group according to the test procedure in the Manual of Tests and Criteria, part III, 34.4.2, in accordance with the following criteria:

.1   Packing group I: any substance which, in the 1:1 mixture (by mass) of substance and cellulose tested, spontaneously ignites; or the mean pressure rise time of a 1:1 mixture (by mass) of substance and cellulose is less than that of a 1:1 mixture (by mass) of 50% perchloric acid and cellulose;

.2   Packing group II: any substance which, in the 1:1 mixture (by mass) of substance and cellulose tested, exhibits a mean pressure rise time less than or equal to the mean pressure rise time of a 1:1 mixture (by mass) of 40% aqueous sodium chlorate solution and cellulose; and the criteria for packing group I are not met;

.3   Packing group III: any substance which, in the 1:1 mixture (by mass) of substance and cellulose tested, exhibits a mean pressure rise time less than or equal to the mean pressure rise time of a 1:1 mixture (by mass) of 65% aqueous nitric acid and cellulose; and the criteria for packing groups I and II are not met;

.4   Not classified as class 5.1: any substance which, in the 1:1 mixture (by mass) of substance and cellulose tested, exhibits a pressure rise of less than 2070 kPa gauge; or exhibits a mean pressure rise time greater than the mean pressure rise time of a 1:1 mixture (by mass) of 65% aqueous nitric acid and cellulose.

2.5.3   Class 5.2 – Organic peroxides

2.5.3.1   Properties

2.5.3.1.1   Organic peroxides are liable to exothermic decomposition at normal or elevated temperatures. The decomposition can be initiated by heat, contact with impurities (such as acids, heavy-metal compounds, amines), friction or impact. The rate of decomposition increases with temperature and varies with the organic peroxide formulation. Decomposition may result in the evolution of harmful, or flammable, gases or vapours. For certain organic peroxides the temperature shall be controlled during transport. Some organic peroxides may decompose explosively, particularly if confined. This characteristic may be modified by the addition of diluents or by the use of appropriate packagings. Many organic peroxides burn vigorously.

2.5.3.1.2   Contact of organic peroxides with the eyes is to be avoided. Some organic peroxides will cause serious injury to the cornea, even after brief contact, or will be corrosive to the skin.

2.5.3.2   Classification of organic peroxides

2.5.3.2.1   Any organic peroxide shall be considered for classification in class 5.2, unless the organic peroxide formulation contains:

.1   not more than 1.0% available oxygen from the organic peroxides when containing not more than 1.0% hydrogen peroxide; or

.2   not more than 0.5% available oxygen from the organic peroxides when containing more than 1.0% but not more than 7.0% hydrogen peroxide.

Note: The available oxygen content (%) of an organic peroxide formulation is given by the formula:

$$16 \times \Sigma(n_i \times c_i/m_i)$$

where:

n_i = number of peroxygen groups per molecule of organic peroxide i;

c_i = concentration (mass %) of organic peroxide i;

m_i = molecular mass of organic peroxide i.

2.5.3.2.2 Organic peroxides are classified into seven types according to the degree of danger they present. The types of organic peroxide range from type A, which may not be accepted for transport in the packaging in which it is tested, to type G, which is not subject to the provisions for organic peroxides of class 5.2. The classification of types B to F is directly related to the maximum quantity allowed in one packaging.

2.5.3.2.3 Organic peroxides permitted for transport in packagings are listed in 2.5.3.2.4, those permitted for transport in IBCs are listed in packing instruction IBC520 and those permitted for transport in portable tanks are listed in portable tank instruction T23. For each permitted substance listed, the generic entry of the Dangerous Goods List (UN 3101 to UN 3120) is assigned, appropriate subsidiary risks and remarks providing relevant transport information are given. The generic entries specify:

.1 organic peroxide type (B to F);

.2 physical state (liquid or solid); and

.3 temperature control, when required (see 2.5.3.4).

2.5.3.2.3.1 Mixtures of the listed formulations may be classified as the same type of organic peroxide as that of the most dangerous component and be transported under the conditions of transport given for this type. However, as two stable components can form a thermally less stable mixture, the self-accelerating decomposition temperature (SADT) of the mixture shall be determined and, if necessary, temperature control applied as required by 2.5.3.4.

2.5.3.2.4   List of currently assigned organic peroxides in packagings

Note: Packing Method codes "OP1" to "OP8" refer to packing methods in packing instruction P520. Peroxides to be transported shall fulfil the classification and the control and emergency temperatures (derived from the SADT) as listed. For substances permitted in IBCs, see packing instruction IBC520, and for those permitted in tanks, see portable tank instruction T23.

Number (generic entry)	ORGANIC PEROXIDE	Concentration (%)	Diluent type A (%)	Diluent type B (%)(1)	Inert solid (%)	Water (%)	Packing method	Control temperature (°C)	Emergency temperature (°C)	Subsidiary risks and remarks
3101	tert-BUTYL PEROXYACETATE	> 52 – 77	≥ 23				OP5			(3)
	1,1-DI-(tert-BUTYLPEROXY)CYCLOHEXANE	> 80 – 100					OP5			(3)
	1,1-DI-(tert-BUTYLPEROXY)-3,3,5-TRIMETHYL-CYCLOHEXANE	> 90 – 100					OP5			(3)
	METHYL ETHYL KETONE PEROXIDE(S)	see remark (8)	≥ 48				OP5			(3) (8) (13)
	2,5-DIMETHYL-2,5-DI-(tert-BUTYLPEROXY)-HEXYNE-3	> 86 – 100					OP5			(3)
3102	tert-BUTYL MONOPEROXYMALEATE	> 52 – 100					OP5			(3)
	3-CHLOROPEROXYBENZOIC ACID	> 57 – 86			≥ 14		OP1			(3)
	DIBENZOYL PEROXIDE	> 52 – 100			≤ 48		OP2			(3)
	DIBENZOYL PEROXIDE	> 77 – 94				≥ 6	OP4			(3)
	DI-4-CHLOROBENZOYL PEROXIDE	≤ 77				≥ 23	OP5			(3)
	DI-2,4-DICHLOROBENZOYL PEROXIDE	≤ 77				≥ 23	OP5			(3)
	2,2-DIHYDROPEROXYPROPANE	≤ 27			≥ 73		OP5			(3)
	2,5-DIMETHYL-2,5-DI-(BENZOYLPEROXY)HEXANE	> 82 – 100					OP5			(3)
	DI-(2-PHENOXYETHYL) PEROXYDICARBONATE	> 85 – 100					OP5			(3)
	DISUCCINIC ACID PEROXIDE	> 72 – 100					OP4			(3) (17)
3103	tert-AMYL PEROXYBENZOATE	≤ 100					OP5			
	tert-AMYLPEROXY ISOPROPYL CARBONATE	≤ 77	≥ 23				OP5			
	n-BUTYL 4,4-DI-(tert-BUTYLPEROXY)VALERATE	> 52 – 100					OP5			
	tert-BUTYL HYDROPEROXIDE	> 79 – 90				≥ 10	OP5			(13)
	tert-BUTYL HYDROPEROXIDE + DI-tert-BUTYL PEROXIDE	< 82 + > 9				≥ 7	OP5			(13)
	tert-BUTYL MONOPEROXYMALEATE	≤ 52	≥ 48				OP6			
	tert-BUTYL PEROXYACETATE	> 32 – 52	≥ 48				OP6			
	tert-BUTYL PEROXYBENZOATE	> 77 – 100					OP5			
	tert-BUTYLPEROXY ISOPROPYLCARBONATE	≤ 77	≥ 23				OP5			
	tert-BUTYLPEROXY-2-METHYLBENZOATE	≤ 100					OP5			
	1,1-DI-(tert-AMYLPEROXY)CYCLOHEXANE	≤ 82	≥ 18				OP6			

Number (generic entry)	ORGANIC PEROXIDE	Concentration (%)	Diluent type A (%)	Diluent type B (%)(t)	Inert solid (%)	Water (%)	Packing method	Control temperature (°C)	Emergency temperature (°C)	Subsidiary risks and remarks
3103 (cont.)	2,2-DI-(tert-BUTYLPEROXY)BUTANE	≤ 52	≥ 48				OP6			
	1,6-DI-(tert-BUTYLPEROXYCARBONYLOXY)-HEXANE	≤ 72	≥ 28				OP5			
	1,1-DI-(tert-BUTYLPEROXY)CYCLOHEXANE	> 52 – 80	≥ 20				OP5			
	1,1-DI-(tert-BUTYLPEROXY)CYCLOHEXANE	≤ 72		≥ 28			OP5			(30)
	1,1-DI-(tert-BUTYLPEROXY)-3,3,5-TRIMETHYL-CYCLOHEXANE	> 57 – 90	≥ 10				OP5			
	1,1-DI-(tert-BUTYLPEROXY)-3,3,5-TRIMETHYL-CYCLOHEXANE	≤ 77		≥ 23			OP5			(30)
	1,1-DI-(tert-BUTYLPEROXY)-3,3,5-TRIMETHYL-CYCLOHEXANE	≤ 90		≥ 10			OP5			
	2,5-DIMETHYL-2,5-DI-(tert-BUTYLPEROXY)HEXANE	> 90 – 100					OP5			(26)
	2,5-DIMETHYL-2,5-DI-(tert-BUTYLPEROXY)-HEXYNE-3	> 52 – 86	≥ 14				OP5			
	ETHYL 3,3-DI-(tert-BUTYLPEROXY)BUTYRATE	> 77 – 100					OP5			(11)
	ORGANIC PEROXIDE, LIQUID, SAMPLE						OP2			
3104	CYCLOHEXANONE PEROXIDE(S)	≤ 91				≥ 9	OP6			(13)
	DIBENZOYL PEROXIDE	≤ 77				≥ 23	OP6			
	2,5-DIMETHYL-2,5-DI(BENZOYLPEROXY)HEXANE	≤ 82				≥ 18	OP5			
	2,5-DIMETHYL-2,5-DIHYDROPEROXYHEXANE	≤ 82				≥ 18	OP6			
	ORGANIC PEROXIDE, SOLID, SAMPLE						OP2			(11)
3105	ACETYL ACETONE PEROXIDE	≤ 42	≥ 48			≥ 8	OP7			(2)
	tert-AMYL PEROXYACETATE	≤ 62	≥ 38				OP7			
	tert-AMYL PEROXY-2-ETHYLHEXYL CARBONATE	≤ 100					OP7			
	tert-AMYL PEROXY-3,5,5-TRIMETHYLHEXANOATE	≤ 100					OP7			
	tert-BUTYL HYDROPEROXIDE	≤ 80	≥ 20				OP7			
	tert-BUTYL PEROXYBENZOATE	> 52 – 77	≥ 23				OP7			
	tert-BUTYL PEROXYBUTYL FUMARATE	≤ 52	≥ 48				OP7			
	tert-BUTYL PEROXYCROTONATE	≤ 77	≥ 23				OP7			
	tert-BUTYL PEROXY-2-ETHYLHEXYLCARBONATE	≤ 100					OP7			
	1-(2-tert-BUTYLPEROXY ISOPROPYL)-3-ISOPROPENYLBENZENE	> 37 – 100	≥ 23				OP7			(4) (13)
	tert-BUTYL PEROXY-3,5,5-TRIMETHYLHEXANOATE	≤ 77	≥ 23				OP7			
	CYCLOHEXANONE PEROXIDE(S)	≤ 72	≥ 28				OP7			(5)

Number (generic entry)	ORGANIC PEROXIDE	Concentration (%)	Diluent type A (%)	Diluent type B (%)(1)	Inert solid (%)	Water (%)	Packing method	Control temperature (°C)	Emergency temperature (°C)	Subsidiary risks and remarks
3105 (cont.)	2,2-DI-(*tert*-AMYLPEROXY)BUTANE	≤ 57	≥ 43				OP7			
	DI-*tert*-BUTYL PEROXYAZELATE	≤ 52	≥ 48				OP7			
	1,1-DI-(*tert*-BUTYLPEROXY)CYCLOHEXANE	> 42 – 52	≥ 48				OP7			
	1,1-DI-(*tert*-BUTYLPEROXY)CYCLOHEXANE + *tert*-BUTYL PEROXY-2-ETHYLHEXANOATE	≤ 43 + ≤ 16	≥ 41				OP7			
	DI-(*tert*-BUTYLPEROXY)PHTHALATE	> 42 – 52	≥ 48				OP7			
	2,2-DI-(*tert*-BUTYLPEROXY)PROPANE	≤ 52	≥ 48				OP7			
	2,5-DIMETHYL-2,5-DI-(*tert*-BUTYLPEROXY)HEXANE	> 52 – 90	≥ 10				OP7			
	2,5-DIMETHYL-2,5-DI-(3,5,5-TRIMETHYL-HEXANOYLPEROXY)HEXANE	≤ 77	≥ 23				OP7			
	ETHYL 3,3-DI-(*tert*-AMYLPEROXY)BUTYRATE	≤ 67	≥ 33				OP7			
	ETHYL 3,3-DI-(*tert*-BUTYLPEROXY)BUTYRATE	≤ 77	≥ 23				OP7			
	p-MENTHYL HYDROPEROXIDE	> 72 – 100					OP7			(13)
	METHYL ETHYL KETONE PEROXIDE(S)	see remark (9)	≥ 55				OP7			(9)
	METHYL ISOBUTYL KETONE PEROXIDE(S)	≤ 62	≥ 19				OP7			(22)
	PEROXYACETIC ACID, TYPE D, stabilized	≤ 43					OP7			(13) (14) (19)
	PINANYL HYDROPEROXIDE	> 56 – 100					OP7			(13)
	1,1,3,3-TETRAMETHYLBUTYL HYDROPEROXIDE	≤ 100					OP7			
	3,6,9-TRIETHYL-3,6,9-TRIMETHYL-1,4,7-TRIPEROXONANE	≤ 42	≥ 58				OP7			(28)
3106	ACETYL ACETONE PEROXIDE	≤ 32 as a paste					OP7			(20)
	tert-BUTYL PEROXYBENZOATE	≤ 52			≥ 48		OP7			
	tert-BUTYL PEROXY-2-ETHYLHEXANOATE + 2,2-DI-(*tert*-BUTYLPEROXY)BUTANE	≤ 12 + ≤ 14	≥ 14		≥ 60		OP7			
	tert-BUTYLPEROXY STEARYLCARBONATE	≤ 100					OP7			
	tert-BUTYL PEROXY-3,5,5-TRIMETHYLHEXANOATE	≤ 42			≥ 58		OP7			
	3-CHLOROPEROXYBENZOIC ACID	≤ 57			≥ 3	≥ 40	OP7			
	3-CHLOROPEROXYBENZOIC ACID	≤ 77			≥ 6	≥ 17	OP7			
	CYCLOHEXANONE PEROXIDE(S)	≤ 72 as a paste					OP7			(5) (20)
	DIBENZOYL PEROXIDE	≤ 62			≥ 28	≥ 10	OP7			
	DIBENZOYL PEROXIDE	> 52 – 62 as a paste					OP7			(20)
	DIBENZOYL PEROXIDE	> 35 – 52			≥ 48		OP7			
	1,1-DI-(*tert*-BUTYLPEROXY)CYCLOHEXANE	≤ 42	≥ 13		≥ 45		OP7			
	DI-(*tert*-BUTYLPEROXYISOPROPYL)BENZENE(S)	> 42 – 100			≤ 57		OP7			

IMDG Code (amendment 38-16)

Number (generic entry)	ORGANIC PEROXIDE	Concentration (%)	Diluent type A (%)	Diluent type B (%)[(f)]	Inert solid (%)	Water (%)	Packing method	Control temperature (°C)	Emergency temperature (°C)	Subsidiary risks and remarks
3106 (cont.)	DI-(*tert*-BUTYLPEROXY)PHTHALATE	≤ 52 as a paste					OP7			(20)
	2,2-DI-(*tert*-BUTYLPEROXY)PROPANE	≤ 42	≥ 13		≥ 45		OP7			
	DI-4-CHLOROBENZOYL PEROXIDE	≤ 52 as a paste			≥ 58		OP7			(20)
	2,2-DI-(4,4-DI-(*tert*-BUTYLPEROXY)CYCLOHEXYL)-PROPANE	≤ 42			≥ 58		OP7			
	DI-2,4-DICHLOROBENZOYL PEROXIDE	≤ 52 as a paste with silicon oil					OP7			
	DI-(1-HYDROXYCYCLOHEXYL)PEROXIDE	≤ 100					OP7			
	DIISOPROPYLBENZENE DIHYDROPEROXIDE	≤ 82	≥ 5			≥ 5	OP7			(24)
	DILAUROYL PEROXIDE	≤ 100					OP7			
	DI-(4-METHYLBENZOYL) PEROXIDE	≤ 52 as paste with silicon oil					OP7			
	2,5-DIMETHYL-2,5-DI-(BENZOYLPEROXY)HEXANE	≤ 82			≥ 18		OP7			
	2,5-DIMETHYL-2,5-DI-(*tert*-BUTYLPEROXY)-HEXYNE-3	≤ 52			≥ 48		OP7			
	DI-(2-PHENOXYETHYL)PEROXYDICARBONATE	≤ 85				≥ 15	OP7			
	ETHYL 3,3-DI-(*tert*-BUTYLPEROXY)BUTYRATE	≤ 52			≥ 48		OP7			
	([3R-(3R,5aS,6S,8aS,9R,10R,12S,12aR**)]-DECAHYDRO-10-METHOXY-3,6,9-TRIMETHYL-3,12-EPOXY-12H-PYRANO[4,3-I]-1,2-BENZODIOXEPIN)	≤ 100					OP7			
3107	*tert*-AMYL HYDROPEROXIDE	≤ 88	≥ 6			≥ 6	OP8			
	tert-BUTYL HYDROPEROXIDE	≤ 79	≤ 10			> 14	OP8			(13) (23)
	CUMYL HYDROPEROXIDE	> 90 – 98	≤ 10				OP8			(13)
	DI-*tert*-AMYL PEROXIDE	≤ 100					OP8			
	DIBENZOYL PEROXIDE	> 36 – 42	≥ 18			≤ 40	OP8			
	DI-*tert*-BUTYL PEROXIDE	> 52 – 100					OP8			
	1,1-DI-(*tert*-BUTYLPEROXY)CYCLOHEXANE	≤ 27	≥ 25				OP8			
	DI-(*tert*-BUTYLPEROXY)PHTHALATE	≤ 42	≥ 58				OP8			(21)
	1,1-DI-(*tert*-BUTYLPEROXY)-3,3,5-TRIMETHYL-CYCLOHEXANE	≤ 57	≥ 43				OP8			
	1,1-DI-(*tert*-BUTYLPEROXY)-3,3,5-TRIMETHYL-CYCLOHEXANE	≤ 32	≥ 26	≥ 42			OP8			
	2,2-DI-(4,4-DI-(*tert*-BUTYLPEROXY)CYCLOHEXYL)-PROPANE	≤ 22		≥ 78			OP8			

⊗

2

Number (generic entry)	ORGANIC PEROXIDE	Concentration (%)	Diluent type A (%)	Diluent type B (%)(1)	Inert solid (%)	Water (%)	Packing method	Control temperature (°C)	Emergency temperature (°C)	Subsidiary risks and remarks
3107 *(cont.)*	METHYL ETHYL KETONE PEROXIDE(S)	see remark (10)	≥ 60				OP8			(10)
	3,3,5,7,7-PENTAMETHYL-1,2,4-TRIOXEPANE	≤ 100					OP8			
	PEROXYACETIC ACID, TYPE E, stabilized	≤ 43		≥ 48			OP8			(13) (15) (19)
	POLYETHER POLY-*tert*-BUTYLPEROXY-CARBONATE	≤ 52					OP8			
3108	*tert*-BUTYL CUMYL PEROXIDE	≤ 52			≥ 48		OP8			
	n-BUTYL 4,4-DI-(*tert*-BUTYLPEROXY)VALERATE	≤ 52			≥ 48		OP8			
	tert-BUTYL MONOPEROXYMALEATE	≤ 52			≥ 48		OP8			
	tert-BUTYL MONOPEROXYMALEATE	≤ 52 as a paste					OP8			
	1-(2-*tert*-BUTYLPEROXYISOPROPYL)-3-ISOPROPENYLBENZENE	≤ 42			≥ 58		OP8			
	DIBENZOYL PEROXIDE	≤ 56.5 as a paste				≥ 15	OP8			(20)
	DIBENZOYL PEROXIDE	≤ 52 as a paste					OP8			
	2,5-DIMETHYL-2,5-DI-(*tert*-BUTYLPEROXY)HEXANE	≤ 47 as a paste					OP8			
	2,5-DIMETHYL-2,5-DI-(*tert*-BUTYLPEROXY)HEXANE	≤ 77			≥ 23		OP8			
3109	*tert*-BUTYL CUMYL PEROXIDE	> 42 – 100	≥ 10				OP8			
	tert-BUTYL HYDROPEROXIDE	≤ 72				≥ 28	OP8			(13)
	tert-BUTYL PEROXYACETATE	≤ 32		≥ 68			OP8			
	tert-BUTYL PEROXY-3,5,5-TRIMETHYL-HEXANOATE	≤ 37		≥ 63			OP8			
	CUMYL HYDROPEROXIDE	≤ 90	≥ 10				OP8			(13) (18)
	DIBENZOYL PEROXIDE	≤ 42 as a stable dispersion in water					OP8			
	DI-*tert*-BUTYL PEROXIDE	≤ 52		≥ 48			OP8			(25)
	1,1-DI-(*tert*-BUTYLPEROXY)CYCLOHEXANE	≤ 42	≥ 58				OP8			
	1,1-DI-(*tert*-BUTYLPEROXY)CYCLOHEXANE	≤ 13	≥ 13	≥ 74			OP8			
	DILAUROYL PEROXIDE	≤ 42 as a stable dispersion in water					OP8			
	2,5-DIMETHYL-2,5-DI-(*tert*-BUTYLPEROXY)HEXANE	≤ 52	≥ 48				OP8			(13)
	ISOPROPYLCUMYL HYDROPEROXIDE	≤ 72	≥ 28				OP8			(27)
	p-MENTHYL HYDROPEROXIDE	≤ 72	≥ 28				OP8			(31)
	METHYL ISOPROPYL KETONE PEROXIDE(S)	See remark (31)	≥ 70				OP8			
	PEROXYACETIC ACID, TYPE F, stabilized	≤ 43					OP8			(13) (16) (19)
	PINANYL HYDROPEROXIDE	≤ 56	≥ 44				OP8			

Number (generic entry)	ORGANIC PEROXIDE	Concentration (%)	Diluent type A (%)	Diluent type B (%)(1)	Inert solid (%)	Water (%)	Packing method	Control temperature (°C)	Emergency temperature (°C)	Subsidiary risks and remarks (12)
3110	DICUMYL PEROXIDE	> 52 – 100					OP8			
	1,1-DI-(tert-BUTYLPEROXY)-3,3,5-TRIMETHYL-CYCLOHEXANE	≤ 57			≥ 43		OP8			
	3,6,9-TRIETHYL-3,6,9-TRIMETHYL-1,4,7-TRIPEROXONANE	≤ 17	≥ 18		≥ 65		OP8			
3111	tert-BUTYL PEROXYISOBUTYRATE	> 52 – 77		≥ 23			OP5	+15	+20	(3)
	DIISOBUTYRYL PEROXIDE	> 32 – 52		≥ 48			OP5	–20	–10	(3)
	ISOPROPYL sec-BUTYL PEROXYDICARBONATE + DI-sec-BUTYL PEROXYDICARBONATE + DIISOPROPYL PEROXYDICARBONATE	≤ 52 + ≤ 28 + ≤ 22					OP5	–20	–10	(3)
3112	ACETYL CYCLOHEXANESULPHONYL PEROXIDE	≤ 82				≥ 12	OP4	–10	0	(3)
	DICYCLOHEXYL PEROXYDICARBONATE	> 91 – 100					OP3	+10	+15	(3)
	DIISOPROPYL PEROXYDICARBONATE	> 52 – 100					OP2	–15	–5	(3)
	DI-(2-METHYLBENZOYL) PEROXIDE	≤ 87				≥ 13	OP5	+30	+35	(3)
3113	tert-AMYL PEROXYPIVALATE	≤ 77		≥ 23			OP5	+10	+15	
	tert-BUTYL PEROXYDIETHYLACETATE	≤ 100					OP5	+20	+25	
	tert-BUTYL PEROXY-2-ETHYLHEXANOATE	> 52 – 100					OP6	+20	+25	
	tert-BUTYL PEROXYPIVALATE	> 67 – 77	≥ 23				OP5	0	+10	
	DI-sec-BUTYL PEROXYDICARBONATE	> 52 – 100					OP4	–20	–10	
	DI-(2-ETHYLHEXYL)PEROXYDICARBONATE	> 77 – 100					OP5	–20	–10	
	2,5-DIMETHYL-2,5-DI-(2-ETHYLHEXANOYLPEROXY)-HEXANE	≤ 100					OP5	+20	+25	
	DI-n-PROPYL PEROXYDICARBONATE	≤ 100					OP3	–25	–15	
	DI-n-PROPYL PEROXYDICARBONATE	≤ 77		≥ 23			OP5	–20	–10	
	ORGANIC PEROXIDE, LIQUID, SAMPLE, TEMPERATURE CONTROLLED						OP2			(11)
3114	DI-(4-tert-BUTYLCYCLOHEXYL)-PEROXYDICARBONATE	≤ 100					OP6	+30	+35	
	DICYCLOHEXYL PEROXYDICARBONATE	≤ 91				≥ 9	OP5	+10	+15	
	DIDECANOYL PEROXIDE	≤ 100					OP6	+30	+35	
	DI-n-OCTANOYL PEROXIDE	≤ 100					OP5	+10	+15	
	ORGANIC PEROXIDE, SOLID, SAMPLE, TEMPERATURE CONTROLLED						OP2			(11)

Number (generic entry)	ORGANIC PEROXIDE	Concentration (%)	Diluent type A (%)	Diluent type B (%)(1)	Inert solid (%)	Water (%)	Packing method	Control temperature (°C)	Emergency temperature (°C)	Subsidiary risks and remarks
3115	ACETYL CYCLOHEXANESULPHONYL PEROXIDE	≤ 32		≥ 68			OP7	−10	0	
	tert-AMYL PEROXY-2-ETHYLHEXANOATE	≤ 100					OP7	+20	+25	
	tert-AMYL PEROXYNEODECANOATE	≤ 77		≥ 23			OP7	0	+10	
	tert-BUTYL PEROXY-2-ETHYLHEXANOATE + 2,2-DI-(*tert*-BUTYLPEROXY)BUTANE	≤ 31 + ≤ 36		≥ 33			OP7	+35	+40	
	tert-BUTYL PEROXYISOBUTYRATE	≤ 52		≥ 48			OP7	+15	+20	
	tert-BUTYL PEROXYNEODECANOATE	> 77 – 100					OP7	−5	+5	
	tert-BUTYL PEROXYNEODECANOATE	≤ 77		≥ 23			OP7	0	+10	
	tert-BUTYL PEROXYNEOHEPTANOATE	≤ 77	≥ 23				OP7	0	+10	
	tert-BUTYL PEROXYPIVALATE	> 27 – 67		≥ 33			OP7	0	+10	
	CUMYL PEROXYNEODECANOATE	≤ 77		≥ 23			OP7	−10	0	
	CUMYL PEROXYNEODECANOATE	≤ 87	≥ 13				OP7	−10	0	
	CUMYL PEROXYNEOHEPTANOATE	≤ 77	≥ 23				OP7	−10	0	
	CUMYL PEROXYPIVALATE	≤ 77		≥ 23			OP7	−5	+5	
	DIACETONE ALCOHOL PEROXIDES	≤ 57		≥ 26		≥ 8	OP7	+40	+45	(6)
	DIACETYL PEROXIDE	≤ 27		≥ 73			OP7	+20	+25	(7) (13)
	DI-*n*-BUTYL PEROXYDICARBONATE	> 27 – 52		≥ 48			OP7	−15	−5	
	DI-*sec*-BUTYL PEROXYDICARBONATE	≤ 52		≥ 48			OP7	−15	−5	
	DI-(2-ETHOXYETHYL)PEROXYDICARBONATE	≤ 52		≥ 48			OP7	−10	0	
	DI-(2-ETHYLHEXYL)PEROXYDICARBONATE	≤ 77		≥ 23			OP7	−15	−5	
	DIISOBUTYRYL PEROXIDE	≤ 32		≥ 68			OP7	−20	−10	
	DIISOPROPYL PEROXYDICARBONATE	≤ 52		≥ 48			OP7	−20	−10	
	DIISOPROPYL PEROXYDICARBONATE	≤ 32	≥ 68				OP7	−15	−5	
	DI-(3-METHOXYBUTYL) PEROXYDICARBONATE	≤ 52		≥ 48			OP7	−5	+5	
	DI-(3-METHYLBENZOYL) PEROXIDE + BENZOYL (3-METHYLBENZOYL) PEROXIDE + DIBENZOYL PEROXIDE	≤ 20 + ≤ 18 + ≤ 4		≥ 58			OP7	+35	+40	
	DI-(2-NEODECANOYLPEROXYISOPROPYL)-BENZENE	≤ 52	≥ 48				OP7	−10	0	
	DI-(3,5,5-TRIMETHYLHEXANOYL) PEROXIDE	> 52 – 82	≥ 18				OP7	0	+10	
	1-(2-ETHYLHEXANOYLPEROXY)-1,3-DIMETHYLBUTYL PEROXYPIVALATE	≤ 52	≥ 45	≥ 10			OP7	−20	−10	
	tert-HEXYL PEROXYNEODECANOATE	≤ 71	≥ 29				OP7	0	+10	
	tert-HEXYL PEROXYPIVALATE	≤ 72		≥ 28			OP7	+10	+15	

Number (generic entry)	ORGANIC PEROXIDE	Concentration (%)	Diluent type A (%)	Diluent type B (%)(1)	Inert solid (%)	Water (%)	Packing method	Control temperature (°C)	Emergency temperature (°C)	Subsidiary risks and remarks
3115 (cont.)	3-HYDROXY-1,1-DIMETHYLBUTYL PEROXYNEODECANOATE	≤ 77	≥ 23				OP7	–5	+ 5	
	ISOPROPYL sec-BUTYL PEROXYDICARBONATE + DI-sec-BUTYL PEROXYDICARBONATE + DI-ISOPROPYL PEROXYDICARBONATE	≤ 32 + ≤ 15 – 18 + ≤ 12 – 15	≥ 38				OP7	–20	–10	
	METHYLCYCLOHEXANONE PEROXIDE(S)	≤ 67		≥ 33			OP7	+35	+40	
	1,1,3,3-TETRAMETHYLBUTYL PEROXY-2-ETHYLHEXANOATE	≤ 100					OP7	+15	+20	
	1,1,3,3-TETRAMETHYLBUTYL PEROXY-NEODECANOATE	≤ 72		≥ 28			OP7	–5	+5	
	1,1,3,3-TETRAMETHYLBUTYL PEROXYPIVALATE	≤ 77	≥ 23				OP7	0	+10	
3116	DIMYRISTYL PEROXYDICARBONATE	≤ 100					OP7	+20	+25	
	DI-n-NONANOYL PEROXIDE	≤ 100					OP7	0	+10	
	DISUCCINIC ACID PEROXIDE	≤ 72				≥ 28	OP7	+10	+15	
3117	tert-BUTYL PEROXY-2-ETHYLHEXANOATE	> 32 – 52		≥ 48			OP8	+30	+35	
	DI-n-BUTYL PEROXYDICARBONATE	≤ 27		≥ 73			OP8	–10	0	
	tert-BUTYL PEROXYNEOHEPTANOATE	≤ 42 as a stable dispersion in water					OP8	0	+10	
	1,1-DIMETHYL-3-HYDROXYBUTYL PEROXY-NEOHEPTANOATE	≤ 52	≥ 48				OP8	0	+10	
	DIPROPIONYL PEROXIDE	≤ 27		≥ 73			OP8	+15	+20	
	3-HYDROXY-1,1-DIMETHYLBUTYL PEROXY-NEODECANOATE	≤ 52	≥ 48				OP8	–5	+5	
3118	tert-BUTYL PEROXY-2-ETHYLHEXANOATE	≤ 52			≥ 48		OP8	+20	+25	
	tert-BUTYL PEROXYNEODECANOATE	≤ 42 as a stable dispersion in water (frozen)					OP8	0	+10	
	DI-n-BUTYL PEROXYDICARBONATE	≤ 42 as a stable dispersion in water (frozen)					OP8	–15	–5	
	DI-2,4-DICHLOROBENZOYL PEROXIDE	≤ 52 as a paste					OP8	+ 20	+ 25	
	PEROXYLAURIC ACID	≤ 100					OP8	+35	+40	
3119	tert-AMYL PEROXYNEODECANOATE	≤ 47	≥ 53				OP8	0	+ 10	
	tert-BUTYL PEROXY-2-ETHYLHEXANOATE	≤ 32		≥ 68			OP8	+40	+45	
	tert-BUTYL PEROXYNEODECANOATE	≤ 52 as a stable dispersion in water					OP8	0	+10	

2

Number (generic entry)	ORGANIC PEROXIDE	Concentration (%)	Diluent type A (%)	Diluent type B (%)[1]	Inert solid (%)	Water (%)	Packing method	Control temperature (°C)	Emergency temperature (°C)	Subsidiary risks and remarks
3119 (cont.)	tert-BUTYL PEROXYNEODECANOATE	≤ 32	≥ 68				OP8	0	+10	
	tert-BUTYL PEROXYPIVALATE	≤ 27		≥ 73			OP8	+30	+35	
	CUMYL PEROXYNEODECANOATE	≤ 52 as a stable dispersion in water					OP8	−10	0	
	DI-(4-tert-BUTYLCYCLOHEXYL) PEROXYDICARBONATE	≤ 42 as a stable dispersion in water					OP8	+30	+35	
	DICETYL PEROXYDICARBONATE	≤ 42 as a stable dispersion in water					OP8	+30	+35	
	DICYCLOHEXYL PEROXYDICARBONATE	≤ 42 as a stable dispersion in water					OP8	+15	+20	
	DI-(2-ETHYLHEXYL) PEROXYDICARBONATE	≤ 62 as a stable dispersion in water					OP8	−15	−5	
	DIMYRISTYL PEROXYDICARBONATE	≤ 42 as a stable dispersion in water					OP8	+20	+25	
	DI-(3,5,5-TRIMETHYLHEXANOYL) PEROXIDE	≤ 52 as a stable dispersion in water					OP8	+10	+15	
	DI-(3,5,5-TRIMETHYLHEXANOYL) PEROXIDE	≤ 38	≥ 62				OP8	+20	+25	
	DI-(3,5,5-TRIMETHYLHEXANOYL) PEROXIDE	> 38 – 52	≥ 48				OP8	+10	+15	
	3-HYDROXY-1,1-DIMETHYLBUTYL PEROXYNEODECANOATE	≤ 52 as a stable dispersion in water					OP 8	−5	+5	
	1,1,3,3-TETRAMETHYLBUTYL PEROXYNEODECANOATE	≤ 52 as a stable dispersion in water					OP8	−5	+5	
3120	DI-(2-ETHYLHEXYL)PEROXYDICARBONATE	≤ 52 as a stable dispersion in water (frozen)					OP8	−15	−5	
	DICETYL PEROXYDICARBONATE	≤ 100					OP8	+30	+35	
Exempt	CYCLOHEXANONE PEROXIDE(S)	≤ 32			≥ 68					(29)
Exempt	DIBENZOYL PEROXIDE	≤ 35			≥ 65					(29)
Exempt	DI-(2-tert-BUTYLPEROXYISOPROPYL)BENZENE(S)	≤ 42			≥ 58					(29)
Exempt	DI-4-CHLOROBENZOYL PEROXIDE	≤ 32			≥ 68					(29)
Exempt	DICUMYL PEROXIDE	≤ 52			≥ 48					(29)

◁

Remarks

(1)   Diluent type B may always be replaced by diluent type A. The boiling point of diluent type B shall be at least 60°C higher than the SADT of the organic peroxide

(2)   Available oxygen ≤ 4.7%

(3)   "EXPLOSIVE" subsidiary risk label required. (Model No. 1, see 5.2.2.2.2)

(4)   Diluent may be replaced by di-*tert*-butyl peroxide

(5)   Available oxygen ≤ 9%

(6)   With ≤ 9% hydrogen peroxide; available oxygen ≤ 10%

(7)   Only non-metallic packagings are allowed

(8)   Available oxygen > 10% and ≤ 10.7%, with or without water

(9)   Available oxygen ≤ 10%, with or without water

(10)   Available oxygen ≤ 8.2%, with or without water

(11)   See 2.5.3.2.5.1

(12)   Up to 2000 kg per receptacle assigned to ORGANIC PEROXIDE TYPE F on the basis of large-scale trials

(13)   "CORROSIVE" subsidiary risk label required (Model No. 8, see 5.2.2.2.2)

(14)   Peroxyacetic acid formulations which fulfil the criteria of 2.5.3.3.2.4

(15)   Peroxyacetic acid formulations which fulfil the criteria of 2.5.3.3.2.5

(16)   Peroxyacetic acid formulations which fulfil the criteria of 2.5.3.3.2.6

(17)   Addition of water to this organic peroxide will decrease its thermal stability

(18)   No "CORROSIVE" subsidiary risk label required for concentrations below 80%

(19)   Mixtures with hydrogen peroxide, water and acid(s)

(20)   With diluent type A, with or without water

(21)   With ≥ 25% diluent type A by mass, and in addition ethylbenzene

(22)   With ≥ 19% diluent type A by mass, and in addition methyl isobutyl ketone

(23)   With < 6% di-*tert*-butyl peroxide

(24)   With ≤ 8% 1-isopropylhydroperoxy-4-isopropylhydroxybenzene

(25)   Diluent type B with boiling point > 110°C

(26)   With < 0.5% hydroperoxides content

(27)   For concentrations more than 56%, "CORROSIVE" subsidiary risk label required (Model No. 8, see 5.2.2.2.2)

(28)   Available active oxygen ≤ 7.6% in diluent type A having a 95% boil-off point in the range 200–260°C

(29)   Not subject to the provisions for peroxide, class 5.2

(30)   Diluent type B with boiling point > 130°C

(31)   Active oxygen ≤ 6.7%

2.5.3.2.5   Classification of organic peroxides not listed in 2.5.3.2.4, packing instruction IBC520 or portable tank instruction T23 and assignment to a generic entry shall be made by the competent authority of the country of origin on the basis of a test report. Principles applying to the classification of such substances are provided in 2.5.3.3. Test methods and criteria and an example of a report are given in the current edition of the Manual of Tests and Criteria, part II. The statement of approval shall contain the classification and the relevant transport conditions (see 5.4.4.1.3).

2.5.3.2.5.1   Samples of new organic peroxides or new formulations of currently assigned organic peroxides for which complete test data are not available and which are to be transported for further testing or evaluation may be assigned to one of the appropriate entries for ORGANIC PEROXIDE TYPE C provided the following conditions are met:

.1   the available data indicate that the sample would be no more dangerous than ORGANIC PEROXIDE TYPE B;

.2   the sample is packaged in accordance with packing method OP2 and the quantity per cargo transport unit is limited to 10 kg; and

.3   the available data indicate that the control temperature, if any, is sufficiently low to prevent any dangerous decomposition and sufficiently high to prevent any dangerous phase separation.

2.5.3.3   **Principles for classification of organic peroxides**

Note: This section refers only to those properties of organic peroxides which are decisive for their classification. A flow chart, presenting the classification principles in the form of a graphically arranged scheme of questions concerning the decisive properties together with the possible answers, is given in figure 2.5.1 in chapter 2.5 of the United Nations *Recommendations on the Transport of Dangerous Goods*. These properties shall be determined experimentally. Suitable test methods with pertinent evaluation criteria are given in the Manual of Tests and Criteria, part II.

2.5.3.3.1   Any organic peroxide formulation shall be regarded as possessing explosive properties when, in laboratory testing, the formulation is liable to detonate, to deflagrate rapidly or to show a violent effect when heated under confinement.

2.5.3.3.2 The following principles apply to the classification of organic peroxide formulations not listed in 2.5.3.2.4:

.1 Any organic peroxide formulation which can detonate or deflagrate rapidly, as packaged for transport, is prohibited from transport in that packaging under class 5.2 (defined as ORGANIC PEROXIDE TYPE A);

.2 Any organic peroxide formulation possessing explosive properties and which, as packaged for transport, neither detonates nor deflagrates rapidly, but is liable to undergo a thermal explosion in that package, shall bear an "EXPLOSIVE" subsidiary risk label (Model No. 1, see 5.2.2.2.2). Such an organic peroxide may be packaged in amounts of up to 25 kg unless the maximum quantity has to be limited to a lower amount to preclude detonation or rapid deflagration in the package (defined as ORGANIC PEROXIDE TYPE B);

.3 Any organic peroxide formulation possessing explosive properties may be transported without an "EXPLOSIVE" subsidiary risk label when the substance as packaged (maximum 50 kg) for transport cannot detonate or deflagrate rapidly or undergo a thermal explosion (defined as ORGANIC PEROXIDE TYPE C);

.4 Any organic peroxide formulation which, in laboratory testing:

.1 detonates partially, does not deflagrate rapidly and shows no violent effect when heated under confinement; or

.2 does not detonate at all, deflagrates slowly and shows no violent effect when heated under confinement; or

.3 does not detonate or deflagrate at all and shows a medium effect when heated under confinement

is acceptable for transport in packages of not more than 50 kg net mass (defined as ORGANIC PEROXIDE TYPE D);

.5 Any organic peroxide formulation which, in laboratory testing, neither detonates nor deflagrates at all and shows low or no effect when heated under confinement is acceptable for transport in packages of not more than 400 kg/450 L (defined as ORGANIC PEROXIDE TYPE E);

.6 Any organic peroxide formulation which, in laboratory testing, neither detonates in the cavitated state nor deflagrates at all and shows only a low or no effect when heated under confinement as well as low or no explosive power may be considered for transport in IBCs or tanks (defined as ORGANIC PEROXIDE TYPE F); for additional provisions see 4.1.7 and 4.2.1.13;

.7 Any organic peroxide formulation which, in laboratory testing, neither detonates in the cavitated state nor deflagrates at all and shows no effect when heated under confinement nor any explosive power shall be exempted from class 5.2, provided that the formulation is thermally stable (self-accelerating decomposition temperature is 60°C or higher for a 50 kg package) and for liquid formulations diluent type A is used for desensitization (defined as ORGANIC PEROXIDE TYPE G). If the formulation is not thermally stable or a diluent other than type A is used for desensitization, the formulation shall be defined as ORGANIC PEROXIDE TYPE F.

2.5.3.4 Temperature control provisions

2.5.3.4.0 The properties of some organic peroxides require that they be transported under temperature control. Control and emergency temperatures for currently assigned organic peroxides are shown in the list 2.5.3.2.4. The controlled temperature provisions are given in chapter 7.3.7.

2.5.3.4.1 The following organic peroxides shall be subjected to temperature control during transport:

.1 organic peroxides type B and C with a SADT $\leq$ 50°C;

.2 organic peroxides type D showing a medium effect when heated under confinement[*] with a SADT $\leq$ 50°C or showing a low or no effect when heated under confinement with a SADT $\leq$ 45°C; and

.3 organic peroxides types E and F with a SADT $\leq$ 45°C.

2.5.3.4.2 Test methods for determining the SADT are given in the Manual of Tests and Criteria, part II, chapter 28. The test selected shall be conducted in a manner which is representative, both in size and material, of the package to be transported.

2.5.3.4.3 Test methods for determining the flammability are given in the Manual of Tests and Criteria, part III, chapter 32.4. Because organic peroxides may react vigorously when heated, it is recommended to determine their flashpoint using small sample sizes such as described in ISO 3679.

2.5.3.5 Desensitization of organic peroxides

2.5.3.5.1 In order to ensure safety during transport, organic peroxides are in many cases desensitized by organic liquids or solids, inorganic solids or water. Where a percentage of a substance is stipulated, this refers to the percentage by mass, rounded to the nearest whole number. In general, desensitization shall be such that, in case of spillage or fire, the organic peroxide will not concentrate to a dangerous extent.

---

[*] As determined by test series E as prescribed in the Manual of Tests and Criteria, part II.

2.5.3.5.2   Unless otherwise stated for the individual organic peroxide formulation, the following definitions apply for diluents used for desensitization:

.1   Diluents type A are organic liquids which are compatible with the organic peroxide and which have a boiling point of not less than 150°C. Type A diluents may be used for desensitizing all organic peroxides.

.2   Diluents type B are organic liquids which are compatible with the organic peroxide and which have a boiling point of less than 150°C but not less than 60°C and a flashpoint of not less than 5°C. Type B diluents may be used for desensitization of all organic peroxides provided that the boiling point is at least 60°C higher than the SADT in a 50 kg package.

2.5.3.5.3   Diluents, other than type A or type B, may be added to organic peroxide formulations as listed in 2.5.3.2.4 provided that they are compatible. However, replacement of all or part of a type A or type B diluent by another diluent with differing properties requires that the organic peroxide formulation be re-assessed in accordance with the normal acceptance procedure for class 5.2.

2.5.3.5.4   Water may only be used for the desensitization of organic peroxides which are shown in 2.5.3.2.4 or in the statement of approval according to 2.5.3.2.5 as being with water or as a stable dispersion in water.

2.5.3.5.5   Organic and inorganic solids may be used for desensitization of organic peroxides provided that they are compatible.

2.5.3.5.6   Compatible liquids and solids are those which have no detrimental influence on the thermal stability and hazard type of the organic peroxide formulation.

Chapter 2.6

Class 6 – Toxic and infectious substances

2.6.0 Introductory notes

Note 1: The word "toxic" has the same meaning as "poisonous".

Note 2: Genetically modified microorganisms which do not meet the definition of a toxic or an infectious substance shall be considered for classification in class 9 and assigned to UN 3245.

Note 3: Toxins from plant, animal or bacterial sources which do not contain any infectious substances, or toxins that are contained in substances which are not infectious substances, shall be considered for classification in class 6.1 and assigned to UN 3172.

2.6.1 Definitions

Class 6 is subdivided into two classes as follows:

Class 6.1 – Toxic substances
These are substances liable either to cause death or serious injury or to harm human health if swallowed or inhaled, or by skin contact.

Class 6.2 – Infectious substances
These are substances known or reasonably expected to contain pathogens. Pathogens are defined as micro-organisms (including bacteria, viruses, rickettsiae, parasites, fungi) and other agents such as prions, which can cause disease in humans or animals.

2.6.2 Class 6.1 – Toxic substances

2.6.2.1 Definitions and properties

2.6.2.1.1 LD_{50} *(median lethal dose) for acute oral toxicity* is the statistically derived single dose of a substance that can be expected to cause death within 14 days in 50 per cent of young adult albino rats when administered by the oral route. The LD_{50} value is expressed in terms of mass of test substance per mass of test animal (mg/kg).

2.6.2.1.2 LD_{50} *for acute dermal toxicity* is that dose of the substance which, administered by continuous contact for 24 hours with the bare skin of the albino rabbit, is most likely to cause death within 14 days in one half of the animals tested. The number of animals tested shall be sufficient to give a statistically significant result and be in conformity with good pharmacological practices. The result is expressed in milligrams per kilogram body mass.

2.6.2.1.3 LC_{50} *for acute toxicity on inhalation* is that concentration of vapour, mist or dust which, administered by continuous inhalation to both male and female young adult albino rats for one hour, is most likely to cause death within 14 days in one half of the animals tested. A solid substance shall be tested if at least 10% (by mass) of its total mass is likely to be dust in the respirable range, such as the aerodynamic diameter of that particle fraction is 10 microns or less. A liquid substance shall be tested if a mist is likely to be generated in a leakage of the transport containment. For both solid and liquid substances, more than 90% (by mass) of a specimen prepared for inhalation toxicity testing shall be in the respirable range as defined above. The result is expressed in milligrams per litre of air for dusts and mists or in millilitres per cubic metre of air (parts per million) for vapours.

2.6.2.1.4 *Properties*

.1 The dangers of poisoning which are inherent in these substances depend upon contact with the human body, that is by inhalation of vapours by unsuspecting persons at some distance from the cargo or the immediate dangers of physical contact with the substance. These have been considered in the context of the probability of accident occurring during transport by sea.

.2 Nearly all toxic substances evolve toxic gases when involved in a fire or when heated to decomposition.

.3 A substance specified as "stabilized" shall not be transported in an unstabilized condition.

2.6.2.2 Assignment of packing groups to toxic substances

2.6.2.2.1 Toxic substances have for packing purposes been apportioned among packing groups according to the degree of their toxic hazards in transport:

.1 Packing group I: substances and preparations presenting a high toxicity risk;

.2 Packing group II: substances and preparations presenting a medium toxicity risk;

.3 Packing group III: substances and preparations presenting a low toxicity risk.

2.6.2.2.2 In making this grouping, account has been taken of human experience in instances of accidental poisoning, and of special properties possessed by any individual substance, such as liquid state, high volatility, any special likelihood of penetration, and special biological effects.

2.6.2.2.3 In the absence of human experience, the grouping has been based on data obtained from animal experiments. Three possible routes of administration have been examined. These routes are exposure through:

– oral ingestion;

– dermal contact; and

– inhalation of dusts, mists or vapours.

2.6.2.2.3.1 For appropriate animal test data for the various routes of exposure, see 2.6.2.1. When a substance exhibits a different order of toxicity by two or more routes of administration, the highest degree of danger indicated by the tests has been used in assigning the packing group.

2.6.2.2.4 The criteria to be applied for grouping a substance according to the toxicity it exhibits by all three routes of administration are presented in the following paragraphs.

2.6.2.2.4.1 The grouping criteria for the oral and dermal routes as well as for inhalation of dusts and mists are shown in the following table:

Grouping criteria for administration through oral ingestion, dermal contact and inhalation of dusts and mists

Packing group	Oral toxicity LD_{50} (mg/kg)	Dermal toxicity LD_{50} (mg/kg)	Inhalation toxicity by dusts and mists LC_{50} (mg/L)
I	≤ 5.0	≤ 50	≤ 0.2
II	> 5.0 and ≤ 50	> 50 and ≤ 200	> 0.2 and ≤ 2.0
III*	> 50 and ≤ 300	> 200 and ≤ 1000	> 2.0 and ≤ 4.0

* Tear gas substances shall be included in packing group II even if their toxicity data correspond to packing group III values.

Note: Substances meeting the criteria of class 8 and with an inhalation toxicity of dusts and mists (LC_{50}) leading to packing group I are only accepted for an allocation to class 6.1 if the toxicity through oral ingestion or dermal contact is at least in the range of packing group I or II. Otherwise an allocation to class 8 is made when appropriate (see 2.8.2.3).

2.6.2.2.4.2 The criteria for inhalation toxicity of dusts and mists in 2.6.2.2.4.1 are based on LC_{50} data relating to one hour exposures, and where such information is available it shall be used. However, where only LC_{50} data relating to 4-hour exposures to dusts and mists are available, such figures can be multiplied by four and the product substituted in the above criteria, i.e. LC_{50} (4 hours) $\times$ 4 is considered the equivalent of LC_{50} (1 hour).

2.6.2.2.4.3 Liquids having toxic vapours shall be assigned to the following packing groups, where "V" is the saturated vapour concentration in mL/m^3 air at 20°C and standard atmospheric pressure:

Packing group I: if $V \geq 10\ LC_{50}$ and $LC_{50} \leq 1,000\ mL/m^3$.

Packing group II: if $V \geq LC_{50}$ and $LC_{50} \leq 3,000\ mL/m^3$, and do not meet the criteria for packing group I.

Packing group III: if $V \geq \frac{1}{5} LC_{50}$ and $LC_{50} \leq 5,000\ mL/m^3$, and do not meet the criteria for packing groups I or II.

Note: Tear gas substances shall be included in packing group II even if their toxicity data correspond to packing group III values.

2.6.2.2.4.4 In figure 2-3 the criteria according to 2.6.2.2.4.3 are expressed in graphical form, as an aid to easy classification. Because of approximations inherent in the use of graphs, substances falling on or near packing group borderlines shall be checked using numerical criteria.

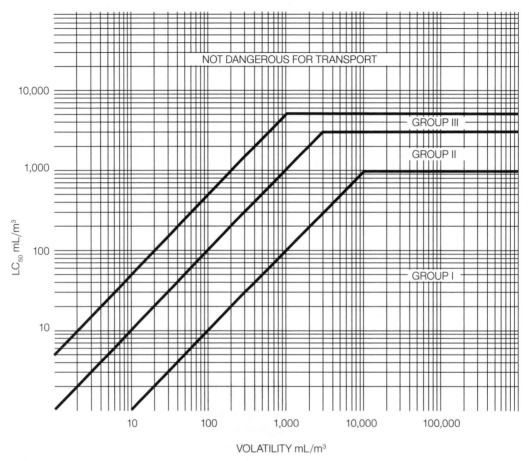

Figure 2-3 – *Inhalation toxicity: packing group borderlines*

2.6.2.2.4.5 The criteria for inhalation toxicity of vapours in 2.6.2.2.4.3 are based on LC_{50} data relating to one hour exposures, and where such information is available it shall be used. However, where only LC_{50} data relating to 4-hour exposures to the vapours are available, such figures can be multiplied by two and the product substituted in the above criteria, i.e. LC_{50} (4 hours) $\times$ 2 is considered the equivalent of LC_{50} (1 hour).

2.6.2.2.4.6 Mixtures of liquids that are toxic by inhalation shall be assigned to packing groups according to 2.6.2.2.4.7 or 2.6.2.2.4.8.

2.6.2.2.4.7 If LC_{50} data are available for each of the toxic substances comprising a mixture, the packing group may be determined as follows:

.1 Estimate the LC_{50} of the mixture using the formula:

$$LC_{50} \text{ (mixture)} = \frac{1}{\sum\limits_{i=1}^{n} \left(\dfrac{f_i}{LC_{50i}} \right)}$$

where: f_i = mole fraction of the ith component substance of the mixture

LC_{50i} = mean lethal concentration of the ith component substance in mL/m^3.

.2 Estimate the volatility of each component substance comprising the mixture using the formula:

$$V_i = \left(\frac{P_i \times 10^6}{101.3} \right) mL/m^3$$

where: P_i = the partial pressure of the ith component substance in kPa at 20°C and one atmosphere pressure.

.3 Calculate the ratio of the volatility to the LC_{50} using the formula:

$$R = \sum\limits_{i=1}^{n} \left(\frac{V_i}{LC_{50i}} \right)$$

.4   Using the calculated values of LC_{50} (mixture) and R, the packing group for the mixture is determined:

Packing group I: $R \geq 10$ and LC_{50} (mixture) $\leq 1,000$ mL/m^3.

Packing group II: $R \geq 1$ and LC_{50} (mixture) $\leq 3,000$ mL/m^3 and not meeting criteria for packing group I.

Packing group III: $R \geq \frac{1}{5}$ and LC_{50} (mixture) $\leq 5,000$ mL/m^3 and not meeting criteria for packing groups I or II.

2.6.2.2.4.8   In the absence of LC_{50} data on the toxic constituent substances, the mixture may be assigned a packing group based on the following simplified threshold toxicity tests. When these threshold tests are used, the most restrictive packing group shall be determined and used for transporting the mixture.

    .1   A mixture is assigned to packing group I only if it meets both of the following criteria:

       –   A sample of the liquid mixture is vaporized and diluted with air to create a test atmosphere of 1,000 mL/m^3 vaporized mixture in air. Ten albino rats (five male and five female) are exposed to the test atmosphere for one hour and observed for 14 days. If five or more of the animals die within the 14-day observation period, the mixture is presumed to have an LC_{50} equal to or less than 1,000 mL/m^3.

       –   A sample of the vapour in equilibrium with the liquid mixture at 20°C is diluted with 9 equal volumes of air to form a test atmosphere. Ten albino rats (five male and five female) are exposed to the test atmosphere for one hour and observed for 14 days. If five or more of the animals die within the 14-day observation period, the mixture is presumed to have a volatility equal to or greater than 10 times the mixture LC_{50}.

    .2   A mixture is assigned to packing group II only if it meets both of the following criteria, and the mixture does not meet the criteria for packing group I:

       –   A sample of the liquid mixture is vaporized and diluted with air to create a test atmosphere of 3,000 mL/m^3 vaporized mixture in air. Ten albino rats (five male and five female) are exposed to the test atmosphere for one hour and observed for 14 days. If five or more of the animals die within the 14-day observation period, the mixture is presumed to have an LC_{50} equal to or less than 3,000 mL/m^3.

       –   A sample of the vapour in equilibrium with the liquid mixture at 20°C is used to form a test atmosphere. Ten albino rats (five male and five female) are exposed to the test atmosphere for one hour and observed for 14 days. If five or more of the animals die within the 14-day observation period, the mixture is presumed to have a volatility equal to or greater than the mixture LC_{50}.

    .3   A mixture is assigned to packing group III only if it meets both of the following criteria, and the mixture does not meet the criteria for packing groups I or II:

       –   A sample of the liquid mixture is vaporized and diluted with air to create a test atmosphere of 5,000 mL/m^3 vaporized mixture in air. Ten albino rats (five male and five female) are exposed to the test atmosphere for one hour and observed for 14 days. If five or more of the animals die within the 14-day observation period, the mixture is presumed to have an LC_{50} equal to or less than 5,000 mL/m^3.

       –   The vapour pressure of the liquid mixture is measured and if the vapour concentration is equal to or greater than 1,000 mL/m^3, the mixture is presumed to have a volatility equal to or greater than $\frac{1}{5}$ the mixture LC_{50}.

2.6.2.3   Methods for determining oral and dermal toxicity of mixtures

2.6.2.3.1   When classifying and assigning the appropriate packing group to mixtures in class 6.1, in accordance with the oral and dermal toxicity criteria in 2.6.2.2, it is necessary to determine the acute LD_{50} of the mixture.

2.6.2.3.2   If a mixture contains only one active substance, and the LD_{50} of that constituent is known, in the absence of reliable acute oral and dermal toxicity data on the actual mixture to be transported, the oral or dermal LD_{50} may be obtained by the following method:

$$LD_{50} \text{ value of preparation} = \frac{LD_{50} \text{ value of active substance} \times 100}{\text{percentage of active substance by mass}}$$

2.6.2.3.3   If a mixture contains more than one active constituent, there are three possible approaches that may be used to determine the oral or dermal LD_{50} of the mixture. The preferred method is to obtain reliable acute oral and dermal toxicity data on the actual mixture to be transported. If reliable, accurate data are not available, then either of the following methods may be performed:

    .1   Classify the formulation according to the most hazardous constituent of the mixture as if that constituent were present in the same concentration as the total concentration of all active constituents; or

.2 Apply the formula:

$$\frac{C_A}{T_A} + \frac{C_B}{T_B} + \dots \frac{C_Z}{T_Z} = \frac{100}{T_M}$$

where:

C = the % concentration of constituent A, B ... Z in the mixture;

T = the oral LD_{50} value of constituent A, B ... Z;

T_M = the oral LD_{50} value of the mixture.

Note: This formula can also be used for dermal toxicities provided that this information is available on the same species for all constituents. The use of this formula does not take into account any potentiation or protective phenomena.

2.6.2.4 Classification of pesticides

2.6.2.4.1 All active pesticide substances and their preparations for which the LC_{50} and/or LD_{50} values are known and which are classified in class 6.1 shall be classified under appropriate packing groups in accordance with the criteria given in 2.6.2.2. Substances and preparations which are characterized by subsidiary risks shall be classified according to the precedence of hazard table in 2.0.3 with the assignment of appropriate packing groups.

2.6.2.4.2 If the oral or dermal LD_{50} value for a pesticide preparation is not known, but the LD_{50} value of its active substance(s) is known, the LD_{50} value for the preparation may be obtained by applying the procedures in 2.6.2.3.

Note: LD_{50} toxicity data for a number of common pesticides may be obtained from the most current edition of "The WHO Recommended Classification of Pesticides by Hazard and Guidelines to Classification", available from the International Programme on Chemical Safety, World Health Organization (WHO), 1211 Geneva 27, Switzerland. While that publication may be used as a source of LD_{50} data for pesticides, its classification system shall not be used for purposes of transport classification of, or assignment of packing groups to, pesticides, which shall be in accordance with the provisions of this Code.

2.6.2.4.3 The proper shipping name used in the transport of the pesticide shall be selected from those referenced on the basis of the active ingredient, of the physical state of the pesticide and any subsidiary risks which it may exhibit.

■ 2.6.2.5 Substances not accepted for transport

Chemically unstable substances of class 6.1 shall not be accepted for transport unless the necessary precautions have been taken to prevent the possibility of a dangerous decomposition or polymerization under normal conditions of transport. For the precautions necessary to prevent polymerization, see special provision 386 of chapter 3.3. To this end particular care shall be taken to ensure that receptacles and tanks do not contain any substances liable to promote these reactions.

2.6.3 Class 6.2 – Infectious substances

2.6.3.1 Definitions

For the purposes of this Code:

2.6.3.1.1 *Infectious substances* are substances which are known or are reasonably expected to contain pathogens. Pathogens are defined as micro-organisms (including bacteria, viruses, rickettsiae, parasites, fungi) and other agents such as prions, which can cause disease in humans or animals.

2.6.3.1.2 *Biological products* are those products derived from living organisms which are manufactured and distributed in accordance with the requirements of appropriate national authorities, which may have special licensing requirements, and are used either for prevention, treatment, or diagnosis of disease in humans or animals, or for development, experimental or investigation purposes related thereto. They include, but are not limited to, finished or unfinished products such as vaccines.

2.6.3.1.3 *Cultures* are the result of a process by which pathogens are intentionally propagated. This definition does not include human or animal patient specimens as defined in 2.6.3.1.4.

2.6.3.1.4   *Patient specimens* are human or animal materials, collected directly from humans or animals, including, but not limited to, excreta, secreta, blood and its components, tissue and tissue fluid swabs, and body parts being transported for purposes such as research, diagnosis, investigational activities, disease treatment and prevention.

2.6.3.1.5   [Reserved]

2.6.3.1.6   *Medical or clinical wastes* are wastes derived from the medical treatment of animals or humans or from bio-research.

2.6.3.2   Classification of infectious substances

2.6.3.2.1   Infectious substances shall be classified in class 6.2 and assigned to UN 2814, UN 2900, UN 3291 or UN 3373, as appropriate.

2.6.3.2.2   Infectious substances are divided into the following categories:

2.6.3.2.2.1   *Category A:* An infectious substance which is transported in a form that, when exposure to it occurs, is capable of causing permanent disability, life-threatening or fatal disease in otherwise healthy humans or animals. Indicative examples of substances that meet these criteria are given in the table in this paragraph.

Note: An exposure occurs when an infectious substance is released outside the protective packaging, resulting in physical contact with humans or animals.

.1   Infectious substances meeting these criteria which cause disease in humans or in both humans and animals shall be assigned to UN 2814. Infectious substances which cause disease only in animals shall be assigned to UN 2900.

.2   Assignment to UN 2814 or UN 2900 shall be based on the known medical history and symptoms of the source, human or animal, endemic local conditions, or professional judgement concerning individual circumstances of the human or animal source.

   Note 1:   The proper shipping name for UN 2814 is INFECTIOUS SUBSTANCE, AFFECTING HUMANS. The proper shipping name for UN 2900 is INFECTIOUS SUBSTANCE, AFFECTING ANIMALS only.

   Note 2:   The following table is not exhaustive. Infectious substances, including new or emerging pathogens, which do not appear in the table but which meet the same criteria shall be assigned to category A. In addition, if there is doubt as to whether or not a substance meets the criteria it shall be included in category A.

   Note 3:   In the following table, the microorganism names written in italics are bacteria, mycoplasmas, rickettsiae or fungi.

**Indicative examples of infectious substances included in category A in any form
unless otherwise indicated (2.6.3.2.2.1.1)**

UN number and proper shipping name	Microorganism
UN 2814 Infectious substance, affecting humans	*Bacillus anthracis* (cultures only) *Brucella abortus* (cultures only) *Brucella melitensis* (cultures only) *Brucella suis* (cultures only) *Burkholderia mallei – Pseudomonas mallei –* Glanders (cultures only) *Burkholderia pseudomallei – Pseudomonas pseudomallei* (cultures only) *Chlamydia psittaci –* avian strains (cultures only) *Clostridium botulinum* (cultures only) *Coccidioides immitis* (cultures only) *Coxiella burnetii* (cultures only) Crimean-Congo hemorrhagic fever virus Dengue virus (cultures only) Eastern equine encephalitis virus (cultures only) *Escherichia coli*, verotoxigenic (cultures only) Ebola virus Flexal virus *Francisella tularensis* (cultures only) Guanarito virus Hantaan virus

UN number and proper shipping name	Microorganism
UN 2814 Infectious substance, affecting humans *(cont.)*	Hantavirus causing hemorragic fever with renal syndrome
	Hendra virus
	Hepatitis B virus (cultures only)
	Herpes B virus (cultures only)
	Human immunodeficiency virus (cultures only)
	Highly pathogenic avian influenza virus (cultures only)
	Japanese Encephalitis virus (cultures only)
	Junin virus
	Kyasanur Forest disease virus
	Lassa virus
	Machupo virus
	Marburg virus
	Monkeypox virus
	Mycobacterium tuberculosis (cultures only)
	Nipah virus
	Omsk hemorrhagic fever virus
	Poliovirus (cultures only)
	Rabies virus (cultures only)
	Rickettsia prowazekii (cultures only)
	Rickettsia rickettsii (cultures only)
	Rift Valley fever virus (cultures only)
	Russian spring–summer encephalitis virus (cultures only)
	Sabia virus
	Shigella dysenteriae type 1 (cultures only)
	Tick-borne encephalitis virus (cultures only)
	Variola virus
	Venezuelan equine encephalitis virus (cultures only)
	West Nile virus (cultures only)
	Yellow fever virus (cultures only)
	Yersinia pestis (cultures only)
UN 2900 Infectious substance, affecting animals only	African swine fever virus (cultures only)
	Avian paramyxovirus Type 1 – Velogenic Newcastle disease virus (cultures only)
	Classical swine fever virus (cultures only)
	Foot and mouth disease virus (cultures only)
	Lumpy skin disease virus (cultures only)
	Mycoplasma mycoides – Contagious bovine pleuropneumonia (cultures only)
	Peste des petits ruminants virus (cultures only)
	Rinderpest virus (cultures only)
	Sheep-pox virus (cultures only)
	Goatpox virus (cultures only)
	Swine vesicular disease virus (cultures only)
	Vesicular stomatitis virus (cultures only)

2.6.3.2.2.2   *Category B:* An infectious substance which does not meet the criteria for inclusion in category A. Infectious substances in category B shall be assigned to UN 3373.

Note: The proper shipping name for UN 3373 is BIOLOGICAL SUBSTANCE, CATEGORY B.

2.6.3.2.3   *Exemptions*

2.6.3.2.3.1   Substances which do not contain infectious substances or substances which are unlikely to cause disease in humans or animals are not subject to the provisions of this Code, unless they meet the criteria for inclusion in another class.

2.6.3.2.3.2   Substances containing microorganisms which are non-pathogenic to humans or animals are not subject to the provisions of this Code unless they meet the criteria for inclusion in another class.

2.6.3.2.3.3   Substances in a form that any present pathogens have been neutralized or inactivated such that they no longer pose a health risk are not subject to the provisions of this Code unless they meet the criteria for inclusion in another class.

Note: Medical equipment which has been drained of free liquid is deemed to meet the requirements of this paragraph and is not subject to the provisions of this Code.

2.6.3.2.3.4 Environmental samples (including food and water samples) which are not considered to pose a significant risk of infection are not subject to the provisions of this Code unless they meet the criteria for inclusion in another class.

2.6.3.2.3.5 Dried blood spots, collected by applying a drop of blood onto absorbent material, are not subject to the provisions of this Code.

2.6.3.2.3.6 Faecal occult blood screening samples are not subject to the provisions of this Code.

2.6.3.2.3.7 Blood or blood components which have been collected for the purposes of transfusion or for the preparation of blood products to be used for transfusion or transplantation and any tissues or organs intended for use in transplantation as well as samples drawn in connection with such purposes are not subject to the provisions of this Code.

2.6.3.2.3.8 Human or animal specimens for which there is minimal likelihood that pathogens are present are not subject to the provisions of this Code if the specimen is transported in a packaging which will prevent any leakage and which is marked with the words "EXEMPT HUMAN SPECIMEN" or "EXEMPT ANIMAL SPECIMEN", as appropriate. The packaging should meet the following conditions:

   .1   The packaging should consist of three components:

      .1   a leak-proof primary receptacle(s);

      .2   a leak-proof secondary packaging; and

      .3   an outer packaging of adequate strength for its capacity, mass and intended use, and with at least one surface having minimum dimensions of 100 mm × 100 mm.

   .2   For liquids, absorbent material in sufficient quantity to absorb the entire contents should be placed between the primary receptacle(s) and the secondary packaging so that, during transport, any release or leak of a liquid substance will not reach the outer packaging and will not compromise the integrity of the cushioning material.

   .3   When multiple fragile primary receptacles are placed in a single secondary packaging, they should be either individually wrapped or separated to prevent contact between them.

Note: An element of professional judgement is required to determine if a substance is exempt under this paragraph. That judgement should be based on the known medical history, symptoms and individual circumstances of the source, human or animal, and endemic local conditions. Examples of specimens which may be transported under this paragraph include the blood or urine tests to monitor cholesterol levels, blood glucose levels, hormone levels, or prostate specific antibodies (PSA); those required to monitor organ function such as heart, liver or kidney function for humans or animals with non-infectious diseases, or therapeutic drug monitoring; those conducted for insurance or employment purposes and are intended to determine the presence of drugs or alcohol; pregnancy test; biopsies to detect cancer; and antibody detection in humans or animals in the absence of any concern for infection (e.g. evaluation of vaccine-induced immunity, diagnosis of autoimmune disease, etc.).

2.6.3.2.3.9 Except for:

   .1   medical waste (UN 3291);

   .2   medical devices or equipment contaminated with or containing infectious substances in category A (UN 2814 or UN 2900); and

   .3   medical devices or equipment contaminated with or containing other dangerous goods that meet the definition of another hazard class,

medical devices or equipment potentially contaminated with or containing infectious substances which are being transported for disinfection, cleaning, sterilization, repair, or equipment evaluation are not subject to the provisions of this Code if packed in packagings designed and constructed in such a way that, under normal conditions of transport, they cannot break, be punctured or leak their contents. Packagings shall be designed to meet the construction requirements listed in 6.1.4 or 6.6.4.

These packagings shall meet the general packing requirements of 4.1.1.1 and 4.1.1.2 and be capable of retaining the medical devices and equipment when dropped from a height of 1.2 m.

The packagings shall be marked "USED MEDICAL DEVICE" or "USED MEDICAL EQUIPMENT". When using overpacks or unit loads these shall be marked in the same way, except when the inscription remains visible.

2.6.3.3   Biological products

2.6.3.3.1 For the purposes of this Code, biological products are divided into the following groups:

.1 those which are manufactured and packaged in accordance with the requirements of appropriate national authorities and transported for the purposes of final packaging or distribution, and use for personal health care by medical professionals or individuals. Substances in this group are not subject to the provisions of this Code;

.2 those which do not fall under .1 and are known or reasonably believed to contain infectious substances and which meet the criteria for inclusion in category A or category B. Substances in this group shall be assigned to UN 2814, UN 2900 or UN 3373, as appropriate.

Note: Some licensed biological products may present a biohazard only in certain parts of the world. Competent authorities may require that such biological products comply with local requirements for infectious substances or may impose other restrictions.

2.6.3.4 Genetically modified microorganisms and organisms

2.6.3.4.1 Genetically modified microorganisms not meeting the definition of infectious substance shall be classified in accordance with chapter 2.9.

2.6.3.5 Medical or clinical wastes

2.6.3.5.1 Medical or clinical wastes containing category A infectious substances shall be assigned to UN 2814 or UN 2900, as appropriate. Medical or clinical wastes containing infectious substances in category B shall be assigned to UN 3291.

2.6.3.5.2 Medical or clinical wastes which are reasonably believed to have a low probability of containing infectious substances shall be assigned to UN 3291. For the assignment, international, regional or national waste catalogues may be taken into account.

Note: The proper shipping name for UN 3291 is CLINICAL WASTE, UNSPECIFIED, N.O.S. or (BIO) MEDICAL WASTE, N.O.S. or REGULATED MEDICAL WASTE, N.O.S.

2.6.3.5.3 Decontaminated medical or clinical wastes which previously contained infectious substances are not subject to the provisions of this Code unless they meet the criteria for inclusion in another class.

2.6.3.6 Infected animals

2.6.3.6.1 Unless an infectious substance cannot be consigned by any other means, live animals shall not be used to consign such a substance. A live animal which has been intentionally infected and is known or suspected to contain an infectious substance shall only be transported under terms and conditions approved by the competent authority.

2.6.3.6.2 Animal material affected by pathogens of category A or which would be assigned to category A in cultures only, shall be assigned to UN 2814 or UN 2900 as appropriate. Animal material affected by pathogens of category B other than those which would be assigned to category A if they were in cultures shall be assigned to UN 3373.

Chapter 2.7

Class 7 – Radioactive material

Note: For class 7, the type of packaging may have a decisive effect on classification.

2.7.1 Definitions

2.7.1.1 *Radioactive material* means any material containing radionuclides where both the activity concentration and the total activity in the consignment exceed the values specified in 2.7.2.2.1 to 2.7.2.2.6.

2.7.1.2 Contamination

Contamination means the presence of a radioactive substance on a surface in quantities in excess of $0.4\,\text{Bq/cm}^2$ for beta and gamma emitters and low-toxicity alpha emitters, or $0.04\,\text{Bq/cm}^2$ for all other alpha emitters.

Non-fixed contamination means contamination that can be removed from a surface during routine conditions of transport.

Fixed contamination means contamination other than non-fixed contamination.

2.7.1.3 Definitions of specific terms

A_1 and A_2

A_1 means the activity value of special form radioactive material which is listed in the table in 2.7.2.2.1 or derived in 2.7.2.2.2 and is used to determine the activity limits for the provisions of this Code.

A_2 means the activity value of radioactive material, other than special form radioactive material, which is listed in the table in 2.7.2.2.1 or derived in 2.7.2.2.2 and is used to determine the activity limits for the provisions of this Code.

Fissile nuclides means uranium-233, uranium-235, plutonium-239 and plutonium-241. *Fissile material* means a material containing any of the fissile nuclides. Excluded from the definition of fissile material are the following:

.1 natural uranium or depleted uranium which is unirradiated;

.2 natural uranium or depleted uranium which has been irradiated in thermal reactors only;

.3 material with fissile nuclides less than a total of 0.25 g;

.4 any combination of .1, .2 and/or .3.

These exclusions are only valid if there is no other material with fissile nuclides in the package or in the consignment if shipped unpackaged.

Low dispersible radioactive material means either a solid radioactive material or a solid radioactive material in a sealed capsule, that has limited dispersibility and is not in powder form.

Low specific activity (LSA) material means radioactive material which by its nature has a limited specific activity, or radioactive material for which limits of estimated average specific activity apply. External shielding materials surrounding the LSA material shall not be considered in determining the estimated average specific activity.

Low toxicity alpha emitters are: natural uranium; depleted uranium; natural thorium; uranium-235 or uranium-238; thorium-232; thorium-228 and thorium-230 when contained in ores or physical and chemical concentrates; or alpha emitters with a half-life of less than 10 days.

Specific activity of a radionuclide means the activity per unit mass of that nuclide. The specific activity of a material shall mean the activity per unit mass of the material in which the radionuclides are essentially uniformly distributed.

Special form radioactive material means either:

.1 an indispersible solid radioactive material; or

.2 a sealed capsule containing radioactive material.

Surface contaminated object (SCO) means a solid object which is not itself radioactive but which has radioactive material distributed on its surface.

Unirradiated thorium means thorium containing not more than 10^{-7} g of uranium-233 per gram of thorium-232.

Unirradiated uranium means uranium containing not more than 2×10^3 Bq of plutonium per gram of uranium-235, not more than 9×10^6 Bq of fission products per gram of uranium-235 and not more than 5×10^{-3} g of uranium-236 per gram of uranium-235.

Uranium – natural, depleted, enriched means the following:

> *Natural uranium* means uranium (which may be chemically separated) containing the naturally occurring distribution of uranium isotopes (approximately 99.28% uranium-238, and 0.72% uranium-235 by mass).

> *Depleted uranium* means uranium containing a lesser mass percentage of uranium-235 than in natural uranium.

> *Enriched uranium* means uranium containing a greater mass percentage of uranium-235 than 0.72%.

In all cases, a very small mass percentage of uranium-234 is present.

2.7.2 Classification

2.7.2.1 General provisions

2.7.2.1.1 Radioactive material shall be assigned to one of the UN numbers specified in table 2.7.2.1.1, in accordance with 2.7.2.4 and 2.7.2.5, taking into account the material characteristics determined in 2.7.2.3.

Table 2.7.2.1.1 – Assignment of UN numbers

UN numbers	Proper shipping name[a] and description
Excepted packages (1.5.1.5)	
2908	RADIOACTIVE MATERIAL, EXCEPTED PACKAGE – EMPTY PACKAGING
2909	RADIOACTIVE MATERIAL, EXCEPTED PACKAGE – ARTICLES MANUFACTURED FROM NATURAL URANIUM or DEPLETED URANIUM or NATURAL THORIUM
2910	RADIOACTIVE MATERIAL, EXCEPTED PACKAGE – LIMITED QUANTITY OF MATERIAL
2911	RADIOACTIVE MATERIAL, EXCEPTED PACKAGE – INSTRUMENTS or ARTICLES
3507	URANIUM HEXAFLUORIDE, RADIOACTIVE MATERIAL, EXCEPTED PACKAGE less than 0.1 kg per package, non-fissile or fissile-excepted[b, c]
Low specific activity radioactive material (2.7.2.3.1)	
2912	RADIOACTIVE MATERIAL, LOW SPECIFIC ACTIVITY (LSA-I), non-fissile or fissile-excepted[b]
3321	RADIOACTIVE MATERIAL, LOW SPECIFIC ACTIVITY (LSA-II), non-fissile or fissile-excepted[b]
3322	RADIOACTIVE MATERIAL, LOW SPECIFIC ACTIVITY (LSA-III), non-fissile or fissile-excepted[b]
3324	RADIOACTIVE MATERIAL, LOW SPECIFIC ACTIVITY (LSA-II), FISSILE
3325	RADIOACTIVE MATERIAL, LOW SPECIFIC ACTIVITY (LSA-III), FISSILE
Surface contaminated objects (2.7.2.3.2)	
2913	RADIOACTIVE MATERIAL, SURFACE CONTAMINATED OBJECTS (SCO-I or SCO-II), non-fissile or fissile–excepted[b]
3326	RADIOACTIVE MATERIAL, SURFACE CONTAMINATED OBJECTS (SCO-I or SCO-II), FISSILE
Type A packages (2.7.2.4.4)	
2915	RADIOACTIVE MATERIAL, TYPE A PACKAGE, non-special form, non-fissile or fissile-excepted[b]
3327	RADIOACTIVE MATERIAL, TYPE A PACKAGE, FISSILE, non-special form
3332	RADIOACTIVE MATERIAL, TYPE A PACKAGE, SPECIAL FORM, non-fissile or fissile-excepted[b]
3333	RADIOACTIVE MATERIAL, TYPE A PACKAGE, SPECIAL FORM, FISSILE
Type B(U) package (2.7.2.4.6)	
2916	RADIOACTIVE MATERIAL, TYPE B(U) PACKAGE, non-fissile or fissile-excepted[b]
3328	RADIOACTIVE MATERIAL, TYPE B(U) PACKAGE, FISSILE

UN numbers	Proper shipping name[a] and description
Type B(M) package **(2.7.2.4.6)**	
2917	RADIOACTIVE MATERIAL, TYPE B(M) PACKAGE, non-fissile or fissile-excepted[b]
3329	RADIOACTIVE MATERIAL, TYPE B(M) PACKAGE, FISSILE
Type C package **(2.7.2.4.6)**	
3323	RADIOACTIVE MATERIAL, TYPE C PACKAGE, non-fissile or fissile-excepted[b]
3330	RADIOACTIVE MATERIAL, TYPE C PACKAGE, FISSILE
Special arrangement **(2.7.2.5)**	
2919	RADIOACTIVE MATERIAL, TRANSPORTED UNDER SPECIAL ARRANGEMENT, non-fissile or fissile-excepted[b]
3331	RADIOACTIVE MATERIAL, TRANSPORTED UNDER SPECIAL ARRANGEMENT, FISSILE
Uranium hexafluoride **(2.7.2.4.5)**	
2977	RADIOACTIVE MATERIAL, URANIUM HEXAFLUORIDE, FISSILE
2978	RADIOACTIVE MATERIAL, URANIUM HEXAFLUORIDE, non-fissile or fissile-excepted[b]
3507	URANIUM HEXAFLUORIDE, RADIOACTIVE MATERIAL, EXCEPTED PACKAGE less than 0.1 kg per package, non-fissile or fissile-excepted[b, c]

[a] The proper shipping name is found in the column "Proper shipping name and description" and is restricted to that part shown in capital letters. In the cases of UN Nos. 2909, 2911, 2913 and 3326, where alternative proper shipping names are separated by the word "or", only the relevant proper shipping name shall be used.

[b] The term "fissile-excepted" refers only to material excepted under 2.7.2.3.5.

[c] For UN 3507, see also special provision 369 in chapter 3.3.

2.7.2.2 Determination of activity level

2.7.2.2.1 The following basic values for individual radionuclides are given in table 2.7.2.2.1:

.1 A_1 and A_2 in TBq;

.2 Activity concentration limits for exempt material in Bq/g; and

.3 Activity limits for exempt consignments in Bq.

Table 2.7.2.2.1 – Basic radionuclides values for individual radionuclides

Radionuclide (atomic number)	A_1 (TBq)	A_2 (TBq)	Activity concentration limit for exempt material (Bq/g)	Activity limit for an exempt consignment (Bq)
Actinium (89)				
Ac-225 *(a)*	8×10^{-1}	6×10^{-3}	1×10^1	1×10^4
Ac-227 *(a)*	9×10^{-1}	9×10^{-5}	1×10^{-1}	1×10^3
Ac-228	6×10^{-1}	5×10^{-1}	1×10^1	1×10^6
Silver (47)				
Ag-105	2×10^0	2×10^0	1×10^2	1×10^6
Ag-108m *(a)*	7×10^{-1}	7×10^{-1}	1×10^1 *(b)*	1×10^6 *(b)*
Ag-110m *(a)*	4×10^{-1}	4×10^{-1}	1×10^1	1×10^6
Ag-111	2×10^0	6×10^{-1}	1×10^3	1×10^6
Aluminium (13)				
Al-26	1×10^{-1}	1×10^{-1}	1×10^1	1×10^5
Americium (95)				
Am-241	1×10^1	1×10^{-3}	1×10^0	1×10^4
Am-242m *(a)*	1×10^1	1×10^{-3}	1×10^0 *(b)*	1×10^4 *(b)*
Am-243 *(a)*	5×10^0	1×10^{-3}	1×10^0 *(b)*	1×10^3 *(b)*
Argon (18)				
Ar-37	4×10^1	4×10^1	1×10^6	1×10^8
Ar-39	4×10^1	2×10^1	1×10^7	1×10^4
Ar-41	3×10^{-1}	3×10^{-1}	1×10^2	1×10^9

Radionuclide (atomic number)	A_1 (TBq)	A_2 (TBq)	Activity concentration limit for exempt material (Bq/g)	Activity limit for an exempt consignment (Bq)
Arsenic (33)				
As-72	3×10^{-1}	3×10^{-1}	1×10^1	1×10^5
As-73	4×10^1	4×10^1	1×10^3	1×10^7
As-74	1×10^0	9×10^{-1}	1×10^1	1×10^6
As-76	3×10^{-1}	3×10^{-1}	1×10^2	1×10^5
As-77	2×10^1	7×10^{-1}	1×10^3	1×10^6
Astatine (85)				
At-211 *(a)*	2×10^1	5×10^{-1}	1×10^3	1×10^7
Gold (79)				
Au-193	7×10^0	2×10^0	1×10^2	1×10^7
Au-194	1×10^0	1×10^0	1×10^1	1×10^6
Au-195	1×10^1	6×10^0	1×10^2	1×10^7
Au-198	1×10^0	6×10^{-1}	1×10^2	1×10^6
Au-199	1×10^1	6×10^{-1}	1×10^2	1×10^6
Barium (56)				
Ba-131 *(a)*	2×10^0	2×10^0	1×10^2	1×10^6
Ba-133	3×10^0	3×10^0	1×10^2	1×10^6
Ba-133m	2×10^1	6×10^{-1}	1×10^2	1×10^6
Ba-140 *(a)*	5×10^{-1}	3×10^{-1}	1×10^1 *(b)*	1×10^5 *(b)*
Beryllium (4)				
Be–7	2×10^1	2×10^1	1×10^3	1×10^7
Be-10	4×10^1	6×10^{-1}	1×10^4	1×10^6
Bismuth (83)				
Bi-205	7×10^{-1}	7×10^{-1}	1×10^1	1×10^6
Bi-206	3×10^{-1}	3×10^{-1}	1×10^1	1×10^5
Bi-207	7×10^{-1}	7×10^{-1}	1×10^1	1×10^6
Bi-210	1×10^0	6×10^{-1}	1×10^3	1×10^6
Bi-210m *(a)*	6×10^{-1}	2×10^{-2}	1×10^1	1×10^5
Bi-212 *(a)*	7×10^{-1}	6×10^{-1}	1×10^1 *(b)*	1×10^5 *(b)*
Berkelium (97)				
Bk-247	8×10^0	8×10^{-4}	1×10^0	1×10^4
Bk-249 *(a)*	4×10^1	3×10^{-1}	1×10^3	1×10^6
Bromine (35)				
Br-76	4×10^{-1}	4×10^{-1}	1×10^1	1×10^5
Br-77	3×10^0	3×10^0	1×10^2	1×10^6
Br-82	4×10^{-1}	4×10^{-1}	1×10^1	1×10^6
Carbon (6)				
C-11	1×10^0	6×10^{-1}	1×10^1	1×10^6
C-14	4×10^1	3×10^0	1×10^4	1×10^7
Calcium (20)				
Ca-41	Unlimited	Unlimited	1×10^5	1×10^7
Ca-45	4×10^1	1×10^0	1×10^4	1×10^7
Ca-47 *(a)*	3×10^0	3×10^{-1}	1×10^1	1×10^6
Cadmium (48)				
Cd-109	3×10^1	2×10^0	1×10^4	1×10^6
Cd-113m	4×10^1	5×10^{-1}	1×10^3	1×10^6
Cd-115 *(a)*	3×10^0	4×10^{-1}	1×10^2	1×10^6
Cd-115m	5×10^{-1}	5×10^{-1}	1×10^3	1×10^6
Cerium (58)				
Ce-139	7×10^0	2×10^0	1×10^2	1×10^6
Ce-141	2×10^1	6×10^{-1}	1×10^2	1×10^7
Ce-143	9×10^{-1}	6×10^{-1}	1×10^2	1×10^6
Ce-144 *(a)*	2×10^{-1}	2×10^{-1}	1×10^2 *(b)*	1×10^5 *(b)*
Californium (98)				
Cf-248	4×10^1	6×10^{-3}	1×10^1	1×10^4
Cf-249	3×10^0	8×10^{-4}	1×10^0	1×10^3
Cf-250	2×10^1	2×10^{-3}	1×10^1	1×10^4
Cf-251	7×10^0	7×10^{-4}	1×10^0	1×10^3

Radionuclide (atomic number)	A_1 (TBq)	A_2 (TBq)	Activity concentration limit for exempt material (Bq/g)	Activity limit for an exempt consignment (Bq)
Cf-252	1×10^{-1}	3×10^{-3}	1×10^{1}	1×10^{4}
Cf-253 *(a)*	4×10^{1}	4×10^{-2}	1×10^{2}	1×10^{5}
Cf-254	1×10^{-3}	1×10^{-3}	1×10^{0}	1×10^{3}
Chlorine (17)				
Cl-36	1×10^{1}	6×10^{-1}	1×10^{4}	1×10^{6}
Cl-38	2×10^{-1}	2×10^{-1}	1×10^{1}	1×10^{5}
Curium (96)				
Cm-240	4×10^{1}	2×10^{-2}	1×10^{2}	1×10^{5}
Cm-241	2×10^{0}	1×10^{0}	1×10^{2}	1×10^{6}
Cm-242	4×10^{1}	1×10^{-2}	1×10^{2}	1×10^{5}
Cm-243	9×10^{0}	1×10^{-3}	1×10^{0}	1×10^{4}
Cm-244	2×10^{1}	2×10^{-3}	1×10^{1}	1×10^{4}
Cm-245	9×10^{0}	9×10^{-4}	1×10^{0}	1×10^{3}
Cm-246	9×10^{0}	9×10^{-4}	1×10^{0}	1×10^{3}
Cm-247 *(a)*	3×10^{0}	1×10^{-3}	1×10^{0}	1×10^{4}
Cm-248	2×10^{-2}	3×10^{-4}	1×10^{0}	1×10^{3}
Cobalt (27)				
Co-55	5×10^{-1}	5×10^{-1}	1×10^{1}	1×10^{6}
Co-56	3×10^{-1}	3×10^{-1}	1×10^{1}	1×10^{5}
Co-57	1×10^{1}	1×10^{1}	1×10^{2}	1×10^{6}
Co-58	1×10^{0}	1×10^{0}	1×10^{1}	1×10^{6}
Co-58m	4×10^{1}	4×10^{1}	1×10^{4}	1×10^{7}
Co-60	4×10^{-1}	4×10^{-1}	1×10^{1}	1×10^{5}
Chromium (24)				
Cr-51	3×10^{1}	3×10^{1}	1×10^{3}	1×10^{7}
Caesium (55)				
Cs-129	4×10^{0}	4×10^{0}	1×10^{2}	1×10^{5}
Cs-131	3×10^{1}	3×10^{1}	1×10^{3}	1×10^{6}
Cs-132	1×10^{0}	1×10^{0}	1×10^{1}	1×10^{5}
Cs-134	7×10^{-1}	7×10^{-1}	1×10^{1}	1×10^{4}
Cs-134m	4×10^{1}	6×10^{-1}	1×10^{3}	1×10^{5}
Cs-135	4×10^{1}	1×10^{0}	1×10^{4}	1×10^{7}
Cs-136	5×10^{-1}	5×10^{-1}	1×10^{1}	1×10^{5}
Cs-137 *(a)*	2×10^{0}	6×10^{-1}	1×10^{1} *(b)*	1×10^{4} *(b)*
Copper (29)				
Cu-64	6×10^{0}	1×10^{0}	1×10^{2}	1×10^{6}
Cu-67	1×10^{1}	7×10^{-1}	1×10^{2}	1×10^{6}
Dysprosium (66)				
Dy-159	2×10^{1}	2×10^{1}	1×10^{3}	1×10^{7}
Dy-165	9×10^{-1}	6×10^{-1}	1×10^{3}	1×10^{6}
Dy-166 *(a)*	9×10^{-1}	3×10^{-1}	1×10^{3}	1×10^{6}
Erbium (68)				
Er-169	4×10^{1}	1×10^{0}	1×10^{4}	1×10^{7}
Er-171	8×10^{-1}	5×10^{-1}	1×10^{2}	1×10^{6}
Europium (63)				
Eu-147	2×10^{0}	2×10^{0}	1×10^{2}	1×10^{6}
Eu-148	5×10^{-1}	5×10^{-1}	1×10^{1}	1×10^{6}
Eu-149	2×10^{1}	2×10^{1}	1×10^{2}	1×10^{7}
Eu-150 (short-lived)	2×10^{0}	7×10^{-1}	1×10^{3}	1×10^{6}
Eu-150 (long-lived)	7×10^{-1}	7×10^{-1}	1×10^{1}	1×10^{6}
Eu-152	1×10^{0}	1×10^{0}	1×10^{1}	1×10^{6}
Eu-152m	8×10^{-1}	8×10^{-1}	1×10^{2}	1×10^{6}
Eu-154	9×10^{-1}	6×10^{-1}	1×10^{1}	1×10^{6}
Eu-155	2×10^{1}	3×10^{0}	1×10^{2}	1×10^{7}
Eu-156	7×10^{-1}	7×10^{-1}	1×10^{1}	1×10^{6}
Fluorine (9)				
F-18	1×10^{0}	6×10^{-1}	1×10^{1}	1×10^{6}

Radionuclide (atomic number)	A_1 (TBq)	A_2 (TBq)	Activity concentration limit for exempt material (Bq/g)	Activity limit for an exempt consignment (Bq)
Iron (26)				
Fe-52 *(a)*	3×10^{-1}	3×10^{-1}	1×10^1	1×10^6
Fe-55	4×10^1	4×10^1	1×10^4	1×10^6
Fe-59	9×10^{-1}	9×10^{-1}	1×10^1	1×10^6
Fe-60 *(a)*	4×10^1	2×10^{-1}	1×10^2	1×10^5
Gallium (31)				
Ga-67	7×10^0	3×10^0	1×10^2	1×10^6
Ga-68	5×10^{-1}	5×10^{-1}	1×10^1	1×10^5
Ga-72	4×10^{-1}	4×10^{-1}	1×10^1	1×10^5
Gadolinium (64)				
Gd-146 *(a)*	5×10^{-1}	5×10^{-1}	1×10^1	1×10^6
Gd-148	2×10^1	2×10^{-3}	1×10^1	1×10^4
Gd-153	1×10^1	9×10^0	1×10^2	1×10^7
Gd-159	3×10^0	6×10^{-1}	1×10^3	1×10^6
Germanium (32)				
Ge-68 *(a)*	5×10^{-1}	5×10^{-1}	1×10^1	1×10^5
Ge-71	4×10^1	4×10^1	1×10^4	1×10^8
Ge-77	3×10^{-1}	3×10^{-1}	1×10^1	1×10^5
Hafnium (72)				
Hf-172 *(a)*	6×10^{-1}	6×10^{-1}	1×10^1	1×10^6
Hf-175	3×10^0	3×10^0	1×10^2	1×10^6
Hf-181	2×10^0	5×10^{-1}	1×10^1	1×10^6
Hf-182	Unlimited	Unlimited	1×10^2	1×10^6
Mercury (80)				
Hg-194 *(a)*	1×10^0	1×10^0	1×10^1	1×10^6
Hg-195m *(a)*	3×10^0	7×10^{-1}	1×10^2	1×10^6
Hg-197	2×10^1	1×10^1	1×10^2	1×10^7
Hg-197m	1×10^1	4×10^{-1}	1×10^2	1×10^6
Hg-203	5×10^0	1×10^0	1×10^2	1×10^5
Holmium (67)				
Ho-166	4×10^{-1}	4×10^{-1}	1×10^3	1×10^5
Ho-166m	6×10^{-1}	5×10^{-1}	1×10^1	1×10^6
Iodine (53)				
I-123	6×10^0	3×10^0	1×10^2	1×10^7
I-124	1×10^0	1×10^0	1×10^1	1×10^6
I-125	2×10^1	3×10^0	1×10^3	1×10^6
I-126	2×10^0	1×10^0	1×10^2	1×10^6
I-129	Unlimited	Unlimited	1×10^2	1×10^5
I-131	3×10^0	7×10^{-1}	1×10^2	1×10^6
I-132	4×10^{-1}	4×10^{-1}	1×10^1	1×10^5
I-133	7×10^{-1}	6×10^{-1}	1×10^1	1×10^6
I-134	3×10^{-1}	3×10^{-1}	1×10^1	1×10^5
I-135 *(a)*	6×10^{-1}	6×10^{-1}	1×10^1	1×10^6
Indium (49)				
In-111	3×10^0	3×10^0	1×10^2	1×10^6
In-113m	4×10^0	2×10^0	1×10^2	1×10^6
In-114m *(a)*	1×10^1	5×10^{-1}	1×10^2	1×10^6
In-115m	7×10^0	1×10^0	1×10^2	1×10^6
Iridium (77)				
Ir-189 *(a)*	1×10^1	1×10^1	1×10^2	1×10^7
Ir-190	7×10^{-1}	7×10^{-1}	1×10^1	1×10^6
Ir-192	1×10^0 *(c)*	6×10^{-1}	1×10^1	1×10^4
Ir-194	3×10^{-1}	3×10^{-1}	1×10^2	1×10^5
Potassium (19)				
K-40	9×10^{-1}	9×10^{-1}	1×10^2	1×10^6
K-42	2×10^{-1}	2×10^{-1}	1×10^2	1×10^6
K-43	7×10^{-1}	6×10^{-1}	1×10^1	1×10^6

Radionuclide (atomic number)	A_1 (TBq)	A_2 (TBq)	Activity concentration limit for exempt material (Bq/g)	Activity limit for an exempt consignment (Bq)
Krypton (36)				
Kr-79	4×10^0	2×10^0	1×10^3	1×10^5
Kr-81	4×10^1	4×10^1	1×10^4	1×10^7
Kr-85	1×10^1	1×10^1	1×10^5	1×10^4
Kr-85m	8×10^0	3×10^0	1×10^3	1×10^{10}
Kr-87	2×10^{-1}	2×10^{-1}	1×10^2	1×10^9
Lanthanum (57)				
La-137	3×10^1	6×10^0	1×10^3	1×10^7
La-140	4×10^{-1}	4×10^{-1}	1×10^1	1×10^5
Lutetium (71)				
Lu-172	6×10^{-1}	6×10^{-1}	1×10^1	1×10^6
Lu-173	8×10^0	8×10^0	1×10^2	1×10^7
Lu-174	9×10^0	9×10^0	1×10^2	1×10^7
Lu-174m	2×10^1	1×10^1	1×10^2	1×10^7
Lu-177	3×10^1	7×10^{-1}	1×10^3	1×10^7
Magnesium (12)				
Mg-28 *(a)*	3×10^{-1}	3×10^{-1}	1×10^1	1×10^5
Manganese (25)				
Mn-52	3×10^{-1}	3×10^{-1}	1×10^1	1×10^5
Mn-53	Unlimited	Unlimited	1×10^4	1×10^9
Mn-54	1×10^0	1×10^0	1×10^1	1×10^6
Mn-56	3×10^{-1}	3×10^{-1}	1×10^1	1×10^5
Molybdenum (42)				
Mo-93	4×10^1	2×10^1	1×10^3	1×10^8
Mo-99 *(a)*	1×10^0	6×10^{-1}	1×10^2	1×10^6
Nitrogen (7)				
N-13	9×10^{-1}	6×10^{-1}	1×10^2	1×10^9
Sodium (11)				
Na-22	5×10^{-1}	5×10^{-1}	1×10^1	1×10^6
Na-24	2×10^{-1}	2×10^{-1}	1×10^1	1×10^5
Niobium (41)				
Nb-93m	4×10^1	3×10^1	1×10^4	1×10^7
Nb-94	7×10^{-1}	7×10^{-1}	1×10^1	1×10^6
Nb-95	1×10^0	1×10^0	1×10^1	1×10^6
Nb-97	9×10^{-1}	6×10^{-1}	1×10^1	1×10^6
Neodymium (60)				
Nd-147	6×10^0	6×10^{-1}	1×10^2	1×10^6
Nd-149	6×10^{-1}	5×10^{-1}	1×10^2	1×10^6
Nickel (28)				
Ni-59	Unlimited	Unlimited	1×10^4	1×10^8
Ni-63	4×10^1	3×10^1	1×10^5	1×10^8
Ni-65	4×10^{-1}	4×10^{-1}	1×10^1	1×10^6
Neptunium (93)				
Np-235	4×10^1	4×10^1	1×10^3	1×10^7
Np-236 (short-lived)	2×10^1	2×10^0	1×10^3	1×10^7
Np-236 (long-lived)	9×10^0	2×10^{-2}	1×10^2	1×10^5
Np-237	2×10^1	2×10^{-3}	1×10^0 *(b)*	1×10^3 *(b)*
Np-239	7×10^0	4×10^{-1}	1×10^2	1×10^7
Osmium (76)				
Os-185	1×10^0	1×10^0	1×10^1	1×10^6
Os-191	1×10^1	2×10^0	1×10^2	1×10^7
Os-191m	4×10^1	3×10^1	1×10^3	1×10^7
Os-193	2×10^0	6×10^{-1}	1×10^2	1×10^6
Os-194 *(a)*	3×10^{-1}	3×10^{-1}	1×10^2	1×10^5
Phosphorus (15)				
P-32	5×10^{-1}	5×10^{-1}	1×10^3	1×10^5
P-33	4×10^1	1×10^0	1×10^5	1×10^8

Radionuclide (atomic number)	A_1 (TBq)	A_2 (TBq)	Activity concentration limit for exempt material (Bq/g)	Activity limit for an exempt consignment (Bq)
Protactinium (91)				
Pa-230 *(a)*	2×10^0	7×10^{-2}	1×10^1	1×10^6
Pa-231	4×10^0	4×10^{-4}	1×10^0	1×10^3
Pa-233	5×10^0	7×10^{-1}	1×10^2	1×10^7
Lead (82)				
Pb-201	1×10^0	1×10^0	1×10^1	1×10^6
Pb-202	4×10^1	2×10^1	1×10^3	1×10^6
Pb-203	4×10^0	3×10^0	1×10^2	1×10^6
Pb-205	Unlimited	Unlimited	1×10^4	1×10^7
Pb-210 *(a)*	1×10^0	5×10^{-2}	1×10^1 *(b)*	1×10^4 *(b)*
Pb-212 *(a)*	7×10^{-1}	2×10^{-1}	1×10^1 *(b)*	1×10^5 *(b)*
Palladium (46)				
Pd-103 *(a)*	4×10^1	4×10^1	1×10^3	1×10^8
Pd-107	Unlimited	Unlimited	1×10^5	1×10^8
Pd-109	2×10^0	5×10^{-1}	1×10^3	1×10^6
Promethium (61)				
Pm-143	3×10^0	3×10^0	1×10^2	1×10^6
Pm-144	7×10^{-1}	7×10^{-1}	1×10^1	1×10^6
Pm-145	3×10^1	1×10^1	1×10^3	1×10^7
Pm-147	4×10^1	2×10^0	1×10^4	1×10^7
Pm-148m *(a)*	8×10^{-1}	7×10^{-1}	1×10^1	1×10^6
Pm-149	2×10^0	6×10^{-1}	1×10^3	1×10^6
Pm-151	2×10^0	6×10^{-1}	1×10^2	1×10^6
Polonium (84)				
Po-210	4×10^1	2×10^{-2}	1×10^1	1×10^4
Praseodymium (59)				
Pr-142	4×10^{-1}	4×10^{-1}	1×10^2	1×10^5
Pr-143	3×10^0	6×10^{-1}	1×10^4	1×10^6
Platinum (78)				
Pt-188 *(a)*	1×10^0	8×10^{-1}	1×10^1	1×10^6
Pt-191	4×10^0	3×10^0	1×10^2	1×10^6
Pt-193	4×10^1	4×10^1	1×10^4	1×10^7
Pt-193m	4×10^1	5×10^{-1}	1×10^3	1×10^7
Pt-195m	1×10^1	5×10^{-1}	1×10^2	1×10^6
Pt-197	2×10^1	6×10^{-1}	1×10^3	1×10^6
Pt-197m	1×10^1	6×10^{-1}	1×10^2	1×10^6
Plutonium (94)				
Pu-236	3×10^1	3×10^{-3}	1×10^1	1×10^4
Pu-237	2×10^1	2×10^1	1×10^3	1×10^7
Pu-238	1×10^1	1×10^{-3}	1×10^0	1×10^4
Pu-239	1×10^1	1×10^{-3}	1×10^0	1×10^4
Pu-240	1×10^1	1×10^{-3}	1×10^0	1×10^3
Pu-241 *(a)*	4×10^1	6×10^{-2}	1×10^2	1×10^5
Pu-242	1×10^1	1×10^{-3}	1×10^0	1×10^4
Pu-244 *(a)*	4×10^{-1}	1×10^{-3}	1×10^0	1×10^4
Radium (88)				
Ra-223 *(a)*	4×10^{-1}	7×10^{-3}	1×10^2 *(b)*	1×10^5 *(b)*
Ra-224 *(a)*	4×10^{-1}	2×10^{-2}	1×10^1 *(b)*	1×10^5 *(b)*
Ra-225 *(a)*	2×10^{-1}	4×10^{-3}	1×10^2	1×10^5
Ra-226 *(a)*	2×10^{-1}	3×10^{-3}	1×10^1 *(b)*	1×10^4 *(b)*
Ra-228 *(a)*	6×10^{-1}	2×10^{-2}	1×10^1 *(b)*	1×10^5 *(b)*
Rubidium (37)				
Rb-81	2×10^0	8×10^{-1}	1×10^1	1×10^6
Rb-83 *(a)*	2×10^0	2×10^0	1×10^2	1×10^6
Rb-84	1×10^0	1×10^0	1×10^1	1×10^6
Rb-86	5×10^{-1}	5×10^{-1}	1×10^2	1×10^5
Rb-87	Unlimited	Unlimited	1×10^4	1×10^7
Rb (nat)	Unlimited	Unlimited	1×10^4	1×10^7

IMDG Code (amendment 38-16)

Radionuclide (atomic number)	A_1 (TBq)	A_2 (TBq)	Activity concentration limit for exempt material (Bq/g)	Activity limit for an exempt consignment (Bq)
Rhenium (75)				
Re-184	1×10^0	1×10^0	1×10^1	1×10^6
Re-184m	3×10^0	1×10^0	1×10^2	1×10^6
Re-186	2×10^0	6×10^{-1}	1×10^3	1×10^6
Re-187	Unlimited	Unlimited	1×10^6	1×10^9
Re-188	4×10^{-1}	4×10^{-1}	1×10^2	1×10^5
Re-189 (a)	3×10^0	6×10^{-1}	1×10^2	1×10^6
Re (nat)	Unlimited	Unlimited	1×10^6	1×10^9
Rhodium (45)				
Rh-99	2×10^0	2×10^0	1×10^1	1×10^6
Rh-101	4×10^0	3×10^0	1×10^2	1×10^7
Rh-102	5×10^{-1}	5×10^{-1}	1×10^1	1×10^6
Rh-102m	2×10^0	2×10^0	1×10^2	1×10^6
Rh-103m	4×10^1	4×10^1	1×10^4	1×10^8
Rh-105	1×10^1	8×10^{-1}	1×10^2	1×10^7
Radon (86)				
Rn-222 (a)	3×10^{-1}	4×10^{-3}	1×10^1 (b)	1×10^8 (b)
Ruthenium (44)				
Ru-97	5×10^0	5×10^0	1×10^2	1×10^7
Ru-103 (a)	2×10^0	2×10^0	1×10^2	1×10^6
Ru-105	1×10^0	6×10^{-1}	1×10^1	1×10^6
Ru-106 (a)	2×10^{-1}	2×10^{-1}	1×10^2 (b)	1×10^5 (b)
Sulphur (16)				
S-35	4×10^1	3×10^0	1×10^5	1×10^8
Antimony (51)				
Sb-122	4×10^{-1}	4×10^{-1}	1×10^2	1×10^4
Sb-124	6×10^{-1}	6×10^{-1}	1×10^1	1×10^6
Sb-125	2×10^0	1×10^0	1×10^2	1×10^6
Sb-126	4×10^{-1}	4×10^{-1}	1×10^1	1×10^5
Scandium (21)				
Sc-44	5×10^{-1}	5×10^{-1}	1×10^1	1×10^5
Sc-46	5×10^{-1}	5×10^{-1}	1×10^1	1×10^6
Sc-47	1×10^1	7×10^{-1}	1×10^2	1×10^6
Sc-48	3×10^{-1}	3×10^{-1}	1×10^1	1×10^5
Selenium (34)				
Se-75	3×10^0	3×10^0	1×10^2	1×10^6
Se-79	4×10^1	2×10^0	1×10^4	1×10^7
Silicon (14)				
Si-31	6×10^{-1}	6×10^{-1}	1×10^3	1×10^6
Si-32	4×10^1	5×10^{-1}	1×10^3	1×10^6
Samarium (62)				
Sm-145	1×10^1	1×10^1	1×10^2	1×10^7
Sm-147	Unlimited	Unlimited	1×10^1	1×10^4
Sm-151	4×10^1	1×10^1	1×10^4	1×10^8
Sm-153	9×10^0	6×10^{-1}	1×10^2	1×10^6
Tin (50)				
Sn-113 (a)	4×10^0	2×10^0	1×10^3	1×10^7
Sn-117m	7×10^0	4×10^{-1}	1×10^2	1×10^6
Sn-119m	4×10^1	3×10^1	1×10^3	1×10^7
Sn-121m (a)	4×10^1	9×10^{-1}	1×10^3	1×10^7
Sn-123	8×10^{-1}	6×10^{-1}	1×10^3	1×10^6
Sn-125	4×10^{-1}	4×10^{-1}	1×10^2	1×10^5
Sn-126 (a)	6×10^{-1}	4×10^{-1}	1×10^1	1×10^5
Strontium (38)				
Sr-82 (a)	2×10^{-1}	2×10^{-1}	1×10^1	1×10^5
Sr-85	2×10^0	2×10^0	1×10^2	1×10^6
Sr-85m	5×10^0	5×10^0	1×10^2	1×10^7
Sr-87m	3×10^0	3×10^0	1×10^2	1×10^6

2

Radionuclide (atomic number)	A_1 (TBq)	A_2 (TBq)	Activity concentration limit for exempt material (Bq/g)	Activity limit for an exempt consignment (Bq)
Sr-89	6×10^{-1}	6×10^{-1}	1×10^3	1×10^6
Sr-90 *(a)*	3×10^{-1}	3×10^{-1}	1×10^2 *(b)*	1×10^4 *(b)*
Sr-91 *(a)*	3×10^{-1}	3×10^{-1}	1×10^1	1×10^5
Sr-92 *(a)*	1×10^0	3×10^{-1}	1×10^1	1×10^6
Tritium (1)				
T (H-3)	4×10^1	4×10^1	1×10^6	1×10^9
Tantalum (73)				
Ta-178 (long-lived)	1×10^0	8×10^{-1}	1×10^1	1×10^6
Ta-179	3×10^1	3×10^1	1×10^3	1×10^7
Ta-182	9×10^{-1}	5×10^{-1}	1×10^1	1×10^4
Terbium (65)				
Tb-157	4×10^1	4×10^1	1×10^4	1×10^7
Tb-158	1×10^0	1×10^0	1×10^1	1×10^6
Tb-160	1×10^0	6×10^{-1}	1×10^1	1×10^6
Technetium (43)				
Tc-95m *(a)*	2×10^0	2×10^0	1×10^1	1×10^6
Tc-96	4×10^{-1}	4×10^{-1}	1×10^1	1×10^6
Tc-96m *(a)*	4×10^{-1}	4×10^{-1}	1×10^3	1×10^7
Tc-97	Unlimited	Unlimited	1×10^3	1×10^8
Tc-97m	4×10^1	1×10^0	1×10^3	1×10^7
Tc-98	8×10^{-1}	7×10^{-1}	1×10^1	1×10^6
Tc-99	4×10^1	9×10^{-1}	1×10^4	1×10^7
Tc-99m	1×10^1	4×10^0	1×10^2	1×10^7
Tellurium (52)				
Te-121	2×10^0	2×10^0	1×10^1	1×10^6
Te-121m	5×10^0	3×10^0	1×10^2	1×10^6
Te-123m	8×10^0	1×10^0	1×10^2	1×10^7
Te-125m	2×10^1	9×10^{-1}	1×10^3	1×10^7
Te-127	2×10^1	7×10^{-1}	1×10^3	1×10^6
Te-127m *(a)*	2×10^1	5×10^{-1}	1×10^3	1×10^7
Te-129	7×10^{-1}	6×10^{-1}	1×10^2	1×10^6
Te-129m *(a)*	8×10^{-1}	4×10^{-1}	1×10^3	1×10^6
Te-131m *(a)*	7×10^{-1}	5×10^{-1}	1×10^1	1×10^6
Te-132 *(a)*	5×10^{-1}	4×10^{-1}	1×10^2	1×10^7
Thorium (90)				
Th-227	1×10^1	5×10^{-3}	1×10^1	1×10^4
Th-228 *(a)*	5×10^{-1}	1×10^{-3}	1×10^0 *(b)*	1×10^4 *(b)*
Th-229	5×10^0	5×10^{-4}	1×10^0 *(b)*	1×10^3 *(b)*
Th-230	1×10^1	1×10^{-3}	1×10^0	1×10^4
Th-231	4×10^1	2×10^{-2}	1×10^3	1×10^7
Th-232	Unlimited	Unlimited	1×10^1	1×10^4
Th-234 *(a)*	3×10^{-1}	3×10^{-1}	1×10^3 *(b)*	1×10^5 *(b)*
Th (nat)	Unlimited	Unlimited	1×10^0 *(b)*	1×10^3 *(b)*
Titanium (22)				
Ti-44 *(a)*	5×10^{-1}	4×10^{-1}	1×10^1	1×10^5
Thallium (81)				
Tl-200	9×10^{-1}	9×10^{-1}	1×10^1	1×10^6
Tl-201	1×10^1	4×10^0	1×10^2	1×10^6
Tl-202	2×10^0	2×10^0	1×10^2	1×10^6
Tl-204	1×10^1	7×10^{-1}	1×10^4	1×10^4
Thulium (69)				
Tm-167	7×10^0	8×10^{-1}	1×10^2	1×10^6
Tm-170	3×10^0	6×10^{-1}	1×10^3	1×10^6
Tm-171	4×10^1	4×10^1	1×10^4	1×10^8
Uranium (92)				
U-230 (fast lung absorption) *(a) (d)*	4×10^1	1×10^{-1}	1×10^1 *(b)*	1×10^5 *(b)*
U-230 (medium lung absorption) *(a) (e)*	4×10^1	4×10^{-3}	1×10^1	1×10^4

IMDG Code (amendment 38-16)

Radionuclide (atomic number)	A_1 (TBq)	A_2 (TBq)	Activity concentration limit for exempt material (Bq/g)	Activity limit for an exempt consignment (Bq)
U-230 (slow lung absorption) *(a) (f)*	3×10^1	3×10^{-3}	1×10^1	1×10^4
U-232 (fast lung absorption) *(d)*	4×10^1	1×10^{-2}	1×10^0 *(b)*	1×10^3 *(b)*
U-232 (medium lung absorption) *(e)*	4×10^1	7×10^{-3}	1×10^1	1×10^4
U-232 (slow lung absorption) *(f)*	1×10^1	1×10^{-3}	1×10^1	1×10^4
U-233 (fast lung absorption) *(d)*	4×10^1	9×10^{-2}	1×10^1	1×10^4
U-233 (medium lung absorption) *(e)*	4×10^1	2×10^{-2}	1×10^2	1×10^5
U-233 (slow lung absorption) *(f)*	4×10^1	6×10^{-3}	1×10^1	1×10^5
U-234 (fast lung absorption) *(d)*	4×10^1	9×10^{-2}	1×10^1	1×10^4
U-234 (medium lung absorption) *(e)*	4×10^1	2×10^{-2}	1×10^2	1×10^5
U-234 (slow lung absorption) *(f)*	4×10^1	6×10^{-3}	1×10^1	1×10^5
U-235 (all lung absorption types) *(a) (d) (e) (f)*	Unlimited	Unlimited	1×10^1 *(b)*	1×10^4 *(b)*
U-236 (fast lung absorption) *(d)*	Unlimited	Unlimited	1×10^1	1×10^4
U-236 (medium lung absorption) *(e)*	4×10^1	2×10^{-2}	1×10^2	1×10^5
U-236 (slow lung absorption) *(f)*	4×10^1	6×10^{-3}	1×10^1	1×10^4
U-238 (all lung absorption types) *(d) (e) (f)*	Unlimited	Unlimited	1×10^1 *(b)*	1×10^4 *(b)*
U (nat)	Unlimited	Unlimited	1×10^0 *(b)*	1×10^3 *(b)*
U (enriched to 20% or less) *(g)*	Unlimited	Unlimited	1×10^0	1×10^3
U (dep)	Unlimited	Unlimited	1×10^0	1×10^3
Vanadium (23)				
V-48	4×10^{-1}	4×10^{-1}	1×10^1	1×10^5
V-49	4×10^1	4×10^1	1×10^4	1×10^7
Tungsten (74)				
W-178 *(a)*	9×10^0	5×10^0	1×10^1	1×10^6
W-181	3×10^1	3×10^1	1×10^3	1×10^7
W-185	4×10^1	8×10^{-1}	1×10^4	1×10^7
W-187	2×10^0	6×10^{-1}	1×10^2	1×10^6
W-188 *(a)*	4×10^{-1}	3×10^{-1}	1×10^2	1×10^5
Xenon (54)				
Xe-122 *(a)*	4×10^{-1}	4×10^{-1}	1×10^2	1×10^9
Xe-123	2×10^0	7×10^{-1}	1×10^2	1×10^9
Xe-127	4×10^0	2×10^0	1×10^3	1×10^5
Xe-131m	4×10^1	4×10^1	1×10^4	1×10^4
Xe-133	2×10^1	1×10^1	1×10^3	1×10^4
Xe-135	3×10^0	2×10^0	1×10^3	1×10^{10}
Yttrium (39)				
Y-87 *(a)*	1×10^0	1×10^0	1×10^1	1×10^6
Y-88	4×10^{-1}	4×10^{-1}	1×10^1	1×10^6
Y-90	3×10^{-1}	3×10^{-1}	1×10^3	1×10^5
Y-91	6×10^{-1}	6×10^{-1}	1×10^3	1×10^6
Y-91m	2×10^0	2×10^0	1×10^2	1×10^6
Y-92	2×10^{-1}	2×10^{-1}	1×10^2	1×10^5
Y-93	3×10^{-1}	3×10^{-1}	1×10^2	1×10^5
Ytterbium (70)				
Yb-169	4×10^0	1×10^0	1×10^2	1×10^7
Yb-175	3×10^1	9×10^{-1}	1×10^3	1×10^7
Zinc (30)				
Zn-65	2×10^0	2×10^0	1×10^1	1×10^6
Zn-69	3×10^0	6×10^{-1}	1×10^4	1×10^6
Zn-69m *(a)*	3×10^0	6×10^{-1}	1×10^2	1×10^6
Zirconium (40)				
Zr-88	3×10^0	3×10^0	1×10^2	1×10^6
Zr-93	Unlimited	Unlimited	1×10^3 *(b)*	1×10^7 *(b)*
Zr-95 *(a)*	2×10^0	8×10^{-1}	1×10^1	1×10^6
Zr-97 *(a)*	4×10^{-1}	4×10^{-1}	1×10^1 *(b)*	1×10^5 *(b)*

(a) A_1 and/or A_2 values for these parent radionuclides include contributions from their progeny with half-lives less than 10 days, as listed in the following:

    Mg-28   Al-28

Ar-42	K-42
Ca-47	Sc-47
Ti-44	Sc-44
Fe-52	Mn-52m
Fe-60	Co-60m
Zn-69m	Zn-69
Ge-68	Ga-68
Rb-83	Kr-83m
Sr-82	Rb-82
Sr-90	Y-90
Sr-91	Y-91m
Sr-92	Y-92
Y-87	Sr-87m
Zr-95	Nb-95m
Zr-97	Nb-97m, Nb-97
Mo-99	Tc-99m
Tc-95m	Tc-95
Tc-96m	Tc-96
Ru-103	Rh-103m
Ru-106	Rh-106
Pd-103	Rh-103m
Ag-108m	Ag-108
Ag-110m	Ag-110
Cd-115	In-115m
In-114m	In-114
Sn-113	In-113m
Sn-121m	Sn-121
Sn-126	Sb-126m
Te-118	Sb-118
Te-127m	Te-127
Te-129m	Te-129
Te-131m	Te-131
Te-132	I-132
I-135	Xe-135m
Xe-122	I-122
Cs-137	Ba-137m
Ba-131	Cs-131
Ba-140	La-140
Ce-144	Pr-144m, Pr-144
Pm-148m	Pm-148
Gd-146	Eu-146
Dy-166	Ho-166
Hf-172	Lu-172
W-178	Ta-178
W-188	Re-188
Re-189	Os-189m
Os-194	Ir-194
Ir-189	Os-189m
Pt-188	Ir-188
Hg-194	Au-194
Hg-195m	Hg-195
Pb-210	Bi-210
Pb-212	Bi-212, Tl-208, Po-212
Bi-210m	Tl-206

Bi-212	Tl-208, Po-212
At-211	Po-211
Rn-222	Po-218, Pb-214, At-218, Bi-214, Po-214
Ra-223	Rn-219, Po-215, Pb-211, Bi-211, Po-211, Tl-207
Ra-224	Rn-220, Po-216, Pb-212, Bi-212, Tl-208, Po-212
Ra-225	Ac-225, Fr-221, At-217, Bi-213, Tl-209, Po-213, Pb-209
Ra-226	Rn-222, Po-218, Pb-214, At-218, Bi-214, Po-214
Ra-228	Ac-228
Ac-225	Fr-221, At-217, Bi-213, Tl-209, Po-213, Pb-209
Ac-227	Fr-223
Th-228	Ra-224, Rn-220, Po-216, Pb-212, Bi-212, Tl-208, Po-212
Th-234	Pa-234m, Pa-234
Pa-230	Ac-226, Th-226, Fr-222, Ra-222, Rn-218, Po-214
U-230	Th-226, Ra-222, Rn-218, Po-214
U-235	Th-231
Pu-241	U-237
Pu-244	U-240, Np-240m
Am-242m	Am-242, Np-238
Am-243	Np-239
Cm-247	Pu-243
Bk-249	Am-245
Cf-253	Cm-249

(b) Parent nuclides and their progeny included in secular equilibrium are listed in the following:

Sr-90	Y-90
Zr-93	Nb-93m
Zr-97	Nb-97
Ru-106	Rh-106
Ag-108m	Ag-108
Cs-137	Ba-137m
Ce-144	Pr-144
Ba-140	La-140
Bi-212	Tl-208 (0.36), Po-212 (0.64)
Pb-210	Bi-210, Po-210
Pb-212	Bi-212, Tl-208 (0.36), Po-212 (0.64)
Rn-222	Po-218, Pb-214, Bi-214, Po-214
Ra-223	Rn-219, Po-215, Pb-211, Bi-211, Tl-207
Ra-224	Rn-220, Po-216, Pb-212, Bi-212, Tl-208 (0.36), Po-212 (0.64)
Ra-226	Rn-222, Po-218, Pb-214, Bi-214, Po-214, Pb-210, Bi-210, Po-210
Ra-228	Ac-228
Th-228	Ra-224, Rn-220, Po-216, Pb-212, Bi-212, Tl-208 (0.36), Po-212 (0.64)
Th-229	Ra-225, Ac-225, Fr-221, At-217, Bi-213, Po-213, Pb-209
Th (nat)	Ra-228, Ac-228, Th-228, Ra-224, Rn-220, Po-216, Pb-212, Bi-212, Tl-208 (0.36), Po-212 (0.64)
Th-234	Pa-234m
U-230	Th-226, Ra-222, Rn-218, Po-214
U-232	Th-228, Ra-224, Rn-220, Po-216, Pb-212, Bi-212, Tl-208 (0.36), Po-212 (0.64)
U-235	Th-231
U-238	Th-234, Pa-234m
U (nat)	Th-234, Pa-234m, U-234, Th-230, Ra-226, Rn-222, Po-218, Pb-214, Bi-214, Po-214, Pb-210, Bi-210, Po-210
Np-237	Pa-233
Am-242m	Am-242
Am-243	Np-239

(c) The quantity may be determined from a measurement of the rate of decay or a measurement of the radiation level at a prescribed distance from the source.

(d) These values apply only to compounds of uranium that take the chemical form of UF_6, UO_2F_2 and $UO_2(NO_3)_2$ in both normal and accident conditions of transport.

(e) These values apply only to compounds of uranium that take the chemical form of UO_3, UF_4, UCl_4 and hexavalent compounds in both normal and accident conditions of transport.

(f) These values apply to all compounds of uranium other than those specified in (d) and (e) above.

(g) These values apply to unirradiated uranium only.

2.7.2.2.2   For individual radionuclides:

.1   which are not listed in table 2.7.2.2.1, the determination of the basic radionuclide values referred to in 2.7.2.2.1 shall require multilateral approval. For these radionuclides, activity concentration limits for exempt material and activity limits for exempt consignments shall be calculated in accordance with the principles established in the *International Basic Safety Standards for Protection against Ionizing Radiation and for the Safety of Radiation Sources*, Safety Series No. 115, IAEA, Vienna (1996). It is permissible to use an A_2 value calculated using a dose coefficient for the appropriate lung absorption type as recommended by the International Commission on Radiological Protection, if the chemical forms of each radionuclide under both normal and accident conditions of transport are taken into consideration. Alternatively, the radionuclide values in table 2.7.2.2.2 may be used without obtaining competent authority approval;

.2   In instruments or articles in which the radioactive material is enclosed or is included as a component part of the instrument or other manufactured article and which meet 2.7.2.4.1.3.3, alternative basic radionuclide values to those in table 2.7.2.2.1 for the activity limit for an exempt consignment are permitted and shall require multilateral approval. Such alternative activity limits for an exempt consignment shall be calculated in accordance with the principles set out in the *International Basic Safety Standards for Protection against Ionizing Radiation and for the Safety of Radiation Sources*, Safety Series No. 115, IAEA, Vienna (1996).

Table 2.7.2.2.2 – Basic radionuclide values for unknown radionuclides or mixtures

Radioactive contents	A_1 (TBq)	A_2 (TBq)	Activity concentration limit for exempt material (Bq/g)	Activity limit for exempt consignments (Bq)
Only beta or gamma emitting nuclides are known to be present	0.1	0.02	1×10^1	1×10^4
Alpha emitting nuclides but no neutron emitters are known to be present	0.2	9×10^{-5}	1×10^{-1}	1×10^3
Neutron emitting nuclides are known to be present or no relevant data are available	0.001	9×10^{-5}	1×10^{-1}	1×10^3

2.7.2.2.3   In the calculations of A_1 and A_2 for a radionuclide not in table 2.7.2.2.1, a single radioactive decay chain in which the radionuclides are present in their naturally occurring proportions, and in which no daughter nuclide has a half-life either longer than 10 days or longer than that of the parent nuclide, shall be considered as a single radionuclide; and the activity to be taken into account and the A_1 or A_2 value to be applied shall be those corresponding to the parent nuclide of that chain. In the case of radioactive decay chains in which any daughter nuclide has a half-life either longer than 10 days or greater than that of the parent nuclide, the parent and such daughter nuclides shall be considered as mixtures of different nuclides.

2.7.2.2.4   For mixtures of radionuclides, the basic radionuclide values referred to in 2.7.2.2.1 may be determined as follows:

$$X_m = \frac{1}{\sum_i \frac{f(i)}{X(i)}}$$

where:

$f(i)$ is the fraction of activity or activity concentration of radionuclide i in the mixture;

$X(i)$ is the appropriate value of A_1 or A_2, or the activity concentration limit for exempt material or the activity limit for an exempt consignment, as appropriate, for the radionuclide i; and

X_m is the derived value of A_1 or A_2, or the activity concentration limit for exempt material or the activity limit for an exempt consignment in the case of a mixture.

2.7.2.2.5   When the identity of each radionuclide is known but the individual activities of some of the radionuclides are not known, the radionuclides may be grouped and the lowest radionuclide value, as appropriate, for the radionuclides in each group may be used in applying the formulae in 2.7.2.2.4 and 2.7.2.4.4. Groups may be based on the total alpha activity and the total beta/gamma activity when these are known, using the lowest radionuclide values for the alpha emitters or beta/gamma emitters, respectively.

2.7.2.2.6   For individual radionuclides or for mixtures of radionuclides for which relevant data are not available, the values shown in table 2.7.2.2.2 shall be used.

2.7.2.3   Determination of other material characteristics

2.7.2.3.1   *Low specific activity (LSA) material*

2.7.2.3.1.1   [Reserved]

2.7.2.3.1.2   LSA material shall be in one of three groups:

  .1   LSA-I

   .1   uranium and thorium ores and concentrates of such ores, and other ores containing naturally occurring radionuclides;

   .2   Natural uranium, depleted uranium, natural thorium or their compounds or mixtures, that are unirradiated and in solid or liquid form;

   .3   radioactive material for which the A_2 value is unlimited. Fissile material may be included only if excepted under 2.7.2.3.5; or

   .4   other radioactive material in which the activity is distributed throughout and the estimated average specific activity does not exceed 30 times the values for activity concentration specified in 2.7.2.2.1 to 2.7.2.2.6. Fissile material may be included only if excepted under 2.7.2.3.5;

  .2   LSA-II

   .1   water with tritium concentration up to 0.8 TBq/L;

   .2   other material in which the activity is distributed throughout and the estimated average specific activity does not exceed $10^{-4}A_2$/g for solids and gases, and $10^{-5}A_2$/g for liquids;

  .3   LSA-III – Solids (e.g. consolidated wastes, activated materials), excluding powders, that meet the requirements of 2.7.2.3.1.3, in which:

   .1   the radioactive material is distributed throughout a solid or a collection of solid objects, or is essentially uniformly distributed in a solid compact binding agent (such as concrete, bitumen and ceramic);

   .2   the radioactive material is relatively insoluble, or it is intrinsically contained in a relatively insoluble matrix, so that, even under loss of packaging, the loss of radioactive material per package by leaching when placed in water for seven days would not exceed $0.1A_2$; and

   .3   the estimated average specific activity of the solid, excluding any shielding material, does not exceed $2 \times 10^{-3}A_2$/g.

2.7.2.3.1.3   LSA-III material shall be a solid of such a nature that, if the entire contents of a package were subjected to the test specified in 2.7.2.3.1.4, the activity in the water would not exceed $0.1A_2$.

2.7.2.3.1.4   LSA-III material shall be tested as follows:

A solid material sample representing the entire contents of the package shall be immersed for 7 days in water at ambient temperature. The volume of water to be used in the test shall be sufficient to ensure that at the end of the 7-day test period the free volume of the unabsorbed and unreacted water remaining shall be at least 10% of the volume of the solid test sample itself. The water shall have an initial pH of 6 to 8 and a maximum conductivity of 1 mS/m at 20°C. The total activity of the free volume of water shall be measured following the 7-day immersion of the test sample.

2.7.2.3.1.5   Demonstration of compliance with the performance standards in 2.7.2.3.1.4 shall be in accordance with 6.4.12.1 and 6.4.12.2.

2.7.2.3.2   *Surface contaminated object (SCO)*

SCO is classified in one of two groups:

  .1   SCO-I: A solid object on which:

   .1   the non-fixed contamination on the accessible surface averaged over 300 cm^2 (or the area of the surface if less than 300 cm^2) does not exceed 4 Bq/cm^2 for beta and gamma emitters and low-toxicity alpha emitters, or 0.4 Bq/cm^2 for all other alpha emitters;

.2   the fixed contamination on the accessible surface averaged over 300 cm^2 (or the area of the surface if less than 300 cm^2) does not exceed 4×10^4 Bq/cm^2 for beta and gamma emitters and low-toxicity alpha emitters, or 4×10^3 Bq/cm^2 for all other alpha emitters; or

.3   the non-fixed contamination plus the fixed contamination on the inaccessible surface averaged over 300 cm^2 (or the area of the surface if less than 300 cm^2) does not exceed 4×10^4 Bq/cm^2 for beta and gamma emitters and low-toxicity alpha emitters, or 4×10^3 Bq/cm^2 for all other alpha emitters;

.2   SCO-II: A solid object on which either the fixed or non-fixed contamination on the surface exceeds the applicable limits specified for SCO-I in 2.7.2.3.2.1 above and on which:

.1   the non-fixed contamination on the accessible surface averaged over 300 cm^2 (or the area of the surface if less than 300 cm^2) does not exceed 400 Bq/cm^2 for beta and gamma emitters and low-toxicity alpha emitters, or 40 Bq/cm^2 for all other alpha emitters;

.2   the fixed contamination on the accessible surface averaged over 300 cm^2 (or the area of the surface if less than 300 cm^2) does not exceed 8×10^5 Bq/cm^2 for beta and gamma emitters and low-toxicity alpha emitters, or 8×10^4 Bq/cm^2 for all other alpha emitters; or

.3   the non-fixed contamination plus the fixed contamination on the inaccessible surface averaged over 300 cm^2 (or the area of the surface if less than 300 cm^2) does not exceed 8×10^5 Bq/cm^2 for beta and gamma emitters and low-toxicity alpha emitters, or 8×10^4 Bq/cm^2 for all other alpha emitters.

2.7.2.3.3   *Special form radioactive material*

2.7.2.3.3.1   .1   Special form radioactive material shall have at least one dimension not less than 5 mm.

.2   When a sealed capsule constitutes part of the special form radioactive material, the capsule shall be so manufactured that it can be opened only by destroying it.

.3   The design for special form radioactive material requires unilateral approval.

2.7.2.3.3.2   Special form radioactive material shall be of such a nature or shall be so designed that, if it is subjected to the tests specified in 2.7.2.3.3.4 to 2.7.2.3.3.8, it shall meet the following requirements:

.1   It would not break or shatter under the impact, percussion and bending tests 2.7.2.3.3.5.1, 2.7.2.3.3.5.2, 2.7.2.3.3.5.3, and 2.7.2.3.3.6.1 as applicable;

.2   It would not melt or disperse in the applicable heat test 2.7.2.3.3.5.4 or 2.7.2.3.3.6.2 as applicable; and

.3   The activity in the water from the leaching tests specified in 2.7.2.3.3.7 and 2.7.2.3.3.8 would not exceed 2 kBq; or alternatively for sealed sources, the leakage rate for the volumetric leakage assessment test specified in ISO 9978:1992, *Radiation protection – Sealed radioactive sources – Leakage test methods,* would not exceed the applicable acceptance threshold acceptable to the competent authority.

2.7.2.3.3.3   Demonstration of compliance with the performance standards in 2.7.2.3.3.2 shall be in accordance with 6.4.12.1 and 6.4.12.2.

2.7.2.3.3.4   Specimens that comprise or simulate special form radioactive material shall be subjected to the impact test, the percussion test, the bending test, and the heat test specified in 2.7.2.3.3.5 or alternative tests as authorized in 2.7.2.3.3.6. A different specimen may be used for each of the tests. Following each test, a leaching assessment or volumetric leakage test shall be performed on the specimen by a method no less sensitive than the methods given in 2.7.2.3.3.7 for indispersible solid material or 2.7.2.3.3.8 for encapsulated material.

2.7.2.3.3.5   The relevant test methods are:

.1   Impact test: The specimen shall drop onto the target from a height of 9 m. The target shall be as defined in 6.4.14;

.2   Percussion test: The specimen shall be placed on a sheet of lead which is supported by a smooth solid surface and struck by the flat face of a mild steel bar so as to cause an impact equivalent to that resulting from a free drop of 1.4 kg through 1 m. The lower part of the bar shall be 25 mm in diameter with the edges rounded off to a radius of (3.0 ± 0.3) mm. The lead, of hardness number 3.5 to 4.5 on the Vickers scale and not more than 25 mm thick, shall cover an area greater than that covered by the specimen. A fresh surface of lead shall be used for each impact. The bar shall strike the specimen so as to cause maximum damage;

.3   Bending test: The test shall apply only to long, slender sources with both a minimum length of 10 cm and a length to minimum width ratio of not less than 10. The specimen shall be rigidly clamped in a horizontal position so that one half of its length protrudes from the face of the clamp. The orientation of the specimen shall be such that the specimen will suffer maximum damage when its free end is struck by the flat face of a steel bar. The bar shall strike the specimen so as to cause an impact equivalent to that resulting from a free vertical drop of 1.4 kg through 1 m. The lower part of the bar shall be 25 mm in diameter with the edges rounded off to a radius of (3.0 ± 0.3) mm;

.4   Heat test: The specimen shall be heated in air to a temperature of 800°C and held at that temperature for a period of 10 minutes and shall then be allowed to cool.

2.7.2.3.3.6   Specimens that comprise or simulate radioactive material enclosed in a sealed capsule may be excepted from:

    .1   The tests prescribed in 2.7.2.3.3.5.1 and 2.7.2.3.3.5.2 provided that the specimens are alternatively subjected to the impact test prescribed in ISO 2919:2012, *Radiation Protection – Sealed Radioactive Sources – General requirements and classification:*

        .1   the class 4 impact test if the mass of the special form radioactive material is less than 200 g; and

        .2   the class 5 impact test if the mass of the special form radioactive material is equal to or more than 200 g but is less than 500 g.

    .2   The test prescribed in 2.7.2.3.3.5.4 provided they are alternatively subjected to the class 6 temperature test specified in ISO 2919:2012, *Radiation protection – Sealed radioactive sources – General requirements and classification.*

2.7.2.3.3.7   For specimens which comprise or simulate indispersible solid material, a leaching assessment shall be performed as follows:

    .1   The specimen shall be immersed for 7 days in water at ambient temperature. The volume of water to be used in the test shall be sufficient to ensure that at the end of the 7-day test period the free volume of the unabsorbed and unreacted water remaining shall be at least 10% of the volume of the solid test sample itself. The water shall have an initial pH of 6 to 8 and a maximum conductivity of 1 mS/m at 20°C;

    .2   The water with specimen shall then be heated to a temperature of (50 ± 5)°C and maintained at this temperature for 4 hours;

    .3   The activity of the water shall then be determined;

    .4   The specimen shall then be kept for at least 7 days in still air at not less than 30°C and relative humidity not less than 90%;

    .5   The specimen shall then be immersed in water of the same specification as in 2.7.2.3.3.7.1 above and the water with the specimen heated to (50 ± 5)°C and maintained at this temperature for 4 hours;

    .6   The activity of the water shall then be determined.

2.7.2.3.3.8   For specimens which comprise or simulate radioactive material enclosed in a sealed capsule, either a leaching assessment or a volumetric leakage assessment shall be performed as follows:

    .1   The leaching assessment shall consist of the following steps:

        .1   the specimen shall be immersed in water at ambient temperature. The water shall have an initial pH of 6 to 8 with a maximum conductivity of 1 mS/m at 20°C;

        .2   the water and specimen shall be heated to a temperature of (50 ± 5)°C and maintained at this temperature for 4 hours;

        .3   the activity of the water shall then be determined;

        .4   the specimen shall then be kept for at least 7 days in still air at not less than 30°C and relative humidity of not less than 90%;

        .5   the process in .1, .2 and .3 shall be repeated.

    .2   The alternative volumetric leakage assessment shall comprise any of the tests prescribed in ISO 9978:1992, *Radiation protection – Sealed radioactive sources – Leakage test methods,* provided that they are acceptable to the competent authority.

2.7.2.3.4   *Low dispersible material*

2.7.2.3.4.1   The design for low dispersible radioactive material shall require multilateral approval. Low dispersible radioactive material shall be such that the total amount of this radioactive material in a package, taking into account the provisions of 6.4.8.14, shall meet the following provisions:

    .1   The radiation level at 3 m from the unshielded radioactive material does not exceed 10 mSv/h;

    .2   If subjected to the tests specified in 6.4.20.3 and 6.4.20.4, the airborne release in gaseous and particulate forms of up to 100 μm aerodynamic equivalent diameter would not exceed $100A_2$. A separate specimen may be used for each test; and

    .3   If subjected to the test specified in 2.7.2.3.1.4, the activity in the water would not exceed $100A_2$. In the application of this test, the damaging effects of the tests specified in 2.7.2.3.4.1.2 above shall be taken into account.

2.7.2.3.4.2   Low dispersible material shall be tested as follows:

A specimen that comprises or simulates low dispersible radioactive material shall be subjected to the enhanced thermal test specified in 6.4.20.3 and the impact test specified in 6.4.20.4. A different specimen may be used for each of the tests. Following each test, the specimen shall be subjected to the leach test specified in 2.7.2.3.1.4. After each test it shall be determined if the applicable provisions of 2.7.2.3.4.1 have been met.

2.7.2.3.4.3 Demonstration of compliance with the performance standards in 2.7.2.3.4.1 and 2.7.2.3.4.2 shall be in accordance with 6.4.12.1 and 6.4.12.2.

2.7.2.3.5 *Fissile material*

Fissile material and packages containing fissile material shall be classified under the relevant entry as "FISSILE" in accordance with table 2.7.2.1.1 unless excepted by one of the provisions of subparagraphs .1 to .6 below and transported subject to the requirements of 5.1.5.5. All provisions apply only to material in packages that meets the requirements of 6.4.7.2 unless unpackaged material is specifically allowed in the provision.

   .1 uranium enriched in uranium-235 to a maximum of 1% by mass, and with a total plutonium and uranium-233 content not exceeding 1% of the mass of uranium-235, provided that the fissile nuclides are distributed essentially homogeneously throughout the material. In addition, if uranium-235 is present in metallic, oxide or carbide forms, it shall not form a lattice arrangement;

   .2 liquid solutions of uranyl nitrate enriched in uranium-235 to a maximum of 2% by mass, with a total plutonium and uranium-233 content not exceeding 0.002% of the mass of uranium, and with a minimum nitrogen to uranium atomic ratio (N/U) of 2;

   .3 uranium with a maximum uranium enrichment of 5% by mass uranium-235 provided:

      .1 there is no more than 3.5 g of uranium-235 per package;

      .2 the total plutonium and uranium-233 content does not exceed 1% of the mass of uranium-235 per package;

      .3 Transport of the package is subject to the consignment limit provided in 5.1.5.5.3;

   .4 fissile nuclides with a total mass not greater than 2 g per package provided the package is transported subject to the consignment limit provided in 5.1.5.5.4;

   .5 fissile nuclides with a total mass not greater than 45 g either packaged or unpackaged subject to limits provided in 5.1.5.5.5;

   .6 a fissile material that meets the requirements of 5.1.5.5.2, 2.7.2.3.6 and 5.1.5.2.1.

2.7.2.3.6 A fissile material excepted from classification as "FISSILE" under 2.7.2.3.5.6 shall be subcritical without the need for accumulation control under the following conditions:

   .1 the conditions of 6.4.11.1 (a);

   .2 the conditions consistent with the assessment provisions stated in 6.4.11.12 (b) and 6.4.11.13 (b) for packages; and

   .3 the conditions specified in 6.4.11.11 (a), if transported by air.

2.7.2.4 **Classification of packages or unpacked material**

The quantity of radioactive material in a package shall not exceed the relevant limits for the package type as specified below.

2.7.2.4.1 *Classification as excepted package*

2.7.2.4.1.1 A package may be classified as an excepted package if it meets one of the following conditions:

   .1 it is an empty package having contained radioactive material;

   .2 it contains instruments or articles not exceeding the activity limits specified in columns (2) and (3) of table 2.7.2.4.1.2;

   .3 it contains articles manufactured of natural uranium, depleted uranium or natural thorium;

   .4 it contains radioactive material not exceeding the activity limits specified in column (4) of table 2.7.2.4.1.2; or

   .5 it contains less than 0.1 kg of uranium hexafluoride not exceeding the activity limits specified in column (4) of table 2.7.2.4.1.2.

2.7.2.4.1.2 A package containing radioactive material may be classified as an excepted package provided that the radiation level at any point on its external surface does not exceed 5 µSv/h.

Table 2.7.2.4.1.2 – Activity limits for excepted packages

Physical state of contents	Instruments or article		Material package limits[a]
	Item limits[a]	Package limits[a]	
(1)	(2)	(3)	(4)
Solids			
special form	$10^{-2} A_1$	A_1	$10^{-3} A_1$
other form	$10^{-2} A_2$	A_2	$10^{-3} A_2$
Liquids	$10^{-3} A_2$	$10^{-1} A_2$	$10^{-4} A_2$
Gases			
tritium	$2 \times 10^{-2} A_2$	$2 \times 10^{-1} A_2$	$2 \times 10^{-2} A_2$
special form	$10^{-3} A_1$	$10^{-2} A_1$	$10^{-3} A_1$
other forms	$10^{-3} A_2$	$10^{-2} A_2$	$10^{-3} A_2$

[a] For mixtures of radionuclides, see 2.7.2.2.4 to 2.7.2.2.6.

2.7.2.4.1.3 Radioactive material which is enclosed in or is included as a component part of an instrument or other manufactured article may be classified under UN 2911, RADIOACTIVE MATERIAL, EXCEPTED PACKAGE – INSTRUMENTS or ARTICLES provided that:

.1 the radiation level at 10 cm from any point on the external surface of any unpackaged instrument or article is not greater than 0.1 mSv/h; and

△ .2 each instrument or manufactured article bears the mark "RADIOACTIVE" on its external surface except for the following:

.1 radioluminescent time-pieces or devices;

.2 consumer products that either have received regulatory approval in accordance with 1.5.1.4.5 or do not individually exceed the activity limit for an exempt consignment in table 2.7.2.2.1 (column 5), provided such products are transported in a package that bears the mark "RADIOACTIVE" on its internal surface in such a manner that a warning of the presence of radioactive material is visible on opening the package;

.3 other instruments or articles too small to bear the mark "RADIOACTIVE", provided that they are transported in a package that bears the mark "RADIOACTIVE" on its internal surface in such a manner that a warning of the presence of radioactive material is visible on opening the package; and

.3 the active material is completely enclosed by non-active components (a device performing the sole function of containing radioactive material shall not be considered to be an instrument or manufactured article); and

.4 the limits specified in columns 2 and 3 of table 2.7.2.4.1.2 are met for each individual item and each package, respectively.

2.7.2.4.1.4 Radioactive material in forms other than as specified in 2.7.2.4.1.3 and with an activity not exceeding the limits specified in column 4 of table 2.7.2.4.1.2, may be classified under UN 2910, RADIOACTIVE MATERIAL, EXCEPTED PACKAGE – LIMITED QUANTITY OF MATERIAL provided that:

.1 the package retains its radioactive contents under routine conditions of transport; and

△ .2 the package bears the mark "RADIOACTIVE" on either:

.1 an internal surface in such a manner that a warning of the presence of radioactive material is visible on opening the package; or

.2 the outside of the package, where it is impractical to mark an internal surface.

2.7.2.4.1.5 Uranium hexafluoride not exceeding the limits specified in column 4 of table 2.7.2.4.1.2 may be classified under UN 3507 URANIUM HEXAFLUORIDE, RADIOACTIVE MATERIAL, EXCEPTED PACKAGE, less than 0.1 kg per package, non-fissile or fissile-excepted, provided that:

.1 the mass of uranium hexafluoride in the package is less than 0.1 kg; and

.2 the conditions of 2.7.2.4.5.1 and 2.7.2.4.1.4.1 and 2.7.2.4.1.4.2 are met.

2.7.2.4.1.6 Articles manufactured of natural uranium, depleted uranium or natural thorium and articles in which the sole radioactive material is unirradiated natural uranium, unirradiated depleted uranium or unirradiated natural thorium may be classified under UN 2909, RADIOACTIVE MATERIAL, EXCEPTED PACKAGE – ARTICLES MANUFACTURED FROM NATURAL URANIUM or DEPLETED URANIUM or NATURAL THORIUM, provided that the outer surface of the uranium or thorium is enclosed in an inactive sheath made of metal or some other substantial material.

2.7.2.4.1.7 An empty packaging which had previously contained radioactive material may be classified under UN 2908, RADIOACTIVE MATERIAL, EXCEPTED PACKAGE – EMPTY PACKAGING, provided that:

.1 it is in a well-maintained condition and securely closed;

.2 the outer surface of any uranium or thorium in its structure is covered with an inactive sheath made of metal or some other substantial material;

.3 the level of internal non-fixed contamination, when averaged over any 300 cm^2, does not exceed:

.1 400 Bq/cm^2 for beta and gamma emitters and low-toxicity alpha emitters; and

.2 40 Bq/cm^2 for all other alpha emitters; and

.4 any labels which may have been displayed on it in conformity with 5.2.2.1.12.1 are no longer visible.

2.7.2.4.2 *Classification as Low specific activity (LSA) material*

Radioactive material may only be classified as LSA material if the definition of LSA in 2.7.1.3 and the conditions of 2.7.2.3.1, 4.1.9.2 and 7.1.4.5.1 are met.

2.7.2.4.3 *Classification as Surface contaminated object (SCO)*

Radioactive material may be classified as SCO if the definition of SCO in 2.7.1.3 and the conditions of 2.7.2.3.2, 4.1.9.2 and 7.1.4.5.1 are met.

2.7.2.4.4 *Classification as Type A package*

Packages containing radioactive material may be classified as Type A packages provided that the following conditions are met:

Type A packages shall not contain activities greater than either of the following:

.1 for special form radioactive material – A_1;

.2 for all other radioactive material – A_2.

For mixtures of radionuclides whose identities and respective activities are known, the following condition shall apply to the radioactive contents of a Type A package:

$$\sum_i \frac{B(i)}{A_1(i)} + \sum_j \frac{C(j)}{A_2(j)} \leq 1$$

where:

$B(i)$ is the activity of radionuclide i as special form radioactive material;

$A_1(i)$ is the A_1 value for radionuclide i;

$C(j)$ is the activity of radionuclide j as other than special form radioactive material;

$A_2(j)$ is the A_2 value for radionuclide j.

2.7.2.4.5 *Classification of uranium hexafluoride*

2.7.2.4.5.1 Uranium hexafluoride shall only be assigned to:

.1 UN 2977, RADIOACTIVE MATERIAL, URANIUM HEXAFLUORIDE, FISSILE;

.2 UN 2978, RADIOACTIVE MATERIAL, URANIUM HEXAFLUORIDE, non-fissile or fissile-excepted; or

.3 UN 3507, URANIUM HEXAFLUORIDE, RADIOACTIVE MATERIAL, EXCEPTED PACKAGE less than 0.1 kg per package, non-fissile or fissile-excepted.

2.7.2.4.5.2 The contents of a package containing uranium hexafluoride shall comply with the following requirements:

.1 for UN Nos. 2977 and 2978, the mass of uranium hexafluoride shall not be different from that allowed for the package design, and for UN 3507, the mass of uranium hexafluoride shall be less than 0.1 kg;

.2 the mass of uranium hexafluoride shall not be greater than a value that would lead to an ullage smaller than 5% at the maximum temperature of the package as specified for the plant systems where the package shall be used; and

.3 the uranium hexafluoride shall be in solid form and the internal pressure shall not be above atmospheric pressure when presented for transport.

2.7.2.4.6 *Classification as Type B(U), Type B(M) or Type C packages*

2.7.2.4.6.1 Packages not otherwise classified in 2.7.2.4 (2.7.2.4.1 to 2.7.2.4.5) shall be classified in accordance with the competent authority certificate of approval for the package issued by the country of origin of design.

2.7.2.4.6.2   The contents of a Type B(U), Type B(M) or Type C package shall be as specified in the certificate of approval.

2.7.2.5   **Special arrangements**

Radioactive material shall be classified as transported under special arrangement when it is intended to be transported in accordance with 1.5.4.

2

Chapter 2.8

Class 8 – Corrosive substances

2.8.1 Definition and properties

2.8.1.1 Definition

Class 8 substances (corrosive substances) means substances which, by chemical action, will cause severe damage when in contact with living tissue or, in the case of leakage, will materially damage, or even destroy, other goods or the means of transport.

2.8.1.2 Properties

2.8.1.2.1 In cases where particularly severe personal damage is to be expected, a note to that effect is made in the Dangerous Goods List in chapter 3.2 in the wording "causes (severe) burns to skin, eyes and mucous membranes".

2.8.1.2.2 Many substances are sufficiently volatile to evolve vapour irritating to the nose and eyes. If so, this fact is mentioned in the Dangerous Goods List in chapter 3.2 in the wording "vapour irritates mucous membranes".

2.8.1.2.3 A few substances may produce toxic gases when decomposed by very high temperatures. In these cases the statement "when involved in a fire, evolves toxic gases" appears in the Dangerous Goods List in chapter 3.2.

2.8.1.2.4 In addition to direct destructive action in contact with skin or mucous membranes, some substances in this class are toxic or harmful. Poisoning may result if they are swallowed, or if their vapour is inhaled; some of them even may penetrate the skin. Where appropriate, a statement is made to that effect in the Dangerous Goods List in chapter 3.2.

2.8.1.2.5 All substances in this class have a more or less destructive effect on materials such as metals and textiles.

2.8.1.2.5.1 In the Dangerous Goods List, the term "corrosive to most metals" means that any metal likely to be present in a ship, or in its cargo, may be attacked by the substance or its vapour.

2.8.1.2.5.2 The term "corrosive to aluminium, zinc, and tin" implies that iron or steel is not damaged in contact with the substance.

2.8.1.2.5.3 A few substances in this class can corrode glass, earthenware and other siliceous materials. Where appropriate, this is stated in the Dangerous Goods List in chapter 3.2.

2.8.1.2.6 Many substances in this class only become corrosive after having reacted with water, or with moisture in the air. This fact is indicated in the Dangerous Goods List in chapter 3.2 by the words "in the presence of moisture...". The reaction of water with many substances is accompanied by the liberation of irritating and corrosive gases. Such gases usually become visible as fumes in the air.

2.8.1.2.7 A few substances in this class generate heat in reaction with water or organic materials, including wood, paper, fibres, some cushioning materials and certain fats and oils. Where appropriate, this is indicated in the Dangerous Goods List in chapter 3.2.

2.8.1.2.8 A substance which is designated as "stabilized" shall not be transported in the unstabilized state.

2.8.2 Assignment of packing groups

2.8.2.1 Substances and preparations of class 8 are divided among the three packing groups according to their degree of hazard in transport as follows:

Packing group I: Very dangerous substances and preparations;

Packing group II: Substances and preparations presenting medium danger;

Packing group III: Substances and preparations presenting minor danger.

The packing group to which a substance has been assigned is given in the Dangerous Goods List in chapter 3.2.

2.8.2.2   Allocation of substances listed in the Dangerous Goods List in chapter 3.2 to the packing groups in class 8 has been on the basis of experience, taking into account such additional factors as inhalation risk (see 2.8.2.3) and reactivity with water (including the formation of dangerous decomposition products). New substances, including mixtures, can be assigned to packing groups on the basis of the length of time of contact necessary to produce full thickness destruction of human skin in accordance with the criteria in 2.8.2.5. Liquids, and solids which may become liquid during transport, which are judged not to cause full thickness destruction of human skin shall still be considered for their potential to cause corrosion in certain metal surfaces in accordance with the criteria in 2.8.2.5.3.2.

2.8.2.3   A substance or preparation meeting the criteria of class 8 and having an inhalation toxicity of dusts and mists (LC_{50}) in the range of packing group I, but toxicity through oral ingestion or dermal contact only in the range of packing group III or less, shall be allocated to class 8 (see note under 2.6.2.2.4.1).

2.8.2.4   In assigning the packing group to a substance in accordance with 2.8.2.2, account shall be taken of human experience in instances of accidental exposure. In the absence of human experience, the grouping shall be based on data obtained from experiments in accordance with OECD Test Guideline 404[*] or 435[†]. A substance which is determined not to be corrosive in accordance with OECD Test Guideline 430[‡] or 431[§] may be considered not to be corrosive to skin for the purposes of this Code without further testing.

2.8.2.5   Packing groups are assigned to corrosive substances in accordance with the following criteria:

.1   Packing group I is assigned to substances that cause full thickness destruction of intact skin tissue within an observation period of up to 60 minutes starting after an exposure time of 3 minutes or less.

.2   Packing group II is assigned to substances that cause full thickness destruction of intact skin tissue within an observation period of up to 14 days starting after an exposure time of more than 3 but not more than 60 minutes.

.3   Packing group III is assigned to substances that:

.1   cause full thickness destruction of intact skin tissue within an observation period of up to 14 days starting after an exposure time of more than 60 minutes but not more than 4 hours; or

.2   are judged not to cause full thickness destruction of intact skin tissue but which exhibit a corrosion rate on either steel or aluminium surfaces exceeding 6.25 mm a year at a test temperature of 55°C when tested on both materials. For the purposes of testing steel, type S235JR+CR (1.0037 resp. St 37-2), S275J2G3+CR (1.0144 resp. St 44-3), ISO 3574:1999, Unified Numbering System (UNS) G10200 or SAE 1020, and for testing aluminium, non-clad, types 7075-T6 or AZ5GU T6 shall be used. An acceptable test is prescribed in the Manual of Tests and Criteria, part III, section 37.

Note: Where an initial test on either steel or aluminium indicates the substance being tested is corrosive, the follow-up test on the other metal is not required.

Table 2.8.2.5 – Table summarizing the criteria in 2.8.2.5

Packing group	Exposure time	Observation period	Effect
I	≤ 3 min	≤ 60 min	Full thickness destruction of intact skin
II	> 3 min ≤ 1 h	≤ 14 d	Full thickness destruction of intact skin
III	> 1 h ≤ 4 h	≤ 14 d	Full thickness destruction of intact skin
III	–	–	Corrosion rate on either steel or aluminium surfaces exceeding 6.25 mm a year at a test temperature of 55°C when tested on both materials

■ 2.8.3   Substances not accepted for transport

Chemically unstable substances of class 8 shall not be accepted for transport unless the necessary precautions have been taken to prevent the possibility of a dangerous decomposition or polymerization under normal conditions of transport. For the precautions necessary to prevent polymerization, see special provision 386 of chapter 3.3. To this end particular care shall be taken to ensure that receptacles and tanks do not contain any substances liable to promote these reactions.

---

[*] OECD Guideline for the testing of chemicals No. 404, Acute Dermal Irritation/Corrosion, 2002.

[†] OECD Guideline for the testing of chemicals No. 435, *In Vitro* Membrane Barrier Test Method for Skin Corrosion, 2006.

[‡] OECD Guideline for the testing of chemicals No. 430, *In Vitro* Skin Corrosion: Transcutaneous Electrical Resistance Test (TER), 2004.

[§] OECD Guideline for the testing of chemicals No. 431, *In Vitro* Skin Corrosion: Human Skin Model Test, 2004.

Chapter 2.9

Miscellaneous dangerous substances and articles (class 9) and environmentally hazardous substances

Note 1: For the purposes of this Code, the environmentally hazardous substances (aquatic environment) criteria contained in this chapter apply to the classification of marine pollutants (see 2.10).

Note 2: Although the environmentally hazardous substances (aquatic environment) criteria apply to all hazard classes, except for class 7 (see paragraphs 2.10.2.3, 2.10.2.5 and 2.10.3.2), the criteria have been included in this chapter.

2.9.1 Definitions

2.9.1.1 *Class 9 substances and articles (miscellaneous dangerous substances and articles)* are substances and articles which, during transport, present a danger not covered by other classes.

2.9.2 Assignment to class 9

2.9.2.1 Class 9 includes, inter alia:

.1 substances and articles not covered by other classes which experience has shown, or may show, to be of such a dangerous character that the provisions of part A of chapter VII of SOLAS, as amended, shall apply.

.2 substances not subject to the provisions of part A in chapter VII of the aforementioned Convention, but to which the provisions of Annex III of MARPOL, as amended, apply.

2.9.2.2 The substances and articles of class 9 are subdivided as follows:

Substances which, on inhalation as fine dust, may endanger health

2212 ASBESTOS, AMPHIBOLE (amosite, tremolite, actinolite, anthophyllite, crocidolite)

2590 ASBESTOS, CHRYSOTILE

Substances evolving flammable vapour

2211 POLYMERIC BEADS, EXPANDABLE, evolving flammable vapour

3314 PLASTICS MOULDING COMPOUND in dough, sheet or extruded rope form evolving flammable vapour

Lithium batteries

3090 LITHIUM METAL BATTERIES (including lithium alloy batteries)

3091 LITHIUM METAL BATTERIES CONTAINED IN EQUIPMENT (including lithium alloy batteries) or

3091 LITHIUM METAL BATTERIES PACKED WITH EQUIPMENT (including lithium alloy batteries)

3480 LITHIUM ION BATTERIES (including lithium ion polymer batteries)

3481 LITHIUM ION BATTERIES CONTAINED IN EQUIPMENT (including lithium ion polymer batteries) or

3481 LITHIUM ION BATTERIES PACKED WITH EQUIPMENT (including lithium ion polymer batteries)

Note: See 2.9.4.

Capacitors

3499   CAPACITOR, ELECTRIC DOUBLE LAYER (with an energy storage capacity greater than 0.3 Wh)

3508   CAPACITOR, ASYMMETRIC (with an energy storage capacity greater than 0.3 Wh)

Life-saving appliances

2990   LIFE-SAVING APPLIANCES, SELF-INFLATING

3072   LIFE-SAVING APPLIANCES, NOT SELF-INFLATING containing dangerous goods as equipment

3268   SAFETY DEVICES, electrically initiated

Substances and articles which, in the event of fire, may form dioxins

This group of substances includes:

2315   POLYCHLORINATED BIPHENYLS, LIQUID

3432   POLYCHLORINATED BIPHENYLS, SOLID

3151   POLYHALOGENATED BIPHENYLS, LIQUID or

■ 3151   HALOGENATED MONOMETHYLDIPHENYLMETHANES, LIQUID or

3151   POLYHALOGENATED TERPHENYLS, LIQUID

3152   POLYHALOGENATED BIPHENYLS, SOLID or

■ 3152   HALOGENATED MONOMETHYLDIPHENYLMETHANES, SOLID or

3152   POLYHALOGENATED TERPHENYLS, SOLID

Examples of articles are transformers, condensers and apparatus containing those substances.

Substances transported or offered for transport at elevated temperatures

3257   ELEVATED TEMPERATURE LIQUID, N.O.S., at or above 100°C and below its flashpoint (including molten metal, molten salts, etc.)

3258   ELEVATED TEMPERATURE SOLID, N.O.S., at or above 240°C

Environmentally hazardous substances

3077   ENVIRONMENTALLY HAZARDOUS SUBSTANCE, SOLID, N.O.S.

3082   ENVIRONMENTALLY HAZARDOUS SUBSTANCE, LIQUID, N.O.S.

These entries are used for substances and mixtures which are dangerous to the aquatic environment that do not meet the classification criteria of any other class or another substance within class 9. These entries may also be used for wastes not otherwise subject to the provisions of this Code but which are covered under the Basel Convention on the Control of Transboundary Movements of Hazardous Wastes and their Disposal and for substances designated to be environmentally hazardous substances by the competent authority of the country of origin, transit or destination which do not meet the criteria for an environmentally hazardous substance according to the provisions of this Code or for any other hazard class. The criteria for substances which are hazardous to the aquatic environment are given in section 2.9.3.

Genetically modified microorganisms (GMMOs) and genetically modified organisms (GMOs)

3245   GENETICALLY MODIFIED MICROORGANISMS or

3245   GENETICALLY MODIFIED ORGANISMS

GMMOs and GMOs which do not meet the definition of toxic substances (see 2.6.2) or infectious substances (see 2.6.3) shall be assigned to UN 3245.

GMMOs or GMOs are not subject to the provisions of this Code when authorized for use by the competent authorities of the countries of origin, transit and destination.

Genetically modified live animals shall be transported under terms and conditions of the competent authorities of the countries of origin and destination.

Other substances or articles presenting a danger during transport, but not meeting the definitions of another class:

1841 ACETALDEHYDE AMMONIA

1845 CARBON DIOXIDE, SOLID (DRY ICE)

1931 ZINC DITHIONITE (ZINC HYDROSULPHITE)

1941 DIBROMODIFLUOROMETHANE

1990 BENZALDEHYDE

2071 AMMONIUM NITRATE BASED FERTILIZER

2216 FISH MEAL (FISH SCRAP), STABILIZED

2807 MAGNETIZED MATERIAL[*]

2969 CASTOR BEANS or

2969 CASTOR MEAL or

2969 CASTOR POMACE or

2969 CASTOR FLAKE

⊗

3166 VEHICLE, FLAMMABLE GAS POWERED or

3166 VEHICLE, FLAMMABLE LIQUID POWERED or

⊗

3166 VEHICLE, FUEL CELL, FLAMMABLE GAS POWERED or

3166 VEHICLE, FUEL CELL, FLAMMABLE LIQUID POWERED

3171 BATTERY-POWERED VEHICLE or

3171 BATTERY-POWERED EQUIPMENT

3316 CHEMICAL KIT or

3316 FIRST AID KIT

3334 AVIATION REGULATED LIQUID, N.O.S.[*]

3335 AVIATION REGULATED SOLID, N.O.S.[*]

3359 FUMIGATED CARGO TRANSPORT UNIT

3363 DANGEROUS GOODS IN MACHINERY or

3363 DANGEROUS GOODS IN APPARATUS

3496 BATTERIES, NICKEL-METAL HYDRIDE

△ 3509 PACKAGINGS, DISCARDED, EMPTY, UNCLEANED[†]

■ 3530 ENGINE, INTERNAL COMBUSTION or

■ 3530 MACHINERY, INTERNAL COMBUSTION

2.9.3 Environmentally hazardous substances (aquatic environment)

2.9.3.1 General definitions

2.9.3.1.1 Environmentally hazardous substances include, inter alia, liquid or solid substances pollutant to the aquatic environment and solutions and mixtures of such substances (such as preparations and wastes).

For the purposes of this section,

---

[*] Not subject to the provisions of this Code but may be subject to provisions governing the transport of dangerous goods by other modes (see also special provision 960).

[†] This entry shall not be used for sea transport. Discarded packaging shall meet the requirements of 4.1.1.11.

Substance means chemical elements and their compounds in the natural state or obtained by any production process, including any additive necessary to preserve the stability of the product and any impurities deriving from the process used, but excluding any solvent which may be separated without affecting the stability of the substance or changing its composition.

2.9.3.1.2   The aquatic environment may be considered in terms of the aquatic organisms that live in the water, and the aquatic ecosystem of which they are part.[*] The basis, therefore, of the identification of hazard is the aquatic toxicity of the substance or mixture, although this may be modified by further information on the degradation and bioaccumulation behaviour.

2.9.3.1.3   While the following classification procedure is intended to apply to all substances and mixtures, it is recognized that in some cases, e.g. metals or poorly soluble inorganic compounds, special guidance will be necessary.[†]

2.9.3.1.4   The following definitions apply for acronyms or terms used in this section:

BCF	bioconcentration factor;
BOD	biochemical oxygen demand;
COD	chemical oxygen demand;
GLP	good laboratory practices;
EC_x	the concentration associated with x% response;
EC_{50}	the effective concentration of substance that causes 50% of the maximum response;
ErC_{50}	EC_{50} in terms of reduction of growth;
K_{ow}	octanol/water partition coefficient;
LC_{50} (50% lethal concentration)	the concentration of a substance in water which causes the death of 50% (one half) in a group of test animals;
$L(E)C_{50}$	LC_{50} or EC_{50};
NOEC (no observed effect concentration)	the test concentration immediately below the lowest tested concentration with statistically significant adverse effect. The NOEC has no statistically significant adverse effect compared to the control;
OECD Test Guidelines	Test guidelines published by the Organization for Economic Co-operation and Development (OECD).

2.9.3.2   Definitions and data requirements

2.9.3.2.1   The basic elements for classification of environmentally hazardous substances (aquatic environment) are:

    .1   acute aquatic toxicity;

    .2   chronic aquatic toxicity;

    .3   potential for or actual bioaccumulation; and

    .4   degradation (biotic or abiotic) for organic chemicals;

2.9.3.2.2   While data from internationally harmonized test methods are preferred, in practice, data from national methods may also be used where they are considered as equivalent. In general, it has been agreed that freshwater and marine species toxicity data can be considered as equivalent data and are preferably to be derived using OECD Test Guidelines or equivalent according to the principles of good laboratory practices (GLP). Where such data are not available, classification shall be based on the best available data.

2.9.3.2.3   *Acute aquatic toxicity* means the intrinsic property of a substance to be injurious to an organism in a short-term aquatic exposure to that substance.

Acute (short-term) hazard, for classification purposes, means the hazard of a chemical caused by its acute toxicity to an organism during short-term aquatic exposure to that chemical.

Acute aquatic toxicity shall normally be determined using a fish 96 h LC_{50} (OECD Test Guideline 203 or equivalent), a crustacea species 48 h EC_{50} (OECD Test Guideline 202 or equivalent) and/or an algal species 72 or 96 h EC_{50} (OECD Test Guideline 201 or equivalent). These species are considered as surrogate for all

---

[*] This does not address aquatic pollutants for which there may be a need to consider effects beyond the aquatic environment such as the impacts on human health, etc.

[†] This can be found in annex 10 of the GHS.

aquatic organisms and data on other species such as Lemna may also be considered if the test methodology is suitable.

2.9.3.2.4 Chronic aquatic toxicity means the intrinsic property of a substance to cause adverse effects to aquatic organisms during aquatic exposures which are determined in relation to the life cycle of the organism.

Long-term hazard, for classification purposes, means the hazard of a chemical caused by its chronic toxicity following long-term exposure in the aquatic environment.

Chronic toxicity data are less available than acute data and the range of testing procedures less standardized. Data generated according to the OECD Test Guidelines 210 (Fish Early Life Stage) or 211 (Daphnia Reproduction) and 201 (Algal Growth Inhibition) may be accepted. Other validated and internationally accepted tests may also be used. The NOECs or other equivalent EC_x shall be used.

△ 2.9.3.2.5 *Bioaccumulation* means net result of uptake, transformation and elimination of a substance in an organism due to all routes of exposure (i.e. air, water, sediment/soil and food).

The potential for bioaccumulation shall normally be determined by using the octanol/water partition coefficient, usually reported as a log K_{ow} determined according to OECD Test Guidelines 107, 117 or 123. While this represents a potential to bioaccumulate, an experimentally determined bioconcentration factor (BCF) provides a better measure and shall be used in preference when available. A BCF shall be determined according to OECD Test Guideline 305.

2.9.3.2.6 *Degradation* means the decomposition of organic molecules to smaller molecules and eventually to carbon dioxide, water and salts.

Environmental degradation may be biotic or abiotic (e.g. hydrolysis) and the criteria used reflect this fact. Ready biodegradation is most easily defined using the biodegradability tests (A to F) of OECD Test Guidelines 301. A pass level in these tests may be considered as indicative of rapid degradation in most environments. These are freshwater tests and thus the use of the results from OECD Test Guideline 306, which is more suitable for marine environments, has also been included. Where such data are not available, a BOD(5 days)/COD ratio $\geq$ 0.5 is considered as indicative of rapid degradation. Abiotic degradation such as hydrolysis, primary degradation, both abiotic and biotic, degradation in non-aquatic media and proven rapid degradation in the environment may all be considered in defining rapid degradability.[*]

Substances are considered rapidly degradable in the environment if the following criteria are met:

.1 In 28-day ready biodegradation studies, the following levels of degradation are achieved:

    .1 tests based on dissolved organic carbon: 70%;

    .2 tests based on oxygen depletion or carbon dioxide generation: 60% of theoretical maxima.

These levels of biodegradation shall be achieved within 10 days of the start of degradation which point is taken as the time when 10% of the substance has been degraded, unless the substance is identified as a complex, multi-component substance with structurally similar constituents. In this case, and where there is sufficient justification, the 10-day window condition may be waived and the pass level applied at 28 days;[†]

.2 in those cases where only BOD and COD data are available, when the ratio of BOD_5/COD is $\geq$ 0.5; or

.3 if other convincing scientific evidence is available to demonstrate that the substance or mixture can be degraded (biotically and/or abiotically) in the aquatic environment to a level above 70% within a 28-day period.

2.9.3.3 Substance classification categories and criteria

2.9.3.3.1 Substances shall be classified as "environmentally hazardous substances (aquatic environment)", if they satisfy the criteria for Acute 1, Chronic 1 or Chronic 2, according to table 2.9.1. These criteria describe in detail the classification categories. They are diagrammatically summarized in table 2.9.2.

Table 2.9.1 – Categories for substances hazardous to the aquatic environment (see note 1)

(a) Acute (short-term) aquatic hazard

Category: Acute 1 (see note 2)	
96 hr LC_{50} (for fish)	$\leq$ 1 mg/L and/or
48 hr EC_{50} (for crustacea)	$\leq$ 1 mg/L and/or
72 or 96 hr ErC_{50} (for algae or other aquatic plants)	$\leq$ 1 mg/L (see note 3)

---

[*] Special guidance on data interpretation is provided in chapter 4.1 and annex 9 of the GHS.

[†] See chapter 4.1 and annex 9, paragraph A9.4.2.2.3 of the GHS.

(b) Long-term aquatic hazard (see also figure 2.9.1)

(i) Non-rapidly degradable substances (see note 4) for which there are adequate chronic toxicity data available

Category: Chronic 1 (see note 2)	
Chronic NOEC or EC_x (for fish)	≤ 0.1 mg/L and/or
Chronic NOEC or EC_x (for crustacea)	≤ 0.1 mg/L and/or
Chronic NOEC or EC_x (for algae or other aquatic plants)	≤ 0.1 mg/L
Category: Chronic 2	
Chronic NOEC or EC_x (for fish)	≤ 1 mg/L and/or
Chronic NOEC or EC_x (for crustacea)	≤ 1 mg/L and/or
Chronic NOEC or EC_x (for algae or other aquatic plants)	≤ 1 mg/L

(ii) Rapidly degradable substances for which there are adequate chronic toxicity data available

Category: Chronic 1 (see note 2)	
Chronic NOEC or EC_x (for fish)	≤ 0.01 mg/L and/or
Chronic NOEC or EC_x (for crustacea)	≤ 0.01 mg/L and/or
Chronic NOEC or EC_x (for algae or other aquatic plants)	≤ 0.01 mg/L
Category: Chronic 2	
Chronic NOEC or EC_x (for fish)	≤ 0.1 mg/L and/or
Chronic NOEC or EC_x (for crustacea)	≤ 0.1 mg/L and/or
Chronic NOEC or EC_x (for algae or other aquatic plants)	≤ 0.1 mg/L

(iii) Substances for which adequate chronic toxicity data are not available

Category: Chronic 1 (see note 2)	
96 hr LC_{50} (for fish)	≤ 1 mg/L and/or
48 hr EC_{50} (for crustacea)	≤ 1 mg/L and/or
72 or 96 hr ErC_{50} (for algae or other aquatic plants)	≤ 1 mg/L (see note 3)
and the substance is not rapidly degradable and/or the experimentally determined BCF is ≥ 500 (or, if absent, the log $K_{ow} \geq 4$) (see notes 4 and 5)	
Category: Chronic 2	
96 hr LC_{50} (for fish)	> 1 but ≤ 10 mg/L and/or
48 hr EC_{50} (for crustacea)	> 1 but ≤ 10 mg/L and/or
72 or 96 hr ErC_{50} (for algae or other aquatic plants)	> 1 but ≤ 10 mg/L and/or (see note 3)
and the substance is not rapidly degradable and/or the experimentally determined BCF is ≥ 500 (or, if absent, the log $K_{ow} \geq 4$) (see notes 4 and 5)	

Note 1: The organisms fish, crustacea and algae are tested as surrogate species covering a range of trophic levels and taxa, and the test methods are highly standardized. Data on other organisms may also be considered, however, provided they represent equivalent species and test endpoints.

Note 2: When classifying substances as Acute 1 and/or Chronic 1 it is necessary at the same time to indicate an appropriate M factor (see 2.9.3.4.6.4) to apply the summation method.

Note 3: Where the algal toxicity ErC50 (= EC_{50} (growth rate)) falls more than 100 times below the next most sensitive species and results in a classification based solely on this effect, consideration shall be given to whether this toxicity is representative of the toxicity to aquatic plants. Where it can be shown that this is not the case, professional judgment shall be used in deciding if classification shall be applied. Classification shall be based on the ErC_{50}. In circumstances where the basis of the EC_{50} is not specified and no ErC_{50} is recorded, classification shall be based on the lowest EC_{50} available.

Note 4: Lack of rapid degradability is based on either a lack of ready biodegradability or other evidence of lack of rapid degradation. When no useful data on degradability are available, either experimentally determined or estimated data, the substance shall be regarded as not rapidly degradable.

Note 5: Potential to bioaccumulate, based on an experimentally derived BCF ≥ 500 or, if absent, a log $K_{ow} \geq 4$ provided log K_{ow} is an appropriate descriptor for the bioaccumulation potential of the substance. Measured log K_{ow} values take precedence over estimated values and measured BCF values take precedence over log K_{ow} values.

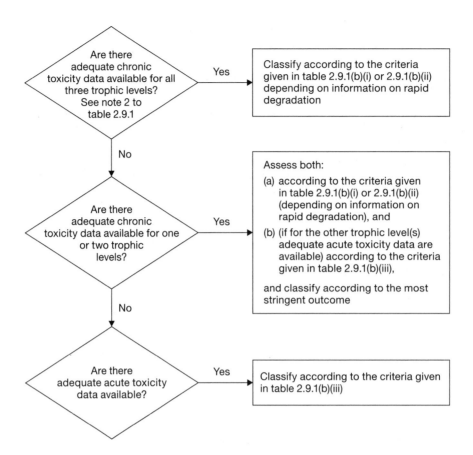

Figure 2.9.1 – *Categories for substances long-term hazardous to the aquatic environment*

2.9.3.3.2   The classification scheme in table 2.9.2 below summarizes the classification criteria for substances.

Table 2.9.2 – Classification scheme for substances hazardous to the aquatic environment

Classification categories			
Acute hazard (see note 1)	Long-term hazard (see note 2)		
	Adequate chronic toxicity data available		Adequate chronic toxicity data not available (see note 1)
	Non-rapidly degradable substances (see note 3)	Rapidly degradable substances (see note 3)	
Category: Acute 1	**Category: Chronic 1**	**Category: Chronic 1**	**Category: Chronic 1**
$L(E)C_{50} \leq 1.00$	NOEC or $EC_x \leq 0.1$	NOEC or $EC_x \leq 0.01$	$L(E)C_{50} \leq 1.00$ and lack of rapid degradability and/or BCF $\geq$ 500 or, if absent, log $K_{ow} \geq 4$
	Category: Chronic 2	**Category: Chronic 2**	**Category: Chronic 2**
	$0.1 <$ NOEC or $EC_x \leq 1$	$0.01 <$ NOEC or $EC_x \leq 0.1$	$1.00 < L(E)C_{50} \leq 10.0$ and lack of rapid degradability and/or BCF $\geq$ 500 or, if absent, log $K_{ow} \geq 4$

Note 1: Acute toxicity band based on $L(E)C_{50}$ values in mg/L for fish, crustacea and/or algae or other aquatic plants (or Quantitative Structure Activity Relationships (QSAR) estimation if no experimental data).[*]

Note 2: Substances are classified in the various chronic categories unless there are adequate chronic toxicity data available for all three trophic levels above the water solubility or above 1 mg/L. ("Adequate" means that the data sufficiently cover the endpoint of concern. Generally this would mean measured test data, but in order to avoid unnecessary testing it can on a case by case basis also be estimated data, e.g. (Q)SAR, or for obvious cases expert judgment).

[*] Special guidance is provided in chapter 4.1, paragraph 4.1.2.13 and annex 9, section A9.6 of the GHS.

Note 3: Chronic toxicity band based on NOEC or equivalent EC_x values in mg/L for fish or crustacea or other recognized measures for chronic toxicity.

2.9.3.4 **Mixtures classification categories and criteria**

2.9.3.4.1 The classification system for mixtures covers the classification categories which are used for substances, meaning categories Acute 1 and Chronic 1 and 2. In order to make use of all available data for purposes of classifying the aquatic environmental hazards of the mixture, the following assumption is made and is applied where appropriate:

The "relevant ingredients" of a mixture are those which are present in a concentration equal to or greater than 0.1% (by mass) for ingredients classified as Acute and/or Chronic 1 and equal to or greater than 1% for other ingredients, unless there is a presumption (e.g. in the case of highly toxic ingredients) that an ingredient present at less than 0.1% can still be relevant for classifying the mixture for aquatic environmental hazards.

2.9.3.4.2 The approach for classification of aquatic environmental hazards is tiered, and is dependent upon the type of information available for the mixture itself and for its ingredients. Elements of the tiered approach include:

.1 classification based on tested mixtures;

.2 classification based on bridging principles;

.3 the use of "summation of classified ingredients" and/or an "additivity formula".

Figure 2.9.2 outlines the process to be followed.

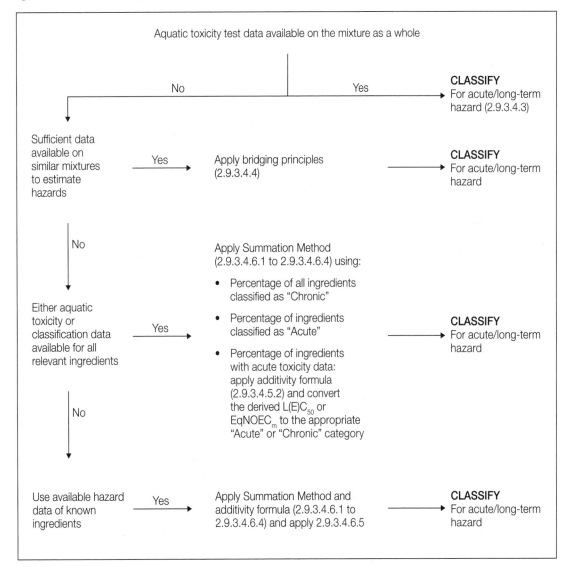

Figure 2.9.2 – *Tiered approach to classification of mixtures for acute and long-term aquatic environmental hazards*

2.9.3.4.3 *Classification of mixtures when toxicity data are available for the complete mixture*

2.9.3.4.3.1 When the mixture as a whole has been tested to determine its aquatic toxicity, this information shall be used for classifying the mixture according to the criteria that have been agreed for substances. The classification is normally based on the data for fish, crustacea and algae/plants (see 2.9.3.2.3 and 2.9.3.2.4). When adequate acute or chronic data for the mixture as a whole are lacking, "bridging principles" or "summation method" shall be applied (see 2.9.3.4.4 to 2.9.3.4.6).

2.9.3.4.3.2 The long-term hazard classification of mixtures requires additional information on degradability and in certain cases bioaccumulation. There are no degradability and bioaccumulation data for mixtures as a whole. Degradability and bioaccumulation tests for mixtures are not used as they are usually difficult to interpret, and such tests may be meaningful only for single substances.

2.9.3.4.3.3 *Classification for category Acute 1*

(a) When there are adequate acute toxicity test data (LC_{50} or EC_{50}) available for the mixture as a whole showing $L(E)C_{50} \leq 1$ mg/L:

Classify the mixture as Acute 1 in accordance with table 2.9.1 (a);

(b) When there are acute toxicity test data ($LC_{50}(s)$ or $EC_{50}(s)$ available for the mixture as a whole showing $L(E)C_{50}(s) > 1$ mg/L, or above the water solubility:

No need to classify for acute hazard under these Regulations.

2.9.3.4.3.4 *Classification for categories Chronic 1 and 2*

(a) When there are adequate chronic toxicity data (EC_x or NOEC) available for the mixture as a whole showing EC_x or NOEC of the tested mixture ≤ 1 mg/L:

(i) classify the mixture as Chronic 1 or 2 in accordance with table 2.9.1 (b)(ii) (rapidly degradable) if the available information allows the conclusion that all relevant ingredients of the mixture are rapidly degradable;

(ii) classify the mixture as Chronic 1 or 2 in all other cases in accordance with table 2.9.1 (b)(i) (non-rapidly degradable);

(b) When there are adequate chronic toxicity data (EC_x or NOEC) available for the mixture as a whole showing $EC_x(s)$ or NOEC(s) of the tested mixture > 1 mg/L or above the water solubility:

No need to classify for long-term hazard under these Regulations.

2.9.3.4.4 *Classification of mixtures when toxicity data are not available for the complete mixture: bridging principles*

2.9.3.4.4.1 Where the mixture itself has not been tested to determine its aquatic environmental hazard, but there are sufficient data on the individual ingredients and similar tested mixtures to adequately characterize the hazards of the mixture, these data shall be used in accordance with the following agreed bridging rules. This ensures that the classification process uses the available data to the greatest extent possible in characterizing the hazards of the mixture without the necessity for additional testing in animals.

2.9.3.4.4.2 *Dilution*

2.9.3.4.4.2.1 Where a new mixture is formed by diluting a tested mixture or a substance with a diluent which has an equivalent or lower aquatic hazard classification than the least toxic original ingredient and which is not expected to affect the aquatic hazards of other ingredients, then the resulting mixture shall be classified as equivalent to the original tested mixture or substance. Alternatively, the method explained in 2.9.3.4.5 may be applied.

2.9.3.4.4.2.2 If a mixture is formed by diluting another classified mixture or a substance with water or other totally non-toxic material, the toxicity of the mixture shall be calculated from the original mixture or substance.

2.9.3.4.4.3 *Batching*

2.9.3.4.4.3.1 The aquatic hazard classification of a tested production batch of a mixture shall be assumed to be substantially equivalent to that of another untested production batch of the same commercial product when produced by or under the control of the same manufacturer, unless there is reason to believe there is significant variation such that the aquatic hazard classification of the untested batch has changed. If the latter occurs, new classification is necessary.

2.9.3.4.4.4 *Concentration of mixtures which are classified with the most severe classification categories (Chronic 1 and Acute 1)*

2.9.3.4.4.4.1 If a tested mixture is classified as Chronic 1 and/or Acute 1, and the ingredients of the mixture which are classified as Chronic 1 and/or Acute 1 are further concentrated, the more concentrated untested mixture shall be classified with the same classification category as the original tested mixture without additional testing.

2.9.3.4.4.5   *Interpolation within one toxicity category*

2.9.3.4.4.5.1 For three mixtures (A, B and C) with identical ingredients, where mixtures A and B have been tested and are in the same toxicity category, and where untested mixture C has the same toxicologically active ingredients as mixtures A and B but has concentrations of toxicologically active ingredients intermediate to the concentrations in mixtures A and B, then mixture C is assumed to be in the same category as A and B.

2.9.3.4.4.6   *Substantially similar mixtures*

2.9.3.4.4.6.1 Given the following:

(a)   Two mixtures:

   (i)   A + B

   (ii)   C + B

(b)   The concentration of ingredient B is essentially the same in both mixtures;

(c)   The concentration of ingredient A in mixture (i) equals that of ingredient C in mixture (ii);

(d)   Data on aquatic hazards for A and C are available and are substantially equivalent, i.e. they are in the same hazard category and are not expected to affect the aquatic toxicity of B.

If mixture (i) or (ii) is already classified based on test data, then the other mixture can be assigned the same hazard category.

2.9.3.4.5   *Classification of mixtures when toxicity data are available for all ingredients or only for some ingredients of the mixture*

2.9.3.4.5.1 The classification of a mixture shall be based on summation of the concentrations of its classified ingredients. The percentage of ingredients classified as Acute or Chronic will feed straight into the summation method. Details of the summation method are described in 2.9.3.4.6.1 to 2.9.3.4.6.4.1.

2.9.3.4.5.2 Mixtures may be made of a combination of both ingredients that are classified (as Acute 1 and/or Chronic 1, 2) and those for which adequate toxicity test data are available. When adequate toxicity data are available for more than one ingredient in the mixture, the combined toxicity of those ingredients shall be calculated using the following additivity formulas (a) or (b), depending on the nature of the toxicity data:

(a)   Based on acute aquatic toxicity:

$$\frac{\sum C_i}{L(E)C_{50m}} = \sum_n \frac{C_i}{L(E)C_{50i}}$$

where: C_i = concentration of ingredient i (mass percentage);

$L(E)C_{50i}$ = LC_{50} or EC_{50} for ingredient i (mg/L);

n = number of ingredients, and i is running from 1 to n; and

$L(E)C_{50m}$ = $L(E)C_{50}$ of the part of the mixture with test data

The calculated toxicity shall be used to assign that portion of the mixture an acute hazard category which is then subsequently used in applying the summation method;

(b)   Based on chronic aquatic toxicity:

$$\frac{\sum C_i + \sum C_j}{EqNOEC_m} = \sum_n \frac{C_i}{NOEC_i} + \sum_n \frac{C_j}{0.1 \times NOEC_j}$$

where: C_i = concentration of ingredient i (mass percentage) covering the rapidly degradable ingredients;

C_j = concentration of ingredient j (mass percentage) covering the non-rapidly degradable ingredients;

$NOEC_i$ = NOEC (or other recognized measures for chronic toxicity) for ingredient i covering the rapidly degradable ingredients, in mg/L;

$NOEC_j$ = NOEC (or other recognized measures for chronic toxicity) for ingredient j covering the non-rapidly degradable ingredients, in mg/L;

n = number of ingredients, and i and j are running from 1 to n;

$EqNOEC_m$ = equivalent NOEC of the part of the mixture with test data;

The equivalent toxicity thus reflects the fact that non-rapidly degrading substances are classified one hazard category level more "severe" than rapidly degrading substances.

The calculated equivalent toxicity shall be used to assign that portion of the mixture a long-term hazard category, in accordance with the criteria for rapidly degradable substances (table 2.9.1 (b)(ii)), which is then subsequently used in applying the summation method.

2.9.3.4.5.3   When applying the additivity formula for part of the mixture, it is preferable to calculate the toxicity of this part of the mixture using for each ingredient toxicity values that relate to the same taxonomic group (i.e. fish, crustacea or algae) and then to use the highest toxicity (lowest value) obtained (i.e. use the most sensitive of the three groups). However, when toxicity data for each ingredient are not available in the same taxonomic group, the toxicity value of each ingredient shall be selected in the same manner that toxicity values are selected for the classification of substances, i.e. the higher toxicity (from the most sensitive test organism) is used. The calculated acute and chronic toxicity shall then be used to classify this part of the mixture as Acute 1 and/or Chronic 1 or 2 using the same criteria described for substances.

2.9.3.4.5.4   If a mixture is classified in more than one way, the method yielding the more conservative result shall be used.

2.9.3.4.6   *Summation method*

2.9.3.4.6.1   *Classification procedure*

2.9.3.4.6.1.1   In general a more severe classification for mixtures overrides a less severe classification, e.g. a classification with Chronic 1 overrides a classification with Chronic 2. As a consequence the classification procedure is already completed if the results of the classification is Chronic 1. A more severe classification than Chronic 1 is not possible; therefore, it is not necessary to pursue the classification procedure further.

2.9.3.4.6.2   *Classification for category Acute 1*

2.9.3.4.6.2.1   First, all ingredients classified as Acute 1 are considered. If the sum of the concentrations (in %) of these ingredients is greater than or equal to 25% the whole mixture shall be classified as Acute 1. If the result of the calculation is a classification of the mixture as Acute 1, the classification process is completed.

2.9.3.4.6.2.2   The classification of mixtures for acute hazards based on this summation of the concentrations of classified ingredients is summarized in table 2.9.3 below.

Table 2.9.3 – Classification of a mixture for acute hazards based on summation of the concentrations of classified ingredients

Sum of the concentrations (in %) of ingredients classified as:	Mixture is classified as:
Acute 1 $\times$ M^* $\geq$ 25%	Acute 1

* For explanation of the M factor, see 2.9.3.4.6.4.

2.9.3.4.6.3   *Classification for categories Chronic 1 and 2*

2.9.3.4.6.3.1   First, all ingredients classified as Chronic 1 are considered. If the sum of the concentrations (in %) of these ingredients is greater than or equal to 25% the mixture shall be classified as Chronic 1. If the result of the calculation is a classification of the mixture as Chronic 1 the classification procedure is completed

2.9.3.4.6.3.2   In cases where the mixture is not classified as Chronic 1, classification of the mixture as Chronic 2 is considered. A mixture shall be classified as Chronic 2 if 10 times the sum of the concentrations (in %) of all ingredients classified as Chronic 1 plus the sum of the concentrations (in %) of all ingredients classified as Chronic 2 is greater than or equal to 25%. If the result of the calculation is classification of the mixture as Chronic 2, the classification process is completed.

2.9.3.4.6.3.3   The classification of mixtures for long-term hazards based on this summation of the concentrations of classified ingredients is summarized in table 2.9.4 below.

Table 2.9.4 – Classification of a mixture for long-term hazards based on summation of the concentrations of classified ingredients

Sum of the concentrations (in %) of ingredients classified as:	Mixture classified as:
Chronic 1 $\times$ M^* $\geq$ 25%	Chronic 1
(M $\times$ 10 $\times$ Chronic 1) + Chronic 2 $\geq$ 25%	Chronic 2

* For explanation of the M factor, see 2.9.3.4.6.4.

2.9.3.4.6.4 *Mixtures with highly toxic ingredients*

2.9.3.4.6.4.1 Acute 1 or Chronic 1 ingredients with acute toxicities well below 1 mg/L and/or chronic toxicities well below 0.1 mg/L (if non-rapidly degradable) and 0.01 mg/L (if rapidly degradable) may influence the toxicity of the mixture and are given increased weight in applying the summation method. When a mixture contains ingredients classified as Acute 1 or Chronic 1, the tiered approach described in 2.9.3.4.6.2 and 2.9.3.4.6.3 shall be applied using a weighted sum by multiplying the concentrations of Acute 1 and Chronic 1 ingredients by a factor, instead of merely adding up the percentages. This means that the concentration of Acute 1 in the left column of table 2.9.3 and the concentration of Chronic 1 in the left column of table 2.9.4 are multiplied by the appropriate multiplying factor. The multiplying factors to be applied to these ingredients are defined using the toxicity value, as summarized in table 2.9.5 below. Therefore, in order to classify a mixture containing Acute 1 and/or Chronic 1 ingredients, the classifier needs to be informed of the value of the *M* factor in order to apply the summation method. Alternatively, the additivity formula (2.9.3.4.5.2) may be used when toxicity data are available for all highly toxic ingredients in the mixture and there is convincing evidence that all other ingredients, including those for which specific acute and/or chronic toxicity data are not available, are of low or no toxicity and do not significantly contribute to the environmental hazard of the mixture.

Table 2.9.5 – Multiplying factors for highly toxic ingredients of mixtures

Acute toxicity	M factor	Chronic toxicity	M factor	
$L(E)C_{50}$ value		NOEC value	NRD[*] ingredients	RD[†] ingredients
$0.1 < L(E)C_{50} \leq 1$	1	$0.01 < NOEC \leq 0.1$	1	–
$0.01 < L(E)C_{50} \leq 0.1$	10	$0.001 < NOEC \leq 0.01$	10	1
$0.001 < L(E)C_{50} \leq 0.01$	100	$0.0001 < NOEC \leq 0.001$	100	10
$0.0001 < L(E)C_{50} \leq 0.001$	1,000	$0.00001 < NOEC \leq 0.0001$	1,000	100
$0.00001 < L(E)C_{50} \leq 0.0001$	10,000	$0.000001 < NOEC \leq 0.00001$	10,000	1,000
(continue in factor 10 intervals)		(continue in factor 10 intervals)		

[*] Non-rapidly degradable.

[†] Rapidly degradable.

2.9.3.4.6.5 *Classification of mixtures with ingredients without any useable information*

2.9.3.4.6.5.1 In the event that no useable information on acute and/or chronic aquatic toxicity is available for one or more relevant ingredients, it is concluded that the mixture cannot be attributed (a) definitive hazard category(ies). In this situation the mixture shall be classified based on the known ingredients only with the additional statement that: "*x* percent of the mixture consists of ingredient(s) of unknown hazards to the aquatic environment."

2.9.4 Lithium batteries

Cells and batteries, cells and batteries contained in equipment, or cells and batteries packed with equipment, containing lithium in any form shall be assigned to UN Nos. 3090, 3091, 3480 or 3481 as appropriate. They may be transported under these entries if they meet the following provisions:

.1 Each cell or battery is of the type proved to meet the requirements of each test of the Manual of Tests and Criteria, part III, subsection 38.3. Cells and batteries manufactured according to a type meeting the requirements of subsection 38.3 of the Manual of Tests and Criteria, revision 3, amendment 1 or any subsequent revision and amendment applicable at the date of the type testing may continue to be transported, unless otherwise provided in this Code.

Cell and battery types only meeting the requirements of the Manual of Tests and Criteria, revision 3, are no longer valid. However, cells and batteries manufactured in conformity with such types before 1 July 2003 may continue to be transported if all other applicable requirements are fulfilled.

Note: Batteries shall be of a type proved to meet the testing requirements of the Manual of Tests and Criteria, part III, subsection 38.3, irrespective of whether the cells of which they are composed are of a tested type.

.2 Each cell and battery incorporates a safety venting device or is designed to preclude a violent rupture under conditions normally incident to transport.

.3 Each cell and battery is equipped with an effective means of preventing external short circuits.

.4 Each battery containing cells or series of cells connected in parallel is equipped with effective means as necessary to prevent dangerous reverse current flow (e.g. diodes, fuses, etc.).

.5 Cells and batteries shall be manufactured under a quality management programme that includes:

.1 a description of the organizational structure and responsibilities of personnel with regard to design and product quality;

.2 the relevant inspection and test, quality control, quality assurance, and process operation instructions that will be used;

.3 process controls that should include relevant activities to prevent and detect internal short circuit failure during manufacture of cells;

.4 quality records, such as inspection reports, test data, calibration data and certificates. Test data shall be kept and made available to the competent authority upon request;

.5 management reviews to ensure the effective operation of the quality management programme;

.6 a process for control of documents and their revision;

.7 a means for control of cells or batteries that are not conforming to the type tested as mentioned in 2.9.4.1 above;

.8 training programmes and qualification procedures for relevant personnel; and

.9 procedures to ensure that there is no damage to the final product.

Note: In-house quality management programmes may be accepted. Third party certification is not required, but the procedures listed in .1 to .9 above shall be properly recorded and traceable. A copy of the quality management programme shall be made available to the competent authority upon request.

Chapter 2.10

Marine pollutants

2.10.1   **Definition**

Marine pollutants means substances which are subject to the provisions of Annex III of MARPOL, as amended.

2.10.2   **General provisions**

2.10.2.1   Marine pollutants shall be transported under the provisions of Annex III of MARPOL, as amended.

2.10.2.2   The Index indicates by the symbol P in the column headed **MP** those substances, materials and articles that are identified as marine pollutants.

2.10.2.3   Marine pollutants shall be transported under the appropriate entry according to their properties if they fall within the criteria of any of the classes 1 to 8. If they do not fall within the criteria of any of these classes, they shall be transported under the entry: ENVIRONMENTALLY HAZARDOUS SUBSTANCE, SOLID, N.O.S., UN 3077 or ENVIRONMENTALLY HAZARDOUS SUBSTANCE, LIQUID, N.O.S., UN 3082, as appropriate, unless there is a specific entry in class 9.

2.10.2.4   Column 4 of the Dangerous Goods List also provides information on marine pollutants using the symbol P for single entries. The absence of the symbol P or the presence of a "–" in that column does not preclude the application of 2.10.3.

2.10.2.5   When a substance, material or article possesses properties that meet the criteria of a marine pollutant but is not identified in this Code, such substance, material or article shall be transported as a marine pollutant in accordance with the Code.

2.10.2.6   With the approval of the competent authority (see 7.9.2), substances, materials or articles that are identified as marine pollutants in this Code but which no longer meet the criteria as a marine pollutant need not be transported in accordance with the provisions of this Code applicable to marine pollutants.

2.10.2.7   Marine pollutants packaged in single or combination packagings containing a net quantity per single or inner packaging of 5 L or less for liquids or having a net mass per single or inner packaging of 5 kg or less for solids are not subject to any other provisions of this Code relevant to marine pollutants provided the packagings meet the general provisions of 4.1.1.1, 4.1.1.2 and 4.1.1.4 to 4.1.1.8. In the case of marine pollutants also meeting the criteria for inclusion in another hazard class, all provisions of this Code relevant to any additional hazards continue to apply.

2.10.3   **Classification**

2.10.3.1   Marine pollutants shall be classified in accordance with chapter 2.9.3.

2.10.3.2   The classification criteria of 2.9.3 are not applicable to substances or materials of class 7.

2

Part 3 is in volume 2

PART 4

PACKING AND TANK PROVISIONS

4

Chapter 4.1

Use of packagings, including intermediate bulk containers (IBCs) and large packagings

4.1.0 Definitions

Effectively closed: liquid-tight closure.

Hermetically sealed: vapour-tight closure.

Securely closed: so closed that dry contents cannot escape during normal handling; the minimum provisions for any closure.

4.1.1 General provisions for the packing of dangerous goods in packagings, including IBCs and large packagings

Note: For the packing of goods of classes 2, 6.2 and 7, the general provisions of this section only apply as indicated in 4.1.8.2 (class 6.2), 4.1.9.1.5 (class 7) and in the applicable packing instructions of 4.1.4 (P201 and LP02 for class 2 and P620, P621, P650, IBC620 and LP621 for class 6.2).

4.1.1.1   Dangerous goods shall be packed in good quality packagings, including IBCs and large packagings, which shall be strong enough to withstand the shocks and loadings normally encountered during transport, including trans-shipment between cargo transport units and between cargo transport units and warehouses as well as any removal from a pallet or overpack for subsequent manual or mechanical handling. Packagings, including IBCs and large packagings, shall be constructed and closed so as to prevent any loss of contents when prepared for transport which may be caused under normal conditions of transport, by vibration, or by changes in temperature, humidity or pressure (resulting from altitude, for example). Packagings, including IBCs and large packagings, shall be closed in accordance with the information provided by the manufacturer. No dangerous residue shall adhere to the outside of packages, IBCs and large packagings during transport. These provisions apply, as appropriate, to new, reused, reconditioned or remanufactured packagings, and to new, reused, repaired or remanufactured IBCs, and to new, reused or remanufactured large packagings.

4.1.1.2   Parts of packagings, including IBCs and large packagings, which are in direct contact with dangerous goods:

.1   shall not be affected or significantly weakened by those dangerous goods; and

.2   shall not cause a dangerous effect, such as catalysing a reaction or reacting with the dangerous goods; and

.3   shall not allow permeation of the dangerous goods that could constitute a danger under normal conditions of transport.

Where necessary, they shall be provided with a suitable inner coating or treatment.

4.1.1.3   Unless otherwise provided elsewhere in this Code, each packaging, including IBCs and large packagings, except inner packagings, shall conform to a design type successfully tested in accordance with the provisions of 6.1.5, 6.3.5, 6.5.6 or 6.6.5, as applicable. However, IBCs manufactured before 1 January 2011 and conforming to a design type which has not passed the vibration test of 6.5.6.13 or which was not required to meet the criteria of 6.5.6.9.5.4 at the time it was subjected to the drop test may still be used.

4.1.1.4   When filling packagings, including IBCs and large packagings, with liquids,[*] sufficient ullage (outage) shall be left to ensure that neither leakage nor permanent distortion of the packaging occurs as a result of an expansion of the liquid caused by temperatures likely to occur during transport. Unless specific provisions are prescribed, liquids shall not completely fill a packaging at a temperature of 55°C. However, sufficient

---

[*] With respect to ullage limits only, the provisions applicable for packagings for solid substances may be used if the viscous substance has an outflow time via a DIN-cup with a 4 mm diameter outlet exceeding 10 minutes at 20°C (corresponding to an outflow time via a Ford cup 4 of more than 690 seconds at 20°C, or to a viscosity of more than 2680 centistokes at 20°C).

---

ullage shall be left in an IBC to ensure that at the mean bulk temperature of 50°C it is not filled to more than 98% of its water capacity.[*]

4.1.1.4.1 For air transport, packagings intended to contain liquids shall also be capable of withstanding a pressure differential without leakage as specified in the international regulations for air transport.

△ **4.1.1.5** Inner packagings shall be packed in an outer packaging in such a way that, under normal conditions of transport, they cannot break, be punctured or leak their contents into the outer packaging. Inner packagings containing liquids shall be packaged with their closures upward and placed within outer packagings consistent with the orientation marks prescribed in 5.2.1.7.1 of this Code. Inner packagings that are liable to break or be punctured easily, such as those made of glass, porcelain or stoneware or of certain plastics materials, etc., shall be secured in outer packagings with suitable cushioning material. Any leakage of the contents shall not substantially impair the protective properties of the cushioning material or of the outer packaging.

4.1.1.5.1 Where an outer packaging of a combination packaging or a large packaging has been successfully tested with different types of inner packagings, a variety of such different inner packagings may also be assembled in this outer packaging or large packagings. In addition, provided an equivalent level of performance is maintained, the following variations in inner packagings are allowed without further testing of the package:

.1 Inner packagings of equivalent or smaller size may be used provided:

– the inner packagings are of similar design to the tested inner packagings (such as shape – round, rectangular, etc.);

– the material of construction of inner packagings (glass, plastics, metal, etc.) offers resistance to impact and stacking forces equal to or greater than that of the originally tested inner packaging;

– the inner packagings have the same or smaller openings and the closure is of similar design (such as screw cap, friction lid, etc.);

– sufficient additional cushioning material is used to take up void spaces and to prevent significant movement of the inner packagings;

– inner packagings are oriented within the outer packaging in the same manner as in the tested package; and

.2 A lesser number of the tested inner packagings or of the alternative types of inner packagings identified in .1 above may be used, provided sufficient cushioning is added to fill the void space(s) and to prevent significant movement of the inner packagings.

4.1.1.5.2 Use of supplementary packagings within an outer packaging (e.g. an intermediate packaging or a receptacle inside a required inner packaging) additional to what is required by the packing instructions is authorized provided all relevant requirements are met, including those of 4.1.1.3, and, if appropriate, suitable cushioning is used to prevent movement within the packaging.

4.1.1.5.3 Cushioning and absorbent material shall be inert and suited to the nature of the contents.

4.1.1.5.4 The nature and the thickness of the outer packagings shall be such that friction during transport does not generate any heating likely to alter dangerously the chemical stability of the contents.

4.1.1.6 Dangerous goods shall not be packed together in the same outer packaging, or in large packagings, with dangerous or other goods if they react dangerously with each other and cause:

.1 combustion and/or evolution of considerable heat;

.2 evolution of flammable, toxic or asphyxiant gases;

.3 the formation of corrosive substances; or

.4 the formation of unstable substances.

4.1.1.7 The closures of packagings containing wetted or diluted substances shall be such that the percentage of liquid (water, solvent or phlegmatizer) does not fall below the prescribed limits during transport.

4.1.1.7.1 Where two or more closure systems are fitted in series on an IBC, that nearest to the substance being transported shall be closed first.

---

[*] For a differing temperature, the maximum degree of filling may be determined as follows:

$$\text{Degree of filling} = \frac{98}{1 + \alpha\,(50 - t_F)} \text{ per cent of the capacity of the IBC}$$

In this formula α represents the mean coefficient of cubic expansion of the liquid substance between 15°C and 50°C; that is to say, for a maximum rise in the temperature of 35°C, "α" is calculated according to the formula:

$$\alpha = \frac{d_{15} - d_{50}}{35 \times d_{50}}$$

where d_{15} and d_{50} are the relative densities of the liquid at 15°C and 50°C and t_F is the mean temperature of the liquid at the time of filling.

4.1.1.7.2 Unless otherwise specified in the Dangerous Goods List, packages containing substances which:

.1 evolve flammable gases or vapour;

.2 may become explosive if allowed to dry;

.3 evolve toxic gases or vapour;

.4 evolve corrosive gases or vapour; or

.5 may react dangerously with the atmosphere

should be hermetically sealed.

4.1.1.8 Where pressure may develop in a package by the emission of gas from the contents (as a result of temperature increase or other causes), the packaging or IBC may be fitted with a vent provided that the gas emitted will not cause danger on account of its toxicity, its flammability, the quantity released, etc.

A venting device shall be fitted if dangerous overpressure may develop due to normal decomposition of substances. The vent shall be so designed that, when the packaging or IBC is in the attitude in which it is intended to be transported, leakages of liquid and the penetration of foreign substances are prevented under normal conditions of transport.

4.1.1.8.1 Liquids may only be filled into inner packagings which have an appropriate resistance to internal pressure that may be developed under normal conditions of transport.

4.1.1.9 New, remanufactured or re-used packagings, including IBCs and large packagings, or reconditioned packagings and repaired or routinely maintained IBCs shall be capable of passing the tests prescribed in 6.1.5, 6.3.5, 6.5.6 or 6.6.5, as applicable. Before being filled and handed over for transport, every packaging, including IBCs and large packagings, shall be inspected to ensure that it is free from corrosion, contamination or other damage and every IBC shall be inspected with regard to the proper functioning of any service equipment. Any packaging which shows signs of reduced strength as compared with the approved design type shall no longer be used or shall be so reconditioned that it is able to withstand the design type tests. Any IBC which shows signs of reduced strength as compared with the tested design type shall no longer be used or shall be so repaired or routinely maintained that it is able to withstand the design type tests.

4.1.1.10 Liquids shall be filled only into packagings, including IBCs, which have an appropriate resistance to the internal pressure that may develop under normal conditions of transport. As the vapour pressure of low-boiling-point liquids is usually high, the strength of receptacles for these liquids shall be sufficient to withstand, with an ample factor of safety, the internal pressure likely to be generated. Packagings and IBCs marked with the hydraulic test pressure prescribed in 6.1.3.1(d) and 6.5.2.2.1, respectively, shall be filled only with a liquid having a vapour pressure:

.1 such that the total gauge pressure in the packaging or IBC (i.e. the vapour pressure of the filling substance plus the partial pressure of air or other inert gases, less 100 kPa) at 55°C, determined on the basis of a maximum degree of filling in accordance with 4.1.1.4 and a filling temperature of 15°C, will not exceed two thirds of the marked test pressure; or

.2 at 50°C, less than four sevenths of the sum of the marked test pressure plus 100 kPa; or

.3 at 55°C, less than two thirds of the sum of the marked test pressure plus 100 kPa.

IBCs intended for the transport of liquids shall not be used to carry liquids having a vapour pressure of more than 110 kPa (1.1 bar) at 50°C or 130 kPa (1.3 bar) at 55°C.

Examples of required marked test pressures for packagings, including IBCs, calculated as in 4.1.1.10.3

UN No.	Name	Class	Packing group	Vp_{55} (kPa)	$Vp_{55} \times 1.5$ (kPa)	$(Vp_{55} \times 1.5)$ minus 100 (kPa)	Required minimum test pressure (gauge) under 6.1.5.5.4.3 (kPa)	Minimum test pressure (gauge) to be marked on the packaging (kPa)
2056	Tetrahydrofuran	3	I	70	105	5	100	100
2247	*n*-Decane	3	II	1.4	2.1	−97.9	100	100
1593	Dichloromethane	6.1	III	164	246	146	146	150
1155	Diethyl ether	3	I	199	299	199	199	250

Note 1: For pure liquids, the vapour pressure at 55°C (Vp_{55}) can often be obtained from scientific tables.

Note 2: The table refers to the use of 4.1.1.10.3 only, which means that the marked test pressure shall exceed 1.5 times the vapour pressure at 55°C less 100 kPa. When, for example, the test pressure for *n*-decane is determined according to 6.1.5.5.4.1, the minimum marked test pressure may be lower.

Note 3: For diethyl ether, the required minimum test pressure under 6.1.5.5.5 is 250 kPa.

4.1.1.11　Empty packagings, including IBCs and large packagings, that have contained a dangerous substance shall be treated in the same manner as is required by this Code for a filled packaging, unless adequate measures have been taken to nullify any hazard.

△ 4.1.1.12　Every packaging as specified in chapter 6.1 intended to contain liquids shall successfully undergo a suitable leakproofness test. This test is part of a quality assurance programme as stipulated in 6.1.1.3 which shows the capability of meeting the appropriate test level indicated in 6.1.5.4.4:

.1　before it is first used for transport;

.2　after remanufacturing or reconditioning of any packaging, before it is re-used for transport.

For this test, the packaging need not have its closures fitted. The inner receptacle of a composite packaging may be tested without the outer packaging, provided the test results are not affected. This test is not necessary for inner packagings of combination packagings or large packagings.

4.1.1.13　Packagings, including IBCs, used for solids which may become liquid at temperatures likely to be encountered during transport shall also be capable of containing the substance in the liquid state.

4.1.1.14　Packagings, including IBCs, used for powdery or granular substances shall be sift-proof or shall be provided with a liner.

4.1.1.15　For plastics drums and jerricans, rigid plastics IBCs and composite IBCs with plastics inner receptacles, unless otherwise approved by the competent authority, the period of use permitted for the transport of dangerous substances shall be five years from the date of manufacture of the receptacles, except where a shorter period of use is prescribed because of the nature of the substance to be transported.

4.1.1.16　Where ice is used as a coolant it shall not affect the integrity of the packaging.

4.1.1.17　Explosives, self-reactive substances and organic peroxides

Unless specific provision to the contrary is made in this Code, the packagings, including IBCs and large packagings, used for goods of class 1, self-reactive substances of class 4.1 and organic peroxides of class 5.2 shall comply with the provisions for the medium danger group (packing group II).

△ 4.1.1.18　Use of salvage packagings and large salvage packagings

△ 4.1.1.18.1　Damaged, defective, leaking or non-conforming packages, or dangerous goods that have spilled or leaked may be transported in salvage packagings mentioned in 6.1.5.1.11 and 6.6.5.1.9. This does not prevent the use of a larger size packaging or large packaging of appropriate type and performance level and under the conditions of 4.1.1.18.2 and 4.1.1.18.3.

4.1.1.18.2　Appropriate measures shall be taken to prevent excessive movement of the damaged or leaking packages within a salvage packaging. When the salvage packaging contains liquids, sufficient inert absorbent material shall be added to eliminate the presence of free liquid.

4.1.1.18.3　Appropriate measures shall be taken to ensure there is no dangerous build-up of pressure.

⊗

4.1.1.19　Use of salvage pressure receptacles

△ 4.1.1.19.1　In the case of damaged, defective, leaking or non-conforming pressure receptacles, salvage pressure receptacles according to 6.2.3 may be used.

Note: A salvage pressure receptacle may be used as an overpack in accordance with 5.1.2. When used as an overpack, marks shall be in accordance with 5.1.2.1 instead of 5.2.1.3.

△ 4.1.1.19.2　Pressure receptacles shall be placed in salvage pressure receptacles of suitable size. The maximum size of the placed pressure receptacle is limited to a water capacity of 1,000 litres. More than one pressure receptacle may be placed in the same salvage pressure receptacle only if the contents are known and do not react dangerously with each other (see 4.1.1.6). In this case the total sum of water capacities of the placed pressure receptacles shall not exceed 1,000 litres. Measures shall be taken to prevent movement of the pressure receptacles within the salvage pressure receptacle, e.g. by partitioning, securing or cushioning.

4.1.1.19.3　A pressure receptacle may only be placed in a salvage pressure receptacle if:

.1　the salvage pressure receptacle is in accordance with 6.2.3.5 and a copy of the approval certificate is available;

.2　parts of the salvage pressure receptacle which are, or are likely to be in direct contact with the dangerous goods will not be affected or weakened by those dangerous goods and will not cause a dangerous effect (e.g. catalysing reaction or reacting with the dangerous goods); and

.3　the contents of the contained pressure receptacle(s) is limited in pressure and volume so that if totally discharged into the salvage pressure receptacle, the pressure in the salvage pressure receptacle at 65°C will not exceed the test pressure of the salvage pressure receptacle (for gases, see packing instruction in P200 (3) 4.1.4.1). The reduction of the useable water capacity of the salvage pressure receptacle, e.g. by any contained equipment and cushioning, shall be taken into account.

4.1.1.19.4   The proper shipping name, the UN number preceded by the letters "UN" and label(s) as required for packages in chapter 5.2 applicable to the dangerous goods inside the contained pressure receptacle(s) shall be applied to the salvage pressure receptacle for transport.

4.1.1.19.5   Salvage pressure receptacles shall be cleaned, purged and visually inspected internally and externally after each use. They shall be periodically inspected and tested in accordance with 6.2.1.6 at least once every five years.

4.1.1.20   During transport, packagings, including IBCs and large packagings, shall be securely fastened to or contained within the cargo transport unit, so that lateral or longitudinal movement or impact is prevented and adequate external support is provided.

4.1.2   Additional general provisions for the use of IBCs

4.1.2.1   When IBCs are used for the transport of liquids with a flashpoint of 60°C (closed cup) or lower, or of powders liable to dust explosion, measures shall be taken to prevent a dangerous electrostatic discharge.

4.1.2.2.1   Every metal, rigid plastics and composite IBC shall be inspected and tested, as relevant, in accordance with 6.5.4.4 or 6.5.4.5:

.1   before it is put into service;

.2   thereafter at intervals not exceeding two and a half and five years, as appropriate; and

.3   after the repair or remanufacture, before it is re-used for transport.

4.1.2.2.2   An IBC shall not be filled and offered for transport after the date of expiry of the last periodic test or inspection. However, an IBC filled prior to the date of expiry of the last periodic test or inspection may be transported for a period not to exceed three months beyond the date of expiry of the last periodic test or inspection. In addition, an IBC may be transported after the date of expiry of the last periodic test or inspection:

.1   after emptying but before cleaning, for purposes of performing the required test or inspection prior to refilling; and

.2   unless otherwise approved by the competent authority, for a period not to exceed six months beyond the date of expiry of the last periodic test or inspection in order to allow the return of dangerous goods or residues for proper disposal or recycling. Reference to this exemption shall be entered in the transport document.

4.1.2.3   IBCs of type 31HZ2 when transporting liquids shall be filled to at least 80% of the volume of the outer casing and shall be transported in closed cargo transport units.

△ **4.1.2.4**   Except for routine maintenance of metal, rigid plastics, composite and flexible IBCs performed by the owner of the IBC, whose State and name or authorized symbol is durably marked on the IBC, the party performing routine maintenance shall durably mark the IBC near the manufacturer's UN design type mark to show:

.1   the State in which the routine maintenance was carried out; and

.2   the name or authorized symbol of the party performing the routine maintenance.

4.1.3   General provisions concerning packing instructions

4.1.3.1   Packing instructions applicable to dangerous goods of classes 1 to 9 are specified in 4.1.4. They are subdivided in three subsections depending on the type of packagings to which they apply:

subsection 4.1.4.1   for packagings other than IBCs and large packagings; these packing instructions are designated by an alphanumeric code comprising the letter "P";

subsection 4.1.4.2   for IBCs; these are designated by an alphanumeric code comprising the letters "IBC";

subsection 4.1.4.3   for large packagings; these are designated by an alphanumeric code comprising the letters "LP".

Generally, packing instructions specify that the general provisions of 4.1.1, 4.1.2 and/or 4.1.3, as appropriate, are applicable. They may also require compliance with the special provisions of 4.1.5, 4.1.6, 4.1.7, 4.1.8 or 4.1.9 when appropriate. Special packing provisions may also be specified in the packing instruction for individual substances or articles. They are also designated by an alphanumeric code comprising the letters:

"PP"   for packagings other than IBCs and large packagings

"B"   for IBCs

"L"   for large packagings.

Unless otherwise specified, each packaging shall conform to the applicable provisions of part 6. Generally, packing instructions do not provide guidance on compatibility and the user shall not select a packaging without checking that the substance is compatible with the packaging material selected (such as, most fluorides are unsuitable for glass receptacles). Where glass receptacles are permitted in the packing instructions, porcelain, earthenware and stoneware packagings are also allowed.

4.1.3.2   Column 8 of the Dangerous Goods List shows for each article or substance the packing instruction(s) that shall be used. Column 9 indicates the special packing provisions applicable to specific substances or articles.

4.1.3.3   Each packing instruction shows, where applicable, the acceptable single and combination packagings. For combination packagings, the acceptable outer packagings, inner packagings and, when applicable, the maximum quantity permitted in each inner or outer packaging are shown. *Maximum net mass* and *maximum capacity* are as defined in 1.2.1.

4.1.3.4   The following packagings shall not be used when the substances being transported are liable to become liquid during transport:

Packagings

Drums: 1D and 1G

Boxes: 4C1, 4C2, 4D, 4F, 4G and 4H1

Bags: 5L1, 5L2, 5L3, 5H1, 5H2, 5H3, 5H4, 5M1 and 5M2

Composite: 6HC, 6HD1, 6HD2, 6HG1, 6HG2, 6PC, 6PD1, 6PD2, 6PG1, 6PG2 and 6PH1

Large packagings

Flexible plastics: 51H (outer packaging)

IBCs

For substances of packing group I:
  All types of IBCs

For substances of packing groups II and III:

Wooden: 11C, 11D and 11F

Fibreboard: 11G

Flexible: 13H1, 13H2, 13H3, 13H4, 13H5, 13L1, 13L2, 13L3, 13L4, 13M1 and 13M2

Composite: 11HZ2 and 21HZ2

4.1.3.5   Where the packing instructions in this chapter authorize the use of a particular type of packaging (such as 4G; 1A2), packagings bearing the same packaging identification code followed by the letters "V", "U" or "W" marked in accordance with the provisions of part 6 (such as "4GV", "4GU" or "4GW"; "1A2V", "1A2U" or "1A2W") may also be used under the same conditions and limitations applicable to the use of that type of packaging according to the relevant packing instructions. For example, a combination packaging marked with the packaging code "4GV" may be used whenever a combination packaging marked "4G" is authorized, provided the provisions in the relevant packing instruction regarding types of inner packagings and quantity limitations are respected.

4.1.3.6   Pressure receptacles for liquids and solids

4.1.3.6.1   Unless otherwise indicated in this Code, pressure receptacles conforming to:

.1   the applicable requirements of chapter 6.2; or

.2   the National or International standards on the design, construction, testing, manufacturing and inspection, as applied by the country in which the pressure receptacles are manufactured, provided that the provisions of 4.1.3.6 and 6.2.3.3 are met,

are authorized for the transport of any liquid or solid substance other than explosives, thermally unstable substances, organic peroxides, self-reactive substances, substances where significant pressure may develop by evolution of chemical reaction and radioactive material (unless permitted in 4.1.9).

This subsection is not applicable to the substances mentioned in 4.1.4.1, packing instruction P200, table 3.

4.1.3.6.2   Every design type of pressure receptacle shall be approved by the competent authority of the country of manufacture or as indicated in chapter 6.2.

4.1.3.6.3   Unless otherwise indicated, pressure receptacles having a minimum test pressure of 0.6 MPa shall be used.

4.1.3.6.4   Unless otherwise indicated, pressure receptacles may be provided with an emergency pressure relief device designed to avoid bursting in case of overfill or fire accidents.

Pressure receptacle valves shall be designed and constructed in such a way that they are inherently able to withstand damage without release of the contents or shall be protected from damage which could cause inadvertent release of the contents of the pressure receptacle, by one of the methods as given in 4.1.6.1.8.1 to 4.1.6.1.8.5.

4.1.3.6.5   The level of filling shall not exceed 95% of the capacity of the pressure receptacle at 50°C. Sufficient ullage (outage) shall be left to ensure that the pressure receptacle will not be liquid-full at a temperature of 55°C.

4.1.3.6.6   Unless otherwise indicated, pressure receptacles shall be subjected to a periodic inspection and test every five years. The periodic inspection shall include an external examination, an internal examination or alternative method as approved by the competent authority, a pressure test or equivalent effective non-destructive testing with the agreement of the competent authority, including an inspection of all accessories (e.g. tightness of valves, emergency relief valves or fusible elements). Pressure receptacles shall not be filled after they become due for periodic inspection and test but may be transported after the expiry of the time limit. Pressure receptacle repairs shall meet the requirements of 4.1.6.1.11.

4.1.3.6.7   Prior to filling, the filler shall perform an inspection of the pressure receptacle and ensure that the pressure receptacle is authorized for the substances to be transported and that the provisions of this Code have been met. Shut-off valves shall be closed after filling and remain closed during transport. The consignor shall verify that the closures and equipment are not leaking.

4.1.3.6.8   Refillable pressure receptacles shall not be filled with a substance different from that previously contained unless the necessary operations for change of service have been performed.

4.1.3.6.9   Marking of pressure receptacles for liquids and solids according to 4.1.3.6 (not conforming to the requirements of chapter 6.2) shall be in accordance with the requirements of the competent authority of the country of manufacturing.

4.1.3.7   Packagings, including IBCs and large packagings, not specifically authorized in the applicable packing instruction shall not be used for the transport of a substance or article unless specifically approved by the competent authority and provided:

.1   the alternative packaging complies with the general provisions of this chapter;

.2   when the packing instruction indicated in the Dangerous Goods List so specifies, the alternative packaging meets the provisions of part 6;

.3   the competent authority determines that the alternative packaging provides at least the same level of safety as if the substance were packed in accordance with a method specified in the particular packing instruction indicated in the Dangerous Goods List; and

.4   a copy of the competent authority approval accompanies each consignment or the transport document includes an indication that alternative packaging was approved by the competent authority.

Note: The competent authorities granting such approvals shall take action to amend the Code to include the provisions covered by the approval as appropriate.

4.1.3.8   Unpackaged articles other than class 1 articles

4.1.3.8.1   Where large and robust articles cannot be packaged in accordance with the requirements of chapter 6.1 or 6.6 and they have to be transported empty, uncleaned and unpackaged, the competent authority may approve such transport. In doing so, the competent authority shall take into account that:

.1   Large and robust articles shall be strong enough to withstand the shocks and loadings normally encountered during transport, including trans-shipment between cargo transport units and between cargo transport units and warehouses, as well as any removal from a pallet for subsequent manual or mechanical handling.

.2   All closures and openings shall be sealed so that there can be no loss of contents which might be caused under normal conditions of transport, by vibration, or by changes in temperature, humidity or pressure (resulting from altitude, for example). No dangerous residue shall adhere to the outside of the large and robust articles.

.3   Parts of large and robust articles, which are in direct contact with dangerous goods:

.1   shall not be affected or significantly weakened by those dangerous goods; and

.2   shall not cause a dangerous effect, e.g. catalysing a reaction or reacting with the dangerous goods.

.4   Large and robust articles containing liquids shall be stowed and secured to ensure that neither leakage nor permanent distortion of the article occurs during transport.

.5   They shall be fixed in cradles or crates or other handling devices in such a way that they will not become loose during normal conditions of transport.

4.1.3.8.2   Unpackaged articles approved by the competent authority in accordance with the provisions of 4.1.3.8.1 shall be subject to the consignment procedures of part 5. In addition the consignor of such articles shall ensure that a copy of any such approval is transported with the large and robust articles.

Note: A large and robust article may include flexible fuel containment systems, military equipment, machinery or equipment containing dangerous goods above the limited quantity thresholds.

4.1.3.9   Where, in 4.1.3.6 and in the individual packing instructions, cylinders and other pressure receptacles for gases are authorized for the transport of any liquid or solid substance, use is also authorized of cylinders and pressure receptacles of a kind normally used for gases which conform to the requirements of the competent authority of the country in which the cylinder or pressure receptacle is filled. Valves shall be suitably protected. Pressure receptacles with capacities of 1 L or less shall be packed in outer packagings constructed of suitable material of adequate strength and design in relation to the capacity of the packaging and its intended use and secured or cushioned so as to prevent significant movement within the outer packaging during normal conditions of transport.

4

4.1.4 List of packing instructions

4.1.4.1 Packing instructions concerning the use of packagings (except IBCs and large packagings)

P001	PACKING INSTRUCTION (LIQUIDS)			P001
The following packagings are authorized provided the general provisions of 4.1.1 and 4.1.3 are met.				
Combination packagings		Maximum capacity/net mass (see 4.1.3.3)		
Inner packagings	Outer packagings	Packing group I	Packing group II	Packing group III
Glass 10 L	**Drums**			
Plastics 30 L	steel (1A1, 1A2)	75 kg	400 kg	400 kg
Metal 40 L	aluminium (1B1, 1B2)	75 kg	400 kg	400 kg
	other metal (1N1, 1N2)	75 kg	400 kg	400 kg
	plastics (1H1, 1H2)	75 kg	400 kg	400 kg
	plywood (1D)	75 kg	400 kg	400 kg
	fibre (1G)	75 kg	400 kg	400 kg
	Boxes			
	steel (4A)	75 kg	400 kg	400 kg
	aluminium (4B)	75 kg	400 kg	400 kg
	other metal (4N)	75 kg	400 kg	400 kg
	natural wood (4C1, 4C2)	75 kg	400 kg	400 kg
	plywood (4D)	75 kg	400 kg	400 kg
	reconstituted wood (4F)	75 kg	400 kg	400 kg
	fibreboard (4G)	75 kg	400 kg	400 kg
	expanded plastics (4H1)	40 kg	60 kg	60 kg
	solid plastics (4H2)	75 kg	400 kg	400 kg
	Jerricans			
	steel (3A1, 3A2)	60 kg	120 kg	120 kg
	aluminium (3B1, 3B2)	60 kg	120 kg	120 kg
	plastics (3H1, 3H2)	30 kg	120 kg	120 kg
Single packagings				
Drums				
steel, non-removable head (1A1)		250 L	450 L	450 L
steel, removable head (1A2)		prohibited	250 L	250 L
aluminium, non-removable head (1B1)		250 L	450 L	450 L
aluminium, removable head (1B2)		prohibited	250 L	250 L
other metal, non-removable head (1N1)		250 L	450 L	450 L
other metal, removable head (1N2)		prohibited	250 L	250 L
plastics, non-removable head (1H1)		250 L*	450 L	450 L
plastics, removable head (1H2)		prohibited	250 L	250 L
Jerricans				
steel, non-removable head (3A1)		60 L	60 L	60 L
steel, removable head (3A2)		prohibited	60 L	60 L
aluminium, non-removable head (3B1)		60 L	60 L	60 L
aluminium, removable head (3B2)		prohibited	60 L	60 L
plastics, non-removable head (3H1)		60 L*	60 L	60 L
plastics, removable head (3H2)		prohibited	60 L	60 L
Composite packagings				
Plastics receptacle in steel or aluminium drum (6HA1, 6HB1)		250 L	250 L	250 L
Plastics receptacle in fibre, plastics or plywood drum (6HG1, 6HH1, 6HD1)		120 L*	250 L	250 L
Plastics receptacle in steel or aluminium crate or box or plastics receptacle in wood, plywood, fibreboard or solid plastics box (6HA2, 6HB2, 6HC, 6HD2, 6HG2 or 6HH2)		60 L*	60 L	60 L
Glass receptacle in steel, aluminium, fibre, plywood, solid plastics or expanded plastics drum (6PA1, 6PB1, 6PG1, 6PD1, 6PH1 or 6PH2) or in a steel, aluminium, wood or fibreboard box or in a wickerwork hamper (6PA2, 6PB2, 6PC, 6PG2 or 6PD2)		60 L	60 L	60 L
Pressure receptacles, provided that the general provisions of 4.1.3.6 are met				

* Not permitted for class 3, packing group I.

P001	PACKING INSTRUCTION (LIQUIDS) *(continued)*	P001

Special packing provisions:

PP1   For UN Nos. 1133, 1210, 1263 and 1866 and for adhesives, printing inks, printing ink related materials, paints, paint related materials and resin solutions which are assigned to UN 3082, metal or plastics packagings for substances of packing groups II and III in quantities of 5 L or less per packaging are not required to meet the performance tests in chapter 6.1 when transported:

    (a)   in palletized loads, a pallet box or a unit load device, such as individual packagings placed or stacked and secured by strapping, shrink- or stretch-wrapping or other suitable means to a pallet. For sea transport, the palletized loads, pallet boxes or unit load devices shall be firmly packed and secured in closed cargo transport units. On roll-on/roll-off ships the unit loads may be carried in vehicles other than closed vehicles provided they are securely fenced to the full height of the cargo carried; or

    (b)   as an inner packaging of a combination packaging with a maximum net mass of 40 kg.

PP2   For UN 3065, wooden barrels with a maximum capacity of 250 L and which do not meet the provisions of chapter 6.1 may be used.

PP4   For UN 1774, packagings shall meet the packing group II performance level.

PP5   For UN 1204, packagings shall be so constructed that explosion is not possible by reason of increased internal pressure. Gas cylinders and gas receptacles shall not be used for these substances.

PP10   For UN 1791, for packing group II, the packaging shall be vented.

PP31   For UN Nos. 1131, 1553, 1693, 1694, 1699, 1701, 2478, 2604, 2785, 3148, 3183, 3184, 3185, 3186, 3187, 3188, 3398 (PG II and III), 3399 (PG II and III), 3413 and 3414, packagings shall be hermetically sealed.

PP33   For UN 1308, for packing groups I and II, only combination packagings with a maximum gross mass of 75 kg are allowed.

PP81   For UN 1790 with more than 60% but not more than 85% hydrogen fluoride and UN 2031 with more than 55% nitric acid, the permitted use of plastics drums and jerricans as single packagings shall be two years from their date of manufacture

PP93   For UN Nos. 3532 and 3534, packagings shall be designed and constructed to permit the release of gas or vapour to prevent a build-up of pressure that could rupture the packagings in the event of loss of stabilization.

P002	PACKING INSTRUCTION (SOLIDS)	P002

The following packagings are authorized provided the general provisions of 4.1.1 and 4.1.3 are met.

Combination packagings		Maximum net mass (see 4.1.3.3)		
Inner packagings	**Outer packagings**	**Packing group I**	**Packing group II**	**Packing group III**
Glass 10 kg	**Drums**			
Plastics[1] 30 kg	steel (1A1, 1A2)	125 kg	400 kg	400 kg
Metal 40 kg	aluminium (1B1, 1B2)	125 kg	400 kg	400 kg
Paper[1, 2, 3] 50 kg	other metal (1N1, 1N2)	125 kg	400 kg	400 kg
Fibre[1, 2, 3] 50 kg	plastics (1H1, 1H2)	125 kg	400 kg	400 kg
	plywood (1D)	125 kg	400 kg	400 kg
	fibre (1G)	125 kg	400 kg	400 kg
	Boxes			
	steel (4A)	125 kg	400 kg	400 kg
	aluminium (4B)	125 kg	400 kg	400 kg
	other metal (4N)	125 kg	400 kg	400 kg
	natural wood (4C1)	125 kg	400 kg	400 kg
	natural wood with sift-proof walls (4C2)	250 kg	400 kg	400 kg
	plywood (4D)	125 kg	400 kg	400 kg
[1] These inner packagings shall be sift-proof.	reconstituted wood (4F)	125 kg	400 kg	400 kg
[2] These inner packagings shall not be used when the	fibreboard (4G)	75 kg	400 kg	400 kg
substances being transported may become liquid during	expanded plastics (4H1)	40 kg	60 kg	60 kg
transport.	solid plastics (4H2)	125 kg	400 kg	400 kg
[3] Paper and fibre inner	**Jerricans**			
packagings shall not be used for substances of packing	steel (3A1, 3A2)	75 kg	120 kg	120 kg
group I.	aluminium (3B1, 3B2)	75 kg	120 kg	120 kg
	plastics (3H1, 3H2)	75 kg	120 kg	120 kg
Single packagings				
Drums				
steel (1A1 or 1A2[4])		400 kg	400 kg	400 kg
aluminium (1B1 or 1B2[4])		400 kg	400 kg	400 kg
metal, other than steel or aluminium (1N1 or 1N2[4])		400 kg	400 kg	400 kg
plastics (1H1 or 1H2[4])		400 kg	400 kg	400 kg
fibre (1G[5])		400 kg	400 kg	400 kg
plywood (1D[5])		400 kg	400 kg	400 kg

[4] These packagings shall not be used for substances of packing group I that may become liquid during transport (see 4.1.3.4).

[5] These packagings shall not be used when the substances being transported may become liquid during transport (see 4.1.3.4).

P002	PACKING INSTRUCTION (SOLIDS) *(continued)*		P002

The following packagings are authorized provided the general provisions of 4.1.1 and 4.1.3 are met.

Single packagings *(continued)*	Maximum net mass (see 4.1.3.3)		
	Packing group I	Packing group II	Packing group III
Jerricans			
steel (3A1 or 3A2[4])	120 kg	120 kg	120 kg
aluminium (3B1 or 3B2[4])	120 kg	120 kg	120 kg
plastics (3H1 or 3H2[4])	120 kg	120 kg	120 kg
Boxes			
steel (4A)[5]	Not allowed	400 kg	400 kg
aluminium (4B)[5]	Not allowed	400 kg	400 kg
other metal (4N)[5]	Not allowed	400 kg	400 kg
natural wood (4C1)[5]	Not allowed	400 kg	400 kg
natural wood with sift-proof walls (4C2)[5]	Not allowed	400 kg	400 kg
plywood (4D)[5]	Not allowed	400 kg	400 kg
reconstituted wood (4F)[5]	Not allowed	400 kg	400 kg
fibreboard (4G)[5]	Not allowed	400 kg	400 kg
solid plastics (4H2)[5]	Not allowed	400 kg	400 kg
Bags			
bags (5H3, 5H4, 5L3, 5M2)[5]	Not allowed	50 kg	50 kg
Composite packagings			
Plastics receptacle in steel, aluminium, plywood, fibre or plastics drum (6HA1, 6HB1, 6HG1[5], 6HD1[5], or 6HH1)	400 kg	400 kg	400 kg
Plastics receptacle in steel or aluminium crate or box, wooden box, plywood box, fibreboard box or solid plastics box (6HA2, 6HB2, 6HC, 6HD2[5], 6HG2[5] or 6HH2)	75 kg	75 kg	75 kg
Glass receptacle in steel, aluminium, plywood or fibre drum (6PA1, 6PB1, 6PD1[5] or 6PG1[5]) or in steel, aluminium, wood, or fibreboard box or in wickerwork hamper (6PA2, 6PB2, 6PC, 6PG2[5] or 6PD2[5]) or in solid or expanded plastics packaging (6PH2 or 6PH1[5])	75 kg	75 kg	75 kg

[4] These packagings shall not be used for substances of packing group I that may become liquid during transport (see 4.1.3.4).
[5] These packagings shall not be used when the substances being transported may become liquid during transport (see 4.1.3.4).

Pressure receptacles, provided that the general provisions of 4.1.3.6 are met.

Special packing provisions:

PP7   For UN 2000, celluloid may be transported unpacked on pallets, wrapped in plastic film and secured by appropriate means, such as steel bands, as a single commodity in closed cargo transport units. Each pallet shall not exceed 1000 kg.

PP8   For UN 2002, packagings shall be so constructed that explosion is not possible by reason of increased internal pressure. Gas cylinders and gas receptacles shall not be used for these substances.

PP9   For UN Nos. 3175, 3243 and 3244, packagings shall conform to a design type that has passed a leakproofness test at the packing group II performance level. For UN 3175 the leakproofness test is not required when the liquids are fully absorbed in solid material contained in sealed bags.

PP11   For UN 1309, packing group III, and UN Nos. 1361 and 1362, 5M1 bags are allowed if they are overpacked in plastic bags and are wrapped in shrink or stretch wrap on pallets.

PP12   For UN Nos. 1361, 2213 and 3077, 5H1, 5L1 and 5M1 bags are allowed when transported in closed cargo transport units.

PP13   For articles classified under UN 2870, only combination packagings meeting the packing group I performance level are authorized.

PP14   For UN Nos. 2211, 2698 and 3314, packagings are not required to meet the performance tests in chapter 6.1.

PP15   For UN Nos. 1324 and 2623, packagings shall meet the packing group III performance level.

PP20   For UN 2217, any sift-proof, tearproof receptacle may be used.

PP30   For UN 2471, paper or fibre inner packagings are not permitted.

PP31   For UN Nos. 1362, 1463, 1565, 1575, 1626, 1680, 1689, 1698, 1868, 1889, 1932, 2471, 2545, 2546, 2881, 3048, 3088, 3170, 3174, 3181, 3182, 3189, 3190, 3205, 3206, 3341, 3342, 3448, 3449 and 3450, packagings shall be hermetically sealed.

PP34   For UN 2969 (as whole beans), 5H1, 5L1 and 5M1 bags are permitted.

PP37   For UN Nos. 2590 and 2212, 5M1 bags are permitted. All bags of any type shall be transported in closed cargo transport units or be placed in closed rigid overpacks.

PP38   For UN 1309, bags are permitted only in closed cargo transport units or as unit loads.

PP84   For UN 1057, rigid outer packagings meeting the packing group II performance level shall be used. The packagings shall be designed and constructed and arranged to prevent movement, inadvertent ignition of the devices or inadvertent release of flammable gas or liquid.

PP85   For UN Nos. 1748, 2208, 2880, 3485, 3486 and 3487, bags are not allowed.

■ PP92   For UN Nos. 3531 and 3533, packagings shall be designed and constructed to permit the release of gas or vapour to prevent a build-up of pressure that could rupture the packagings in the event of loss of stabilization.

■ PP100 For UN numbers 1309, 1323, 1333, 1376, 1435, 1449, 1457, 1472, 1476, 1483, 1509, 1516, 1567, 1869, 2210, 2858, 2878, 2968, 3089, 3096 and 3125, flexible, fibreboard or wooden packagings shall be sift-proof and water-resistant or shall be fitted with a sift-proof and water-resistant liner.

P003	PACKING INSTRUCTION	P003

Dangerous goods shall be placed in suitable outer packagings. The packagings shall meet the provisions of 4.1.1.1, 4.1.1.2, 4.1.1.4, 4.1.1.8 and 4.1.3 and be so designed that they meet the construction provisions of 6.1.4. Outer packagings constructed of suitable material, and of adequate strength and design in relation to the packaging capacity and its intended use, shall be used. Where this packing instruction is used for the transport of articles or inner packagings of combination packagings, the packaging shall be designed and constructed to prevent inadvertent discharge of articles during normal conditions of transport.

Special packing provisions:

PP16 For UN 2800, batteries shall be protected from short circuit within the packagings.

PP17 For UN 2037, packages shall not exceed 55 kg net mass for fibreboard packagings or 125 kg net mass for other packagings.

PP18 For UN 1845, packagings shall be designed and constructed to permit the release of carbon dioxide gas to prevent a build-up of pressure that could rupture the packagings.

PP19 For UN Nos. 1327, 1364, 1365, 1856 and 3360, transport as bales is authorized.

PP20 For UN Nos. 1363, 1386, 1408 and 2793, any sift-proof, tearproof receptacle may be used.

PP32 UN Nos. 2857 and 3358 may be transported unpackaged, in crates or in appropriate overpacks.

PP90 For UN 3506, sealed inner liners or bags of strong leakproof and puncture resistant material impervious to mercury which will prevent escape of the substance from the package irrespective of the position of the package shall be used.

PP91 For UN 1044, large fire extinguishers may also be transported unpackaged provided that the requirements of 4.1.3.8.1.1 to 4.1.3.8.1.5 are met, the valves are protected by one of the methods in accordance with 4.1.6.1.8.1 to 4.1.6.1.8.4 and other equipment mounted on the fire extinguisher is protected to prevent accidental activation. For the purpose of this special packing provision, "large fire extinguishers" means fire extinguishers as described in subparagraphs .3 to .5 of special provision 225 of chapter 3.3.

■ **PP100** For UN Nos. 1408 and 2793 flexible, fibreboard or wooden packagings shall be sift-proof and water-resistant or shall be fitted with a sift-proof and water-resistant liner.

P004	PACKING INSTRUCTION	P004

This instruction applies to UN Nos. 3473, 3476, 3477, 3478 and 3479.

The following packagings are authorized:

(1) For fuel cell cartridges, provided that the general provisions of 4.1.1.1, 4.1.1.2, 4.1.1.3, 4.1.1.6 and 4.1.3 are met:

Drums (1A2, 1B2, 1N2, 1H2, 1D, 1G);

Boxes (4A, 4B, 4N, 4C1, 4C2, 4D, 4F, 4G, 4H1, 4H2);

Jerricans (3A2, 3B2, 3H2).

Packagings shall conform to the packing group II performance level.

(2) For fuel cell cartridges packed with equipment: strong outer packagings which meet the general provisions of 4.1.1.1, 4.1.1.2, 4.1.1.6 and 4.1.3.

When fuel cell cartridges are packed with equipment, they shall be packed in inner packagings or placed in the outer packaging with cushioning material or divider(s) so that the fuel cell cartridges are protected against damage that may be caused by the movement or placement of the contents within the outer packaging.

The equipment shall be secured against movement within the outer packaging.

For the purpose of this packing instruction, "equipment" means apparatus requiring the fuel cell cartridges with which it is packed for its operation.

(3) For fuel cell cartridges contained in equipment: strong outer packagings which meet the general provisions of 4.1.1.1, 4.1.1.2, 4.1.1.6 and 4.1.3.

Large robust equipment (see 4.1.3.8) containing fuel cell cartridges may be transported unpackaged. For fuel cell cartridges contained in equipment, the entire system shall be protected against short circuit and inadvertent operation.

P005	PACKING INSTRUCTION	P005
This instruction applies to UN Nos. 3528, 3529 and 3530.		

If the engine or machinery is constructed and designed so that the means of containment containing the dangerous goods affords adequate protection, an outer packaging is not required.

Dangerous goods in engines or machinery shall otherwise be packed in outer packagings constructed of suitable material, and of adequate strength and design in relation to the packaging capacity and its intended use, and meeting the applicable requirements of 4.1.1.1, or they shall be fixed in such a way that they will not become loose during normal conditions of transport, e.g. in cradles or crates or other handling devices.

In addition, the manner in which means of containment are contained within the engine or machinery, shall be such that under normal conditions of transport, damage to the means of containment containing the dangerous goods is prevented; and in the event of damage to the means of containment containing liquid dangerous goods, no leakage of the dangerous goods from the engine or machinery is possible (a leakproof liner may be used to satisfy this requirement).

Means of containment containing dangerous goods shall be so installed, secured or cushioned as to prevent their breakage or leakage and so as to control their movement within the engine or machinery during normal conditions of transport. Cushioning material shall not react dangerously with the content of the means of containment. Any leakage of the contents shall not substantially impair the protective properties of the cushioning material.

Additional requirement:

Other dangerous goods (e.g. batteries, fire extinguishers, compressed gas accumulators or safety devices) required for the functioning or safe operation of the engine or machinery shall be securely mounted in the engine or machine.

P010	PACKING INSTRUCTION	P010
The following packagings are authorized, provided that the general provisions of 4.1.1 and 4.1.3 are met.		
Combination packagings		Maximum net mass (see 4.1.3.3)
Inner packagings	Outer packagings	
Glass 1 L Steel 40 L	**Drums**	
	steel (1A1, 1A2)	400 kg
	plastics (1H1, 1H2)	400 kg
	plywood (1D)	400 kg
	fibre (1G)	400 kg
	Boxes	
	steel (4A)	400 kg
	natural wood (4C1, 4C2)	400 kg
	plywood (4D)	400 kg
	reconstituted wood (4F)	400 kg
	fibreboard (4G)	400 kg
	expanded plastics (4H1)	60 kg
	solid plastics (4H2)	400 kg
Single packagings		Maximum capacity (see 4.1.3.3)
Drums		
steel, non-removable head (1A1)		450 L
Jerricans		
steel, non-removable head (3A1)		60 L
Composite packagings		
plastics receptacle in steel drums (6HA1)		250 L
Steel pressure receptacles provided that the general provisions of 4.1.3.6 are met.		

P099	PACKING INSTRUCTION	P099

Only packagings which are approved for these goods by the competent authority may be used (see 4.1.3.7). A copy of the competent authority approval shall accompany each consignment or the transport document shall include an indication that the packaging was approved by the competent authority.

P101	PACKING INSTRUCTION	P101

Only packagings which are approved by the competent authority may be used. The State's distinguishing sign for motor vehicles in international traffic of the country for which the authority acts shall be marked on the transport documents as follows:

"Packaging approved by the competent authority of ..."

P110(a)	PACKING INSTRUCTION	P110(a)

The following packagings are authorized, provided the general packing provisions of 4.1.1, 4.1.3 and special packing provisions of 4.1.5 are met.

Inner packagings	Intermediate packagings	Outer packagings
Bags 　plastics 　textile, plastic coated or lined 　rubber 　textile, rubberized 　textile Receptacles 　wood	Bags 　plastics 　textile, plastic coated or lined 　rubber 　textile, rubberized Receptacles 　plastics 　metal 　wood	Drums 　steel (1A1, 1A2) 　metal, other than steel or aluminium 　　(1N1, 1N2) 　plastics (1H1, 1H2)

Additional provisions:

1　The intermediate packagings shall be filled with water-saturated material such as an anti-freeze solution or wetted cushioning.

2　Outer packagings shall be filled with water-saturated material such as an anti-freeze solution or wetted cushioning. Outer packagings shall be constructed and sealed to prevent evaporation of the wetting solution, except for UN 0224 when transported dry.

P110(b)	PACKING INSTRUCTION	P110(b)

The following packagings are authorized, provided the general packing provisions of 4.1.1, 4.1.3 and special packing provisions of 4.1.5 are met.

Inner packagings	Intermediate packagings	Outer packagings
Receptacles 　metal 　wood 　rubber, conductive 　plastics, conductive Bags 　rubber, conductive 　plastics, conductive	Dividing partitions 　metal 　wood 　plastics 　fibreboard	Boxes 　natural wood, sift-proof wall (4C2) 　plywood (4D) 　reconstituted wood (4F)

Special packing provision:

PP42　For UN Nos. 0074, 0113, 0114, 0129, 0130, 0135 and 0224, the following conditions shall be met:

　　　.1　inner packagings shall not contain more than 50 g of explosive substance (quantity corresponding to dry substance);

　　　.2　compartments between dividing partitions shall not contain more than one inner packaging, firmly fitted; and

　　　.3　the outer packaging may be partitioned into up to 25 compartments.

P111	PACKING INSTRUCTION	P111
The following packagings are authorized, provided the general packing provisions of 4.1.1, 4.1.3 and special packing provisions of 4.1.5 are met.		

Inner packagings	Intermediate packagings	Outer packagings

Bags
  paper, waterproofed
  plastics
  textile, rubberized
 	
Sheets
  plastics
  textile, rubberized
 	
Receptacles
  wood
	Not necessary	**Boxes**
		  steel (4A)
		  aluminium (4B)
		  other metal (4N)
		  natural wood, ordinary (4C1)
		  natural wood, sift-proof (4C2)
		  plywood (4D)
		  reconstituted wood (4F)
		  fibreboard (4G)
		  plastics, expanded (4H1)
		  plastics, solid (4H2)
		
		Drums
		  steel (1A1, 1A2)
		  aluminium (1B1, 1B2)
		  other metal (1N1, 1N2)
		  plywood (1D)
		  fibre (1G)
		  plastics (1H1, 1H2)

Special packing provision:

PP43 For UN 0159, inner packagings are not required when metal (1A1, 1A2, 1B1, 1B2, 1N1 or 1N2) or plastics (1H1 or 1H2) drums are used as outer packagings.

P112(a)	PACKING INSTRUCTION (Solid wetted, 1.1D)	P112(a)
The following packagings are authorized, provided the general packing provisions of 4.1.1, 4.1.3 and special packing provisions of 4.1.5 are met.		

Inner packagings	Intermediate packagings	Outer packagings

Bags
  paper, multiwall, water-resistant
  plastics
  textile
  textile, rubberized
  woven plastics
 	
Receptacles
  metal
  plastics
  wood
	Bags
	  plastics
	  textile, plastic coated or lined
	
	Receptacles
	  metal
	  plastics
	  wood
		Boxes
		  steel (4A)
		  aluminium (4B)
		  other metal (4N)
		  natural wood, ordinary (4C1)
		  natural wood, sift-proof (4C2)
		  plywood (4D)
		  reconstituted wood (4F)
		  fibreboard (4G)
		  plastics, expanded (4H1)
		  plastics, solid (4H2)
		
		Drums
		  steel (1A1, 1A2)
		  aluminium (1B1, 1B2)
		  other metal (1N1, 1N2)
		  plywood (1D)
		  fibre (1G)
		  plastics (1H1, 1H2)

Additional provision:

Intermediate packagings are not required if leakproof removable head drums are used as the outer packaging.

Special packing provisions:

PP26 For UN Nos. 0004, 0076, 0078, 0154, 0219 and 0394, packagings shall be lead-free.

PP45 For UN Nos. 0072 and 0226, intermediate packagings are not required.

4

P112(b)	PACKING INSTRUCTION	P112(b)
	(Solid dry, other than powder 1.1D)	

The following packagings are authorized, provided the general packing provisions of 4.1.1, 4.1.3 and special packing provisions of 4.1.5 are met.

Inner packagings	Intermediate packagings	Outer packagings

Bags
  paper, kraft
  paper, multiwall, water-resistant
  plastics
  textile
  textile, rubberized
  woven plastics
	Bags (for UN 0150 only)
	  plastics
	  textile, plastic coated or lined
		Bags
		  woven plastics, sift-proof (5H2)
		  woven plastics, water-resistant
		    (5H3)
		  plastics, film (5H4)
		  textile, sift-proof (5L2)
		  textile, water-resistant (5L3)
		  paper, multiwall, water-resistant
		    (5M2)
		
		Boxes
		  steel (4A)
		  aluminium (4B)
		  other metal (4N)
		  natural wood, ordinary (4C1)
		  natural wood, sift-proof (4C2)
		  plywood (4D)
		  reconstituted wood (4F)
		  fibreboard (4G)
		  plastics, expanded (4H1)
		  plastics, solid (4H2)
		
		Drums
		  steel (1A1, 1A2)
		  aluminium (1B1, 1B2)
		  other metal (1N1, 1N2)
		  plywood (1D)
		  fibre (1G)
		  plastics (1H1, 1H2)

Special packing provisions:

PP26 For UN Nos. 0004, 0076, 0078, 0154, 0216, 0219 and 0386, packagings shall be lead-free.

PP46 For UN 0209, bags, sift-proof (5H2) are recommended for flake or prilled TNT in the dry state and a maximum net mass of 30 kg.

PP47 For UN 0222, inner packagings are not required when the outer packaging is a bag.

IMDG Code (amendment 38-16)

P112(c)	PACKING INSTRUCTION (Solid dry powder 1.1D)	P112(c)

The following packagings are authorized, provided the general packing provisions of 4.1.1, 4.1.3 and special packing provisions of 4.1.5 are met.

Inner packagings	Intermediate packagings	Outer packagings

Bags
  paper, multiwall, water-resistant
  plastics
  woven plastics
 	
Receptacles
  fibreboard
  metal
  plastics
  wood
	Bags
	  paper, multiwall, water-resistant
	  with inner lining
	  plastics
	
	Receptacles
	  metal
	  plastics
	  wood
		Boxes
		  steel (4A)
		  aluminium (4B)
		  other metal (4N)
		  natural wood, ordinary (4C1)
		  natural wood, sift-proof (4C2)
		  plywood (4D)
		  reconstituted wood (4F)
		  fibreboard (4G)
		  plastics, solid (4H2)
		
		Drums
		  steel (1A1, 1A2)
		  aluminium (1B1, 1B2)
		  other metal (1N1, 1N2)
		  plywood (1D)
		  fibre (1G)
		  plastics (1H1, 1H2)

Additional provisions:

1   Inner packagings are not required if drums are used as the outer packaging.

2   The packaging shall be sift-proof.

Special packing provisions:

PP26 For UN Nos. 0004, 0076, 0078, 0154, 0216, 0219 and 0386, packagings shall be lead-free.

PP46 For UN 0209, bags, sift-proof (5H2) are recommended for flake or prilled TNT in the dry state and a maximum net mass of 30 kg.

△ **PP48** For UN 0504, metal packagings shall not be used. Packagings of other material with a small amount of metal, for example metal closures or other metal fittings such as those mentioned in 6.1.4, are not considered metal packagings.

P113	PACKING INSTRUCTION	P113

The following packagings are authorized, provided the general packing provisions of 4.1.1, 4.1.3 and special packing provisions of 4.1.5 are met.

Inner packagings	Intermediate packagings	Outer packagings

Bags
  paper
  plastics
  textile, rubberized
 	
Receptacles
  fibreboard
  metal
  plastics
  wood
	Not necessary	**Boxes**
		  steel (4A)
		  aluminium (4B)
		  other metal (4N)
		  natural wood, ordinary (4C1)
		  natural wood, sift-proof walls (4C2)
		  plywood (4D)
		  reconstituted wood (4F)
		  fibreboard (4G)
		  plastics, solid (4H2)
		
		Drums
		  steel (1A1, 1A2)
		  aluminium (1B1, 1B2)
		  other metal (1N1, 1N2)
		  plywood (1D)
		  fibre (1G)
		  plastics (1H1, 1H2)

Additional provision:

The packaging shall be sift-proof.

Special packing provisions:

PP49 For UN Nos. 0094 and 0305, no more than 50 g of substance shall be packed in an inner packaging.

PP50 For UN 0027, inner packagings are not necessary when drums are used as the outer packaging.

PP51 For UN 0028, paper kraft or waxed paper sheets may be used as inner packagings.

4

P114(a)	PACKING INSTRUCTION (Solid wetted)	P114(a)

The following packagings are authorized, provided the general packing provisions of 4.1.1, 4.1.3 and special packing provisions of 4.1.5 are met.

Inner packagings	Intermediate packagings	Outer packagings

Bags
  plastics
  textile
  woven plastics
 	
Receptacles
  metal
  plastics
  wood
	Bags
	  plastics
	  textile, plastic coated or lined
	
	Receptacles
	  metal
	  plastics
	
	Dividing partitions
	  wood
		Boxes
		  steel (4A)
		  metal, other than steel or aluminium (4N)
		  natural wood, ordinary (4C1)
		  natural wood, sift-proof walls (4C2)
		  plywood (4D)
		  reconstituted wood (4F)
		  fibreboard (4G)
		  plastics, solid (4H2)
		
		Drums
		  steel (1A1, 1A2)
		  aluminium (1B1, 1B2)
		  other metal (1N1, 1N2)
		  plywood (1D)
		  fibre (1G)
		  plastics (1H1, 1H2)

Additional provision:
Intermediate packagings are not required if leakproof removable head drums are used as the outer packaging.

Special packing provisions:
PP26 For UN Nos. 0077, 0132, 0234, 0235 and 0236, packagings shall be lead-free.
PP43 For UN 0342, inner packagings are not required when metal (1A1, 1A2, 1B1, 1B2, 1N1 or 1N2) or plastics (1H1 or 1H2) drums are used as outer packagings.

P114(b)	PACKING INSTRUCTION (Solid dry)	P114(b)

The following packagings are authorized, provided the general packing provisions of 4.1.1, 4.1.3 and special packing provisions of 4.1.5 are met.

Inner packagings	Intermediate packagings	Outer packagings

Bags
  paper, kraft
  plastics
  textile, sift-proof
  woven plastics, sift-proof
 	
Receptacles
  fibreboard
  metal
  paper
  plastics
  woven plastics, sift-proof
  wood
	Not necessary	**Boxes**
		  natural wood, ordinary (4C1)
		  natural wood, sift-proof walls (4C2)
		  plywood (4D)
		  reconstituted wood (4F)
		  fibreboard (4G)
		
		Drums
		  steel (1A1, 1A2)
		  aluminium (1B1, 1B2)
		  other metal (1N1, 1N2)
		  plywood (1D)
		  fibre (1G)
		  plastics (1H1, 1H2)

Special packing provisions:
PP26 For UN Nos. 0077, 0132, 0234, 0235 and 0236, packagings shall be lead-free.
△ **PP48** For UN Nos. 0508 and 0509, metal packagings shall not be used. Packagings of other material with a small amount of metal, for example metal closures or other metal fittings such as those mentioned in 6.1.4, are not considered metal packagings.
PP50 For UN Nos. 0160, 0161 and 0508, inner packagings are not necessary when drums are used as the outer packaging.
PP52 For UN Nos. 0160 and 0161, when metal drums (1A1, 1A2, 1B1, 1B2, 1N1 or 1N2) are used as the outer packaging, metal packagings shall be so constructed that the risk of explosion, by reason of increase in internal pressure from internal or external causes, is prevented.

P115	PACKING INSTRUCTION	P115

The following packagings are authorized, provided the general packing provisions of 4.1.1, 4.1.3 and special packing provisions of 4.1.5 are met.

Inner packagings	Intermediate packagings	Outer packagings
Receptacles plastics wood	**Bags** plastics in metal receptacles **Drums** metal **Receptacles** wood	**Boxes** natural wood, ordinary (4C1) natural wood, sift-proof walls (4C2) plywood (4D) reconstituted wood (4F) **Drums** steel (1A1, 1A2) aluminium (1B1, 1B2) other metal (1N1, 1N2) plywood (1D) fibre (1G) plastics (1H1, 1H2)

Special packing provisions:

PP45   For UN 0144, intermediate packagings are not required.

PP53   For UN Nos. 0075, 0143, 0495 and 0497, when boxes are used as the outer packaging, inner packagings shall have taped screw-cap closures and be not more than 5 L capacity each. Inner packagings shall be surrounded with non-combustible absorbent cushioning materials. The amount of absorbent cushioning material shall be sufficient to absorb the liquid contents. Metal receptacles shall be cushioned from each other. Net mass of propellant is limited to 30 kg for each package when outer packagings are boxes.

PP54   For UN Nos. 0075, 0143, 0495 and 0497, when drums are used as the outer packaging and when intermediate packagings are drums, they shall be surrounded with non-combustible cushioning material in a quantity sufficient to absorb the liquid contents. A composite packaging consisting of a plastics receptacle in a metal drum may be used instead of the inner and intermediate packagings. The net volume of propellent in each package shall not exceed 120 L.

PP55   For UN 0144, absorbent cushioning material shall be inserted.

PP56   For UN 0144, metal receptacles may be used as inner packagings.

PP57   For UN Nos. 0075, 0143, 0495 and 0497, bags shall be used as intermediate packagings when boxes are used as outer packagings.

PP58   For UN Nos. 0075, 0143, 0495 and 0497, drums shall be used as intermediate packagings when drums are used as outer packagings.

PP59   For UN 0144, fibreboard boxes (4G) may be used as outer packagings.

PP60   For UN 0144, aluminium drums (1B1 or 1B2) and metal, other than steel or aluminium, drums (1N1 or 1N2) shall not be used.

4

P116	PACKING INSTRUCTION	P116

The following packagings are authorized, provided the general packing provisions of 4.1.1, 4.1.3 and special packing provisions of 4.1.5 are met.

Inner packagings	Intermediate packagings	Outer packagings
Bags 　paper, water- and oil-resistant 　plastics 　textile, plastic coated or lined 　woven plastics, sift-proof **Receptacles** 　fibreboard, water-resistant 　metal 　plastics 　wood, sift-proof **Sheets** 　paper, water-resistant 　paper, waxed 　plastics	*Not necessary*	**Bags** 　woven plastics (5H1, 5H2, 5H3) 　paper, multiwall, water-resistant 　　(5M2) 　plastics, film (5H4) 　textile, sift-proof (5L2) 　textile, water-resistant (5L3) **Boxes** 　steel (4A) 　aluminium (4B) 　other metal (4N) 　natural wood, ordinary (4C1) 　natural wood, sift-proof walls (4C2) 　plywood (4D) 　reconstituted wood (4F) 　fibreboard (4G) 　plastics, solid (4H2) **Drums** 　steel (1A1, 1A2) 　aluminium (1B1, 1B2) 　other metal (1N1, 1N2) 　fibre (1G) 　plastics (1H1, 1H2) 　plywood (1D) **Jerricans** 　steel (3A1, 3A2) 　plastics (3H1, 3H2)

Special packing provisions:

PP61 For UN Nos. 0082, 0241, 0331 and 0332, inner packagings are not required if leakproof removable head drums are used as the outer packaging.

PP62 For UN Nos. 0082, 0241, 0331 and 0332, inner packagings are not required when the explosive is contained in a material impervious to liquid.

PP63 For UN 0081, inner packagings are not required when contained in rigid plastic which is impervious to nitric esters.

PP64 For UN 0331, inner packagings are not required when bags (5H2, 5H3 or 5H4) are used as outer packagings.

PP65 [Deleted]

PP66 For UN 0081, bags shall not be used as outer packagings.

P130	PACKING INSTRUCTION	P130

The following packagings are authorized, provided the general packing provisions of 4.1.1, 4.1.3 and special packing provisions of 4.1.5 are met.

Inner packagings	Intermediate packagings	Outer packagings
Not necessary	*Not necessary*	**Boxes** steel (4A) aluminium (4B) other metal (4N) natural wood, ordinary (4C1) natural wood, sift-proof walls (4C2) plywood (4D) reconstituted wood (4F) fibreboard (4G) plastics, expanded (4H1) plastics, solid (4H2) **Drums** steel (1A1, 1A2) aluminium (1B1, 1B2) other metal (1N1, 1N2) plywood (1D) fibre (1G) plastics (1H1, 1H2)

Special packing provision:

△ **PP67** The following applies to UN Nos. 0006, 0009, 0010, 0015, 0016, 0018, 0019, 0034, 0035, 0038, 0039, 0048, 0056, 0137, 0138, 0168, 0169, 0171, 0181, 0182, 0183, 0186, 0221, 0243, 0244, 0245, 0246, 0254, 0280, 0281, 0286, 0287, 0297, 0299, 0300, 0301, 0303, 0321, 0328, 0329, 0344, 0345, 0346, 0347, 0362, 0363, 0370, 0412, 0424, 0425, 0434, 0435, 0436, 0437, 0438, 0451, 0488, 0502 and 0510: large and robust explosives articles, normally intended for military use, without their means of initiation or with their means of initiation containing at least two effective protective features, may be transported unpackaged. When such articles have propelling charges or are self-propelled, their ignition systems shall be protected against stimuli encountered during normal conditions of transport. A negative result in Test Series 4 on an unpackaged article indicates that the article can be considered for transport unpackaged. Such unpackaged articles may be fixed to cradles or contained in crates or other suitable handling devices.

P131	PACKING INSTRUCTION	P131

The following packagings are authorized, provided the general packing provisions of 4.1.1, 4.1.3 and special packing provisions of 4.1.5 are met.

Inner packagings	Intermediate packagings	Outer packagings
Bags paper plastics **Receptacles** fibreboard metal plastics wood **Reels**	*Not necessary*	**Boxes** steel (4A) aluminium (4B) other metal (4N) natural wood, ordinary (4C1) natural wood, sift-proof walls (4C2) plywood (4D) reconstituted wood (4F) fibreboard (4G) plastics, solid (4H2) **Drums** steel (1A1, 1A2) aluminium (1B1, 1B2) other metal (1N1, 1N2) plywood (1D) fibre (1G) plastics (1H1, 1H2)

Special packing provision:

PP68 For UN Nos. 0029, 0267 and 0455, bags and reels shall not be used as inner packagings.

4

P132(a)	PACKING INSTRUCTION	P132(a)
	(Articles consisting of closed metal, plastics or fibreboard casings that contain a detonating explosive, or consisting of plastics-bonded detonating explosives)	

The following packagings are authorized, provided the general packing provisions of 4.1.1, 4.1.3 and special packing provisions of 4.1.5 are met.

Inner packagings	Intermediate packagings	Outer packagings
Not necessary	*Not necessary*	**Boxes** steel (4A) aluminium (4B) other metal (4N) natural wood, ordinary (4C1) natural wood, sift-proof walls (4C2) plywood (4D) reconstituted wood (4F) fibreboard (4G) plastics, solid (4H2)

P132(b)	PACKING INSTRUCTION	P132(b)
	(Articles without closed casings)	

The following packagings are authorized, provided the general packing provisions of 4.1.1, 4.1.3 and special packing provisions of 4.1.5 are met.

Inner packagings	Intermediate packagings	Outer packagings
Receptacles fibreboard metal plastics wood **Sheets** paper plastics	*Not necessary*	**Boxes** steel (4A) aluminium (4B) other metal (4N) natural wood, ordinary (4C1) natural wood, sift-proof walls (4C2) plywood (4D) reconstituted wood (4F) fibreboard (4G) plastics, solid (4H2)

P133	PACKING INSTRUCTION	P133

The following packagings are authorized, provided the general packing provisions of 4.1.1, 4.1.3 and special packing provisions of 4.1.5 are met.

Inner packagings	Intermediate packagings	Outer packagings
Receptacles fibreboard metal plastics wood **Trays, fitted with dividing partitions** fibreboard plastics wood	**Receptacles** fibreboard metal plastics wood	**Boxes** steel (4A) aluminium (4B) other metal (4N) natural wood, ordinary (4C1) natural wood, sift-proof walls (4C2) plywood (4D) reconstituted wood (4F) fibreboard (4G) plastics, solid (4H2)

Additional provision:
Receptacles are only required as intermediate packagings when the inner packagings are trays.

Special packing provision:
PP69 For UN Nos. 0043, 0212, 0225, 0268 and 0306, trays shall not be used as inner packagings.

P134	PACKING INSTRUCTION	P134
The following packagings are authorized, provided the general packing provisions of 4.1.1, 4.1.3 and special packing provisions of 4.1.5 are met.		

Inner packagings	Intermediate packagings	Outer packagings

Bags
  water-resistant
 	
Receptacles
  fibreboard
  metal
  plastics
  wood
 	
Sheets
  fibreboard, corrugated
 	
Tubes
  fibreboard
	Not necessary	**Boxes**
		  steel (4A)
		  aluminium (4B)
		  other metal (4N)
		  natural wood, ordinary (4C1)
		  natural wood, sift-proof walls (4C2)
		  plywood (4D)
		  reconstituted wood (4F)
		  fibreboard (4G)
		  plastics, expanded (4H1)
		  plastics, solid (4H2)
		
		Drums
		  steel (1A1, 1A2)
		  aluminium (1B1, 1B2)
		  other metal (1N1, 1N2)
		  plywood (1D)
		  fibre (1G)
		  plastics (1H1, 1H2)

P135	PACKING INSTRUCTION	P135
The following packagings are authorized, provided the general packing provisions of 4.1.1, 4.1.3 and special packing provisions of 4.1.5 are met.		

Inner packagings	Intermediate packagings	Outer packagings

Bags
  paper
  plastics
 	
Receptacles
  fibreboard
  metal
  plastics
  wood
 	
Sheets
  paper
  plastics
	Not necessary	**Boxes**
		  steel (4A)
		  aluminium (4B)
		  other metal (4N)
		  natural wood, ordinary (4C1)
		  natural wood, sift-proof walls (4C2)
		  plywood (4D)
		  reconstituted wood (4F)
		  fibreboard (4G)
		  plastics, expanded (4H1)
		  plastics, solid (4H2)
		
		Drums
		  steel (1A1, 1A2)
		  aluminium (1B1, 1B2)
		  other metal (1N1, 1N2)
		  plywood (1D)
		  fibre (1G)
		  plastics (1H1, 1H2)

P136	PACKING INSTRUCTION	P136
The following packagings are authorized, provided the general packing provisions of 4.1.1, 4.1.3 and special packing provisions of 4.1.5 are met.		

Inner packagings	Intermediate packagings	Outer packagings

Bags
  plastics
  textile
 	
Boxes
  fibreboard
  plastics
  wood
 	
**Dividing partitions in the outer
  packagings**
	Not necessary	**Boxes**
		  steel (4A)
		  aluminium (4B)
		  other metal (4N)
		  natural wood, ordinary (4C1)
		  natural wood, sift-proof walls (4C2)
		  plywood (4D)
		  reconstituted wood (4F)
		  fibreboard (4G)
		  plastics, solid (4H2)
		
		Drums
		  steel (1A1, 1A2)
		  aluminium (1B1, 1B2)
		  other metal (1N1, 1N2)
		  plywood (1D)
		  fibre (1G)
		  plastics (1H1, 1H2)

4

P137	PACKING INSTRUCTION	P137

The following packagings are authorized, provided the general packing provisions of 4.1.1, 4.1.3 and special packing provisions of 4.1.5 are met.

Inner packagings	Intermediate packagings	Outer packagings

Bags
  plastics
Boxes
  fibreboard
  wood
Tubes
  fibreboard
  metal
  plastics
Dividing partitions in the outer packagings
	Not necessary	**Boxes**
		  steel (4A)
		  aluminium (4B)
		  other metal (4N)
		  natural wood, ordinary (4C1)
		  natural wood, sift-proof walls (4C2)
		  plywood (4D)
		  reconstituted wood (4F)
		  fibreboard (4G)
		  plastics, solid (4H2)
		
		Drums
		  steel (1A1, 1A2)
		  aluminium (1B1, 1B2)
		  other metal (1N1, 1N2)
		  plywood (1D)
		  fibre (1G)
		  plastics (1H1, 1H2)

Special packing provision:

△ **PP70** For UN Nos. 0059, 0439, 0440 and 0441, when the shaped charges are packed singly, the conical cavity shall face downwards and the package shall be marked in accordance with 5.2.1.7.1. When the shaped charges are packed in pairs, the conical cavities shall face inwards to minimize the jetting effect in the event of accidental initiation.

P138	PACKING INSTRUCTION	P138

The following packagings are authorized, provided the general packing provisions of 4.1.1, 4.1.3 and special packing provisions of 4.1.5 are met.

Inner packagings	Intermediate packagings	Outer packagings

Bags
  plastics
	Not necessary	**Boxes**
		  steel (4A)
		  aluminium (4B)
		  other metal (4N)
		  natural wood, ordinary (4C1)
		  natural wood, sift-proof walls (4C2)
		  plywood (4D)
		  reconstituted wood (4F)
		  fibreboard (4G)
		  plastics, solid (4H2)
		
		Drums
		  steel (1A1, 1A2)
		  aluminium (1B1, 1B2)
		  other metal (1N1, 1N2)
		  plywood (1D)
		  fibre (1G)
		  plastics (1H1, 1H2)

Additional provision:
If the ends of the articles are sealed, inner packagings are not necessary.

P139	PACKING INSTRUCTION	P139
\multicolumn{3}{}{The following packagings are authorized, provided the general packing provisions of 4.1.1, 4.1.3 and special packing provisions of 4.1.5 are met.}		

Inner packagings	Intermediate packagings	Outer packagings
Bags plastics **Receptacles** fibreboard metal plastics wood **Reels** **Sheets** paper plastics	*Not necessary*	**Boxes** steel (4A) aluminium (4B) other metal (4N) natural wood, ordinary (4C1) natural wood, sift-proof walls (4C2) plywood (4D) reconstituted wood (4F) fibreboard (4G) plastics, solid (4H2) **Drums** steel (1A1, 1A2) aluminium (1B1, 1B2) other metal (1N1, 1N2) plywood (1D) fibre (1G) plastics (1H1, 1H2)

Special packing provisions:

PP71 For UN Nos. 0065, 0102, 0104, 0289 and 0290, the ends of the detonating cord shall be sealed; for example, by a plug firmly fixed so that the explosive cannot escape. The ends of flexible detonating cord shall be fastened securely.

PP72 For UN Nos. 0065 and 0289, inner packagings are not required when they are in coils.

P140	PACKING INSTRUCTION	P140
\multicolumn{3}{}{The following packagings are authorized, provided the general packing provisions of 4.1.1, 4.1.3 and special packing provisions of 4.1.5 are met.}		

Inner packagings	Intermediate packagings	Outer packagings
Bags plastics **Reels** **Sheets** paper, kraft plastics **Receptacles** wood	*Not necessary*	**Boxes** steel (4A) aluminium (4B) other metal (4N) natural wood, ordinary (4C1) natural wood, sift-proof walls (4C2) plywood (4D) reconstituted wood (4F) fibreboard (4G) plastics, solid (4H2) **Drums** steel (1A1, 1A2) aluminium (1B1, 1B2) other metal (1N1, 1N2) plywood (1D) fibre (1G) plastics (1H1, 1H2)

Special packing provisions:

PP73 For UN 0105, no inner packagings are required if the ends are sealed.

PP74 For UN 0101, the packaging shall be sift-proof except when the fuse is covered by a paper tube and both ends of the tube are covered with removable caps.

PP75 For UN 0101, steel, aluminium or other metal boxes or drums shall not be used.

P141	PACKING INSTRUCTION	P141
The following packagings are authorized, provided the general packing provisions of 4.1.1, 4.1.3 and special packing provisions of 4.1.5 are met.		

Inner packagings	Intermediate packagings	Outer packagings

Receptacles
  fibreboard
  metal
  plastics
  wood
 	
Trays, fitted with dividing partitions
  plastics
  wood
 	
Dividing partitions in the outer
  packagings
	Not necessary	**Boxes**
		  steel (4A)
		  aluminium (4B)
		  other metal (4N)
		  natural wood, ordinary (4C1)
		  natural wood, sift-proof walls (4C2)
		  plywood (4D)
		  reconstituted wood (4F)
		  fibreboard (4G)
		  plastics, solid (4H2)
		
		Drums
		  steel (1A1, 1A2)
		  aluminium (1B1, 1B2)
		  other metal (1N1, 1N2)
		  plywood (1D)
		  fibre (1G)
		  plastics (1H1, 1H2)

P142	PACKING INSTRUCTION	P142
The following packagings are authorized, provided the general packing provisions of 4.1.1, 4.1.3 and special packing provisions of 4.1.5 are met.		

Inner packagings	Intermediate packagings	Outer packagings

Bags
  paper
  plastics
 	
Receptacles
  fibreboard
  metal
  plastics
  wood
 	
Sheets
  paper
 	
Trays, fitted with dividing partitions
  plastics
	Not necessary	**Boxes**
		  steel (4A)
		  aluminium (4B)
		  other metal (4N)
		  natural wood, ordinary (4C1)
		  natural wood, sift-proof walls (4C2)
		  plywood (4D)
		  reconstituted wood (4F)
		  fibreboard (4G)
		  plastics, solid (4H2)
		
		Drums
		  steel (1A1, 1A2)
		  aluminium (1B1, 1B2)
		  other metal (1N1, 1N2)
		  plywood (1D)
		  fibre (1G)
		  plastics (1H1, 1H2)

4

P143	PACKING INSTRUCTION	P143

The following packagings are authorized, provided the general packing provisions of 4.1.1, 4.1.3 and special packing provisions of 4.1.5 are met.

Inner packagings	Intermediate packagings	Outer packagings

Bags
  paper, kraft
  plastics
  textile
  textile, rubberized
 	
Receptacles
  fibreboard
  metal
  plastics
  wood
 	
Trays, fitted with dividing partitions
  plastics
  wood
	Not necessary	**Boxes**
		  steel (4A)
		  aluminium (4B)
		  other metal (4N)
		  natural wood, ordinary (4C1)
		  natural wood, sift-proof walls (4C2)
		  plywood (4D)
		  reconstituted wood (4F)
		  fibreboard (4G)
		  plastics, solid (4H2)
		
		Drums
		  steel (1A1, 1A2)
		  aluminium (1B1, 1B2)
		  other metal (1N1, 1N2)
		  plywood (1D)
		  fibre (1G)
		  plastics (1H1, 1H2)

Additional provision:

Instead of the above inner and outer packagings, composite packagings (6HH2) (plastics receptacle with outer solid box) may be used.

Special packing provision:

PP76 For UN Nos. 0271, 0272, 0415 and 0491, when metal packagings are used, metal packagings shall be so constructed that the risk of explosion, by reason of increase in internal pressure from internal or external causes, is prevented.

P144	PACKING INSTRUCTION	P144

The following packagings are authorized, provided the general packing provisions of 4.1.1, 4.1.3 and special packing provisions of 4.1.5 are met.

Inner packagings	Intermediate packagings	Outer packagings

Receptacles
  fibreboard
  metal
  plastics
  wood
 	
Dividing partitions in the outer packagings
	Not necessary	**Boxes**
		  steel (4A)
		  aluminium (4B)
		  other metal (4N)
		  natural wood, ordinary with
		    metal liner (4C1)
		  plywood (4D) with metal liner
		  reconstituted wood with
		    metal liner (4F)
		  plastics, expanded (4H1)
		  plastics, solid (4H2)
		
		Drums
		  steel (1A1, 1A2)
		  aluminium (1B1, 1B2)
		  other metal (1N1, 1N2)
		  plastics (1H1, 1H2)

Special packing provision:

PP77 For UN Nos. 0248 and 0249, packagings shall be protected against the ingress of water. When water-activated contrivances are transported unpackaged, they shall be provided with at least two independent protective features which prevent the ingress of water.

4

P200	PACKING INSTRUCTION	P200

For pressure receptacles, the general packing provisions of 4.1.6.1 shall be met. In addition, for MEGCs, the general requirements of 4.2.4 shall be met.

Cylinders, tubes, pressure drums, bundles of cylinders constructed as specified in 6.2 and MEGCs constructed as specified in 6.7.5 are authorized for the transport of a specific substance when specified in the following tables. For some substances, the special packing provisions may prohibit a particular type of cylinder, tube, pressure drum or bundle of cylinders.

(1) Pressure receptacles containing toxic substances with an LC_{50} less than or equal to 200 mL/m³ (ppm) as specified in the table shall not be equipped with any pressure relief device. Pressure relief devices shall be fitted on pressure receptacles used for the transport of UN 1013 carbon dioxide and UN 1070 nitrous oxide. Other pressure receptacles shall be fitted with a pressure relief device if specified by the competent authority of the country of use. The type of pressure relief device, the set-to-discharge pressure and relief capacity of pressure relief devices, if required, shall be specified by the competent authority of the country of use.

△ (2) The following three tables cover compressed gases (Table 1), liquefied and dissolved gases (Table 2) and substances not in Class 2 (Table 3). They provide:

  (a) The UN number, name and description, and classification of the substance;

  (b) The LC_{50} for toxic substances;

  (c) The types of pressure receptacles authorized for the substance, shown by the letter "X";

  (d) The maximum test period for periodic inspection of the pressure receptacles.

  Note: For pressure receptacles which make use of composite materials, the maximum test period shall be 5 years. The test period may be extended to that specified in Tables 1 and 2 (i.e. up to 10 years), if approved by the competent authority of the country of use.

  (e) The minimum test pressure of the pressure receptacles;

  (f) The maximum working pressure of the pressure receptacles for compressed gases (where no value is given, the working pressure shall not exceed two thirds of the test pressure) or the maximum filling ratio(s) dependent on the test pressure(s) for liquefied and dissolved gases;

  (g) Special packing provisions that are specific to a substance.

(3) In no case shall pressure receptacles be filled in excess of the limit permitted in the following requirements.

  (a) For compressed gases, the working pressure shall be not more than two thirds of the test pressure of the pressure receptacles. Restrictions to this upper limit on working pressure are imposed by special packing provision "o" in (4) below. In no case shall the internal pressure at 65°C exceed the test pressure.

  (b) For high pressure liquefied gases, the filling ratio shall be such that the settled pressure at 65°C does not exceed the test pressure of the pressure receptacles.

  The use of test pressures and filling ratios other than those in the table is permitted, except where (4), special packing provision "o" applies, provided that:

  (i) the criterion of (4), special packing provision "r" is met when applicable; or

  (ii) the above criterion is met in all other cases.

  For high pressure liquefied gases and gas mixtures for which relevant data are not available, the maximum filling ratio (*FR*) shall be determined as follows:

  $$FR = 8.5 \times 10^{-4} \times d_g \times P_h$$

  where FR = maximum filling ratio
  d_g = gas density (at 15°C, 1 bar) (in g/L)
  P_h = minimum test pressure (in bar)

  If the density of the gas is unknown, the maximum filling ratio shall be determined as follows:

  $$FR = \frac{P_h \times MM \times 10^{-3}}{R \times 338}$$

  where FR = maximum filling ratio
  P_h = minimum test pressure (in bar)
  MM = molecular mass (in g/mol)
  R = 8.31451 × 10⁻² bar·L/mol·K (gas constant)

  For gas mixtures, the average molecular mass is to be taken, taking into account the volumetric concentrations of the various components.

  (c) For low pressure liquefied gases, the maximum mass of contents per litre of water capacity (filling factor) shall equal 0.95 times the density of the liquid phase at 50°C; in addition, the liquid phase shall not fill the pressure receptacle at any temperature up to 60°C. The test pressure of the pressure receptacle shall be at least equal to the vapour pressure (absolute) of the liquid at 65°C, minus 100 kPa (1 bar).

  For low pressure liquefied gases and gas mixtures for which relevant data are not available, the maximum filling ratio shall be determined as follows:

  $$FR = (0.0032 \times BP - 0.24) \times d_l$$

  where FR = maximum filling ratio
  BP = boiling point (in kelvin)
  d_l = density of the liquid at boiling point (in kg/L)

  (d) For UN 1001, acetylene, dissolved, and UN 3374 acetylene, solvent free, see (4), special packing provision "p".

P200	PACKING INSTRUCTION *(continued)*	P200

(e) For liquefied gases charged with compressed gases, both components – the liquid phase and the compressed gas – have to be taken into consideration in the calculation of the internal pressure in the pressure receptacle.

The maximum mass of contents per litre of water capacity shall not exceed 0.95 times the density of the liquid phase at 50°C; in addition, the liquid phase shall not completely fill the pressure receptacle at any temperature up to 60°C.

When filled, the internal pressure at 65°C shall not exceed the test pressure of the pressure receptacles. The vapour pressures and volumetric expansions of all substances in the pressure receptacles shall be considered. When experimental data is not available, the following steps shall be carried out:

(i) calculation of the vapour pressure of the liquid component and of the partial pressure of the compressed gas at 15°C (filling temperature);

(ii) calculation of the volumetric expansion of the liquid phase resulting from the heating from 15°C to 65°C and calculation of the remaining volume for the gaseous phase;

(iii) calculation of the partial pressure of the compressed gas at 65°C considering the volumetric expansion of the liquid phase;

Note: The compressibility factor of the compressed gas at 15°C and 65°C shall be considered.

(iv) calculation of the vapour pressure of the liquid component at 65°C;

(v) the total pressure is the sum of the vapour pressure of the liquid component and the partial pressure of the compressed gas at 65°C;

(vi) consideration of the solubility of the compressed gas at 65°C in the liquid phase.

The test pressure of the pressure receptacle shall not be less than the calculated total pressure minus 100 kPa (1bar).

If the solubility of the compressed gas in the liquid component is not known for the calculation, the test pressure can be calculated without taking the gas solubility (subparagraph (vi)) into account.

(4) The filling of pressure receptacles shall be carried out by qualified staff using appropriate equipment and procedures.

The procedures should include checks of:

– the conformity of receptacles and accessories with the provisions of this Code;

– their compatibility with the product to be transported;

– the absence of damage which might affect safety;

– compliance with the degree or pressure of filling, as appropriate;

– marks and identification.

These requirements are deemed to be met if the following standards are applied:

ISO 10691:2004	Gas cylinders – Refillable welded steel cylinders for liquefied petroleum gas (LPG) – Procedures for checking before, during and after filling.
ISO 11372:2011	Gas cylinders – Acetylene cylinders – Filling conditions and filling inspection
ISO 11755:2005	Gas cylinders – Cylinder bundles for compressed and liquefied gases (excluding acetylene) – Inspection at time of filling
ISO 13088:2011	Gas cylinders – Acetylene cylinder bundles – Filling conditions and filling inspection
ISO 24431:2006	Gas cylinders – Cylinders for compressed and liquefied gases (excluding acetylene) – Inspection at time of filling

(5) Special packing provisions:

Material compatibility

a: Aluminium alloy pressure receptacles shall not be used.

b: Copper valves shall not be used.

c: Metal parts in contact with the contents shall not contain more than 65% copper.

d: When steel pressure receptacles are used, only those bearing the "H" mark in accordance with 6.2.2.7.4 (p) are permitted.

Requirements for toxic substances with an LC_{50} less than or equal to 200 mL/m³ (ppm)

k: Valve outlets shall be fitted with pressure-retaining gas-tight plugs or caps having threads that match those of the valve outlets.

Each cylinder within a bundle shall be fitted with an individual valve that shall be closed during transport. After filling, the manifold shall be evacuated, purged and plugged.

Bundles containing UN 1045 fluorine, compressed, may be constructed with isolation valves on groups of cylinders not exceeding 150 litres total water capacity instead of isolation valves on every cylinder.

Cylinders and individual cylinders in a bundle shall have a test pressure greater than or equal to 200 bar and a minimum wall thickness of 3.5 mm for aluminium alloy or 2 mm for steel. Individual cylinders not complying with this requirement shall be transported in a rigid outer packaging that will adequately protect the cylinder and its fittings and meeting the packing group I performance level. Pressure drums shall have a minimum wall thickness as specified by the competent authority.

Pressure receptacles shall not be fitted with a pressure relief device.

Cylinders and individual cylinders in a bundle shall be limited to a maximum water capacity of 85 L.

Each valve shall be capable of withstanding the test pressure of the pressure receptacle and be connected directly to the pressure receptacle by either a taper thread or other means which meets the requirements of ISO 10692-2:2001.

4

P200	PACKING INSTRUCTION *(continued)*	P200

Each valve shall either be of the packless type with non-perforated diaphragm, or be of a type which prevents leakage through or past the packing.

Each pressure receptacle shall be tested for leakage after filling.

Gas specific provisions

l: UN 1040 ethylene oxide may also be packed in hermetically sealed glass or metal inner packagings suitably cushioned in fibreboard, wooden or metal boxes meeting the packing group I performance level. The maximum quantity permitted in any glass inner packaging is 30 g, and the maximum quantity permitted in any metal inner packaging is 200 g. After filling, each inner packaging shall be determined to be leaktight by placing the inner packaging in a hot water bath at a temperature, and for a period of time, sufficient to ensure that an internal pressure equal to the vapour pressure of ethylene oxide at 55°C is achieved. The maximum net mass in any outer packaging shall not exceed 2.5 kg.

m: Pressure receptacles shall be filled to a working pressure not exceeding 5 bar.

n: Cylinders and individual cylinders in a bundle shall contain not more than 5 kg of the gas. When bundles containing UN 1045 fluorine, compressed are divided into groups of cylinders in accordance with special packing provision "k" each group shall contain not more than 5 kg of the gas.

o: In no case shall the working pressure or filling ratio shown in the table be exceeded.

△ p: For UN 1001 acetylene, dissolved and UN 3374 acetylene, solvent free: cylinders shall be filled with a homogeneous monolithic porous material; the working pressure and the quantity of acetylene shall not exceed the values prescribed in the approval or in ISO 3807-1:2000, ISO 3807-2:2000 or ISO 3807:2013, as applicable.

For UN 1001 acetylene, dissolved: cylinders shall contain a quantity of acetone or suitable solvent as specified in the approval (see ISO 3807-1:2000, ISO 3807-2:2000 or ISO 3807:2013, as applicable); cylinders fitted with pressure relief devices or manifolded together shall be transported vertically.

The test pressure of 52 bar applies only to cylinders fitted with a fusible plug.

q: Valve outlets of pressure receptacles for pyrophoric gases or flammable mixtures of gases containing more than 1% of pyrophoric compounds shall be fitted with gas-tight plugs or caps. When these pressure receptacles are manifolded in a bundle, each of the pressure receptacles shall be fitted with an individual valve that shall be closed during transport, and the outlet of the manifold valve shall be fitted with a pressure-retaining gas-tight plug or cap. Gas-tight plugs or caps shall have threads that match those of the valve outlets.

r: The filling ratio of this gas shall be limited such that, if complete decomposition occurs, the pressure does not exceed two thirds of the test pressure of the pressure receptacle.

ra: This gas may also be packed in capsules under the following conditions:
   (i) The mass of gas shall not exceed 150 g per capsule;
   (ii) The capsules shall be free from faults liable to impair the strength;
   (iii) The leakproofness of the closure shall be ensured by an additional device (cap, crown, seal, binding, etc.) capable of preventing any leakage of the closure during transport;
   (iv) The capsules shall be placed in an outer packaging of sufficient strength. A package shall not weigh more than 75 kg.

s: Aluminium alloy pressure receptacles shall be:
   – equipped only with brass or stainless steel valves; and
   – cleaned in accordance with ISO 11621:1997 and not contaminated with oil.

t: (i) The wall thickness of pressure receptacles shall be not less than 3 mm.
   (ii) Prior to transport, it shall be ensured that the pressure has not risen due to potential hydrogen generation.

Periodic inspection

△ u: The interval between periodic tests may be extended to 10 years for aluminium alloy pressure receptacles when the alloy of the pressure receptacle has been subjected to stress corrosion testing as specified in ISO 7866:2012 + Cor 1:2014.

v: The interval between periodic inspections for steel cylinders may be extended to 15 years if approved by the competent authority of the country of use.

Requirements for N.O.S. descriptions and for mixtures

z: The construction materials of the pressure receptacles and their accessories shall be compatible with the contents and shall not react to form harmful or dangerous compounds therewith.

The test pressure and filling ratio shall be calculated in accordance with the relevant requirements of (3).

Toxic substances with an LC_{50} less than or equal to 200 mL/m^3 shall not be transported in tubes, pressure drums or MEGCs and shall meet the requirements of special packing provision "k". However, UN 1975 nitric oxide and dinitrogen tetroxide mixtures may be transported in pressure drums.

For pressure receptacles containing pyrophoric gases or flammable mixtures of gases containing more than 1% pyrophoric compounds, the requirements of special packing provision "q" shall be met.

The necessary steps shall be taken to prevent dangerous reactions (i.e. polymerization or decomposition) during transport. If necessary, stabilization or addition of an inhibitor shall be required.

Mixtures containing UN 1911 diborane shall be filled to a pressure such that, if complete decomposition of the diborane occurs, two thirds of the test pressure of the pressure receptacle shall not be exceeded. Mixtures containing UN 2192 germane, other than mixtures of up to 35% germane in hydrogen or nitrogen or up to 28% germane in helium or argon, shall be filled to a pressure such that, if complete decomposition of the germane occurs, two thirds of the test pressure of the pressure receptacle shall not be exceeded.

P200	PACKING INSTRUCTION (continued)											P200
	Table 1: COMPRESSED GASES											

UN No.	Proper shipping name	Class	Subsidiary risk	LC_{50}, mL_v/m^3	Cylinders	Tubes	Pressure drums	Bundles of cylinders	MEGCs	Test period, years	Test pressure, bar[*]	Maximum working pressure, bar[*]	Special packing provisions
1002	AIR, COMPRESSED	2.2			X	X	X	X	X	10			
1006	ARGON, COMPRESSED	2.2			X	X	X	X	X	10			
1016	CARBON MONOXIDE, COMPRESSED	2.3	2.1	3760	X	X	X	X	X	5			u
1023	COAL GAS, COMPRESSED	2.3	2.1		X	X	X	X	X	5			
1045	FLUORINE, COMPRESSED	2.3	5.1, 8	185	X			X		5	200	30	a, k, n, o
1046	HELIUM, COMPRESSED	2.2			X	X	X	X	X	10			
1049	HYDROGEN, COMPRESSED	2.1			X	X	X	X	X	10			d
1056	KRYPTON, COMPRESSED	2.2			X	X	X	X	X	10			
1065	NEON, COMPRESSED	2.2			X	X	X	X	X	10			
1066	NITROGEN, COMPRESSED	2.2			X	X	X	X	X	10			
1071	OIL GAS, COMPRESSED	2.3	2.1		X	X	X	X	X	5			
1072	OXYGEN, COMPRESSED	2.2	5.1		X	X	X	X		10			s
1612	HEXAETHYL TETRAPHOSPHATE AND COMPRESSED GAS MIXTURE	2.3			X	X	X	X		5			z
1660	NITRIC OXIDE, COMPRESSED	2.3	5.1, 8	115	X			X		5	225	33	k, o
1953	COMPRESSED GAS, TOXIC, FLAMMABLE, N.O.S.	2.3	2.1	≤5000	X	X	X	X	X	5			z
1954	COMPRESSED GAS, FLAMMABLE, N.O.S	2.1			X	X	X	X	X	10			z
1955	COMPRESSED GAS, TOXIC, N.O.S.	2.3		≤5000	X	X	X	X	X	5			z
1956	COMPRESSED GAS, N.O.S.	2.2			X	X	X	X	X	10			z
1957	DEUTERIUM, COMPRESSED	2.1			X	X	X	X	X	10			d
1964	HYDROCARBON GAS MIXTURE, COMPRESSED, N.O.S.	2.1			X	X	X	X	X	10			z
1971	METHANE, COMPRESSED or NATURAL GAS, COMPRESSED with high methane content	2.1			X	X	X	X	X	10			
2034	HYDROGEN AND METHANE MIXTURE, COMPRESSED	2.1			X	X	X	X	X	10			d
2190	OXYGEN DIFLUORIDE, COMPRESSED	2.3	5.1, 8	2.6	X			X		5	200	30	a, k, n, o
3156	COMPRESSED GAS, OXIDIZING, N.O.S.	2.2	5.1		X	X	X	X	X	10			z
3303	COMPRESSED GAS, TOXIC, OXIDIZING, N.O.S.	2.3	5.1	≤5000	X	X	X	X	X	5			z
3304	COMPRESSED GAS, TOXIC, CORROSIVE, N.O.S.	2.3	8	≤5000	X	X	X	X	X	5			z
3305	COMPRESSED GAS, TOXIC, FLAMMABLE, CORROSIVE, N.O.S.	2.3	2.1, 8	≤5000	X	X	X	X	X	5			z
3306	COMPRESSED GAS, TOXIC, OXIDIZING, CORROSIVE, N.O.S.	2.3	5.1, 8	≤5000	X	X	X	X	X	5			z

[*] Where the entries are blank, the maximum working pressure shall not exceed two thirds of the test pressure.

4

P200	PACKING INSTRUCTION *(continued)*											P200
Table 2: LIQUEFIED GASES AND DISSOLVED GASES												
UN No.	Proper shipping name	Class	Subsidiary risk	LC_{50}, mL/m³	Cylinders	Tubes	Pressure drums	Bundles of cylinders	MEGCs	Test period, years	Test pressure, bar*	Filling ratio	Special packing provisions
1001	ACETYLENE, DISSOLVED	2.1			X			X		10	60 52		c, p
1005	AMMONIA, ANHYDROUS	2.3	8	4000	X	X	X	X	X	5	29	0.54	b
1008	BORON TRIFLUORIDE	2.3	8	387	X	X	X	X	X	5	225 300	0.715 0.86	a
1009	BROMOTRIFLUOROMETHANE (REFRIGERANT GAS R 13B1)	2.2			X	X	X	X	X	10	42 120 250	1.13 1.44 1.60	
1010	BUTADIENES, STABILIZED (1,2-butadiene), or	2.1			X	X	X	X	X	10	10	0.59	
1010	BUTADIENES, STABILIZED (1,3-butadiene), or	2.1			X	X	X	X	X	10	10	0.55	
1010	BUTADIENES AND HYDROCARBON MIXTURE, STABILIZED with more than 40% butadienes	2.1			X	X	X	X	X	10			v, z
1011	BUTANE	2.1			X	X	X	X	X	10	10	0.52	v
1012	BUTYLENE (butylenes mixture) or	2.1			X	X	X	X	X	10	10	0.50	z
1012	BUTYLENE (1-butylene) or	2.1			X	X	X	X	X	10	10	0.53	
1012	BUTYLENE (*cis*-2-butylene) or	2.1			X	X	X	X	X	10	10	0.55	
1012	BUTYLENE (*trans*-2-butylene)	2.1			X	X	X	X	X	10	10	0.54	
1013	CARBON DIOXIDE	2.2			X	X	X	X	X	10	190 250	0.68 0.76	
1017	CHLORINE	2.3	5.1, 8	293	X	X	X	X	X	5	22	1.25	a
1018	CHLORODIFLUOROMETHANE (REFRIGERANT GAS R 22)	2.2			X	X	X	X	X	10	27	1.03	
1020	CHLOROPENTAFLUOROETHANE (REFRIGERANT GAS R 115)	2.2			X	X	X	X	X	10	25	1.05	
1021	1-CHLORO-1,2,2,2-TETRAFLUOROETHANE (REFRIGERANT GAS R 124)	2.2			X	X	X	X	X	10	11	1.20	
1022	CHLOROTRIFLUOROMETHANE (REFRIGERANT GAS R 13)	2.2			X	X	X	X	X	10	100 120 190 250	0.83 0.90 1.04 1.11	
1026	CYANOGEN	2.3	2.1	350	X	X	X	X	X	5	100	0.70	u
1027	CYCLOPROPANE	2.1			X	X	X	X	X	10	18	0.55	
1028	DICHLORODIFLUOROMETHANE (REFRIGERANT GAS R 12)	2.2			X	X	X	X	X	10	16	1.15	
1029	DICHLOROFLUOROMETHANE (REFRIGERANT GAS R 21)	2.2			X	X	X	X	X	10	10	1.23	
1030	1,1-DIFLUOROETHANE (REFRIGERANT GAS R 152a)	2.1			X	X	X	X	X	10	16	0.79	
1032	DIMETHYLAMINE, ANHYDROUS	2.1			X	X	X	X	X	10	10	0.59	b
1033	DIMETHYL ETHER	2.1			X	X	X	X	X	10	18	0.58	
1035	ETHANE	2.1			X	X	X	X	X	10	95 120 300	0.25 0.30 0.40	
1036	ETHYLAMINE	2.1			X	X	X	X	X	10	10	0.61	b
1037	ETHYL CHLORIDE	2.1			X	X	X	X	X	10	10	0.80	a, ra
1039	ETHYL METHYL ETHER	2.1			X	X	X	X	X	10	10	0.64	
1040	ETHYLENE OXIDE or ETHYLENE OXIDE WITH NITROGEN up to a total pressure of 1 MPa (10 bar) at 50°C	2.3	2.1	2900	X	X	X	X	X	5	15	0.78	l

*Where the entries are blank, the maximum working pressure shall not exceed two thirds of the test pressure.

IMDG Code (amendment 38-16)

P200	PACKING INSTRUCTION *(continued)*											P200
Table 2: LIQUEFIED GASES AND DISSOLVED GASES *(continued)*												
UN No.	Proper shipping name	Class	Subsidiary risk	LC_{50}, mL/m³	Cylinders	Tubes	Pressure drums	Bundles of cylinders	MEGCs	Test period, years	Test pressure, bar[*]	Filling ratio	Special packing provisions
1041	ETHYLENE OXIDE AND CARBON DIOXIDE MIXTURE with more than 9% ethylene oxide but not more than 87%	2.1			X	X	X	X	X	10	190 250	0.66 0.75	
1043	FERTILIZER AMMONIATING SOLUTION with free ammonia	2.2			X		X	X		5			b, z
1048	HYDROGEN BROMIDE, ANHYDROUS	2.3	8	2860	X	X	X	X	X	5	60	1.51	a, d
1050	HYDROGEN CHLORIDE, ANHYDROUS	2.3	8	2810	X	X	X	X	X	5	100 120 150 200	0.30 0.56 0.67 0.74	a, d a, d a, d a, d
1053	HYDROGEN SULPHIDE	2.3	2.1	712	X	X	X	X	X	5	48	0.67	d, u
1055	ISOBUTYLENE	2.1			X	X	X	X	X	10	10	0.52	
1058	LIQUEFIED GASES, non-flammable, charged with nitrogen, carbon dioxide or air	2.2			X	X	X	X	X	10			z
1060	METHYLACETYLENE AND PROPADIENE MIXTURE, STABILIZED or	2.1			X	X	X	X	X	10			c, z
1060	METHYLACETYLENE AND PROPADIENE MIXTURE, STABILIZED (Propadiene with 1% to 4% methylacetylene)	2.1			X	X	X	X	X	10	22	0.52	c
1061	METHYLAMINE, ANHYDROUS	2.1			X	X	X	X	X	10	13	0.58	b
1062	METHYL BROMIDE with not more than 2% chloropicrin	2.3		850	X	X	X	X	X	5	10	1.51	a
1063	METHYL CHLORIDE (REFRIGERANT GAS R 40)	2.1			X	X	X	X	X	10	17	0.81	a
1064	METHYL MERCAPTAN	2.3	2.1	1350	X	X	X	X	X	5	10	0.78	d, u
1067	DINITROGEN TETROXIDE (NITROGEN DIOXIDE)	2.3	5.1, 8	115	X		X	X		5	10	1.30	k
1069	NITROSYL CHLORIDE	2.3	8	35	X			X		5	13	1.10	k
1070	NITROUS OXIDE	2.2	5.1		X	X	X	X	X	10	180 225 250	0.68 0.74 0.75	
1075	PETROLEUM GASES, LIQUEFIED	2.1			X	X	X	X	X	10			v, z
1076	PHOSGENE	2.3	8	5	X			X	X	5	20	1.23	k, a
1077	PROPYLENE	2.1			X	X	X	X	X	10	27	0.43	
1078	REFRIGERANT GAS, N.O.S.	2.2			X	X	X	X	X	10			z
1079	SULPHUR DIOXIDE	2.3	8	2520	X	X	X	X	X	5	12	1.23	
1080	SULPHUR HEXAFLUORIDE	2.2			X	X	X	X	X	10	70 140 160	1.06 1.34 1.38	
1081	TETRAFLUOROETHYLENE, STABILIZED	2.1			X	X	X	X	X	10	200		m, o
1082	TRIFLUOROCHLOROETHYLENE, STABILIZED	2.3	2.1	2000	X	X	X	X	X	5	19	1.13	u
1083	TRIMETHYLAMINE, ANHYDROUS	2.1			X	X	X	X	X	10	10	0.56	b
1085	VINYL BROMIDE, STABILIZED	2.1			X	X	X	X	X	10	10	1.37	a
1086	VINYL CHLORIDE, STABILIZED	2.1			X	X	X	X	X	10	12	0.81	a
1087	VINYL METHYL ETHER, STABILIZED	2.1			X	X	X	X	X	10	10	0.67	
1581	CHLOROPICRIN AND METHYL BROMIDE MIXTURE with more than 2% chloropicrin	2.3		850	X	X	X	X	X	5	10	1.51	a
1582	CHLOROPICRIN AND METHYL CHLORIDE MIXTURE	2.3			X	X	X	X	X	5	17	0.81	a
1589	CYANOGEN CHLORIDE, STABILIZED	2.3	8	80	X			X		5	20	1.03	k
1741	BORON TRICHLORIDE	2.3	8	2541	X	X	X	X	X	5	10	1.19	a

[*] Where the entries are blank, the maximum working pressure shall not exceed two thirds of the test pressure.

P200	PACKING INSTRUCTION (continued)											P200

Table 2: LIQUEFIED GASES AND DISSOLVED GASES (continued)

UN No.	Proper shipping name	Class	Subsidiary risk	LC_{50}, mL/m³	Cylinders	Tubes	Pressure drums	Bundles of cylinders	MEGCs	Test period, years	Test pressure, bar[*]	Filling ratio	Special packing provisions
1749	CHLORINE TRIFLUORIDE	2.3	5.1, 8	299	X	X	X	X	X	5	30	1.40	a
1858	HEXAFLUOROPROPYLENE (REFRIGERANT GAS R 1216)	2.2			X	X	X	X	X	10	22	1.11	
1859	SILICON TETRAFLUORIDE	2.3	8	450	X	X	X	X	X	5	200 300	0.74 1.10	a
1860	VINYL FLUORIDE, STABILIZED	2.1			X	X	X	X	X	10	250	0.64	a
1911	DIBORANE	2.3	2.1	80	X			X		5	250	0.07	d, k, o
1912	METHYL CHLORIDE AND METHYLENE CHLORIDE MIXTURE	2.1			X	X	X	X	X	10	17	0.81	a
1952	ETHYLENE OXIDE AND CARBON DIOXIDE MIXTURE with not more than 9% ethylene oxide	2.2			X	X	X	X	X	10	190 250	0.66 0.75	
1958	1,2-DICHLORO-1,1,2,2-TETRAFLUOROETHANE (REFRIGERANT GAS R 114)	2.2			X	X	X	X	X	10	10	1.30	
1959	1,1-DIFLUOROETHYLENE (REFRIGERANT GAS R 1132a)	2.1			X	X	X	X	X	10	250	0.77	
1962	ETHYLENE	2.1			X	X	X	X	X	10	225 300	0.34 0.38	
1965	HYDROCARBON GAS MIXTURE, LIQUEFIED, N.O.S.	2.1			X	X	X	X	X	10			v, z
1967	INSECTICIDE GAS, TOXIC, N.O.S.	2.3			X	X	X	X	X	5			z
1968	INSECTICIDE GAS, N.O.S.	2.2			X	X	X	X	X	10			z
1969	ISOBUTANE	2.1			X	X	X	X	X	10	10	0.49	v
1973	CHLORODIFLUOROMETHANE AND CHLOROPENTAFLUOROETHANE MIXTURE with fixed boiling point, with approximately 49% chlorodifluoromethane (REFRIGERANT GAS R 502)	2.2			X	X	X	X	X	10	31	1.01	
1974	CHLORODIFLUOROBROMOMETHANE (REFRIGERANT GAS R 12B1)	2.2			X	X	X	X		10	10	1.61	
1975	NITRIC OXIDE AND DINITROGEN TETROXIDE MIXTURE (NITRIC OXIDE AND NITROGEN DIOXIDE MIXTURE)	2.3	5.1, 8	115	X		X	X		5			k, z
1976	OCTAFLUOROCYCLOBUTANE (REFRIGERANT GAS RC 318)	2.2			X	X	X	X	X	10	11	1.32	
1978	PROPANE	2.1			X	X	X	X	X	10	23	0.43	v
1982	TETRAFLUOROMETHANE (REFRIGERANT GAS R 14)	2.2			X	X	X	X	X	10	200 300	0.71 0.90	
1983	1-CHLORO-2,2,2-TRIFLUOROETHANE (REFRIGERANT GAS R 133a)	2.2			X	X	X	X	X	10	10	1.18	
1984	TRIFLUOROMETHANE (REFRIGERANT GAS R 23)	2.2			X	X	X	X	X	10	190 250	0.88 0.96	
2035	1,1,1-TRIFLUOROETHANE (REFRIGERANT GAS R 143a)	2.1			X	X	X	X	X	10	35	0.73	
2036	XENON	2.2			X	X	X	X	X	10	130	1.28	
2044	2,2-DIMETHYLPROPANE	2.1			X	X	X	X	X	10	10	0.53	
2073	AMMONIA SOLUTION, relative density less than 0.880 at 15°C in water, with more than 35% but not more than 40% ammonia	2.2			X	X	X	X	X	5	10	0.80	b
	with more than 40% but not more than 50% ammonia				X	X	X	X	X	5	12	0.77	b
2188	ARSINE	2.3	2.1	20	X			X		5	42	1.10	d, k

[*] Where the entries are blank, the maximum working pressure shall not exceed two thirds of the test pressure.

P200	PACKING INSTRUCTION (continued)											P200
	Table 2: LIQUEFIED GASES AND DISSOLVED GASES (continued)											
UN No.	Proper shipping name	Class	Subsidiary risk	LC_{50}, mL/m³	Cylinders	Tubes	Pressure drums	Bundles of cylinders	MEGCs	Test period, years	Test pressure, bar[*]	Filling ratio	Special packing provisions
2189	DICHLOROSILANE	2.3	2.1, 8	314	X	X	X	X	X	5	10 / 200	0.90 / 1.08	a
2191	SULPHURYL FLUORIDE	2.3		3020	X	X	X	X	X	5	50	1.10	u
2192	GERMANE	2.3	2.1	620	X	X	X	X	X	5	250	0.064	d, q, r
2193	HEXAFLUOROETHANE (REFRIGERANT GAS R 116)	2.2			X	X	X	X	X	10	200	1.13	
2194	SELENIUM HEXAFLUORIDE	2.3	8	50	X			X		5	36	1.46	k
2195	TELLURIUM HEXAFLUORIDE	2.3	8	25	X			X		5	20	1.00	k
2196	TUNGSTEN HEXAFLUORIDE	2.3	8	160	X			X		5	10	3.08	a, k
2197	HYDROGEN IODIDE, ANHYDROUS	2.3	8	2860	X	X	X	X	X	5	23	2.25	a, d
2198	PHOSPHORUS PENTAFLUORIDE	2.3	8	190	X			X		5	200 / 300	0.90 / 1.25	k / k
2199	PHOSPHINE	2.3	2.1	20	X			X		5	225 / 250	0.30 / 0.45	d, k, q / d, k, q
2200	PROPADIENE, STABILIZED	2.1			X	X	X	X	X	10	22	0.50	
2202	HYDROGEN SELENIDE, ANHYDROUS	2.3	2.1	2	X			X		5	31	1.60	k
2203	SILANE	2.1			X	X	X	X	X	10	225 / 250	0.32 / 0.36	q / q
2204	CARBONYL SULPHIDE	2.3	2.1	1700	X	X	X	X	X	5	30	0.87	u
2417	CARBONYL FLUORIDE	2.3	8	360	X	X	X	X	X	5	200 / 300	0.47 / 0.70	
2418	SULPHUR TETRAFLUORIDE	2.3	8	40	X			X		5	30	0.91	k, a
2419	BROMOTRIFLUOROETHYLENE	2.1			X	X	X	X	X	10	10	1.19	
2420	HEXAFLUOROACETONE	2.3	8	470	X	X	X	X	X	5	22	1.08	
2421	NITROGEN TRIOXIDE	2.3	5.1, 8	57	X			X		5			k
2422	OCTAFLUOROBUT-2-ENE (REFRIGERANT GAS R 1318)	2.2			X	X	X	X	X	10	12	1.34	
2424	OCTAFLUOROPROPANE (REFRIGERANT GAS R 218)	2.2			X	X	X	X	X	10	25	1.04	
2451	NITROGEN TRIFLUORIDE	2.2	5.1		X	X	X	X	X	10	200	0.50	
2452	ETHYLACETYLENE, STABILIZED	2.1			X	X	X	X	X	10	10	0.57	c
2453	ETHYL FLUORIDE (REFRIGERANT GAS R 161)	2.1			X	X	X	X	X	10	30	0.57	
2454	METHYL FLUORIDE (REFRIGERANT GAS R 41)	2.1			X	X	X	X	X	10	300	0.63	
2455	METHYL NITRITE	2.2		(see special provision 900)									
2517	1-CHLORO-1,1-DIFLUOROETHANE (REFRIGERANT GAS R 142b)	2.1			X	X	X	X	X	10	10	0.99	
2534	METHYLCHLOROSILANE	2.3	2.1, 8	600	X	X	X	X	X	5			z
2548	CHLORINE PENTAFLUORIDE	2.3	5.1, 8	122	X			X		5	13	1.49	a, k
2599	CHLOROTRIFLUOROMETHANE AND TRIFLUOROMETHANE AZEOTROPIC MIXTURE with approximately 60% chlorotrifluoromethane (REFRIGERANT GAS R 503)	2.2			X	X	X	X	X	10	31 / 42 / 100	0.12 / 0.17 / 0.64	
2601	CYCLOBUTANE	2.1			X	X	X	X	X	10	10	0.63	
2602	DICHLORODIFLUOROMETHANE AND DIFLUOROETHANE AZEOTROPIC MIXTURE with approximately 74% dichlorodifluoromethane (REFRIGERANT GAS R 500)	2.2			X	X	X	X	X	10	22	1.01	
2676	STIBINE	2.3	2.1	20	X			X		5	200	0.49	k, r

[*] Where the entries are blank, the maximum working pressure shall not exceed two thirds of the test pressure.

P200	PACKING INSTRUCTION *(continued)*												P200
Table 2: LIQUEFIED GASES AND DISSOLVED GASES *(continued)*													
UN No.	Proper shipping name	Class	Subsidiary risk	LC_{50}, mL/m³	Cylinders	Tubes	Pressure drums	Bundles of cylinders	MEGCs	Test period, years	Test pressure, bar*	Filling ratio	Special packing provisions
2901	BROMINE CHLORIDE	2.3	5.1, 8	290	X	X	X	X	X	5	10	1.50	a
3057	TRIFLUOROACETYL CHLORIDE	2.3	8	10	X		X	X		5	17	1.17	k
3070	ETHYLENE OXIDE AND DICHLORODIFLUORO-METHANE MIXTURE with not more than 12.5% ethylene oxide	2.2			X	X	X	X	X	10	18	1.09	
3083	PERCHLORYL FLUORIDE	2.3	5.1	770	X	X	X	X	X	5	33	1.21	u
3153	PERFLUORO(METHYL VINYL ETHER)	2.1			X	X	X	X	X	10	20	0.75	
3154	PERFLUORO(ETHYL VINYL ETHER)	2.1			X	X	X	X	X	10	10	0.98	
3157	LIQUEFIED GAS, OXIDIZING, N.O.S.	2.2	5.1		X	X	X	X	X	10			z
3159	1,1,1,2-TETRAFLUOROETHANE (REFRIGERANT GAS R 134a)	2.2			X	X	X	X	X	10	18	1.05	
3160	LIQUEFIED GAS, TOXIC, FLAMMABLE, N.O.S.	2.3	2.1	≤5000	X	X	X	X	X	5			z
3161	LIQUEFIED GAS, FLAMMABLE, N.O.S.	2.1			X	X	X	X	X	10			z
3162	LIQUEFIED GAS, TOXIC, N.O.S.	2.3		≤5000	X	X	X	X	X	5			z
3163	LIQUEFIED GAS, N.O.S.	2.2			X	X	X	X	X	10			z
3220	PENTAFLUOROETHANE (REFRIGERANT GAS R 125)	2.2			X	X	X	X	X	10	49 35	0.95 0.87	
3252	DIFLUOROMETHANE (REFRIGERANT GAS R 32)	2.1			X	X	X	X	X	10	48	0.78	
3296	HEPTAFLUOROPROPANE (REFRIGERANT GAS R 227)	2.2			X	X	X	X	X	10	13	1.21	
3297	ETHYLENE OXIDE AND CHLOROTETRA-FLUOROETHANE MIXTURE with not more than 8.8% ethylene oxide	2.2			X	X	X	X	X	10	10	1.16	
3298	ETHYLENE OXIDE AND PENTAFLUOROETHANE MIXTURE with not more than 7.9% ethylene oxide	2.2			X	X	X	X	X	10	26	1.02	
3299	ETHYLENE OXIDE AND TETRAFLUOROETHANE MIXTURE with not more than 5.6% ethylene oxide	2.2			X	X	X	X	X	10	17	1.03	
3300	ETHYLENE OXIDE AND CARBON DIOXIDE MIXTURE with more than 87% ethylene oxide	2.3	2.1	More than 2900	X	X	X	X	X	5	28	0.73	
3307	LIQUEFIED GAS, TOXIC, OXIDIZING, N.O.S.	2.3	5.1	≤5000	X	X	X	X	X	5			z
3308	LIQUEFIED GAS, TOXIC, CORROSIVE, N.O.S.	2.3	8	≤5000	X	X	X	X	X	5			z
3309	LIQUEFIED GAS, TOXIC, FLAMMABLE, CORROSIVE, N.O.S.	2.3	2.1, 8	≤5000	X	X	X	X	X	5			z
3310	LIQUEFIED GAS, TOXIC, OXIDIZING, CORROSIVE, N.O.S.	2.3	5.1, 8	≤5000	X	X	X	X	X	5			z
3318	AMMONIA SOLUTION, relative density less than 0.880 at 15°C in water, with more than 50% ammonia	2.3	8		X	X	X	X		5			b
3337	REFRIGERANT GAS R 404A	2.2			X	X	X	X	X	10	36	0.82	
3338	REFRIGERANT GAS R 407A	2.2			X	X	X	X	X	10	32	0.94	
3339	REFRIGERANT GAS R 407B	2.2			X	X	X	X	X	10	33	0.93	
3340	REFRIGERANT GAS R 407C	2.2			X	X	X	X	X	10	30	0.95	
3354	INSECTICIDE GAS, FLAMMABLE, N.O.S.	2.1			X	X	X	X	X	10			z
3355	INSECTICIDE GAS, TOXIC, FLAMMABLE, N.O.S.	2.3	2.1		X	X	X	X	X	5			z
3374	ACETYLENE, SOLVENT FREE	2.1			X			X		5	60 52		c, p

* Where the entries are blank, the maximum working pressure shall not exceed two thirds of the test pressure.

P200		PACKING INSTRUCTION *(continued)*										P200
		Table 3: SUBSTANCES NOT IN CLASS 2										
UN No.	Proper shipping name	Class	Subsidiary risk	LC_{50}, mL/m³	Cylinders	Tubes	Pressure drums	Bundles of cylinders	MEGCs	Test period, years	Test pressure, bar[*]	Filling ratio	Special packing provisions
1051	HYDROGEN CYANIDE, STABILIZED containing less than 3% water	6.1	3	40	X			X		5	100	0.55	k
1052	HYDROGEN FLUORIDE, ANHYDROUS	8	6.1	966	X		X	X		5	10	0.84	t, a
1745	BROMINE PENTAFLUORIDE	5.1	6.1, 8	25	X		X	X		5	10	[†]	k
1746	BROMINE TRIFLUORIDE	5.1	6.1, 8	50	X		X	X		5	10	[†]	k
2495	IODINE PENTAFLUORIDE	5.1	6.1, 8	120	X		X	X		5	10	[†]	k

[*] Where the entries are blank, the maximum working pressure shall not exceed two thirds of the test pressure.
[†] A minimum ullage of 8% by volume is required.

P201	PACKING INSTRUCTION	P201
This instruction applies to UN Nos. 3167, 3168 and 3169.		

The following packagings are authorized:

(1) Cylinders and gas receptacles conforming to the construction, testing and filling requirements approved by the competent authority.

(2) The following combination packagings provided that the general provisions of 4.1.1 and 4.1.3 are met:

Outer packagings:
Drums (1A1, 1A2, 1B1, 1B2, 1N1, 1N2, 1H1, 1H2, 1D, 1G);
Boxes (4A, 4B, 4N, 4C1, 4C2, 4D, 4F, 4G, 4H1, 4H2);
Jerricans (3A1, 3A2, 3B1, 3B2, 3H1, 3H2).

Inner packagings:

(a) For non-toxic gases, hermetically sealed inner packagings of glass or metal with a maximum capacity of 5 L per package;

(b) For toxic gases, hermetically sealed inner packagings of glass or metal with a maximum capacity of 1 L per package.

Packagings shall conform to the packing group III performance level.

P202	PACKING INSTRUCTION	P202
[Reserved]		

P203	PACKING INSTRUCTION	P203
This instruction applies to class 2 refrigerated liquefied gases.		

4

Requirements for closed cryogenic receptacles:

(1) The general requirements of 4.1.6.1 shall be met.

(2) The requirements of chapter 6.2 shall be met.

(3) The closed cryogenic receptacles shall be so insulated that they do not become coated with frost.

(4) Test pressure

Refrigerated liquids shall be filled in closed cryogenic receptacles with the following minimum test pressures:

(a) For closed cryogenic receptacles with vacuum insulation, the test pressure shall not be less than 1.3 times the sum of the maximum internal pressure of the filled receptacle, including during filling and discharge, plus 100 kPa (1 bar);

(b) For other closed cryogenic receptacles, the test pressure shall be not less than 1.3 times the maximum internal pressure of the filled receptacle, taking into account the pressure developed during filling and discharge.

(5) Degree of filling

For non-flammable, non-toxic refrigerated liquefied gases the volume of liquid phase at the filling temperature and at a pressure of 100 kPa (1 bar) shall not exceed 98% of the water capacity of the pressure receptacle.

For flammable refrigerated liquefied gases the degree of filling shall remain below the level at which, if the contents were raised to the temperature at which the vapour pressure equalled the opening pressure of the relief valve, the volume of the liquid phase would reach 98% of the water capacity at that temperature.

(6) Pressure-relief devices

Closed cryogenic receptacles shall be fitted with at least one pressure-relief device.

(7) Compatibility

Materials used to ensure the leakproofness of the joints or for the maintenance of the closures shall be compatible with the contents. In the case of receptacles intended for the transport of oxidizing gases (i.e. with a subsidiary risk of 5.1), these materials shall not react with these gases in a dangerous manner.

(8) Periodic inspection

The periodic inspection and test frequencies of pressure relief valves in accordance with 6.2.1.6.3 shall not exceed five years.

Requirements for open cryogenic receptacles:

Only the following non-oxidizing refrigerated liquefied gases of class 2.2 may be transported in open cryogenic receptacles: UN Nos. 1913, 1951, 1963, 1970, 1977, 2591, 3136 and 3158.

Open cryogenic receptacles shall be constructed to meet the following requirements:

(1) The receptacles shall be designed, manufactured, tested and equipped in such a way as to withstand all conditions, including fatigue, to which they will be subjected during their normal use and during normal conditions of transport.

(2) The capacity shall be not more than 450 litres.

(3) The receptacle shall have a double wall construction with the space between the inner and outer wall being evacuated (vacuum insulation). The insulation shall prevent the formation of hoar frost on the exterior of the receptacle.

(4) The materials of construction shall have suitable mechanical properties at the service temperature.

(5) Materials which are in direct contact with the dangerous goods shall not be affected or weakened by the dangerous goods intended to be transported and shall not cause a dangerous effect, e.g. catalysing a reaction or reacting with the dangerous goods.

(6) Receptacles of glass double wall construction shall have an outer packaging with suitable cushioning or absorbent materials which withstand the pressures and impacts liable to occur under normal conditions of transport.

(7) The receptacle shall be designed to remain in an upright position during transport, e.g. have a base whose smaller horizontal dimension is greater than the height of the centre of gravity when filled to capacity or be mounted on gimbals.

(8) The openings of the receptacles shall be fitted with devices allowing gases to escape, preventing any splashing out of liquid, and so configured that they remain in place during transport.

(9) Open cryogenic receptacles shall bear the following marks permanently affixed, e.g. by stamping, engraving or etching:

  – The manufacturer's name and address;

  – The model number or name;

  – The serial or batch number;

  – The UN number and proper shipping name of gases for which the receptacle is intended;

  – The capacity of the receptacle in litres.

P205	PACKING INSTRUCTION	P205

This instruction applies to UN 3468.

(1) For metal hydride storage systems, the general packing requirements of 4.1.6.1 shall be met.

(2) Only pressure receptacles not exceeding 150 litres in water capacity and having a maximum developed pressure not exceeding 25 MPa are covered by this packing instruction.

(3) Metal hydride storage systems meeting the applicable requirements for the construction and testing of pressure receptacles containing gas of chapter 6.2 are authorized for the transport of hydrogen only.

(4) When steel pressure receptacles or composite pressure receptacles with steel liners are used, only those bearing the "H" mark, in accordance with 6.2.2.9.2(j), shall be used.

(5) Metal hydride storage systems shall meet the service conditions, design criteria, rated capacity, type tests, batch tests, routine tests, test pressure, rated charging pressure and provisions for pressure relief devices for transportable metal hydride storage systems specified in ISO 16111:2008 and their conformity and approval shall be assessed in accordance with 6.2.2.5.

△ (6) Metal hydride storage systems shall be filled with hydrogen at a pressure not exceeding the rated charging pressure shown in the permanent mark on the system as specified by ISO 16111:2008.

(7) The periodic test requirements for a metal hydride storage system shall be in accordance with ISO 16111:2008 and carried out in accordance with 6.2.2.6, and the interval between periodic inspections shall not exceed five years.

P206	PACKING INSTRUCTION	P206

This instruction applies to UN Nos. 3500, 3501, 3502, 3503, 3504 and 3505.

Unless otherwise indicated in these provisions, cylinders and pressure drums conforming to the applicable requirements of Chapter 6.2 are authorized.

(1) The general packing requirements of 4.1.6.1 shall be met.

(2) The maximum test period for periodic inspection shall be 5 years.

△ (3) Cylinders and pressure drums shall be so filled that at 50°C the non-gaseous phase does not exceed 95% of their water capacity and they are not completely filled at 60°C. When filled, the internal pressure at 65°C shall not exceed the test pressure of the cylinders and pressure drums. The vapour pressures and volumetric expansion of all substances in the cylinders and pressure drums shall be taken into account. For liquids charged with a compressed gas both components – the liquid phase and the compressed gas – have to be taken into consideration in the calculation of the internal pressure in the pressure receptacle. When experimental data is not available, the following steps shall be carried out:

(a) calculation of the vapour pressure of the liquid component and of the partial pressure of the compressed gas at 15°C (filling temperature);

(b) calculation of the volumetric expansion of the liquid phase resulting from the heating from 15°C to 65°C and calculation of the remaining volume for the gaseous phase;

(c) calculation of the partial pressure of the compressed gas at 65°C considering the volumetric expansion of the liquid phase;

Note: The compressibility factor of the compressed gas at 15°C and 65°C shall be considered.

(d) calculation of the vapour pressure of the liquid component at 65°C;

(e) the total pressure is the sum of the vapour pressure of the liquid component and the partial pressure of the compressed gas at 65°C;

(f) consideration of the solubility of the compressed gas at 65°C in the liquid phase.

The test pressure of the cylinders or pressure drums shall not be less than the calculated total pressure minus 100 kPa (1bar).

If the solubility of the compressed gas in the liquid component is not known for the calculation, the test pressure can be calculated without taking the gas solubility (subparagraph (f)) into account.

(4) The minimum test pressure shall be in accordance with P200 for the propellant but shall not be less than 20 bar.

Additional requirement:

Cylinders and pressure drums shall not be offered for transport when connected with spray application equipment such as a hose and wand assembly.

Special packing provision:

PP89 For UN Nos. 3501, 3502, 3503, 3504 and 3505, notwithstanding 4.1.6.1.9.2, non-refillable cylinders used may have a water capacity in L not exceeding 1 000L divided by the test pressure expressed in bars provided capacity and pressure restrictions of the construction standard comply with ISO 11118:1999, which limits the maximum capacity to 50L.

4

P207	PACKING INSTRUCTION	P207

This instruction applies to UN 1950.

The following packagings are authorized, provided that the general provisions of 4.1.1 and 4.1.3 are met:

(a) Drums (1A1, 1A2, 1B1, 1B2, 1N1, 1N2, 1H1, 1H2, 1D, 1G);

   Boxes (4A, 4B, 4N, 4C1, 4C2, 4D, 4F, 4G, 4H1, 4H2).

   Packagings shall conform to the packing group II performance level.

(b) Rigid outer packagings with a maximum net mass as follows:

   Fibreboard   55 kg

   Other than fibreboard   125 kg

   The provisions of 4.1.1.3 need not be met.

△ The packagings shall be designed and constructed to prevent excessive movement of the aerosols and inadvertent discharge during normal conditions of transport.

Special packing provision:

PP87 For UN 1950, waste aerosols transported in accordance with special provision 327, the packagings shall have a means of retaining any free liquid that might escape during transport, e.g. absorbent material. The packaging shall be adequately ventilated to prevent the creation of flammable atmosphere and the build-up of pressure.

P208	PACKING INSTRUCTION	P208

This instruction applies to class 2 adsorbed gases.

△ (1) The following packagings are authorized provided the general packing requirements of 4.1.6.1 are met:

   (a) cylinders constructed as specified in 6.2.2 and in accordance with ISO 11513:2011 or ISO 9809-1:2010; and

   (b) cylinders constructed before 1 January 2016 in accordance with 6.2.3 and a specification approved by the competent authorities of the countries of transport and use.

(2) The pressure of each filled cylinder shall be less than 101.3 kPa at 20°C and less than 300 kPa at 50°C.

(3) The minimum test pressure of the cylinder shall be 21 bar.

(4) The minimum burst pressure of the cylinder shall be 94.5 bar.

(5) The internal pressure at 65°C of the filled cylinder shall not exceed the test pressure of the cylinder.

(6) The adsorbent material shall be compatible with the cylinder and shall not form harmful or dangerous compounds with the gas to be adsorbed. The gas in combination with the adsorbent material shall not affect or weaken the cylinder or cause a dangerous reaction (e.g. a catalyzing reaction).

(7) The quality of the adsorbent material shall be verified at the time of each fill to assure the pressure and chemical stability requirements of this packing instruction are met each time an adsorbed gas package is offered for transport.

(8) The adsorbent material shall not meet the criteria of any of the classes or divisions in this Code.

(9) Requirements for cylinders and closures containing toxic gases with an LC_{50} less than or equal to 200 mL/m^3 (ppm) (see table 1) shall be as follows:

   (a) Valve outlets shall be fitted with pressure retaining gas-tight plugs or caps having threads matching those of the valve outlets.

   (b) Each valve shall either be of the packless type with non-perforated diaphragm, or be of a type which prevents leakage through or past the packing.

   (c) Each cylinder and closure shall be tested for leakage after filling.

   (d) Each valve shall be capable of withstanding the test pressure of the cylinder and be directly connected to the cylinder by either a taper-thread or other means which meets the requirements of ISO 10692-2:2001.

   (e) Cylinders and valves shall not be fitted with a pressure relief device.

(10) Valve outlets for cylinders containing pyrophoric gases shall be fitted with gas-tight plugs or caps having threads matching those of the valve outlets.

(11) The filling procedure shall be in accordance with annex A of ISO 11513:2011.

(12) The maximum period for periodic inspections shall be 5 years.

(13) Special packing provisions that are specific to a substance (see table 1).

   Material compatibility

   a: Aluminium alloy cylinders shall not be used.

   d: When steel cylinders are used, only those bearing the "H" mark in accordance with 6.2.2.7.4 (p) are permitted.

   Gas specific provisions

   r: The filling ratio of this gas shall be limited such that, if complete decomposition occurs, the pressure does not exceed two thirds of the test pressure of the cylinder.

   Material compatibility for N.O.S adsorbed gas entries

   z: The construction materials of the cylinders and their accessories shall be compatible with the contents and shall not react to form harmful or dangerous compounds therewith.

P208	PACKING INSTRUCTION *(continued)*				P208
Table 1: ADSORBED GASES					
UN No.	Proper shipping name	Class or Division	Subsidiary risk	LC_{50} mL/m^3	Special packing provisions
(1)	(2)	(3)	(4)	(5)	(6)
3510	ADSORBED GAS, FLAMMABLE, N.O.S.	2.1			z
3511	ADSORBED GAS, N.O.S.	2.2			z
3512	ADSORBED GAS, TOXIC, N.O.S.	2.3		≤ 5,000	z
3513	ADSORBED GAS, OXIDIZING, N.O.S.	2.2	5.1		z
3514	ADSORBED GAS, TOXIC, FLAMMABLE, N.O.S.	2.3	2.1	≤ 5,000	z
3515	ADSORBED GAS, TOXIC, OXIDIZING, N.O.S.	2.3	5.1	≤ 5,000	z
3516	ADSORBED GAS, TOXIC, CORROSIVE, N.O.S.	2.3	8	≤ 5,000	z
3517	ADSORBED GAS, TOXIC, FLAMMABLE, CORROSIVE, N.O.S.	2.3	2.1 8	≤ 5,000	z
3518	ADSORBED GAS, TOXIC, OXIDIZING, CORROSIVE, N.O.S.	2.3	5.1 8	≤ 5,000	z
3519	BORON TRIFLUORIDE, ADSORBED	2.3	8	387	a
3520	CHLORINE, ADSORBED	2.3	5.1 8	293	a
3521	SILICON TETRAFLUORIDE, ADSORBED	2.3	8	450	a
3522	ARSINE, ADSORBED	2.3	2.1	20	d
3523	GERMANE, ADSORBED	2.3	2.1	620	d, r
3524	PHOSPHORUS PENTAFLUORIDE, ADSORBED	2.3	8	190	
3525	PHOSPHINE, ADSORBED	2.3	2.1	20	d
3526	HYDROGEN SELENIDE, ADSORBED	2.3	2.1	2	

P300	PACKING INSTRUCTION	P300
This instruction applies to UN 3064.		

The following packagings are authorized, provided that the general provisions of 4.1.1 and 4.1.3 are met:

Combination packagings consisting of inner metal cans of not more than 1 L capacity each and outer wooden boxes (4C1, 4C2, 4D or 4F) containing not more than 5 L of solution.

Additional provisions:

1 Metal cans shall be completely surrounded with absorbent cushioning material.
2 Wooden boxes shall be completely lined with suitable material impervious to water and nitroglycerin.

P301	PACKING INSTRUCTION	P301
This instruction applies to UN 3165.		

The following packagings are authorized, provided that the general provisions of 4.1.1 and 4.1.3 are met:

(1) Aluminium pressure receptacle made from tubing and having welded heads

Primary containment of the fuel within this receptacle shall consist of a welded aluminium bladder having a maximum internal volume of 46 L. The outer receptacle shall have a minimum design gauge pressure of 1,275 kPa and a minimum burst gauge pressure of 2,755 kPa. Each receptacle shall be leak-checked during manufacture and before shipment and shall be found leakproof. The complete inner unit shall be securely packed in non-combustible cushioning material, such as vermiculite, in a strong outer tightly closed metal packaging which will adequately protect all fittings. Maximum quantity of fuel per unit and package is 42 L.

(2) Aluminium pressure receptacle

Primary containment of the fuel within this receptacle shall consist of a welded vapourtight fuel compartment with an elastomeric bladder having a maximum internal volume of 46 L. The pressure receptacle shall have a minimum design gauge pressure of 2,680 kPa and a minimum burst pressure of 5,170 kPa. Each receptacle shall be leak-checked during manufacture and before shipment and shall be securely packed in non-combustible cushioning material such as vermiculite, in a strong outer tightly closed metal packaging which will adequately protect all fittings. Maximum quantity of fuel per unit and package is 42 L.

4

P302	PACKING INSTRUCTION	P302

This instruction applies to UN 3269.

The following combination packagings are authorized, provided that the general provisions of 4.1.1 and 4.1.3 are met:
Outer packagings:
    Drums (1A1, 1A2, 1B1, 1B2, 1N1, 1N2, 1H1, 1H2, 1D, 1G).
    Boxes (4A, 4B, 4N, 4C1, 4C2, 4D, 4F, 4G, 4H1, 4H2).
    Jerricans (3A1, 3A2, 3B1, 3B2, 3H1, 3H2).
Inner packagings:
    The activator (organic peroxide) shall have a maximum quantity of 125 ml per inner packaging if liquid, and 500 g per inner packaging if solid.
    The base material and the activator shall be each separately packed in inner packagings.
The components may be placed in the same outer packaging provided that they will not interact dangerously in the event of a leakage.
Packagings shall conform to the packing group II or III performance level according to the criteria for Class 3 applied to the base material.

P400	PACKING INSTRUCTION	P400

The following packagings are authorized, provided that the general provisions of 4.1.1 and 4.1.3 are met:
(1) Pressure receptacles, provided that the general provisions of 4.1.3.6 are met. They shall be made of steel and shall be subjected to an initial test and periodic tests every 10 years at a pressure of not less than 1 MPa (10 bar, gauge pressure). During carriage, the liquid shall be under a layer of inert gas with a gauge pressure of not less than 20 kPa (0.2 bar).

(2) Boxes (4A, 4B, 4N, 4C1, 4C2, 4D, 4F or 4G), drums (1A1, 1A2, 1B1, 1B2, 1N1, 1N2, 1D or 1G) or jerricans (3A1, 3A2, 3B1 or 3B2) enclosing hermetically sealed metal cans with inner packagings of glass or metal, with a capacity of not more than 1 L each, having threaded closures with gaskets. Inner packagings shall be cushioned on all sides with dry, absorbent, non-combustible material in a quantity sufficient to absorb the entire contents. Inner packagings shall not be filled to more than 90% of their capacity. Outer packagings shall have a maximum net mass of 125 kg.

(3) Steel, aluminium or metal drums (1A1, 1A2, 1B1, 1B2, 1N1 or 1N2), jerricans (3A1, 3A2, 3B1 or 3B2) or boxes (4A, 4B, 4N or 4N) with a maximum net mass of 150 kg each with hermetically sealed inner metal cans of not more than 4 L capacity each, with threaded closures fitted with gaskets. Inner packagings shall be cushioned on all sides with dry, absorbent, non-combustible material in a quantity sufficient to absorb the entire contents. Each layer of inner packagings shall be separated by a dividing partition in addition to cushioning material. Inner packagings shall not be filled to more than 90% of their capacity.

Special packing provision:
PP86 For UN Nos. 3392 and 3394, air shall be eliminated from the vapour space by nitrogen or other means.

P401	PACKING INSTRUCTION	P401

The following packagings are authorized, provided that the general provisions of 4.1.1 and 4.1.3 are met:
(1) Pressure receptacles, provided that the general provisions of 4.1.3.6 are met. They shall be made of steel and subjected to an initial test and periodic tests every 10 years at a pressure of not less than 0.6 MPa (6 bar, gauge pressure). During carriage, the liquid shall be under a layer of inert gas with a gauge pressure of not less than 20 kPa (0.2 bar).

(2) Combination packagings
Outer packagings:
    Drums (1A1, 1A2, 1B1, 1B2, 1N1, 1N2, 1H1, 1H2, 1D, 1G);
    Boxes (4A, 4B, 4N, 4C1, 4C2, 4D, 4F, 4G, 4H1,4H2);
    Jerricans (3A1, 3A2, 3B1, 3B2, 3H1, 3H2).
Inner packagings:
    Glass, metal or plastics which have threaded closures with a maximum capacity of 1 L.
Each inner packaging shall be surrounded by inert cushioning and absorbent material in a quantity sufficient to absorb the entire contents.
The maximum net mass per outer packaging shall not exceed 30 kg.

Special packing provision:
PP31 For UN Nos. 1183, 1242, 1295, 2965 and 2988, packagings shall be hermetically sealed.

4

P402	PACKING INSTRUCTION	P402

The following packagings are authorized, provided that the general provisions of 4.1.1 and 4.1.3 are met:

(1) Pressure receptacles, provided that the general provisions of 4.1.3.6 are met. They shall be made of steel and subjected to an initial test and periodic tests every 10 years at a pressure of not less than 0.6 MPa (6 bar, gauge pressure). During carriage, the liquid shall be under a layer of inert gas with a gauge pressure of not less than 20 kPa (0.2 bar).

(2) Combination packagings
Outer packagings:
      Drums (1A1, 1A2, 1B1, 1B2, 1N1, 1N2, 1H1, 1H2, 1D, 1G);
      Boxes (4A, 4B, 4N, 4C1, 4C2, 4D, 4F, 4G, 4H1, 4H2);
      Jerricans (3A1, 3A2, 3B1, 3B2, 3H1, 3H2).
Inner packagings with a maximum net mass as follows:
    Glass   10 kg
    Metal or plastics   15 kg
Each inner packaging shall be fitted with threaded closures.
Each inner packaging shall be surrounded by inert cushioning and absorbent material in a quantity sufficient to absorb the entire contents.
The maximum net mass per outer packaging shall not exceed 125 kg.

(3) Steel drums (1A1) with a maximum capacity of 250 L.

(4) Composite packagings consisting of plastics receptacle in a steel or aluminium drum (6HA1 or 6HB1) with a maximum capacity of 250 L.

Special packing provision:
PP31 For UN Nos. 1389, 1391, 1392, 1420, 1421, 1422, 3148, 3184 (PG II), 3185 (PG II), 3187 (PG II), 3188 (PG II), 3398 (PG I), 3399 (PG I) and 3482, packagings shall be hermetically sealed.

4

P403	PACKING INSTRUCTION	P403

The following packagings are authorized, provided that the general provisions of 4.1.1 and 4.1.3 are met.

Combination packagings		Maximum net mass
Inner packagings	**Outer packagings**	
Glass 2 kg	**Drums**	
Plastic 15 kg	steel (1A1, 1A2)	400 kg
Metal 20 kg	aluminium (1B1, 1B2)	400 kg
	other metal (1N1, 1N2)	400 kg
Inner packagings shall be hermetically sealed (e.g. by taping or by threaded closures).	plastics (1H1, 1H2)	400 kg
	plywood (1D)	400 kg
	fibre (1G)	400 kg
	Boxes	
	steel (4A)	400 kg
	aluminium (4B)	400 kg
	other metal (4N)	400 kg
	natural wood (4C1)	250 kg
	natural wood with sift-proof walls (4C2)	250 kg
	plywood (4D)	250 kg
	reconstituted wood (4F)	125 kg
	fibreboard (4G)	125 kg
	expanded plastics (4H1)	60 kg
	solid plastics (4H2)	250 kg
	Jerricans	
	steel (3A1, 3A2)	120 kg
	aluminium (3B1, 3B2)	120 kg
	plastics (3H1, 3H2)	120 kg
Single packagings		
Drums		
steel (1A1, 1A2)		250 kg
aluminium (1B1, 1B2)		250 kg
metal other than steel or aluminium (1N1, 1N2)		250 kg
plastics (1H1, 1H2)		250 kg
Jerricans		
steel (3A1, 3A2)		120 kg
aluminium (3B1, 3B2)		120 kg
plastics (3H1, 3H2)		120 kg
Composite packagings		
Plastics receptacle in steel or aluminium drum (6HA1 or 6HB1)		250 kg
Plastics receptacle in fibre, plastics or plywood drum (6HG1, 6HH1 or 6HD1)		75 kg
Plastics receptacle in steel, aluminium, wood, plywood, fibreboard or solid plastics box (6HA2, 6HB2, 6HC, 6HD2, 6HG2 or 6HH2)		75 kg
Pressure receptacles, provided that the general provisions of 4.1.3.6 are met		

Special packing provisions:

△ **PP31** For UN Nos. 1360, 1397, 1402, 1404, 1407, 1409, 1410, 1413, 1414, 1415, 1418, 1419, 1423, 1426, 1427, 1428, 1432, 1433, 1436, 1714, 1870, 2010, 2011, 2012, 2013, 2257, 2463, 2806, 2813 (PG I), 3131, 3132, 3134, 3135, 3208, 3209, 3395, 3396, 3397, 3401, 3402, 3403 and 3404, packagings shall be hermetically sealed, except for solid fused material.

△ **PP83** *Deleted*

P404	PACKING INSTRUCTION	P404

This instruction applies to pyrophoric solids: UN Nos. 1383, 1854, 1855, 2008, 2441, 2545, 2546, 2846, 2881, 3200, 3391 and 3393.

The following packagings are authorized, provided that the general provisions of 4.1.1 and 4.1.3 are met:
(1) Combination packagings
Outer packagings: (1A1, 1A2, 1B1, 1B2, 1N1, 1N2, 1H1, 1H2, 1D, 1G, 4A, 4B, 4N, 4C1, 4C2, 4D, 4F, 4G or 4H2)
Inner packagings: Metal packagings with a maximum net mass of 15 kg each. Inner packagings shall be hermetically sealed and have threaded closures. Glass receptacles, with a maximum net mass of 1 kg each, having threaded closures with gaskets, cushioned on all sides and contained in hermetically sealed metal cans.
Outer packagings shall have a maximum net mass of 125 kg.
(2) Metal packagings: (1A1, 1A2, 1B1, 1N1, 1N2, 3A1, 3A2, 3B1 and 3B2)
Maximum gross mass: 150 kg
(3) Composite packagings: Plastics receptacle in a steel or aluminium drum (6HA1 or 6HB1)
Maximum gross mass: 150 kg
Pressure receptacles may be used provided that the general provisions of 4.1.3.6 are met.

Special packing provisions:
PP31 For UN Nos. 1383, 1854, 1855, 2008, 2441, 2545, 2546, 2846, 2881 and 3200, packagings shall be hermetically sealed.
PP86 For UN Nos. 3391 and 3393, air shall be eliminated from the vapour space by nitrogen or other means.

P405	PACKING INSTRUCTION	P405

This instruction applies to UN 1381.

The following packagings are authorized, provided that the general provisions of 4.1.1 and 4.1.3 are met:
(1) For UN 1381, wet phosphorus:
  .1 Combination packagings
  Outer packagings: (4A, 4B, 4N, 4C1, 4C2, 4D or 4F); maximum net mass: 75 kg
  Inner packagings:
  (i) hermetically sealed metal cans, with a maximum net mass of 15 kg; or
  (ii) glass inner packagings cushioned on all sides with dry, absorbent, non-combustible material in a quantity sufficient to absorb the entire contents with a maximum net mass of 2 kg; or
  .2 Drums (1A1, 1A2, 1B1, 1B2, 1N1 or 1N2); maximum net mass: 400 kg
  Jerricans (3A1 or 3B1); maximum net mass: 120 kg.
These packagings shall be capable of passing the leakproofness test specified in 6.1.5.4 at the packing group II performance level.
(2) For UN 1381, dry phosphorus:
  .1 When fused, drums (1A2, 1B2 or 1N2) with a maximum net mass of 400 kg; or
  .2 In projectiles or hard-cased articles when transported without class 1 components, as specified by the competent authority.

Special packing provision:
PP31 For UN 1381, packagings shall be hermetically sealed.

4

P406	PACKING INSTRUCTION	P406

The following packagings are authorized, provided that the general provisions of 4.1.1 and 4.1.3 are met:

(1) Combination packagings

    Outer packagings: (4C1, 4C2, 4D, 4F, 4G, 4H1, 4H2, 1G, 1D, 1H1, 1H2, 3H1 or 3H2)

    Inner packagings shall be water-resistant.

(2) Plastics, plywood or fibreboard drums (1H2, 1D or 1G) or boxes (4A, 4B, 4N, 4C1, 4D, 4F, 4C2, 4G and 4H2) with a water-resistant inner bag, plastics film lining or water-resistant coating.

(3) Metal drums (1A1, 1A2, 1B1, 1B2, 1N1 or 1N2), plastics drums (1H1 or 1H2), metal jerricans (3A1, 3A2, 3B1 or 3B2), plastics jerricans (3H1 or 3H2), plastics receptacle in steel or aluminium drums (6HA1 or 6HB1), plastics receptacle in fibre, plastics or plywood drums (6HG1, 6HH1 or 6HD1), plastics receptacle in steel, aluminium, wood, plywood, fibreboard or solid plastics boxes (6HA2, 6HB2, 6HC, 6HD2, 6HG2 or 6HH2).

Additional provisions:

1   Packagings shall be designed and constructed to prevent the loss of water or alcohol content or the content of the phlegmatizer.

2   Packagings shall be so constructed and closed as to avoid an explosive overpressure or pressure build-up of more than 300 kPa (3 bar).

3   The type of packaging and maximum permitted quantity per packaging are limited by the provisions of 2.1.3.4.

Special packing provisions:

PP24   UN Nos. 2852, 3364, 3365, 3366, 3367, 3368 and 3369 shall not be transported in quantities of more than 500 g per package.

PP25   UN 1347 shall not be transported in quantities of more than 15 kg per package.

PP26   For UN Nos. 1310, 1320, 1321, 1322, 1344, 1347, 1348, 1349, 1517, 2907, 3317, 3344 and 3376, packagings shall be lead-free.

PP31   For UN Nos. 1310, 1320, 1321, 1322, 1336, 1337, 1344, 1347, 1348, 1349, 1354, 1355, 1356, 1357, 1517, 1571, 2555, 2556, 2557, 2852, 3317, 3364, 3365, 3366, 3367, 3368, 3369, 3370 and 3376, packagings shall be hermetically sealed.

△ PP48   For UN 3474, metal packagings shall not be used. Packagings of other material with a small amount of metal, for example metal closures or other metal fittings such as those mentioned in 6.1.4, are not considered metal packagings.

PP78   UN 3370 shall not be transported in quantities of more than 11.5 kg per package.

PP80   For UN Nos. 2907 and 3344, packagings shall meet the packing group II performance level. Packagings meeting the test criteria of packing group I shall not be used.

P407	PACKING INSTRUCTION	P407

This instruction applies to UN Nos. 1331, 1944, 1945 and 2254.

The following packagings are authorized, provided that the general provisions of 4.1.1 and 4.1.3 are met:

Outer packagings:

    Drums (1A1, 1A2, 1B1, 1B2, 1N1, 1N2, 1H1, 1H2, 1D, 1G);

    Boxes (4A, 4B, 4N, 4C1, 4C2, 4D, 4F, 4G, 4H1, 4 H2);

    Jerricans (3A1, 3A2, 3B1, 3B2, 3H1, 3H2).

Inner packagings:

    Matches shall be tightly packed in securely closed inner packagings to prevent accidental ignition under normal conditions of transport.

The maximum gross mass of the package shall not exceed 45 kg except for fibreboard boxes which shall not exceed 30 kg.

Packagings shall conform to the packing group III performance level.

Special packing provision:

PP27   UN 1331, Strike-anywhere matches, shall not be packed in the same outer packaging with any other dangerous goods other than safety matches or wax Vesta matches, which shall be packed in separate inner packagings. Inner packagings shall not contain more than 700 strike-anywhere matches.

4

P408	PACKING INSTRUCTION	P408

This instruction applies to UN 3292.

The following packagings are authorized, provided that the general provisions of 4.1.1 and 4.1.3 are met:

(1) For cells:

Drums (1A2, 1B2, 1N2, 1H2, 1D, 1G);

Boxes (4A, 4B, 4N, 4C1, 4C2, 4D, 4F, 4G, 4H1, 4H2);

Jerricans (3A2, 3B2, 3H2).

There shall be sufficient cushioning material to prevent contact between cells and between cells and the internal surfaces of the outer packaging and to ensure that no dangerous movement of the cells within the outer packaging occurs in transport.

Packagings shall conform to the packing group II performance level.

(2) Batteries may be transported unpacked or in protective enclosures (e.g. fully enclosed or wooden slatted crates). The terminals shall not support the weight of other batteries or materials packed with the batteries.

Packagings need not meet the requirements of 4.1.1.3.

Additional requirement:

Cells and batteries shall be protected against short circuit and shall be isolated in such a manner as to prevent short circuits.

P409	PACKING INSTRUCTION	P409

This instruction applies to UN Nos. 2956, 3242 and 3251.

The following packagings are authorized, provided that the general provisions of 4.1.1 and 4.1.3 are met:

(1) Fibre drum (1G) which may be fitted with a liner or coating; maximum net mass: 50 kg.

(2) Combination packagings: Fibreboard box (4G) with a single inner plastic bag; maximum net mass: 50 kg.

(3) Combination packagings: Fibreboard box (4G) or fibre drum (1G) with inner plastic packagings each containing a maximum of 5 kg; maximum net mass: 25 kg.

4

P410	PACKING INSTRUCTION		P410
The following packagings are authorized, provided that the general provisions of 4.1.1 and 4.1.3 are met.			

Combination packagings		Maximum net mass	
Inner packagings	Outer packagings	Packing group II	Packing group III

Glass 10 kg
Plastics[1] 30 kg
Metal 40 kg
Paper[1,2] 10 kg
Fibre[1,2] 10 kg
	Drums
	  steel (1A1, 1A2)
	  aluminium (1B1, 1B2)
	  other metal (1N1, 1N2)
	  plastics (1H1, 1H2)
	  plywood (1D)
	  fibre (1G)[1]
		400 kg
		400 kg
		400 kg
		400 kg
		400 kg
		400 kg
			400 kg
			400 kg
			400 kg
			400 kg
			400 kg
			400 kg

	Boxes
	  steel (4A)
	  aluminium (4B)
	  other metal (4N)
	  natural wood (4C1)
	  natural wood with sift-proof
	    walls (4C2)
	  plywood (4D)
	  reconstituted wood (4F)
	  fibreboard (4G)[1]
	  expanded plastics (4H1)
	  solid plastics (4H2)
		400 kg
		400 kg
		400 kg
		400 kg
		400 kg
		
		400 kg
		400 kg
		400 kg
		60 kg
		400 kg
			400 kg
			400 kg
			400 kg
			400 kg
			400 kg
			
			400 kg
			400 kg
			400 kg
			60 kg
			400 kg

[1] Packagings shall be sift-proof.
[2] These inner packagings shall not be used when the substances being transported may become liquid during transport.
	Jerricans
	  steel (3A1, 3A2)
	  aluminium (3B1, 3B2)
	  plastics (3H1, 3H2)
		120 kg
		120 kg
		120 kg
			120 kg
			120 kg
			120 kg

Single packagings			

Drums
  steel (1A1 or 1A2)
  aluminium (1B1 or 1B2)
  metal other than steel or aluminium (1N1 or 1N2)
  plastics (1H1 or 1H2)
		400 kg
		400 kg
		400 kg
		400 kg
			400 kg
			400 kg
			400 kg
			400 kg

Jerricans
  steel (3A1 or 3A2)
  aluminium (3B1 or 3B2)
  plastics (3H1 or 3H2)
		120 kg
		120 kg
		120 kg
			120 kg
			120 kg
			120 kg

Boxes
  steel (4A)[3]
  aluminium (4B)[3]
  other metal (4N)[3]
  natural wood (4C1)[3]
  natural wood with sift-proof walls (4C2)[3]
  plywood (4D)[3]
  reconstituted wood (4F)[3]
  fibreboard (4G)[3]
  solid plastics (4H2)[3]
		400 kg
		400 kg
		400 kg
		400 kg
		400 kg
		400 kg
		400 kg
		400 kg
		400 kg
			400 kg
			400 kg
			400 kg
			400 kg
			400 kg
			400 kg
			400 kg
			400 kg
			400 kg

Bags Bags (5H3, 5H4, 5L3, 5M2)[3,4]		50 kg	50 kg
Composite packagings			
Plastics receptacle in steel, aluminium, plywood, fibre or plastics drum (6HA1, 6HB1, 6HG1, 6HD1 or 6HH1)		400 kg	400 kg
Plastics receptacle in steel or aluminium crate or box, wooden box, plywood box, fibreboard box or solid plastics box (6HA2, 6HB2, 6HC, 6HD2, 6HG2 or 6HH2)		75 kg	75 kg
Glass receptacle in steel, aluminium, plywood or fibre drum (6PA1, 6PB1, 6PD1 or 6PG1) or in steel, aluminium, wooden, wickerwork hamper or fibreboard box (6PA2, 6PB2, 6PC, 6PD2 or 6PG2) or in solid or expanded plastics packaging (6PH1 or 6PH2)		75 kg	75 kg
[3] These packagings shall not be used when the substances being transported may become liquid during transport. [4] These packagings shall only be used for packing group II substances when transported in a closed cargo transport unit.			
Pressure receptacles, provided that the general provisions of 4.1.3.6 are met			

P410	PACKING INSTRUCTION *(continued)*	P410

Special packing provisions:

△ PP31 For UN Nos. 1326, 1339, 1340, 1341, 1343, 1352, 1358, 1373, 1374, 1378, 1379, 1382, 1384, 1385, 1390, 1393, 1394, 1395, 1396, 1398, 1400, 1401, 1402, 1405, 1409, 1417, 1418, 1431, 1436, 1437, 1871, 1923, 1929, 2004, 2008, 2318, 2545, 2546, 2624, 2805, 2813, 2830, 2835, 2844, 2881, 2940, 3078, 3088, 3131, 3132, 3134, 3135, 3170, 3182, 3189, 3190, 3205, 3206, 3208, 3209, 3395, 3396 and 3397, packagings shall be hermetically sealed.

PP39 For UN 1378, for metal packagings a venting device is required.

△ PP40 For the following UN Nos., falling in PG II, bags are not allowed: 1326, 1340, 1352, 1358, 1374, 1378, 1382, 1390, 1393, 1394, 1395, 1396, 1398, 1400, 1401, 1402, 1403, 1405, 1409, 1417, 1418, 1436, 1437, 1871, 2624, 2805, 2813, 2830, 2835, 3078, 3131, 3132, 3134, 3170, 3182, 3208 and 3209.

△ PP83 *Deleted*

■ PP100 For UN 2950 flexible, fibreboard or wooden packagings shall be sift-proof and water-resistant or shall be fitted with a sift-proof and water-resistant liner.

P411	PACKING INSTRUCTION	P411

This instruction applies to UN 3270.

The following packagings are authorized, provided that the general provisions of 4.1.1 and 4.1.3 are met:
Drums (1A2, 1B2, 1N2, 1H2, 1D, 1G);
Boxes (4A, 4B, 4N, 4C1, 4C2, 4D, 4F, 4G, 4H1, 4H2);
Jerricans (3A2, 3B2, 3H2),
provided that explosion is not possible by reason of increased internal pressure.
The maximum net mass shall not exceed 30 kg.

■ P412	PACKING INSTRUCTION	P412

This instruction applies to UN No. 3527.

The following combination packagings are authorized, provided that the general provisions of 4.1.1 and 4.1.3 are met:
(1) Outer packagings:
Drums (1A1, 1A2, 1B1, 1B2, 1N1, 1N2, 1H1, 1H2, 1D, 1G);
Boxes (4A, 4B, 4N, 4C1, 4C2, 4D, 4F, 4G, 4H1, 4H2)
Jerricans (3A1, 3A2, 3B1, 3B2, 3H1, 3H2);
(2) Inner packagings:
(a) The activator (organic peroxide) shall have a maximum quantity of 125 ml per inner packaging if liquid, and 500 g per inner packaging if solid.
(b) The base material and the activator shall be each separately packed in inner packagings.
The components may be placed in the same outer packaging provided that they will not interact dangerously in the event of a leakage.
Packagings shall conform to the packing group II or III performance level according to the criteria for class 4.1 applied to the base material.

P500	PACKING INSTRUCTION	P500

This instruction applies to UN 3356.

The following packagings are authorized, provided that the general provisions of 4.1.1 and 4.1.3 are met:
Drums (1A2, 1B2, 1N2, 1H2, 1D, 1G);
Boxes (4A, 4B, 4N, 4C1, 4C2, 4D, 4F, 4G, 4H1, 4H2);
Jerricans (3A2, 3B2, 3H2).
Packagings shall conform to the packing group II performance level.

The generator(s) shall be transported in a package which meets the following requirements when one generator in the package is actuated:
(a) Other generators in the package will not be actuated;
(b) Packaging material will not ignite; and
(c) The outside surface temperature of the completed package shall not exceed 100°C.

4

P501	PACKING INSTRUCTION	P501

This instruction applies to UN 2015.

The following packagings are authorized, provided that the general provisions of 4.1.1 and 4.1.3 are met.

Combination packagings	Inner packagings maximum capacity	Outer packagings maximum net mass
(1) Boxes (4A, 4B, 4N, 4C1, 4C2, 4D, 4H2) or drums (1A1, 1A2, 1B1, 1B2, 1N1, 1N2, 1H1, 1H2, 1D) or jerricans (3A1, 3A2, 3B1, 3B2, 3H1, 3H2) with glass, plastics or metal inner packagings	5 L	125 kg
(2) Fibreboard box (4G) or fibre drum (1G), with plastics or metal inner packagings each in a plastics bag	2 L	50 kg

Single packagings	Maximum capacity
Drums steel (1A1) aluminium (1B1) metal other than steel or aluminium (1N1) plastics (1H1)	250 L 250 L 250 L 250 L
Jerricans steel (3A1) aluminium (3B1) plastics (3H1)	60 L 60 L 60 L
Composite packagings	
Plastics receptacle in steel or aluminium drum (6HA1, 6HB1)	250 L
Plastics receptacle in fibre, plastics or plywood drum (6HG1, 6HH1, 6HD1)	250 L
Plastics receptacle in steel or aluminium crate or box or plastics receptacle in wood, plywood, fibreboard or solid plastics box (6HA2, 6HB2, 6HC, 6HD2, 6HG2 or 6HH2)	60 L
Glass receptacle in steel, aluminium, fibre or plywood drum (6PA1, 6PB1, 6PD1 or 6PG1) or in a steel, aluminium, wood or fibreboard box or in wickerwork hamper (6PA2, 6PB2, 6PC, 6PG2 or 6PD2) or in solid or expanded plastics packaging (6PH1 or 6PH2)	60 L

Additional provisions:
1 Packagings shall have a minimum ullage of 10%.
2 Packagings shall be vented.

P502	PACKING INSTRUCTION		P502
The following packagings are authorized, provided that the general provisions of 4.1.1 and 4.1.3 are met.			

Combination packagings		Maximum net mass
Inner packagings	**Outer packagings**	

Glass   5 L
Metal   5 L
Plastic   5 L
	Drums
	   steel (1A1, 1A2)
	   aluminium (1B1, 1B2)
	   other metal (1N1, 1N2)
	   plywood (1D)
	   fibre (1G)
	   plastics (1H1, 1H2)
		125 kg
		125 kg
		125 kg
		125 kg
		125 kg
		125 kg

	Boxes
	   steel (4A)
	   aluminium (4B)
	   other metal (4N)
	   natural wood (4C1)
	   natural wood with sift-proof
	      walls (4C2)
	   plywood (4D)
	   reconstituted wood (4F)
	   fibreboard (4G)
	   expanded plastics (4H1)
	   solid plastics (4H2)
		125 kg
		125 kg
		125 kg
		125 kg
		125 kg
		
		125 kg
		125 kg
		125 kg
		60 kg
		125 kg

Single packagings	Maximum capacity

Drums
   steel (1A1)
   aluminium (1B1)
   plastics (1H1)
	250 L
	250 L
	250 L

Jerricans
   steel (3A1)
   aluminium (3B1)
   plastics (3H1)
	60 L
	60 L
	60 L

Composite packagings	
Plastics receptacle in steel or aluminium drum (6HA1, 6HB1)	250 L
Plastics receptacle in fibre, plastics or plywood drum (6HG1, 6HH1, 6HD1)	250 L
Plastics receptacle in steel or aluminium crate or box or plastics receptacle in wood, plywood, fibreboard or solid plastics box (6HA2, 6HB2, 6HC, 6HD2, 6HG2 or 6HH2)	60 L
Glass receptacle in steel, aluminium, fibre or plywood drum (6PA1, 6PB1, 6PD1 or 6PG1) or in a steel, aluminium, wood or fibreboard box or in wickerwork hamper (6PA2, 6PB2, 6PC, 6PG2 or 6PD2) or in solid or expanded plastics packaging (6PH1 or 6PH2)	60 L

Special packing provision:

△ **PP28** For UN No. 1873, parts of packagings which are in direct contact with perchloric acid shall be constructed of glass or plastics.

P503	PACKING INSTRUCTION		P503
The following packagings are authorized, provided that the general provisions of 4.1.1 and 4.1.3 are met.			

Combination packagings		Maximum net mass
Inner packagings	Outer packagings	
Glass 5 kg	**Drums**	
Metal 5 kg	steel (1A1, 1A2)	125 kg
Plastic 5 kg	aluminium (1B1, 1B2)	125 kg
	other metal (1N1, 1N2)	125 kg
	fibre (1G)	125 kg
	plywood (1D)	125 kg
	plastics (1H1, 1H2)	125 kg
	Boxes	
	steel (4A)	125 kg
	aluminium (4B)	125 kg
	other metal (4N)	125 kg
	natural wood (4C1)	125 kg
	natural wood with sift-proof walls (4C2)	125 kg
	plywood (4D)	125 kg
	reconstituted wood (4F)	125 kg
	fibreboard (4G)	40 kg
	expanded plastics (4H1)	60 kg
	solid plastics (4H2)	125 kg

Single packagings	Maximum net mass
Metal drums (1A1, 1A2, 1B1, 1B2, 1N1 or 1N2)	250 kg
Fibreboard (1G) or plywood drums (1D) fitted with inner liners	200 kg

P504	PACKING INSTRUCTION	P504
The following packagings are authorized, provided that the general provisions of 4.1.1 and 4.1.3 are met.		

Combination packagings	Maximum net mass
(1) Outer packagings: (1A1, 1A2, 1B1, 1B2, 1N1, 1N2, 1H1, 1H2, 1D, 1G, 4A, 4B, 4N, 4C1, 4C2, 4D, 4F, 4G, 4H2) Inner packagings: Glass receptacles with a maximum capacity of 5 L	75 kg
(2) Outer packagings: (1A1, 1A2, 1B1, 1B2, 1N1, 1N2, 1H1, 1H2, 1D, 1G, 4A, 4B, 4N, 4C1, 4C2, 4D, 4F, 4G, 4H2) Inner packagings: Plastics receptacles with a maximum capacity of 30 L	75 kg
(3) Outer packagings: (1G, 4F or 4G) Inner packagings: Metal receptacles with a maximum capacity of 40 L	125 kg
(4) Outer packagings: (1A1, 1A2, 1B2, 1N1, 1N2, 1H1, 1H2, 1D, 4A, 4B, 4N, 4C1, 4C2, 4D, 4H2) Inner packagings: Metal receptacles with a maximum capacity of 40 L	225 kg

Single packagings	Maximum capacity
Drums	
steel, non-removable head (1A1)	250 L
aluminium, non-removable head (1B1)	250 L
metal, other than steel or aluminium, non-removable head (1N1)	250 L
plastics, non-removable head (1H1)	250 L
Jerricans	
steel, non-removable head (3A1)	60 L
aluminium, non-removable head (3B1)	60 L
plastics, non-removable head (3H1)	60 L
Composite packagings	
Plastics receptacle in steel or aluminium drum (6HA1, 6HB1)	250 L
Plastics receptacle in fibre, plastics or plywood drum (6HG1, 6HH1, 6HD1)	120 L
Plastics receptacle in steel or aluminium crate or box or plastics receptacle in wood, plywood, fibreboard or solid plastics box (6HA2, 6HB2, 6HC, 6HD2, 6HG2 or 6HH2)	60 L
Glass receptacle in steel, aluminium, fibre or plywood drum (6PA1, 6PB1, 6PD1 or 6PG1) or in a steel, aluminium, wood or fibreboard box or in wickerwork hamper (6PA2, 6PB2, 6PC, 6PG2 or 6PD2) or in solid or expanded plastics packaging (6PH1 or 6PH2)	60 L

Special packing provisions:

PP10 For UN Nos. 2014 and 3149, the packaging shall be vented.

PP31 For UN 2626, packagings shall be hermetically sealed.

P505	PACKING INSTRUCTION	P505

This instruction applies to UN 3375.

The following packagings are authorized, provided that the general provisions of 4.1.1 and 4.1.3 are met.

Combination packagings	Inner packagings maximum capacity	Outer packagings maximum net mass
Boxes (4B, 4C1, 4C2, 4D, 4G, 4H2) or drums (1B2, 1G, 1N2, 1H2, 1D) or jerricans (3B2, 3H2) with glass, plastics or metal inner packagings	5 L	125 kg

Single packagings	Maximum capacity

Drums
  aluminium (1B1, 1B2)
  plastics (1H1, 1H2)
	250 L
	250 L

Jerricans
  aluminium (3B1, 3B2),
  plastics (3H1, 3H2)
	60 L
	60 L

Composite packagings	
plastics receptacle with outer aluminium drum (6HB1)	250 L
plastics receptacle with outer fibre, plastics or plywood drum (6HG1, 6HH1, 6HD1)	250 L
plastics receptacle with outer aluminium crate or box or plastics receptacle with outer wooden, plywood, fibreboard or solid plastics box (6HB2, 6HC, 6HD2, 6HG2, 6HH2)	60 L
glass receptacle with outer aluminium, fibre or plywood drum (6PB1, 6PG1, 6PD1) or with outer expanded plastics or solid plastics receptacles (6PH1, 6PH2) or with outer aluminium crate or box or with outer wooden or fibreboard box or with outer wickerwork hamper (6PB2, 6PC, 6PG2, 6PD2)	60 L

4

P520	PACKING INSTRUCTION	P520

This instruction applies to organic peroxides of class 5.2 and self-reactive substances of class 4.1.

The packagings listed below are authorized provided the general provisions of 4.1.1 and 4.1.3 and special provisions of 4.1.7 are met.

The packing methods are designated OP1 to OP8. The packing methods appropriate for the individual currently assigned organic peroxides and self-reactive substances are listed in 2.4.2.3.2.3 and 2.5.3.2.4. The quantities specified for each packing method are the maximum quantities authorized per package. The following packagings are authorized:

(1) Combination packagings with outer packagings comprising boxes (4A, 4B, 4N, 4C1, 4C2, 4D, 4F, 4G, 4H1 and 4H2), drums (1A1, 1A2, 1B1, 1B2, 1G, 1H1, 1H2 and 1D), jerricans (3A1, 3A2, 3B1, 3B2, 3H1 and 3H2);

(2) Single packagings consisting of drums (1A1, 1A2, 1B1, 1B2, 1G, 1H1, 1H2 and 1D) and jerricans (3A1, 3A2, 3B1, 3B2, 3H1 and 3H2);

(3) Composite packagings with plastics inner receptacles (6HA1, 6HA2, 6HB1, 6HB2, 6HC, 6HD1, 6HD2, 6HG1, 6HG2, 6HH1 and 6HH2).

Maximum quantity per packaging/package[1] for packing methods OP1 to OP8								
Packing method Maximum quantity	OP1	OP2[1]	OP3	OP4[1]	OP5	OP6	OP7	OP8
Maximum mass (kg) for solids and for combination packagings (liquid and solid)	0.5	0.5/10	5	5/25	25	50	50	400[2]
Maximum contents in litres for liquids[3]	0.5	–	5	–	30	60	60	225[4]

[1] If two values are given, the first applies to the maximum net mass per inner packaging and the second to the maximum net mass of the complete package.

[2] 60 kg for jerricans/200 kg for boxes and, for solids, 400 kg in combination packagings with outer packagings comprising boxes (4C1, 4C2, 4D, 4F, 4G, 4H1 and 4H2) and with inner packagings of plastics or fibre with a maximum net mass of 25 kg.

[3] Viscous liquids shall be treated as solids when they do not meet the criteria provided in the definition for liquids presented in 1.2.1.

[4] 60 L for jerricans.

Additional provisions:

1   Metal packagings, including inner packagings of combination packagings and outer packagings of combination or composite packagings, may only be used for packing methods OP7 and OP8.

2   In combination packagings, glass receptacles may only be used as inner packagings with a maximum content of 0.5 kg for solids or 0.5 L for liquids.

3   In combination packagings, cushioning materials shall not be readily combustible.

4   The packaging of an organic peroxide or self-reactive substance required to bear an EXPLOSIVE subsidiary risk label (Model No. 1, see 5.2.2.2.2) shall also comply with the provisions given in 4.1.5.10 and 4.1.5.11.

Special packing provisions:

PP21   For certain self-reactive substances of types B or C, UN Nos. 3221, 3222, 3223, 3224, 3231, 3232, 3233 and 3234, a smaller packaging than that allowed by packing methods OP5 or OP6 respectively shall be used (see 4.1.7 and 2.4.2.3.2.3).

PP22   UN 3241, 2-bromo-2-nitropropane-1,3-diol, shall be packed in accordance with packing method OP6.

P600	PACKING INSTRUCTION	P600

This instruction applies to UN Nos. 1700, 2016 and 2017.

The following packagings are authorized, provided the general provisions of 4.1.1 and 4.1.3 are met:

Outer packagings: (1A1, 1A2, 1B1, 1B2, 1N1, 1N2, 1H1, 1H2, 1D, 1G, 4A, 4B, 4N, 4C1, 4C2, 4D, 4F, 4G, 4H2) meeting the packing group II performance level. The articles shall be individually packaged and separated from each other using partitions, dividers, inner packagings or cushioning material to prevent inadvertent discharge during normal conditions of transport.

Maximum net mass: 75 kg

P601	PACKING INSTRUCTION	P601

The following packagings are authorized provided the general provisions of 4.1.1 and 4.1.3 are met and the packagings are hermetically sealed:

(1) Combination packagings with a maximum gross mass of 15 kg, consisting of:

- one or more glass inner packaging(s) with a maximum net quantity of 1 litre each and filled to not more than 90% of their capacity; the closure(s) of which shall be physically held in place by any means capable of preventing back-off or loosening by impact or vibration during transport, individually placed in

- metal receptacles together with cushioning and absorbent material sufficient to absorb the entire contents of the glass inner packaging(s), further packed in

- 1A1, 1A2, 1B1, 1B2, 1N1, 1N2, 1H1, 1H2, 1D, 1G, 4A, 4B, 4N, 4C1, 4C2, 4D, 4F, 4G or 4H2 outer packagings.

(2) Combination packagings consisting of metal or plastics inner packagings not exceeding 5 L in capacity individually packed with absorbent material sufficient to absorb the contents and inert cushioning material in 1A1, 1A2, 1B1, 1B2, 1N1, 1N2, 1H1, 1H2, 1D, 1G, 4A, 4B, 4N, 4C1, 4C2, 4D, 4F, 4G or 4H2 outer packagings with a maximum gross mass of 75 kg. Inner packagings shall not be filled to more than 90% of their capacity. The closure of each inner packaging shall be physically held in place by any means capable of preventing back-off or loosening of the closure by impact or vibration during transport.

(3) Packagings consisting of:

Outer packagings: Steel or plastics drums, (1A1, 1A2, 1H1 or 1H2), tested in accordance with the test provisions in 6.1.5 at a mass corresponding to the mass of the assembled package either as a packaging intended to contain inner packagings, or as a single packaging intended to contain solids or liquids, and marked accordingly.

Inner packagings: Drums and composite packagings (1A1, 1B1, 1N1, 1H1 or 6HA1), meeting the provisions of chapter 6.1 for single packagings, subject to the following conditions:

.1 the hydraulic pressure test shall be conducted at a pressure of at least 3 bar (gauge pressure);

.2 the design and production leakproofness tests shall be conducted at a test pressure of 0.30 bar;

.3 they shall be isolated from the outer drum by the use of inert shock-mitigating cushioning material which surrounds the inner packaging on all sides;

.4 their capacity shall not exceed 125 L;

.5 closures shall be of a screw-cap type that are:

   (i) physically held in place by any means capable of preventing back-off or loosening of the closure by impact or vibration during transport; and

   (ii) provided with a cap seal.

.6 The outer and inner packagings shall be subjected periodically to a leakproofness test according to .2 at intervals of not more than two and a half years; and

.7 The outer and inner packagings shall bear in clearly legible and durable characters:

   (i) the date (month, year) of the initial testing and the latest periodic test;

   (ii) the name or authorized symbol of the party performing the tests and inspections.

(4) Pressure receptacles, provided that the general provisions of 4.1.3.6 are met. They shall be subjected to an initial test and periodic tests every 10 years at a pressure of not less than 1 MPa (10 bar) (gauge pressure). Pressure receptacles may not be equipped with any pressure relief device. Each pressure receptacle containing a toxic by inhalation liquid with an LC_{50} less than or equal to 200 mL/m^3 (ppm) shall be closed with a plug or valve conforming to the following:

(a) Each plug or valve shall have a taper-threaded connection directly to the pressure receptacle and be capable of withstanding the test pressure of the pressure receptacle without damage or leakage;

(b) Each valve shall be of the packless type with non-perforated diaphragm, except that, for corrosive materials, a valve may be of the packed type with an assembly made gas-tight by means of a seal cap with gasket joint attached to the valve body or the pressure receptacle to prevent loss of material through or past the packing;

(c) Each valve outlet shall be sealed by a threaded cap or threaded solid plug and inert gasket material;

(d) The materials of construction for the pressure receptacle, valves, plugs, outlet caps, luting and gaskets shall be compatible with each other and with the lading.

Each pressure receptacle with a wall thickness at any point of less than 2.0 mm and each pressure receptacle that does not have fitted valve protection shall be transported in an outer packaging. Pressure receptacles shall not be manifolded or interconnected.

4

P602	PACKING INSTRUCTION	P602

The following packagings are authorized, provided the general provisions of 4.1.1 and 4.1.3 are met and the packagings are hermetically sealed:

(1) Combination packagings with a maximum gross mass of 15 kg, consisting of:
- one or more glass inner packaging(s) with a maximum net quantity of 1 litre each and filled to not more than 90% of their capacity, the closure(s) of which shall be physically held in place by any means capable of preventing back-off or loosening by impact or vibration during transport, individually placed in
- metal receptacles together with cushioning and absorbent material sufficient to absorb the entire contents of the glass inner packaging(s), further packed in
- 1A1, 1A2, 1B1, 1B2, 1N1, 1N2, 1H1, 1H2, 1D, 1G, 4A, 4B, 4N, 4C1, 4C2, 4D, 4F, 4G or 4H2 outer packagings.

(2) Combination packagings consisting of metal or plastics inner packagings individually packed with absorbent material sufficient to absorb the contents and inert cushioning material in 1A1, 1A2, 1B1, 1B2, 1N1, 1N2, 1H1, 1H2 1D, 1G, 4A, 4B, 4N, 4C1, 4C2, 4D, 4F, 4G or 4H2 outer packagings with a maximum gross mass of 75 kg. Inner packagings shall not be filled to more than 90% of their capacity. The closure of each inner packaging shall be physically held in place by any means capable of preventing back-off or loosening of the closure by impact or vibration during transport. Inner packagings shall not exceed 5 L in capacity.

(3) Drums and composite packagings (1A1, 1B1, 1N1, 1H1, 6HA1 or 6HH1), subject to the following conditions:
  .1 the hydraulic pressure test shall be conducted at a pressure of at least 3 bar (gauge pressure);
  .2 the design and production leakproofness tests shall be conducted at a test pressure of 0.30 bar; and
  .3 closures shall be of a screw-cap type that are:
    (i) physically held in place by any means capable of preventing back-off or loosening of the closure by impact or vibration during transport; and
    (ii) provided with a cap seal.

(4) Pressure receptacles, provided that the general provisions of 4.1.3.6 are met. They shall be subjected to an initial test and periodic tests every 10 years at a pressure of not less than 1 MPa (10 bar) (gauge pressure). Pressure receptacles may not be equipped with any pressure relief device. Each pressure receptacle containing a toxic by inhalation liquid with an LC_{50} less than or equal to 200 mL/m^3 (ppm) shall be closed with a plug or valve conforming to the following:
  (a) Each plug or valve shall have a taper-threaded connection directly to the pressure receptacle and be capable of withstanding the test pressure of the pressure receptacle without damage or leakage;
  (b) Each valve shall be of the packless type with non-perforated diaphragm, except that, for corrosive materials, a valve may be of the packed type with an assembly made gas-tight by means of a seal cap with gasket joint attached to the valve body or the pressure receptacle to prevent loss of material through or past the packing;
  (c) Each valve outlet shall be sealed by a threaded cap or threaded solid plug and inert gasket material;
  (d) The materials of construction for the pressure receptacle, valves, plugs, outlet caps, luting and gaskets shall be compatible with each other and with the lading.

Each pressure receptacle with a wall thickness at any point of less than 2.0 mm and each pressure receptacle that does not have fitted valve protection shall be transported in an outer packaging. Pressure receptacles shall not be manifolded or interconnected.

⚠ P603	PACKING INSTRUCTION	P603

This instruction applies to UN 3507.

The following packagings are authorized provided that the general provisions of 4.1.1 and 4.1.3 and the special packing provisions of 4.1.9.1.2, 4.1.9.1.4 and 4.1.9.1.7 are met:

Packagings consisting of:
  (a) Metal or plastics primary receptacle(s); in
  (b) Leakproof rigid secondary packaging(s); in
  (c) A rigid outer packaging:
      Drums (1A2, 1B2, 1N2, 1H2, 1D, 1G);
      Boxes (4A, 4B, 4C1, 4C2, 4D, 4F, 4G, 4H1, 4H2);
      Jerricans (3A2, 3B2, 3H2).

Additional requirements:

1 Primary inner receptacles shall be packed in secondary packagings in a way that, under normal conditions of transport, they cannot break, be punctured or leak their contents into the secondary packaging. Secondary packagings shall be secured in outer packagings with suitable cushioning material to prevent movement. If multiple primary receptacles are placed in a single secondary packaging, they shall be either individually wrapped or separated so as to prevent contact between them.

2 The contents shall comply with the provisions of 2.7.2.4.5.2;

3 The provisions of 6.4.4 shall be met.

Special packing provision:

In the case of fissile-excepted material, limits specified in 2.7.2.3.5 and 6.4.11.2 shall be met.

P620	PACKING INSTRUCTION	P620

This instruction applies to UN Nos. 2814 and 2900.

The following packagings are authorized, provided the special packing provisions of 4.1.8 are met:

Packagings meeting the provisions of chapter 6.3 and approved accordingly consisting of:

.1   Inner packagings comprising:

(i)   leakproof primary receptacle(s);

(ii)   a leakproof secondary packaging;

(iii)   other than for solid infectious substances, an absorbent material in sufficient quantity to absorb the entire contents placed between the primary receptacle(s) and the secondary packaging; if multiple primary receptacles are placed in a single secondary packaging, they shall be either individually wrapped or separated so as to prevent contact between them;

.2   A rigid outer packaging:

Drums (1A1, 1A2, 1B1, 1B2, 1N1, 1N2, 1H1, 1H2, 1D, 1G);

Boxes (4A, 4B, 4N, 4C1, 4C2, 4D, 4F, 4G, 4H1, 4H2);

Jerricans (3A1, 3A2, 3B1, 3B2, 3H1, 3H2).

The smallest external dimension shall be not less than 100 mm.

Additional provisions:

1   Inner packagings containing infectious substances shall not be consolidated with inner packagings containing unrelated types of goods. Complete packages may be overpacked in accordance with the provisions of 1.2.1 and 5.1.2: such an overpack may contain dry ice.

2   Other than for exceptional consignments, such as whole organs which require special packaging, the following additional provisions shall apply:

(a)   *Substances consigned at ambient temperatures or at a higher temperature.* Primary receptacles shall be of glass, metal or plastics. Positive means of ensuring a leakproof seal shall be provided, e.g. a heat seal, a skirted stopper or a metal crimp seal. If screw caps are used, they shall be secured by positive means, e.g. tape, paraffin sealing tape or a manufactured locking closure;

(b)   *Substances consigned refrigerated or frozen.* Ice, dry ice or other refrigerant shall be placed around the secondary packaging(s) or alternatively in an overpack with one or more complete packages marked in accordance with 6.3.3. Interior supports shall be provided to secure secondary packaging(s) or packages in position after the ice or dry ice has dissipated. If ice is used, the outer packaging or overpack shall be leakproof. If dry ice is used, the outer packaging or overpack shall permit the release of carbon dioxide gas. The primary receptacle and the secondary packaging shall maintain their integrity at the temperature of the refrigerant used;

(c)   *Substances consigned in liquid nitrogen.* Plastics primary receptacles capable of withstanding very low temperature shall be used. The secondary packaging shall also be capable of withstanding very low temperatures, and in most cases will need to be fitted over the primary receptacle individually. Provisions for the consignment of liquid nitrogen shall also be fulfilled. The primary receptacle and the secondary packaging shall maintain their integrity at the temperature of the liquid nitrogen.

(d)   Lyophilized substances may also be transported in primary receptacles that are flame-sealed glass ampoules or rubber-stoppered glass vials fitted with metal seals.

3   Whatever the intended temperature of the consignment, the primary receptacle or the secondary packaging shall be capable of withstanding, without leakage, an internal pressure producing a pressure differential of not less than 95 kPa and temperatures in the range −40°C to +55°C.

4   Other dangerous goods shall not be packed in the same packaging as class 6.2 infectious substances unless they are necessary for maintaining the viability, stabilizing or preventing degradation or neutralizing the hazards of the infectious substances. A quantity of 30 mL or less of dangerous goods included in classes 3, 8 or 9 may be packed in each primary receptacle containing infectious substances. These small quantities of dangerous goods of classes 3, 8 or 9 are not subject to any additional provisions of this Code when packed in accordance with this packing instruction.

5   Alternative packagings for the transport of animal material may be authorized by the competent authority in accordance with the provisions of 4.1.3.7.

4

P621	PACKING INSTRUCTION	P621
This instruction applies to UN 3291.		

The following packagings are authorized provided that the general provisions of 4.1.1 except 4.1.1.15 and 4.1.3 are met:

(1) Provided that there is sufficient absorbent material to absorb the entire amount of liquid present and the packaging is capable of retaining liquids:

        Drums (1A2, 1B2, 1N2, 1H2, 1D, 1G);

        Boxes (4A, 4B, 4N, 4C1, 4C2, 4D, 4F, 4G, 4H1, 4H2);

        Jerricans (3A2, 3B2, 3H2).

Packagings shall conform to the packing group II performance level for solids.

(2) For packages containing larger quantities of liquid:

        Drums (1A1, 1A2, 1B1, 1B2, 1N1, 1N2, 1H1, 1H2, 1D, 1G);

        Jerricans (3A1, 3A2, 3B1, 3B2, 3H1, 3H2);

Composite packagings (6HA1, 6HB1, 6HG1, 6HH1, 6HD1, 6HA2, 6HB2, 6HC, 6HD2, 6HG2, 6HH2, 6PA1, 6PB1, 6PG1, 6PD1, 6PH1, 6PH2, 6PA2, 6PB2, 6PC, 6PG2 or 6PD2).

Packagings shall conform to the packing group II performance level for liquids.

Additional requirement:

Packagings intended to contain sharp objects such as broken glass and needles shall be resistant to puncture and retain liquids under the performance test conditions in Chapter 6.1.

P650	PACKING INSTRUCTION	P650

This instruction applies to UN 3373.

(1) The packaging shall be of good quality, strong enough to withstand the shocks and loadings normally encountered during transport, including transhipment between cargo transport units and between cargo transport units and warehouses as well as any removal from a pallet or overpack for subsequent manual or mechanical handling. Packagings shall be constructed and closed to prevent any loss of contents that might be caused under normal conditions of transport by vibration or by changes in temperature, humidity or pressure.

(2) The packaging shall consist of at least three components:

    (a) a primary receptacle;

    (b) a secondary packaging; and

    (c) an outer packaging

    of which either the secondary or the outer packaging shall be rigid.

(3) Primary receptacles shall be packed in secondary packagings in such a way that, under normal conditions of transport, they cannot break, be punctured or leak their contents into the secondary packaging. Secondary packagings shall be secured in outer packagings with suitable cushioning material. Any leakage of the contents shall not compromise the integrity of the cushioning material or of the outer packaging.

(4) For transport, the mark illustrated below shall be displayed on the external surface of the outer packaging on a background of a contrasting colour and shall be clearly visible and legible. The mark shall be in the form of a square set at an angle of 45° (diamond-shaped) with each side having a length of at least 50 mm, the width of the line shall be at least 2 mm and the letters and numbers shall be at least 6 mm high. The proper shipping name "BIOLOGICAL SUBSTANCE, CATEGORY B" in letters at least 6 mm high shall be marked on the outer packaging adjacent to the diamond-shaped mark.

(5) At least one surface of the outer packaging shall have a minimum dimension of 100 mm × 100 mm.

(6) The completed package shall be capable of successfully passing the drop test in 6.3.5.3 as specified in 6.3.5.2 of this Code at a height of 1.2 m. Following the appropriate drop sequence, there shall be no leakage from the primary receptacle(s) which shall remain protected by absorbent material, when required, in the secondary packaging.

(7) For liquid substances

    (a) The primary receptacle(s) shall be leakproof;

    (b) The secondary packaging shall be leakproof;

    (c) If multiple fragile primary receptacles are placed in a single secondary packaging, they shall either be individually wrapped or separated to prevent contact between them;

    (d) Absorbent material shall be placed between the primary receptacle(s) and the secondary packaging. The absorbent material shall be in a quantity sufficient to absorb the entire contents of the primary receptacle(s) so that any release of the liquid substance will not compromise the integrity of the cushioning material or of the outer packaging;

    (e) The primary receptacle or the secondary packaging shall be capable of withstanding, without leakage, an internal pressure of 95 kPa (0.95 bar).

(8) For solid substances

    (a) The primary receptacle(s) shall be siftproof;

    (b) The secondary packaging shall be siftproof;

    (c) If multiple fragile primary receptacles are placed in a single secondary packaging, they shall either be individually wrapped or separated to prevent contact between them.

    (d) If there is any doubt as to whether or not residual liquid may be present in the primary receptacle during transport then a packaging suitable for liquids, including absorbent materials, shall be used.

P650	PACKING INSTRUCTION *(continued)*	P650

(9) Refrigerated or frozen specimens: ice, dry ice and liquid nitrogen

    (a) When dry ice or liquid nitrogen is used as a coolant, the requirements of 5.5.3 shall apply. When used, ice shall be placed outside the secondary packagings or in the outer packaging or an overpack. Interior supports shall be provided to secure the secondary packagings in the original position. If ice is used, the outside packaging or overpack shall be leakproof.

    (b) The primary receptacle and the secondary packaging shall maintain their integrity at the temperature of the refrigerant used as well as the temperatures and the pressures which could result if refrigeration were lost.

△ (10) When packages are placed in an overpack, the package marks required by this packing instruction shall either be clearly visible or be reproduced on the outside of the overpack.

(11) Infectious substances assigned to UN 3373 which are packed and marked in accordance with this packing instruction are not subject to any other provisions of this Code.

(12) Clear instructions on filling and closing such packages shall be provided by packaging manufacturers and subsequent distributors to the consignor or to the person who prepares the package (e.g. patient) to enable the package to be correctly prepared for transport.

(13) Other dangerous goods shall not be packed in the same packaging as class 6.2 infectious substances unless they are necessary for maintaining the viability, stabilizing or preventing degradation or neutralizing the hazards of the infectious substances. A quantity of 30 mL or less of dangerous goods included in classes 3, 8 or 9 may be packed in each primary receptacle containing infectious substances. When these small quantities of dangerous goods are packed with infectious substances in accordance with this packing instruction, no other provisions of the Code need be met.

Additional provision:

Alternative packagings for the transport of animal material may be authorized by the competent authority in accordance with the provisions of 4.1.3.7.

P800	PACKING INSTRUCTION	P800

This instruction applies to UN Nos. 2803 and 2809.

The following packagings are authorized, provided the general provisions of 4.1.1 and 4.1.3 are met:

(1) Pressure receptacles, provided that the general provisions of 4.1.3.6 are met.

(2) Steel flasks or bottles with threaded closures with a capacity not exceeding 3.0 L; or

(3) Combination packagings which conform to the following provisions:

    (a) Inner packagings shall comprise glass, metal or rigid plastics intended to contain liquids with a maximum net mass of 15 kg each.

    (b) The inner packagings shall be packed with sufficient cushioning material to prevent breakage.

    (c) Either the inner packagings or the outer packagings shall have inner liners or bags of strong leakproof and puncture-resistant material impervious to the contents and completely surrounding the contents to prevent it from escaping from the package irrespective of its position or orientation.

    (d) The following outer packagings and maximum net masses are authorized:

Outer packaging	Maximum net mass
Drums	
steel (1A1, 1A2)	400 kg
metal, other than steel or aluminium (1N1, 1N2)	400 kg
plastics (1H1, 1H2)	400 kg
plywood (1D)	400 kg
fibre (1G)	400 kg
Boxes	
steel (4A)	400 kg
metal, other than steel or aluminium (4N)	400 kg
natural wood (4C1)	250 kg
natural wood with sift-proof walls (4C2)	250 kg
plywood (4D)	250 kg
reconstituted wood (4F)	125 kg
fibreboard (4G)	125 kg
expanded plastics (4H1)	60 kg
solid plastics (4H2)	125 kg

Special packing provision:

PP41   For UN 2803, when it is necessary to transport gallium at low temperatures in order to maintain it in a completely solid state, the above packagings may be overpacked in a strong, water-resistant outer packaging which contains dry ice or other means of refrigeration. If a refrigerant is used, all of the above materials used in the packaging of gallium shall be chemically and physically resistant to the refrigerant and shall have impact resistance at the low temperatures of the refrigerant employed. If dry ice is used, the outer packaging shall permit the release of carbon dioxide gas.

P801	PACKING INSTRUCTION	P801

This instruction applies to new and used batteries assigned to UN Nos. 2794, 2795 or 3028.

The following packagings are authorized, provided the general provisions of 4.1.1, except 4.1.1.3, and 4.1.3 are met, except that packagings need not conform to the provisions of part 6:

(1) Rigid outer packagings;

(2) Wooden slatted crates;

(3) Pallets.

Used storage batteries may also be transported loose in stainless steel or plastics battery boxes capable of containing any free liquid.

Additional provisions:

1   Batteries shall be protected against short circuits.

2   Batteries stacked shall be adequately secured in tiers separated by a layer of non-conductive material.

3   Battery terminals shall not support the mass of other superimposed elements.

4   Batteries shall be packaged or secured to prevent inadvertent movement.

5   For UN Nos. 2794 and 2795, batteries shall be capable of passing a tilt test at an angle of 45° with no spillage of liquid.

P802	PACKING INSTRUCTION	P802

The following packagings are authorized, provided the general provisions of 4.1.1 and 4.1.3 are met:

(1) Combination packagings

Outer packagings: 1A1, 1A2, 1B1, 1B2, 1N1, 1N2, 1H1, 1H2, 1D, 1G, 4A, 4B, 4N, 4C1, 4C2, 4D, 4F, 4G or 4H2; maximum net mass: 75 kg.

Inner packagings: glass or plastics; maximum capacity: 10 L.

(2) Combination packagings

Outer packagings: 1A1, 1A2, 1B1, 1B2, 1N1, 1N2, 1H1, 1H2, 1D, 1G, 4A, 4B, 4N, 4C1, 4C2, 4D, 4F, 4G or 4H2; maximum net mass: 125 kg

Inner packagings: metal; maximum capacity: 40 L

(3) Composite packagings: Glass receptacle in steel, aluminium or plywood drum (6PA1, 6PB1 or 6PD1) or in a steel, aluminium or wood box or in wickerwork hamper (6PA2, 6PB2, 6PC or 6PD2) or in solid plastics packaging (6PH2); maximum capacity: 60 L.

(4) Steel drums (1A1) with a maximum capacity of 250 L.

(5) Pressure receptacles may be used provided that the general provisions of 4.1.3.6 are met.

Special packing provisions:

PP79 For UN 1790 with more than 60% but not more than 85% hydrofluoric acid, see P001.

PP81 For UN 1790 with not more than 85% hydrogen fluoride and UN 2031 with more than 55% nitric acid, the permitted use of plastics drums and jerricans as single packagings shall be two years from their date of manufacture.

P803	PACKING INSTRUCTION	P803

This instruction applies to UN 2028.

The following packagings are authorized, provided the general provisions of 4.1.1 and 4.1.3 are met:

(1) Drums (1A2, 1B2, 1N2, 1H2, 1D, 1G);

(2) Boxes (4A, 4B, 4N, 4C1, 4C2, 4D, 4F, 4G, 4H2);

Maximum net mass: 75 kg.

The articles shall be individually packaged and separated from each other, using partitions, dividers, inner packagings or cushioning material to prevent inadvertent discharge during normal conditions of transport.

P804	PACKING INSTRUCTION	P804

This instruction applies to UN 1744.

The following packagings are authorized provided the general provisions of 4.1.1 and 4.1.3 are met and the packagings are hermetically sealed:

(1) Combination packagings with a maximum gross mass of 25 kg, consisting of one or more glass inner packaging(s) with a maximum capacity of 1.3 litres each and filled to no more than 90% of their capacity; the closure(s) of which shall be physically held in place by any means capable of preventing back-off or loosening by impact or vibration during transport, individually placed in:

– metal or rigid plastics receptacles together with cushioning and absorbent material sufficient to absorb the entire contents of the glass inner packaging(s), further packed in:

– 1A1, 1A2, 1B1, 1B2, 1N1, 1N2, 1H1, 1H2, 1D, 1G, 4A, 4B, 4N, 4C1, 4C2, 4D, 4F, 4G or 4H2 outer packagings.

(2) Combination packagings consisting of metal or polyvinylidene fluoride (PVDF) inner packagings, not exceeding 5 litres in capacity individually packed with absorbent material sufficient to absorb the contents and inert cushioning material in 1A1, 1A2, 1B1, 1B2, 1N1, 1N2, 1H1, 1H2, 1D, 1G, 4A, 4B, 4N, 4C1, 4C2, 4D, 4F, 4G or 4H2 outer packagings with a maximum gross mass of 75 kg. Inner packagings shall not be filled to more than 90% of their capacity. The closure of each inner packaging shall be physically held in place by any means capable of preventing back-off or loosening of the closure by impact or vibration during transport.

(3) Packagings consisting of:

Outer packagings:

Steel or plastics drums (1A1, 1A2, 1H1 or 1H2) tested in accordance with the test requirements in 6.1.5 at a mass corresponding to the mass of the assembled package either as a packaging intended to contain inner packagings, or as a single packaging intended to contain solids or liquids, and marked accordingly;

Inner packagings:

Drums and composite packagings (1A1, 1B1, 1N1, 1H1 or 6HA1) meeting the requirements of chapter 6.1 for single packagings, subject to the following conditions:

(a) The hydraulic pressure test shall be conducted at a pressure of at least 300 kPa (3 bar) (gauge pressure);

(b) The design and production leakproofness tests shall be conducted at a test pressure of 30 kPa (0.3 bar);

(c) They shall be isolated from the outer drum by the use of inert shock-mitigating cushioning material which surrounds the inner packaging on all sides;

(d) Their capacity shall not exceed 125 litres;

(e) Closures shall be of a screw type that are:

  (i) Physically held in place by any means capable of preventing back-off or loosening of the closure by impact or vibration during transport;

  (ii) Provided with a cap seal;

(f) The outer and inner packagings shall be subjected periodically to an internal inspection and leakproofness test according to (b) at intervals of not more than two and a half years; and

(g) The outer and inner packagings shall bear in clearly legible and durable characters:

  (i) the date (month, year) of the initial test and the latest periodic test and inspection of the inner packaging; and

  (ii) the name or authorized symbol of the expert performing the tests and inspections.

(4) Pressure receptacles, provided that the general provisions of 4.1.3.6 are met.

(a) They shall be subjected to an initial test and periodic tests every 10 years at a pressure of not less than 1 MPa (10 bar) (gauge pressure);

(b) They shall be subjected periodically to an internal inspection and leakproofness test at intervals of not more than two and a half years;

(c) They may not be equipped with any pressure relief device;

(d) Each pressure receptacle shall be closed with a plug or valve(s) fitted with a secondary closure device; and

(e) The materials of construction for the pressure receptacle, valves, plugs, outlet caps, luting and gaskets shall be compatible with each other and with the contents.

4

P900	PACKING INSTRUCTION	P900

This instruction applies to UN 2216.

The following packagings are authorized, provided the general provisions of 4.1.1 and 4.1.3 are met:
(1) Packagings according to P002; or
(2) Bags (5H1, 5H2, 5H3, 5H4, 5L1, 5L2, 5L3, 5M1 or 5M2) with a maximum net mass of 50 kg.
Fish meal may also be transported unpackaged when it is packed in closed cargo transport units and the free air space has been restricted to a minimum.

P901	PACKING INSTRUCTION	P901

This instruction applies to UN 3316.

The following combination packagings are authorized provided the general provisions of 4.1.1 and 4.1.3 are met:
      Drums (1A1, 1A2, 1B1, 1B2, 1N1, 1N2, 1H1, 1H2, 1D, 1G);
      Boxes (4A, 4B, 4N, 4C1, 4C2, 4D, 4F, 4G, 4H1, 4H2);
      Jerricans (3A1, 3A2, 3B1, 3B2, 3H1, 3H2).
Packagings shall conform to the performance level consistent with the packing group assigned to the kit as a whole (see 3.3.1, special provision 251). Where the kit contains only dangerous goods to which no packing group is assigned, packagings shall meet Packing Group II performance level.
Maximum quantity of dangerous goods per outer packaging: 10 kg excluding the mass of any carbon dioxide, solid (dry ice) used as a refrigerant.

Additional requirement:

Dangerous goods in kits shall be packed in inner packagings which shall not exceed either 250 mL or 250 g and shall be protected from other materials in the kit.

P902	PACKING INSTRUCTION	P902

This instruction applies to UN 3268.

Packaged articles:
The following packagings are authorized provided the general provisions of 4.1.1 and 4.1.3 are met:
      Drums (1A2, 1B2, 1N2, 1H2, 1D, 1G);
      Boxes (4A, 4B, 4N, 4C1, 4C2, 4D, 4F, 4G, 4H1, 4H2);
      Jerricans (3A2, 3B2, 3H2).
Packagings shall conform to the packing group III performance level.
The packagings shall be designed and constructed so as to prevent movement of the articles and inadvertent operation during normal conditions of transport.
Unpackaged articles:
The articles may also be transported unpackaged in dedicated handling devices, vehicles or containers when moved from where they are manufactured to an assembly plant.

Additional requirement:

Any pressure receptacle shall be in accordance with the requirements of the competent authority for the substance(s) contained therein.

4

P903	PACKING INSTRUCTION	P903

This instruction applies to UN Nos. 3090, 3091, 3480 and 3481.

The following packagings are authorized provided that the general provisions of 4.1.1 and 4.1.3 are met:

(1)   For cells and batteries:

        Drums (1A2, 1B2, 1N2, 1H2, 1D, 1G);

        Boxes (4A, 4B, 4N, 4C1, 4C2, 4D, 4F, 4G, 4H1, 4H2);

        Jerricans (3A2, 3B2, 3H2).

Cells or batteries shall be packed in packagings so that the cells or batteries are protected against damage that may be caused by the movement or placement of the cells or batteries within the packaging.

Packagings shall conform to the packing group II performance level.

(2)   In addition for cells or batteries with a gross mass of 12 kg or more employing a strong, impact resistant outer casing, and assemblies of such cells or batteries:

(a) Strong outer packagings;

(b) Protective enclosures (e.g. fully enclosed or wooden slatted crates); or

(c) Pallets or other handling devices.

Cells or batteries shall be secured to prevent inadvertent movement, and the terminals shall not support the weight of other superimposed elements.

Packagings need not meet the requirements of 4.1.1.3.

(3)   For cells or batteries packed with equipment:

Packagings conforming to the requirements in paragraph (1) of this packing instruction, then placed with the equipment in an outer packaging; or

Packagings that completely enclose the cells or batteries, then placed with equipment in a packaging conforming to the requirements in paragraph (1) of this packing instruction.

The equipment shall be secured against movement within the outer packaging.

For the purpose of this packing instruction, "equipment" means apparatus requiring the lithium metal or lithium ion cells or batteries with which it is packed for its operation.

(4)   For cells or batteries contained in equipment:

Strong outer packagings constructed of suitable material, and of adequate strength and design in relation to the packaging capacity and its intended use. They shall be constructed in such a manner as to prevent accidental operation during transport. Packagings need not meet the requirements of 4.1.1.3.

Large equipment can be offered for transport unpackaged or on pallets when the cells or batteries are afforded equivalent protection by the equipment in which they are contained.

Devices such as radio frequency identification (RFID) tags, watches and temperature loggers, which are not capable of generating a dangerous evolution of heat, may be transported when intentionally active in strong outer packagings.

Additional requirement:

Cells or batteries shall be protected against short circuit.

P904	PACKING INSTRUCTION	P904

This instruction applies to UN 3245.

The following packagings are authorized:

(1) Packagings meeting the provisions of 4.1.1.1, 4.1.1.2, 4.1.1.4, 4.1.1.8 and 4.1.3 and so designed that they meet the construction requirements of 6.1.4. Outer packagings constructed of suitable material, and of adequate strength and design in relation to the packaging capacity and its intended use, shall be used. Where this packing instruction is used for the transport of inner packagings of combination packagings the packaging shall be designed and constructed to prevent inadvertent discharge during normal conditions of transport.

(2) Packagings, which need not conform to the packaging test requirements of part 6, but conforming to the following:

    (a) An inner packaging comprising:

        (i) primary receptacle(s) and a secondary packaging, the primary receptacle(s) or the secondary packaging shall be leakproof for liquids or siftproof for solids;

        (ii) for liquids, absorbent material placed between the primary receptacle(s) and the secondary packaging. The absorbent material shall be in a quantity sufficient to absorb the entire contents of the primary receptacle(s) so that any release of the liquid substance will not compromise the integrity of the cushioning material or of the outer packaging;

        (iii) if multiple fragile primary receptacles are placed in a single secondary packaging they shall be individually wrapped or separated to prevent contact between them;

    (b) An outer packaging shall be strong enough for its capacity, mass and intended use, and with a smallest external dimension of at least 100 mm.

For transport, the mark illustrated below shall be displayed on the external surface of the outer packaging on a background of a contrasting colour and shall be clearly visible and legible. The mark shall be in the form of a square set at an angle of 45° (diamond-shaped) with each side having a length of at least 50 mm; the width of the line shall be at least 2 mm and the letters and numbers shall be at least 6 mm high.

Additional requirement:

Ice, dry ice and liquid nitrogen

When dry ice or liquid nitrogen is used as a coolant, the requirements of 5.5.3 shall apply. When used, ice shall be placed outside the secondary packagings or in the outer packaging or an overpack. Interior supports shall be provided to secure the secondary packaging in the original position. If ice is used, the outside packaging or overpack shall be leakproof.

P905	PACKING INSTRUCTION	P905

This instruction applies to UN Nos. 2990 and 3072.

Any suitable packaging is authorized, provided the general provisions of 4.1.1 and 4.1.3 are met, except that packagings need not conform to the provisions of part 6.

When the life-saving appliances are constructed to incorporate or are contained in rigid outer weatherproof casings (such as for lifeboats), they may be transported unpackaged.

Additional provisions:

1   All dangerous substances and articles contained as equipment within the appliances shall be secured to prevent inadvertent movement and in addition:

   (a)   signal devices of class 1 shall be packed in plastics or fibreboard inner packagings;

   (b)   gases (class 2.2) shall be contained in cylinders as specified by the competent authority, which may be connected to the appliance;

   (c)   electric storage batteries (class 8) and lithium batteries (class 9) shall be disconnected or electrically isolated and secured to prevent any spillage of liquid; and

   (d)   small quantities of other dangerous substances (for example in classes 3, 4.1 and 5.2) shall be packed in strong inner packagings.

2   Preparation for transport and packaging shall include provisions to prevent any accidental inflation of the appliance.

P906	PACKING INSTRUCTION	P906

This instruction applies to UN Nos. 2315, 3151, 3152 and 3432.

The following packagings are authorized, provided the general provisions of 4.1.1 and 4.1.3 are met:

△ (1)   For liquids and solids containing or contaminated with PCBs, polyhalogenated biphenyls, polyhalogenated terphenyls or halogenated monomethyldiphenylmethanes: Packagings in accordance with P001 or P002, as appropriate.

(2)   For transformers and condensers and other devices:

   (a)   Packagings in accordance with packing instructions P001 or P002. The articles shall be secured with suitable cushioning material to prevent inadvertent movement during normal conditions of transport; or

△   (b)   Leakproof packagings which are capable of containing, in addition to the devices, at least 1.25 times the volume of the liquid PCBs, polyhalogenated biphenyls, polyhalogenated terphenyls or halogenated monomethyldiphenylmethanes present in them. There shall be sufficient absorbent material in the packagings to absorb at least 1.1 times the volume of liquid which is contained in the devices. In general, transformers and condensers shall be carried in leakproof metal packagings which are capable of holding, in addition to the transformers and condensers, at least 1.25 times the volume of the liquid present in them.

Notwithstanding the above, liquids and solids not packaged in accordance with P001 and P002 and unpackaged transformers and condensers may be transported in cargo transport units fitted with a leakproof metal tray to a height of at least 800 mm, containing sufficient inert absorbent material to absorb at least 1.1 times the volume of any free liquid.

Additional provision:

Adequate provisions shall be taken to seal the transformers and condensers to prevent leakage during normal conditions of transport.

P907	PACKING INSTRUCTION	P907

If the machinery or apparatus is constructed and designed so that the receptacles containing the dangerous goods are afforded adequate protection, an outer packaging is not required. Dangerous goods in machinery or apparatus shall otherwise be packed in outer packagings constructed of suitable material, and of adequate strength and design in relation to the packaging capacity and its intended use, and meeting the applicable requirements of 4.1.1.1.

Receptacles containing dangerous goods shall conform to the general provisions in 4.1.1, except that 4.1.1.3, 4.1.1.4, 4.1.1.12 and 4.1.1.14 do not apply. For class 2.2 gases, the inner cylinder or receptacle, its contents and filling density shall be to the satisfaction of the competent authority of the country in which the cylinder or receptacle is filled.

In addition, the manner in which receptacles are contained within the machinery or apparatus shall be such that, under normal conditions of transport, damage to receptacles containing the dangerous goods is unlikely; and in the event of damage to the receptacles containing solid or liquid dangerous goods, no leakage of the dangerous goods from the machinery or apparatus is possible (a leakproof liner may be used to satisfy this requirement). Receptacles containing dangerous goods shall be so installed, secured or cushioned as to prevent their breakage or leakage and so as to control their movement within the machinery or apparatus during normal conditions of transport. Cushioning material shall not react dangerously with the content of the receptacles. Any leakage of the contents shall not substantially impair the protective properties of the cushioning material.

P908	PACKING INSTRUCTION	P908

This instruction applies to damaged or defective lithium ion cells and batteries and damaged or defective lithium metal cells and batteries, including those contained in equipment, of UN Nos. 3090, 3091, 3480 and 3481.

The following packagings are authorized provided the general provisions for 4.1.1 and 4.1.3 are met:

For cells and batteries and equipment containing cells and batteries:

    Drums (1A2, 1B2, 1N2, 1H2, 1D, 1G)

    Boxes (4A, 4B, 4N, 4C1, 4C2, 4D, 4F, 4G, 4H1, 4H2)

    Jerricans (3A2, 3B2, 3H2)

Packagings shall conform to the packing group II performance level.

(1) Each damaged or defective cell or battery or equipment containing such cells or batteries shall be individually packed in inner packaging and placed inside of an outer packaging. The inner packaging or outer packaging shall be leakproof to prevent the potential release of electrolyte.

(2) Each inner packaging shall be surrounded by sufficient non-combustible and non-conductive thermal insulation material to protect against a dangerous evolution of heat.

(3) Sealed packagings shall be fitted with a venting device when appropriate.

(4) Appropriate measures shall be taken to minimize the effects of vibrations and shocks, prevent movement of the cells or batteries within the package that may lead to further damage and a dangerous condition during transport. Cushioning material that is non-combustible and non-conductive may also be used to meet this requirement.

(5) Non combustibility shall be assessed according to a standard recognized in the country where the packaging is designed or manufactured.

For leaking cells or batteries, sufficient inert absorbent material shall be added to the inner or outer packaging to absorb any release of electrolyte.

A cell or battery with a net mass of more than 30 kg shall be limited to one cell or battery per outer packaging.

Additional requirement:

Cells or batteries shall be protected against short circuit.

4

P909	PACKING INSTRUCTION	P909

This instruction applies to UN Nos. 3090, 3091, 3480 and 3481 transported for disposal or recycling, either packed together with or packed without non-lithium batteries.

(1) Cells and batteries shall be packed in accordance with the following:

    (a) The following packagings are authorized, provided that the general provisions of 4.1.1 and 4.1.3, are met:
Drums (1A2, 1B2, 1N2, 1H2, 1D, 1G);
Boxes (4A, 4B, 4N, 4C1, 4C2, 4D, 4F, 4G, 4H2); and
Jerricans (3A2, 3B2, 3H2).

    (b) Packagings shall conform to the packing group II performance level.

    (c) Metal packagings shall be fitted with a non-conductive lining material (e.g. plastics) of adequate strength for the intended use.

(2) However, lithium ion cells with a Watt-hour rating of not more than 20 Wh, lithium ion batteries with a Watt-hour rating of not more than 100 Wh, lithium metal cells with a lithium content of not more than 1 g and lithium metal batteries with an aggregate lithium content of not more than 2 g may be packed in accordance with the following:

    (a) In strong outer packaging up to 30 kg gross mass meeting the general provisions of 4.1.1, except 4.1.3.3, and 4.1.3.

    (b) Metal packagings shall be fitted with a non-conductive lining material (e.g. plastics) of adequate strength for the intended use.

△ (3) For cells or batteries contained in equipment, strong outer packagings constructed of suitable material, and of adequate strength and design in relation to the packaging capacity and its intended use, may be used. Packagings need not meet the requirements of 4.1.1.3. Equipment may also be offered for transport unpackaged or on pallets when the cells or batteries are afforded equivalent protection by the equipment in which they are contained.

(4) In addition, for cells or batteries with a gross mass of 12 kg or more employing a strong, impact resistant outer casing, strong outer packagings constructed of suitable material and of adequate strength and design in relation to the packagings capacity and its intended use, may be used.
Packagings need not meet the requirements of 4.1.1.3.

Additional requirements:

1   Cells and batteries shall be designed or packed to prevent short circuits and the dangerous evolution of heat.

2   Protection against short circuits and the dangerous evolution of heat includes, but is not limited to:

    – individual protection of the battery terminals,

    – inner packaging to prevent contact between cells and batteries,

    – batteries with recessed terminals designed to protect against short circuits, or

    – the use of a non-conductive and non-combustible cushioning material to fill empty space between the cells or batteries in the packaging.

3   Cells and batteries shall be secured within the outer packaging to prevent excessive movement during transport (e.g. by using a non-combustible and non-conductive cushioning material or through the use of a tightly closed plastics bag).

■ P910	PACKING INSTRUCTION	P910

This instruction applies to UN Nos. 3090, 3091, 3480 and 3481 production runs consisting of not more than 100 cells and batteries and to pre-production prototypes of cells and batteries when these prototypes are transported for testing.

The following packagings are authorized provided that the general provisions of 4.1.1 and 4.1.3 are met:

(1) For cells and batteries, including when packed with equipment:

Drums (1A2, 1B2, 1N2, 1H2, 1D, 1G);

Boxes (4A, 4B, 4N, 4C1, 4C2, 4D, 4F, 4G, 4H1, 4H2);

Jerricans (3A2, 3B2, 3H2).

Packagings shall conform to the packing group II performance level and shall meet the following requirements:

(a) Batteries and cells, including equipment, of different sizes, shapes or masses shall be packaged in an outer packaging of a tested design type listed above provided the total gross mass of the package does not exceed the gross mass for which the design type has been tested;

(b) Each cell or battery shall be individually packed in an inner packaging and placed inside an outer packaging;

(c) Each inner packaging shall be completely surrounded by sufficient non-combustible and non-conductive thermal insulation material to protect against a dangerous evolution of heat;

(d) Appropriate measures shall be taken to minimize the effects of vibration and shocks and prevent movement of the cells or batteries within the package that may lead to damage and a dangerous condition during transport. Cushioning material that is non-combustible and non-conductive may be used to meet this requirement;

(e) Non-combustibility shall be assessed according to a standard recognized in the country where the packaging is designed or manufactured;

(f) A cell or battery with a net mass of more than 30 kg shall be limited to one cell or battery per outer packaging.

(2) For cells and batteries contained in equipment:

Drums (1A2, 1B2, 1N2, 1H2, 1D, 1G);

Boxes (4A, 4B, 4N, 4C1, 4C2, 4D, 4F, 4G, 4H1, 4H2);

Jerricans (3A2, 3B2, 3H2).

Packagings shall conform to the packing group II performance level and shall meet the following requirements:

(a) Equipment of different sizes, shapes or masses shall be packaged in an outer packaging of a tested design type listed above provided the total gross mass of the package does not exceed the gross mass for which the design type has been tested;

(b) The equipment shall be constructed or packaged in such a manner as to prevent accidental operation during transport;

(c) Appropriate measures shall be taken to minimize the effects of vibration and shocks and prevent movement of the equipment within the package that may lead to damage and a dangerous condition during transport. When cushioning material is used to meet this requirement it shall be non-combustible and non-conductive; and

(d) Non-combustibility shall be assessed according to a standard recognized in the country where the packaging is designed or manufactured.

(3) The equipment or the batteries may be transported unpackaged under conditions specified by the competent authority. Additional conditions that may be considered in the approval process include, but are not limited to:

(a) The equipment or the battery shall be strong enough to withstand the shocks and loadings normally encountered during transport, including transshipment between cargo transport units and between cargo transport units and warehouses as well as any removal from a pallet for subsequent manual or mechanical handling; and

(b) The equipment or the battery shall be fixed in cradles or crates or other handling devices in such a way that it will not become loose during normal conditions of transport.

Additional requirements:

The cells and batteries shall be protected against short circuit;

Protection against short circuits includes, but is not limited to,

– individual protection of the battery terminals,

– inner packaging to prevent contact between cells and batteries,

– batteries with recessed terminals designed to protect against short circuits, or

– the use of a non-conductive and non-combustible cushioning material to fill empty space between the cells or batteries in the packaging.

4

4.1.4.2   Packing instructions concerning the use of IBCs

IBC01	PACKING INSTRUCTION	IBC01

The following IBCs are authorized, provided the general provisions of 4.1.1, 4.1.2 and 4.1.3 are met:

    Metal (31A, 31B and 31N).

IBC02	PACKING INSTRUCTION	IBC02

The following IBCs are authorized, provided the general provisions of 4.1.1, 4.1.2 and 4.1.3 are met:

(1)   Metal (31A, 31B and 31N);

(2)   Rigid plastics (31H1 and 31H2);

(3)   Composite (31HZ1).

Special packing provisions:

B5   For UN Nos. 1791, 2014, 2984 and 3149, IBCs shall be provided with a device to allow venting during transport. The inlet to the venting device shall be sited in the vapour space of the IBC under maximum filling conditions during transport.

B8   The pure form of this substance shall not be transported in IBCs since it is known to have a vapour pressure of more than 110 kPa at 50°C or 130 kPa at 55°C.

B15   For UN 2031 with more than 55% nitric acid, the permitted use of rigid plastics IBCs and of composite IBCs with a rigid plastics inner receptacle shall be two years from their date of manufacture.

B16   For UN 3375, IBCs of type 31A and 31N are not allowed without competent authority approval.

B20   For UN Nos. 1716, 1717, 1736, 1737, 1738, 1742, 1743, 1755, 1764, 1768, 1776, 1778, 1782, 1789, 1790, 1796, 1826, 1830, 1832, 2031, 2308, 2353, 2513, 2584, 2796 and 2817 coming under PG II, IBCs shall be fitted with two shut-off devices.

IBC03	PACKING INSTRUCTION	IBC03

The following IBCs are authorized, provided the general provisions of 4.1.1, 4.1.2 and 4.1.3 are met:

(1)   Metal (31A, 31B and 31N);

(2)   Rigid plastics (31H1 and 31H2);

(3)   Composite (31HZ1 and 31HA2, 31HB2, 31HN2, 31HD2 and 31HH2).

Special packing provisions:

B8   The pure form of this substance shall not be transported in IBCs since it is known to have a vapour pressure of more than 110 kPa at 50°C or 130 kPa at 55°C.

B11   Notwithstanding the provisions of 4.1.1.10, UN 2672 ammonia solution in concentrations not exceeding 25% may be transported in rigid or composite plastics IBCs (31H1, 31H2 and 31HZ1).

■   B19   For UN Nos. 3532 and 3534, IBCs shall be designed and constructed to permit the release of gas or vapour to prevent a build-up of pressure that could rupture the IBCs in the event of loss of stabilization.

IBC04	PACKING INSTRUCTION	IBC04

The following IBCs are authorized, provided the general provisions of 4.1.1, 4.1.2 and 4.1.3 are met:

    Metal (11A, 11B, 11N, 21A, 21B, 21N, 31A, 31B and 31N).

Special packing provision:

B1   For packing group I substances, IBCs shall be carried in closed cargo transport units or in freight containers/ vehicles, which shall have rigid sides or fences at least to the height of the IBC.

IBC05	PACKING INSTRUCTION	IBC05

The following IBCs are authorized, provided the general provisions of 4.1.1, 4.1.2 and 4.1.3 are met:

(1)   Metal (11A, 11B, 11N, 21A, 21B, 21N, 31A, 31B and 31N);

(2)   Rigid plastics (11H1, 11H2, 21H1, 21H2, 31H1 and 31H2);

(3)   Composite (11HZ1, 21HZ1 and 31HZ1).

Special packing provisions:

B1   For packing group I substances, IBCs shall be carried in closed cargo transport units or in freight containers/ vehicles, which shall have rigid sides or fences at least to the height of the IBC.

△   B21   For solid substances in IBCs other than metal or rigid plastics IBCs, the IBCs shall be carried in closed cargo transport units or in freight containers/vehicles, which shall have rigid sides or fences at least to the height of the IBC.

IBC06	PACKING INSTRUCTION	IBC06

The following IBCs are authorized, provided the general provisions of 4.1.1, 4.1.2 and 4.1.3 are met:

(1) Metal (11A, 11B, 11N, 21A, 21B, 21N, 31A, 31B and 31N);

(2) Rigid plastics (11H1, 11H2, 21H1, 21H2, 31H1 and 31H2);

(3) Composite (11HZ1, 11HZ2, 21HZ1, 21HZ2 and 31HZ1).

Additional provision:

Where the solid may become liquid during transport see 4.1.3.4.

Special packing provisions:

B1   For packing group I substances, IBCs shall be carried in closed cargo transport units or in freight containers/vehicles, which shall have rigid sides or fences at least to the height of the IBC.

B12   For UN 2907, IBCs shall meet the packing group II performance level. IBCs meeting the test criteria of packing group I shall not be used.

△   B21   For solid substances in IBCs other than metal or rigid plastics IBCs, the IBCs shall be carried in closed cargo transport units or in freight containers/vehicles, which shall have rigid sides or fences at least to the height of the IBC.

IBC07	PACKING INSTRUCTION	IBC07

The following IBCs are authorized, provided the general provisions of 4.1.1, 4.1.2 and 4.1.3 are met:

(1) Metal (11A, 11B, 11N, 21A, 21B, 21N, 31A, 31B and 31N);

(2) Rigid plastics (11H1, 11H2, 21H1, 21H2, 31H1 and 31H2);

(3) Composite (11HZ1, 11HZ2, 21HZ1, 21HZ2 and 31HZ1);

(4) Wooden (11C, 11D and 11F).

Additional provisions:

1   Where the solid may become liquid during transport see 4.1.3.4.

2   Liners of wooden IBCs shall be sift-proof.

Special packing provisions:

B1   For packing group I substances, IBCs shall be carried in closed cargo transport units or in freight containers/vehicles, which shall have rigid sides or fences at least to the height of the IBC.

■   B4   Flexible, fibreboard or wooden IBCs shall be sift-proof and water-resistant or shall be fitted with a sift-proof and water-resistant liner.

⊗

■   B18   For UN Nos. 3531 and 3533, IBCs shall be designed and constructed to permit the release of gas or vapour to prevent a build-up of pressure that could rupture the IBCs in the event of loss of stabilization.

△   B21   For solid substances in IBCs other than metal or rigid plastics IBCs, the IBCs shall be carried in closed cargo transport units or in freight containers/vehicles, which shall have rigid sides or fences at least to the height of the IBC.

IBC08	PACKING INSTRUCTION	IBC08

The following IBCs are authorized, provided the general provisions of 4.1.1, 4.1.2 and 4.1.3 are met:

(1) Metal (11A, 11B, 11N, 21A, 21B, 21N, 31A, 31B and 31N);

(2) Rigid plastics (11H1, 11H2, 21H1, 21H2, 31H1 and 31H2);

(3) Composite (11HZ1, 11HZ2, 21HZ, 21HZ2 and 31HZ1);

(4) Fibreboard (11G);

(5) Wooden (11C, 11D and 11F);

(6) Flexible (13H1, 13H2, 13H3, 13H4, 13H5, 13L1, 13L2, 13L3, 13L4, 13M1 or 13M2).

Additional provisions:

Where the solid may become liquid during transport see 4.1.3.4.

Special packing provisions:

B3   Flexible IBCs shall be sift-proof and water-resistant or shall be fitted with a sift-proof and water-resistant liner.

B4   Flexible, fibreboard or wooden IBCs shall be sift-proof and water-resistant or shall be fitted with a sift-proof and water-resistant liner.

B6   For UN Nos. 1327, 1363, 1364, 1365, 1386, 1408, 1841, 2211, 2217, 2793 and 3314, IBCs are not required to meet the IBC testing provisions of chapter 6.5.

△   B21   For substances, UN Nos. 1374 and 2590 in IBCs other than metal or rigid plastics IBCs, the IBCs shall be carried in closed cargo transport units or in freight containers/vehicles, which shall have rigid sides or fences at least to the height of the IBC.

IBC99	PACKING INSTRUCTION	IBC99

Only IBCs which are approved for these goods by the competent authority may be used (see 4.1.3.7). A copy of the competent authority approval shall accompany each consignment or the transport document shall include an indication that the packaging was approved by the competent authority.

IBC100	PACKING INSTRUCTION	IBC100

This instruction applies to UN Nos. 0082, 0222, 0241, 0331 and 0332.

The following IBCs are authorized, provided the general provisions of 4.1.1, 4.1.2 and 4.1.3 and special provisions of 4.1.5 are met:

(1) Metal (11A, 11B, 11N, 21A, 21B, 21N, 31A, 31B and 31N);

(2) Flexible (13H2, 13H3, 13H4, 13L2, 13L3, 13L4 and 13M2);

(3) Rigid plastics (11H1, 11H2, 21H1, 21H2, 31H1 and 31H2);

(4) Composite (11HZ1, 11HZ2, 21HZ1, 21HZ2, 31HZ1 and 31HZ2).

Additional provisions:

1   IBCs shall only be used for free-flowing substances.

2   Flexible IBCs shall only be used for solids.

Special packing provisions:

B2   For UN 0222 in IBCs other than metal or rigid plastics IBCs, the IBCs shall be transported in closed cargo transport units.

B3   For UN 0222, flexible IBCs shall be sift-proof and water resistant or shall be fitted with a sift-proof and water resistant liner.

B9   For UN 0082, this packing instruction may only be used when the substances are mixtures of ammonium nitrate or other inorganic nitrates with other combustible substances which are not explosive ingredients. Such explosives shall not contain nitroglycerin, similar liquid organic nitrates, or chlorates. Metal IBCs are not authorized.

B10   For UN 0241, this packing instruction may only be used for substances which consist of water as an essential ingredient and high proportions of ammonium nitrate or other oxidizing substances, some or all of which are in solution. The other constituents may include hydrocarbons or aluminium powder, but shall not include nitro-derivatives such as trinitrotoluene. Metal IBCs are not authorized.

B17   For UN 0222, metal IBCs are not authorized.

IBC520	PACKING INSTRUCTION	IBC520

This instruction applies to organic peroxides and self-reactive substances of type F.

The IBCs listed below are authorized for the formulations listed, provided the general provisions of 4.1.1, 4.1.2 and 4.1.3 and special provisions of 4.1.7.2 are met.

For formulations not listed below, only IBCs which are approved by the competent authority may be used (see 4.1.7.2.2).

UN No.	Organic peroxide	Type of IBC	Maximum quantity (litres)	Control temperature	Emergency temperature
3109	ORGANIC PEROXIDE TYPE F, LIQUID				
	tert-Butyl cumyl peroxide	31HA1	1000		
	tert-Butyl hydroperoxide, not more than 72% with water	31A	1250		
	tert-Butyl peroxyacetate, not more than 32% in diluent type A	31HA1	1000		
	tert-Butyl peroxybenzoate, not more than 32% in diluent type A	31A	1250		
	tert-Butyl peroxy-3,5,5-trimethylhexanoate, not more than 37% in diluent type A	31A 31HA1	1250 1000		
	Cumyl hydroperoxide, not more than 90% in diluent type A	31HA1	1250		
	Dibenzoyl peroxide, not more than 42% as a stable dispersion	31H1	1000		
	Di-*tert*-butyl peroxide, not more than 52% in diluent type A	31A 31HA1	1250 1000		
	1,1-Di-(*tert*-butylperoxy)cyclohexane, not more than 37% in diluent type A	31A	1250		
	1,1-Di-(*tert*-butylperoxy)cyclohexane, not more than 42% in diluent type A	31H1	1000		
	Dilauroyl peroxide, not more than 42%, stable dispersion, in water	31HA1	1000		
	Isopropylcumyl hydroperoxide, not more than 72% in diluent type A	31HA1	1250		
	p-Menthyl hydroperoxide, not more than 72% in diluent type A	31HA1	1250		
	Peroxyacetic acid, stabilized, not more than 17%	31H1 31H2 31HA1 31A	1500 1500 1500 1500		
3110	ORGANIC PEROXIDE TYPE F, SOLID				
	Dicumyl peroxide	31A 31H1 31HA1	2000		

IBC520	PACKING INSTRUCTION *(continued)*					IBC520
UN No.	Organic peroxide	Type of IBC	Maximum quantity (litres)	Control temper-ature	Emergency temper-ature	
3119	ORGANIC PEROXIDE TYPE F, LIQUID, TEMPERATURE CONTROLLED					
	tert-Amyl peroxypivalate, not more than 32% in diluent type A	31A	1250	+10°C	+15°C	
	tert-Butyl peroxy-2-ethylhexanoate, not more than 32% in diluent type B	31HA1 31A	1000 1250	+30°C +30°C	+35°C +35°C	
	tert-Butyl peroxyneodecanoate, not more than 32% in diluent type A	31A	1250	0°C	+10°C	
	tert-Butyl peroxyneodecanoate, not more than 42%, stable dispersion, in water	31A	1250	−5°C	+5°C	
	tert-Butyl peroxyneodecanoate, not more than 52%, stable dispersion, in water	31A	1250	−5°C	+5°C	
	tert-Butyl peroxypivalate, not more than 27% in diluent type B	31HA1 31A	1000 1250	+10°C +10°C	+15°C +15°C	
	Di-(2-neodecanoylperoxyisopropyl)benzene, not more than 42%, stable dispersion, in water	31A	1250	−15°C	−5°C	
	3-Hydroxy-1,1-dimethylbutyl peroxyneodecanoate, not more than 52%, stable dispersion, in water	31A	1250	−15°C	−5°C	
	Cumyl peroxyneodecanoate, not more than 52%, stable dispersion, in water	31A	1250	−15°C	−5°C	
	Di-(4-*tert*-butylcyclohexyl) peroxydicarbonate, not more than 42%, stable dispersion, in water	31HA1	1000	+30°C	+35°C	
	Dicetyl peroxydicarbonate, not more than 42%, stable dispersion, in water	31HA1	1000	+30°C	+35°C	
	Dicyclohexyl peroxydicarbonate, not more than 42% as a stable dispersion, in water	31A	1250	+10°C	+15°C	
	Di-(2-ethylhexyl) peroxydicarbonate, not more than 62%, stable dispersion, in water	31A 31HA1	1250 1000	−20°C −20°C	−10°C −10°C	
	Dimyristyl peroxydicarbonate, not more than 42%, stable dispersion, in water	31HA1	1000	+15°C	+20°C	
	Di-(3,5,5-trimethylhexanoyl) peroxide, not more than 52% in diluent type A	31HA1 31A	1000 1250	+10°C +10°C	+15°C +15°C	
	Di-(3,5,5-trimethylhexanoyl) peroxide, not more than 52%, stable dispersion, in water	31A	1250	+10°C	+15°C	
	Diisobutyryl peroxide, not more than 28% as a stable dispersion in water	31HA1 31A	1000 1250	−20°C −20°C	−10°C −10°C	
	Diisobutyryl peroxide, not more than 42% as a stable dispersion in water	31HA1 31A	1000 1250	−25°C −25°C	−15°C −15°C	
	1,1,3,3-Tetramethylbutyl peroxy-2-ethylhexanoate, not more than 67%, in diluent type A	31HA1	1000	+15°C	+20°C	
	1,1,3,3-Tetramethylbutyl peroxyneodecanoate, not more than 52%, stable dispersion, in water	31A 31HA1	1250 1000	−5°C −5°C	+5°C +5°C	
3120	ORGANIC PEROXIDE, TYPE F, SOLID, TEMPERATURE CONTROLLED					

Additional provisions:

1   IBCs shall be provided with a device to allow venting during transport. The inlet to the pressure relief device shall be sited in the vapour space of the IBC under maximum filling conditions during transport.

2   To prevent explosive rupture of metal IBCs or composite IBCs with complete metal casing, the emergency relief devices shall be designed to vent all the decomposition products and vapours evolved during self-accelerating decomposition or during a period of not less than one hour of fire-engulfment as calculated by the formula in 4.2.1.13.8. The control and emergency temperatures specified in this packing instruction are based on a non-insulated IBC. When consigning an organic peroxide in an IBC in accordance with this instruction, it is the responsibility of the consignor to ensure that:

  (a) the pressure and emergency relief devices installed on the IBC are designed to take appropriate account of the self-accelerating decomposition of the organic peroxide and of fire engulfment; and

  (b) when applicable, the control and emergency temperatures indicated are appropriate, taking into account the design (such as insulation) of the IBC to be used.

IBC620	PACKING INSTRUCTION	IBC620
This instruction applies to UN 3291.		

The following IBCs are authorized, provided that the general provisions of 4.1.1, except 4.1.1.15, 4.1.2 and 4.1.3 are met:
Rigid, leakproof IBCs conforming to the packing group II performance level.

Additional provisions:
1   There shall be sufficient absorbent material to absorb the entire amount of liquid present in the IBC.
2   IBCs shall be capable of retaining liquids.
3   IBCs intended to contain sharp objects such as broken glass and needles shall be resistant to puncture.

4.1.4.3   Packing instructions concerning the use of large packagings

LP01		PACKING INSTRUCTION (LIQUIDS)			LP01
The following large packagings are authorized, provided the general provisions of 4.1.1 and 4.1.3 are met.					
Inner packagings		Large outer packagings	Packing group I	Packing group II	Packing group III
Glass	10 L	Steel (50A)			
Plastics	30 L	Aluminium (50B)	Not allowed	Not allowed	3 m^3
Metal	40 L	Metal other than steel or aluminium (50N)			
		Rigid plastics (50H)			
		Natural wood (50C)			
		Plywood (50D)			
		Reconstituted wood (50F)			
		Rigid fibreboard (50G)			

LP02		PACKING INSTRUCTION (SOLIDS)			LP02
The following large packagings are authorized, provided the general provisions of 4.1.1 and 4.1.3 are met.					
Inner packagings		Large outer packagings	Packing group I	Packing group II	Packing group III
Glass	10 kg	Steel (50A)			
Plastics[b]	50 kg	Aluminium (50B)	Not allowed	Not allowed	3 m^3
Metal	50 kg	Metal other than steel or aluminium (50N)			
Paper[a, b]	50 kg	Rigid plastics (50H)			
Fibre[a, b]	50 kg	Natural wood (50C)			
		Plywood (50D)			
		Reconstituted wood (50F)			
		Rigid fibreboard (50G)			
		Flexible plastics (51H)[c]			

[a] These packagings shall not be used when the substances being transported may become liquid during transport.

[b] Packagings shall be sift-proof.

[c] To be used with flexible inner packagings only.

Special packing provision:
△ L2   *Deleted*
■ L3   For UN Nos.1309, 1376, 1483, 1869, 2793, 2858 and 2878, flexible or fibre inner packagings shall be sift-proof and water-resistant or shall be fitted with a sift-proof and water-resistant liner.
■ L4   For UN Nos.1932, 2008, 2009, 2545, 2546, 2881 and 3189 flexible or fibre inner packagings shall be hermetically sealed.

LP99	PACKING INSTRUCTION	LP99
Only packagings which are approved for these goods by the competent authority may be used (see 4.1.3.7). A copy of the competent authority approval shall accompany each consignment or the transport document shall include an indication that the packaging was approved by the competent authority.		

LP101	PACKING INSTRUCTION	LP101
The following packagings are authorized, provided the general provisions of 4.1.1 and 4.1.3 and special provisions of 4.1.5 are met.		

Inner packagings	Intermediate packagings	Large packagings
Not necessary	*Not necessary*	Steel (50A) Aluminium (50B) Metal other than steel or aluminium (50N) Rigid plastics (50H) Natural wood (50C) Plywood (50D) Reconstituted wood (50F) Rigid fibreboard (50G)

Special packing provision:

△ L1   For UN Nos. 0006, 0009, 0010, 0015, 0016, 0018, 0019, 0034, 0035, 0038, 0039, 0048, 0056, 0137, 0138, 0168, 0169, 0171, 0181, 0182, 0183, 0186, 0221, 0243, 0244, 0245, 0246, 0254, 0280, 0281, 0286, 0287, 0297, 0299, 0300, 0301, 0303, 0321, 0328, 0329, 0344, 0345, 0346, 0347, 0362, 0363, 0370, 0412, 0424, 0425, 0434, 0435, 0436, 0437, 0438, 0451, 0488, 0502 and 0510: Large and robust explosives articles, normally intended for military use, without their means of initiation or with their means of initiation containing at least two effective protective features, may be transported unpackaged. When such articles have propelling charges or are self-propelled, their ignition systems shall be protected against stimuli encountered during normal conditions of transport. A negative result in Test Series 4 on an unpackaged article indicates that the article can be considered for transport unpackaged. Such unpackaged articles may be fixed to cradles or contained in crates or other suitable handling devices.

LP102	PACKING INSTRUCTION	LP102
The following packagings are authorized, provided the general provisions of 4.1.1 and 4.1.3 and special provisions of 4.1.5 are met.		

Inner packagings	Intermediate packagings	Outer packagings

Bags
  water-resistant
 	
Receptacles
  fibreboard
  metal
  plastics
  wood
 	
Sheets
  fibreboard, corrugated
 	
Tubes
  fibreboard
	Not necessary	Steel (50A)
		Aluminium (50B)
		Metal other than steel or aluminium (50N)
		Rigid plastics (50H)
		Natural wood (50C)
		Plywood (50D)
		Reconstituted wood (50F)
		Rigid fibreboard (50G)

■ LP200	PACKING INSTRUCTION	LP200
This instruction applies to UN No. 1950.		

The following large packagings are authorized for aerosols, provided that the general provisions of 4.1.1 and 4.1.3 are met:

Rigid large packagings conforming to the packing group II performance level, made of:

  steel (50A);
  aluminium (50B);
  metal other than steel or aluminium (50N);
  rigid plastics (50H);
  natural wood (50C);
  plywood (50D);
  reconstituted wood (50F);
  rigid fibreboard (50G).

Special packing provision:

L2   The large packagings shall be designed and constructed to prevent dangerous movement of the aerosols and inadvertent discharge during normal conditions of transport. For waste aerosols transported in accordance with special provision 327, the large packagings shall have a means of retaining any free liquid that might escape during transport, e.g. absorbent material. The large packagings shall be adequately ventilated to prevent the creation of a flammable atmosphere and the build-up of pressure.

4

LP621	PACKING INSTRUCTION	LP621

This instruction applies to UN 3291.

The following large packagings are authorized, provided the general provisions of 4.1.1 and 4.1.3 are met:

(1) For clinical waste placed in inner packagings: Rigid, leakproof large packagings conforming to the provisions of chapter 6.6 for solids, at the packing group II performance level, provided there is sufficient absorbent material to absorb the entire amount of liquid present and the large packaging is capable of retaining liquids.

(2) For packages containing larger quantities of liquid: Large rigid packagings conforming to the provisions of chapter 6.6, at the packing group II performance level, for liquids.

Additional provision:

Large packagings intended to contain sharp objects such as broken glass and needles shall be resistant to puncture and retain liquids under the performance test conditions in chapter 6.6.

LP902	PACKING INSTRUCTION	LP902

This instruction applies to UN 3268.

Packaged articles:

The following packagings are authorized, provided the general provisions of 4.1.1 and 4.1.3 are met:

Packagings conforming to the packing group III performance level. The packagings shall be designed and constructed to prevent movement of the articles and inadvertent operation during normal conditions of transport.

Unpackaged articles:

The articles may also be transported unpackaged in dedicated handling devices, vehicles, containers or wagons when moved from where they are manufactured to an assembly plant.

Additional provision:

Any pressure receptacle shall be in accordance with the requirements of the competent authority for the substance(s) contained in the pressure receptacle(s).

LP903	PACKING INSTRUCTION	LP903

This instruction applies to UN Nos. 3090, 3091, 3480 and 3481.

The following large packagings are authorized for a single battery, including for a battery contained in equipment, provided that the general provisions of 4.1.1 and 4.1.3 are met:

Rigid large packagings conforming to the packing group II performance level, made of:

steel (50A);

aluminium (50B);

metal other than steel or aluminium (50N);

rigid plastics (50H);

natural wood (50C);

plywood (50D);

reconstituted wood (50F);

rigid fibreboard (50G).

The battery shall be packed so that the battery is protected against damage that may be caused by its movement or placement within the large packaging.

Additional requirement:

Batteries shall be protected against short circuit.

LP904	PACKING INSTRUCTION	LP904

This instruction applies to single damaged or defective batteries for UN 3090, 3091, 3480, and 3481, including those contained in equipment.

The following large packagings are authorized for a single damaged or defective battery and for a single damaged or defective battery contained in equipment, provided the general provisions of 4.1.1 and 4.1.3 are met:

For batteries and equipment containing batteries:

      steel (50A)

      aluminium (50B)

      metal other than steel or aluminium (50N)

      rigid plastics (50H)

      plywood (50D)

Packagings shall conform to the packing group II performance level.

1. Each damaged or defective cell or battery or equipment containing such battery shall be individually packed in an inner packaging and placed inside of an outer packaging. The inner packaging or outer packaging shall be leakproof to prevent the potential release of electrolyte.

2. Each inner packaging shall be surrounded by sufficient non-combustible and non-conductive thermal insulation material to protect against a dangerous evolution of heat.

3. Sealed packagings shall be fitted with a venting device when appropriate.

4. Appropriate measures shall be taken to minimize the effects of vibrations and shocks, prevent movement of the battery within the package that may lead to further damage and a dangerous condition during transport. Cushioning material that is non-combustible and non-conductive may also be used to meet this requirement.

5. Non combustibility shall be assessed according to a standard recognized in the country where the packaging is designed or manufactured.

For leaking batteries, sufficient inert absorbent material shall be added to the inner or outer packaging to absorb any release of electrolyte.

Additional requirement:

Batteries shall be protected against short circuit.

4.1.5 Special packing provisions for goods of class 1

4.1.5.1 The general provisions of 4.1.1 shall be met.

4.1.5.2 All packagings for class 1 goods shall be so designed and constructed that:

    .1 they will protect the explosives, prevent them escaping and cause no increase in the risk of unintended ignition or initiation when subjected to normal conditions of transport, including foreseeable changes in temperature, humidity and pressure;

    .2 the complete package can be handled safely in normal conditions of transport; and

    .3 the packages will withstand any loading imposed on them by foreseeable stacking to which they will be subject during transport so that they do not add to the risk presented by the explosives, the containment function of the packagings is not harmed, and they are not distorted in a way or to an extent which will reduce their strength or cause instability of a stack.

4.1.5.3 All explosive substances and articles, as prepared for transport, shall have been classified in accordance with the procedures detailed in 2.1.3.

4.1.5.4 Class 1 goods shall be packed in accordance with the appropriate packing instruction shown in columns 8 and 9 of the Dangerous Goods List, as detailed in 4.1.4.

4.1.5.5 Unless otherwise specified in this Code, packagings, including IBCs and large packagings, shall conform to the requirements of chapters 6.1, 6.5 or 6.6, as appropriate, and shall meet their test provisions for packing group II.

4.1.5.6 The closure device of packagings containing liquid explosives shall ensure a double protection against leakage.

4.1.5.7 The closure device of metal drums shall include a suitable gasket; if a closure device includes a screw-thread, the ingress of explosive substances into the screw-thread shall be prevented.

4.1.5.8 Packagings for water-soluble substances shall be water-resistant. Packagings for desensitized or phlegmatized substances shall be closed to prevent changes in concentration during transport.

4.1.5.9 When the packaging includes a double envelope filled with water which may freeze during transport, a sufficient quantity of an anti-freeze agent shall be added to the water to prevent freezing. Anti-freeze that could create a fire hazard because of its inherent flammability shall not be used.

4

4.1.5.10   Nails, staples and other closure devices made of metal without protective covering shall not penetrate to the inside of the outer packaging unless the inner packaging adequately protects the explosives against contact with the metal.

4.1.5.11   Inner packagings, fittings and cushioning materials and the placing of explosive substances or articles in packages shall be accomplished in a manner which prevents the explosive substances or articles from becoming loose in the outer packaging under normal conditions of transport. Metallic components of articles shall be prevented from making contact with metal packagings. Articles containing explosive substances not enclosed in an outer casing shall be separated from each other in order to prevent friction and impact. Padding, trays, partitioning in the inner or outer packaging, mouldings or receptacles may be used for this purpose.

4.1.5.12   Packagings shall be made of materials compatible with, and impermeable to, the explosives contained in the package, so that neither interaction between the explosives and the packaging materials nor leakage causes the explosive to become unsafe to transport, or the hazard division or compatibility group to change.

4.1.5.13   The ingress of explosive substances into the recesses of seamed metal packagings shall be prevented.

4.1.5.14   Plastics packagings shall not be liable to generate or accumulate sufficient static electricity so that a discharge could cause the packaged explosive substances or articles to initiate, ignite or function.

4.1.5.15   Large and robust explosives articles, normally intended for military use, without their means of initiation or with their means of initiation containing at least two effective protective features may be transported unpackaged. When such articles have propelling charges or are self-propelled, their ignition systems shall be protected against stimuli encountered during normal conditions of transport. A negative result in Test Series 4 on an unpackaged article indicates that the article can be considered for transport unpackaged. Such unpackaged articles may be fixed to cradles or contained in crates or other suitable handling, storage or launching devices in such a way that they will not become loose during normal conditions of transport. Where such large explosive articles are, as part of their operational safety and suitability tests, subjected to test regimes that meet the provisions of this Code and such tests have been successfully undertaken, the competent authority may approve such articles to be transported under this Code.

4.1.5.16   Explosive substances shall not be packed in inner or outer packagings where the differences in internal and external pressures, due to thermal or other effects, could cause an explosion or rupture of the package.

4.1.5.17   Whenever loose explosive substances or the explosive substance of an uncased or partly cased article may come into contact with the inner surface of metal packagings (1A1, 1A2, 1B1, 1B2, 4A, 4B and metal receptacles), the metal packaging shall be provided with an inner liner or coating (see 4.1.1.2).

4.1.5.18   Packing instruction P101 may be used for any explosive provided the package has been approved by a competent authority regardless of whether the packaging complies with the packing instruction assignment in the Dangerous Goods List.

4.1.5.19   Government-owned military dangerous goods, packaged prior to 1 January 1990 in accordance with the provisions of the IMDG Code in effect at that time, may be transported provided the packagings maintain their integrity and the goods are declared as government-owned goods packaged prior to 1 January 1990.

4.1.6   Special packing provisions for goods of class 2

4.1.6.1   General provisions

4.1.6.1.1   This section provides general requirements applicable to the use of pressure receptacles for the transport of class 2 gases and other dangerous goods in pressure receptacles (e.g. UN 1051 Hydrogen cyanide, stabilized). Pressure receptacles shall be constructed and closed so as to prevent any loss of contents which might be caused under normal conditions of transport, including by vibration, or by changes in temperature, humidity or pressure (resulting from change in altitude, for example).

△ **4.1.6.1.2**   Parts of pressure receptacles which are in direct contact with dangerous goods shall not be affected or weakened by those dangerous goods and shall not cause a dangerous effect (e.g. catalysing a reaction or reacting with the dangerous goods). The provisions of ISO 11114-1:2012 and ISO 11114-2:2013 shall be met as applicable.

4.1.6.1.3   Pressure receptacles, including their closures, shall be selected to contain a gas or a mixture of gases according to the requirements of 6.2.1.2 and the requirements of the specific packing instructions of 4.1.4.1. This section also applies to pressure receptacles which are elements of MEGCs.

4.1.6.1.4   Refillable pressure receptacles shall not be filled with a gas or gas mixture different from that previously contained unless the necessary operations for change of gas service have been performed. The change of service for compressed and liquefied gases shall be in accordance with ISO 11621:1997, as applicable. In addition, a pressure receptacle that previously contained a class 8 corrosive substance or a substance of another class with a corrosive subsidiary risk shall not be authorized for the transport of a class 2 substance unless the necessary inspection and testing as specified in 6.2.1.6 have been performed.

4.1.6.1.5   Prior to filling, the filler shall perform an inspection of the pressure receptacle and ensure that the pressure receptacle is authorized for the gas and, in case of a chemical under pressure, for the propellant to be transported and that the provisions of this Code have been met. Shut-off valves shall be closed after filling and remain closed during transport. The consignor shall verify that the closures and equipment are not leaking.

4.1.6.1.6   Pressure receptacles shall be filled according to the working pressures, filling ratios and provisions specified in the appropriate packing instruction for the specific substance being filled. Reactive gases and gas mixtures shall be filled to a pressure such that if complete decomposition of the gas occurs, the working pressure of the pressure receptacle shall not be exceeded. Bundles of cylinders shall not be filled in excess of the lowest working pressure of any given cylinder in the bundle.

4.1.6.1.7   Pressure receptacles, including their closures, shall conform to the design, construction, inspection and testing requirements detailed in chapter 6.2. When outer packagings are prescribed, the pressure receptacles shall be firmly secured therein. Unless otherwise specified in the detailed packing instructions, one or more inner packagings may be enclosed in an outer packaging.

4.1.6.1.8   Valves shall be designed and constructed in such a way that they are inherently able to withstand damage without release of the contents or shall be protected from damage which could cause inadvertent release of the contents of the pressure receptacle, by one of the following methods:

   .1   Valves are placed inside the neck of the pressure receptacle and protected by a threaded plug or cap;

   .2   Valves are protected by caps. Caps shall possess vent-holes of sufficient cross-sectional area to evacuate the gas if leakage occurs at the valves;

   .3   Valves are protected by shrouds or guards;

   .4   Pressure receptacles are transported in frames (e.g. bundles); or

   .5   Pressure receptacles are transported in an outer packaging. The packaging as prepared for transport shall be capable of meeting the drop test specified in 6.1.5.3 at the packing group I performance level.

   △ For pressure receptacles with valves as described in .2 and .3, the requirements of either ISO 11117:1998 or ISO 11117:2008 + Cor 1:2009 shall be met; for valves with inherent protection, the provisions of annex A of ISO 10297:2006 or annex A of ISO 10297:2014 shall be met.

   For metal hydride storage systems, the valve protection requirements specified in ISO 16111:2008 shall be met.

4.1.6.1.9   Non-refillable pressure receptacles shall:

   .1   be transported in an outer packaging, such as a box, or crate, or in shrink-wrapped trays or stretch-wrapped trays;

   .2   be of a water capacity less than or equal to 1.25 L when filled with flammable or toxic gas;

   .3   not be used for toxic gases with an LC_{50} less than or equal to 200 mL/m^3; and

   .4   not be repaired after being put into service.

4.1.6.1.10 Refillable pressure receptacles, other than cryogenic receptacles, shall be periodically inspected in accordance with 6.2.1.6 and packing instruction P200, P205 or P206, as applicable. Pressure relief valves for closed cryogenic receptacles shall be subject to periodic inspections and tests according to the provisions of 6.2.1.6.3 and packing instruction P203. Pressure receptacles shall not be filled after they become due for periodic inspection but may be transported after the expiry of the time limit.

4.1.6.1.11 Repairs shall be consistent with the manufacture and testing requirements of the applicable design and construction standards and are only permitted as indicated in the relevant periodic inspection standards specified in 6.2.2.4. Pressure receptacles, other than the jacket of closed cryogenic receptacles, shall not be subjected to repairs of any of the following:

   .1   weld cracks or other weld defects;

   .2   cracks in walls;

   .3   leaks or defects in the material of the wall, head or bottom.

4.1.6.1.12 Pressure receptacles shall not be offered for filling:

   .1   when damaged to such an extent that the integrity of the pressure receptacle or its service equipment may be affected;

   .2   unless the pressure receptacle and its service equipment has been examined and found to be in good working order; or

   △ .3   unless the required certification, retest, and filling marks are legible.

4.1.6.1.13 Filled pressure receptacles shall not be offered for transport:

   .1   when leaking;

   .2   when damaged to such an extent that the integrity of the pressure receptacle or its service equipment may be affected;

.3   unless the pressure receptacle and its service equipment has been examined and found to be in good working order; or

△ .4   unless the required certification, retest, and filling marks are legible.

4.1.6.1.14   Where in packing instruction P200 cylinders and other pressure receptacles for gases conforming to the requirements of this subsection and chapter 6.2 are authorized, use is also authorized of cylinders and pressure receptacles which conform to the requirements of the competent authority of the country in which the cylinder or pressure receptacle is filled. Valves shall be suitably protected. Pressure receptacles with capacities of 1 L or less shall be packed in outer packagings constructed of suitable material of adequate strength and design in relation to the capacity of the packaging and its intended use and secured or cushioned so as to prevent significant movement within the outer packaging during normal conditions of transport.

4.1.7   Special packing provisions for organic peroxides (class 5.2) and self-reactive substances of class 4.1

4.1.7.0   General

4.1.7.0.1   For organic peroxides, all receptacles shall be "effectively closed". Where significant internal pressure may develop in a package by the evolution of gas, a vent may be fitted, provided the gas emitted will not cause danger, otherwise the degree of filling shall be limited. Any venting device shall be so constructed that liquid will not escape when the package is in an upright position and it shall be able to prevent ingress of impurities. The outer packaging, if any, shall be so designed as not to interfere with the operation of the venting device.

4.1.7.1   Use of packagings (except IBCs)

4.1.7.1.1   Packagings for organic peroxides and self-reactive substances shall conform to the provisions of chapter 6.1 and shall meet its test provisions for packing group II.

4.1.7.1.2   The packing methods for organic peroxides and self-reactive substances are listed in packing instruction P520 and are designated OP1 to OP8. The quantities specified for each packing method are the maximum quantities authorized per package.

4.1.7.1.3   The packing methods appropriate for the individual currently assigned self-reactive substances and organic peroxides are listed in 2.4.2.3.2.3 and 2.5.3.2.4.

4.1.7.1.4   For new organic peroxides, new self-reactive substances or new formulations of currently assigned organic peroxides or self-reactive substances, the following procedure shall be used to assign the appropriate packing method:

.1   ORGANIC PEROXIDE TYPE B or SELF-REACTIVE SUBSTANCE TYPE B:
Packing method OP5 shall be assigned, provided that the organic peroxide (or self-reactive substance) satisfies the criteria of 2.5.3.3.2.2 (resp. 2.4.2.3.3.2.2) in a packaging authorized by the packing method. If the organic peroxide (or self-reactive substance) can only satisfy these criteria in a smaller packaging than those authorized by packing method OP5 (viz. one of the packagings listed for OP1 to OP4), then the corresponding packing method with the lower OP number is assigned;

.2   ORGANIC PEROXIDE TYPE C or SELF-REACTIVE SUBSTANCE TYPE C:
Packing method OP6 shall be assigned, provided that the organic peroxide (or self-reactive substance) satisfies the criteria of 2.5.3.3.2.3 (resp. 2.4.2.3.3.2.3) in packaging authorized by the packing method. If the organic peroxide (or self-reactive substance) can only satisfy these criteria in a smaller packaging than those authorized by packing method OP6, then the corresponding packing method with the lower OP number is assigned;

.3   ORGANIC PEROXIDE TYPE D or SELF-REACTIVE SUBSTANCE TYPE D:
Packing method OP7 shall be assigned to this type of organic peroxide or self-reactive substance;

.4   ORGANIC PEROXIDE TYPE E or SELF-REACTIVE SUBSTANCE TYPE E:
Packing method OP8 shall be assigned to this type of organic peroxide or self-reactive substance;

.5   ORGANIC PEROXIDE TYPE F or SELF-REACTIVE SUBSTANCE TYPE F:
Packing method OP8 shall be assigned to this type of organic peroxide or self-reactive substance.

4.1.7.2   Use of intermediate bulk containers

4.1.7.2.1   The currently assigned organic peroxides specifically listed in packing instruction IBC520 may be transported in IBCs in accordance with this packing instruction. IBCs shall conform to the requirements of chapter 6.5 and shall meet its test provisions for packing group II.

4.1.7.2.2   Other organic peroxides and self-reactive substances of type F may be transported in IBCs under conditions established by the competent authority of the country of origin when, on the basis of the appropriate tests, that competent authority is satisfied that such transport may be safely conducted. The tests undertaken shall include those necessary:

.1 to prove that the organic peroxide (or self-reactive substance) complies with the principles for classification;

.2 to prove the compatibility of all materials normally in contact with the substance during the transport;

.3 to determine, when applicable, the control and emergency temperatures associated with the transport of the product in the IBC concerned as derived from the SADT;

.4 to design, when applicable, pressure and emergency relief devices; and

.5 to determine if any special provisions are necessary for safe transport of the substance.

4.1.7.2.3 For self-reactive substances, temperature control is required according to 2.4.2.3.4. For organic peroxides, temperature control is required according to 2.5.3.4.1. Temperature control provisions are given in 7.3.7.

4.1.7.2.4 Emergencies to be taken into account are self-accelerating decomposition and fire engulfment. To prevent explosive rupture of metal or composite IBCs with a complete metal casing, the emergency relief devices shall be designed to vent all the decomposition products and vapours evolved during self-accelerating decomposition or during a period of not less than one hour of complete fire engulfment calculated by the equations given in 4.2.1.13.8.

4.1.8 Special packing provisions for infectious substances of category A (class 6.2, UN Nos. 2814 and 2900)

4.1.8.1 Consignors of infectious substances shall ensure that packages are prepared in such a manner that they arrive at their destination in good condition and present no hazard to persons or animals during transport.

4.1.8.2 The definitions in 1.2.1 and the general packing provisions of 4.1.1.1 to 4.1.1.14, except 4.1.1.10 to 4.1.1.12, apply to infectious substances packages. However, liquids shall only be filled into packagings which have an appropriate resistance to the internal pressure that may develop under normal conditions of transport.

4.1.8.3 An itemized list of contents shall be enclosed between the secondary packaging and the outer packaging. When the infectious substances to be transported are unknown, but suspected of meeting the criteria for inclusion in category A, the words "suspected category A infectious substance" shall be shown, in parentheses, following the proper shipping name on the document inside the outer packaging.

△ **4.1.8.4** Before an empty packaging is returned to the consignor, or sent elsewhere, it shall be disinfected or sterilized to nullify any hazard and any label or mark indicating that it had contained an infectious substance shall be removed or obliterated.

4.1.8.5 Provided an equivalent level of performance is maintained, the following variations in the primary receptacles placed within an intermediate packaging are allowed without further testing of the completed package:

.1 Primary receptacles of equivalent or smaller size as compared to the tested primary receptacles may be used provided:

(a) the primary receptacles are of similar design to the tested primary receptacle (such as shape: round, rectangular, etc.);

(b) the material of construction of the primary receptacle (glass, plastics, metal, etc.) offers resistance to impact and stacking forces equal to or greater than that of the originally tested primary receptacle;

(c) the primary receptacles have the same or smaller openings and the closure is of similar design (such as screw cap, friction lid, etc.);

(d) sufficient additional cushioning material is used to take up void spaces and to prevent significant movement of the primary receptacles; and

(e) primary receptacles are oriented within the intermediate packaging in the same manner as in the tested package.

.2 A lesser number of the tested primary receptacles, or of the alternative types of primary receptacles identified in .1 above, may be used provided sufficient cushioning is added to fill the void space(s) and to prevent significant movement of the primary receptacles.

4.1.9 Special packing provisions for radioactive material

4.1.9.1 General

4.1.9.1.1 Radioactive material, packagings and packages shall meet the provisions of chapter 6.4. The quantity of radioactive material in a package shall not exceed the limits specified in 2.7.2.2, 2.7.2.4.1, 2.7.2.4.4, 2.7.2.4.5, 2.7.2.4.6 and 4.1.9.3.

The types of packages for radioactive materials covered by the provisions of this Code are:

.1 Excepted package (see 1.5.1.5);

4

.2 Industrial package Type 1 (Type IP-1 package);

.3 Industrial package Type 2 (Type IP-2 package);

.4 Industrial package Type 3 (Type IP-3 package);

.5 Type A package;

.6 Type B(U) package;

.7 Type B(M) package;

.8 Type C package.

Packages containing fissile material or uranium hexafluoride are subject to additional requirements.

4.1.9.1.2 The non-fixed contamination on the external surfaces of any package shall be kept as low as practicable and, under routine conditions of transport, shall not exceed the following limits:

(a) 4 Bq/cm^2 for beta and gamma emitters and low-toxicity alpha emitters, and

(b) 0.4 Bq/cm^2 for all other alpha emitters.

These limits are applicable when averaged over any area of 300 cm^2 of any part of the surface.

4.1.9.1.3 A package shall not contain any items other than those that are necessary for the use of the radioactive material. The interaction between these items and the package under the conditions of transport applicable to the design shall not reduce the safety of the package.

4.1.9.1.4 Except as provided in 7.1.4.5.11, the level of non-fixed contamination on the external and internal surfaces of overpacks, cargo transport units, tanks, IBCs and conveyances shall not exceed the limits specified in 4.1.9.1.2.

4.1.9.1.5 For radioactive material having other dangerous properties the package design shall take into account those properties. Radioactive material with a subsidiary risk, packaged in packages that do not require competent authority approval, shall be transported in packagings, IBCs, tanks or bulk containers fully complying with the provisions of the relevant chapters of part 6 as appropriate, as well as applicable provisions of chapters 4.1, 4.2 or 4.3 for that subsidiary risk.

4.1.9.1.6 Before a packaging is first used to transport radioactive material, it shall be confirmed that it has been manufactured in conformity with the design specifications to ensure compliance with the relevant provisions of this Code and any applicable certificate of approval. The following requirements shall also be fulfilled, if applicable:

.1 if the design pressure of the containment system exceeds 35 kPa (gauge), it shall be ensured that the containment system of each packaging conforms to the approved design requirements relating to the capability of that system to maintain its integrity under that pressure;

.2 for each packaging intended for use as a Type B(U), Type B(M) or Type C package and for each packaging intended to contain fissile material, it shall be ensured that the effectiveness of its shielding and containment and, where necessary, the heat transfer characteristics and the effectiveness of the confinement system are within the limits applicable to or specified for the approved design;

.3 for each packaging intended to contain fissile material, it shall be ensured that the effectiveness of the criticality safety features is within the limits applicable to or specified for the design and in particular where, in order to comply with the requirements of 6.4.11.1 neutron poisons are specifically included, checks shall be performed to confirm the presence and distribution of those neutron poisons.

4.1.9.1.7 Before each shipment of any package, it shall be ensured that the package contains neither:

.1 radionuclides different from those specified for the package design; nor

.2 contents in a form, or physical or chemical state different from those specified for the package design.

4.1.9.1.8 Before each shipment of any package, it shall be ensured that all the requirements specified in the relevant provisions of this Code and in the applicable certificates of approval have been fulfilled. The following requirements shall also be fulfilled, if applicable:

.1 it shall be ensured that lifting attachments which do not meet the requirements of 6.4.2.2 have been removed or otherwise rendered incapable of being used for lifting the package, in accordance with 6.4.2.3;

.2 each Type B(U), Type B(M) and Type C package shall be held until equilibrium conditions have been approached closely enough to demonstrate compliance with the requirements for temperature and pressure unless an exemption from these requirements has received unilateral approval;

.3 for each Type B(U), Type B(M) and Type C package, it shall be ensured by inspection and/or appropriate tests that all closures, valves and other openings of the containment system through which the radioactive contents might escape are properly closed and, where appropriate, sealed in the manner for which the demonstrations of compliance with the requirements of 6.4.8.8 and 6.4.10.3 were made;

.4 for packages containing fissile material the measurement specified in 6.4.11.5 (b) and the tests to demonstrate closure of each package as specified in 6.4.11.8 shall be performed.

4.1.9.1.9 The consignor shall also have a copy of any instructions with regard to the proper closing of the package and any preparation for shipment before making any shipment under the terms of the certificates.

4.1.9.1.10 Except for consignments under exclusive use, the transport index of any package or overpack shall not exceed 10, nor shall the criticality safety index of any package or overpack exceed 50.

4.1.9.1.11 Except for packages or overpacks transported under exclusive use by rail or by road under the conditions specified in 7.1.4.5.5.1, or under exclusive use and special arrangement by ship under the conditions specified in 7.1.4.5.7, the maximum radiation level at any point on any external surface of a package or overpack shall not exceed 2 mSv/h.

4.1.9.1.12 The maximum radiation level at any point on any external surface of a package or overpack under exclusive use shall not exceed 10 mSv/h.

4.1.9.1.13 Pyrophoric radioactive material shall be packaged in Type A, Type B(U), Type B(M) or Type C packages and shall also be suitably inerted.

4.1.9.2 Provisions and controls for transport of LSA material and SCO

4.1.9.2.1 The quantity of LSA material or SCO in a single Type IP-1 package, Type IP-2 package, Type IP-3 package, or object or collection of objects, whichever is appropriate, shall be so restricted that the external radiation level at 3 m from the unshielded material or object or collection of objects does not exceed 10 mSv/h.

4.1.9.2.2 For LSA material and SCO which are or contain fissile material, which is not excepted under 2.7.2.3.5, the applicable requirements of 7.1.4.5.15 and 7.1.4.5.16 shall be met.

4.1.9.2.3 For LSA material and SCO which are or contain fissile material, the applicable requirements of 6.4.11.1 shall be met.

4.1.9.2.4 LSA material and SCO in groups LSA-I and SCO-I may be transported unpackaged under the following conditions:

.1 all unpackaged material other than ores containing only naturally occurring radionuclides shall be transported in such a manner that, under routine conditions of transport, there will be no escape of the radioactive contents from the conveyance nor will there be any loss of shielding;

.2 each conveyance shall be under exclusive use, except when only transporting SCO-I on which the contamination on the accessible and the inaccessible surfaces is not greater than ten times the applicable level specified in 2.7.1.2;

.3 for SCO-I where it is suspected that non-fixed contamination exists on inaccessible surfaces in excess of the values specified in 2.7.2.3.2.1.1, measures shall be taken to ensure that the radioactive material is not released into the conveyance; and

.4 unpackaged fissile material shall meet the requirements of 2.7.2.3.5.5.

4.1.9.2.5 LSA material and SCO, except as otherwise specified in 4.1.9.2.4, shall be packaged in accordance with table 4.1.9.2.5.

Table 4.1.9.2.5 – Industrial package provisions for LSA material and SCO

Radioactive contents	Industrial package type	
	Exclusive use	Not under exclusive use
LSA-I		
Solid[a]	Type IP-1	Type IP-1
Liquid	Type IP-1	Type IP-2
LSA-II		
Solid	Type IP-2	Type IP-2
Liquid and gas	Type IP-2	Type IP-3
LSA-III	Type IP-2	Type IP-3
SCO-I[a]	Type IP-1	Type IP-1
SCO-II	Type IP-2	Type IP-2

[a] Under the conditions specified in 4.1.9.2.4, LSA-I material and SCO-I may be transported unpackaged.

4.1.9.3   Packages containing fissile material

The contents of packages containing fissile material shall be as specified for the package design either directly in the provisions of this Code or in the certificate of approval.

Chapter 4.2

Use of portable tanks and multiple-element gas containers (MEGCs)

The provisions of this chapter also apply to road tank vehicles to the extent indicated in chapter 6.8.

4.2.0   Transitional provisions

△ **4.2.0.1**   The provisions for the use and construction of portable tanks in this chapter and chapter 6.7 are based on the United Nations *Recommendations on the Transport of Dangerous Goods*. IMO type portable tanks and road tank vehicles certified and approved prior to 1 January 2003 in accordance with the provisions of the IMDG Code in force on 1 July 1999 (amendment 29) may continue to be used provided that they are found to meet the applicable periodic inspections and test provisions. They shall meet the provisions set out in columns (13) and (14) of chapter 3.2. Detailed explanation and construction provisions may be found in CCC.1/Circ.3 *Revised guidance on the continued use of existing IMO type portable tanks and road tank vehicles for the transport of dangerous goods*.

Note: For ease of reference, the following descriptions of existing IMO type tanks are included:

IMO type 1 tank means a portable tank for the transport of substances of classes 3 to 9 fitted with pressure-relief devices, having a maximum allowable working pressure of 1.75 bar and above.

IMO type 2 tank means a portable tank fitted with pressure-relief devices, having a maximum allowable working pressure equal to or above 1.0 bar but below 1.75 bar, intended for the transport of certain dangerous liquids of low hazard and certain solids.

IMO type 4 tank means a road tank vehicle for the transport of dangerous goods of classes 3 to 9 and includes a semi-trailer with a permanently attached tank or a tank attached to a chassis, with at least four twist locks which comply with ISO standards, (e.g. ISO 1161:1984).

△ *IMO type 5 tank* means a portable tank fitted with pressure-relief devices which is used for non-refrigerated liquefied gases of class 2.

IMO type 6 tank means a road tank vehicle for the transport of non-refrigerated liquefied gases of class 2 and includes a semi-trailer with a permanently attached tank or a tank attached to a chassis which is fitted with items of service equipment and structural equipment necessary for the transport of gases.

IMO type 7 tank means a thermally insulated portable tank fitted with items of service and structural equipment necessary for the transport of refrigerated liquefied gases. The portable tank shall be capable of being transported, loaded and discharged without the need of removal of its structural equipment, and shall be capable of being lifted when full. It shall not be permanently secured on board the ship.

IMO type 8 tank means a road tank vehicle for the transport of refrigerated liquefied gases of class 2 and includes a semi-trailer with a permanently attached thermally insulated tank fitted with items of service equipment and structural equipment necessary for the transport of refrigerated liquefied gases.

Note: IMO type 4, 6 and 8 road tank vehicles may be constructed after 1 January 2003 in accordance with the provisions of chapter 6.8.

4.2.0.2   UN portable tanks and MEGCs constructed according to a design approval certificate which has been issued before 1 January 2008 may continue to be used provided that they are found to meet the applicable periodic inspection and test provisions.

4.2.0.3   Portable tanks and MEGCs manufactured before 1 January 2012, that conform to the marking provisions of 6.7.2.20.1, 6.7.3.16.1, 6.7.4.15.1 or 6.7.5.13.1 of the IMDG Code in force on 1 January 2010 (amendment 34-08), as relevant, may continue to be used if they comply with all other relevant provisions of the current edition of the Code including, when applicable, the requirement of 6.7.2.20.1 (g) for marking the symbol "S" on the plate when the shell or the compartment is divided by surge plates into sections of not more than 7500 litres capacity. When the shell, or the compartment, was already divided by surge plates into sections of not more than 7500 litres capacity before 1 January 2012, the capacity of the shell, or respectively of the compartment, need not be supplemented with the symbol "S" until the next periodic inspection or test according to 6.7.2.19.5 is performed.

Portable tanks manufactured before 1 January 2014 need not be marked with the portable tank instruction as required in 6.7.2.20.2, 6.7.3.16.2 and 6.7.4.15.2 until the next periodic inspection and test.

Portable tanks and MECGs manufactured before 1 January 2014 need not comply with the requirements of 6.7.2.13.1.6, 6.7.3.9.1.5, 6.7.4.8.1.5 and 6.7.5.6.1 (d) concerning the marking of the pressure relief devices.

■ IMO portable tanks manufactured before 1 January 2003 shall be marked with an indication of the portable tank instruction for which it meets the minimum test pressure, minimum shell thickness, pressure relief requirements and bottom opening requirements as shown in 4.2.5.2.6 as required in 6.7.2.20.2, 6.7.3.16.2 and 6.7.4.15.2. These portable tanks need not be marked with the portable tank instruction until the next periodic inspection and test.

4.2.1 General provisions for the use of portable tanks for the transport of substances of class 1 and classes 3 to 9

4.2.1.1 This section provides general provisions applicable to the use of portable tanks for the transport of substances of classes 1, 3, 4, 5, 6, 7, 8 and 9. In addition to these general provisions, portable tanks shall conform to the design, construction, inspection and testing provisions detailed in 6.7.2. Substances shall be transported in portable tanks conforming to the applicable portable tank instruction and the portable tank special provisions assigned to each substance in the Dangerous Goods List.

4.2.1.2 During transport, portable tanks shall be adequately protected against damage to the shell and service equipment resulting from lateral and longitudinal impact and overturning. If the shell and service equipment are so constructed as to withstand impact or overturning, it need not be protected in this way. Examples of such protection are given in 6.7.2.17.5.

4.2.1.3 Certain substances are chemically unstable. They are accepted for transport only when the necessary steps have been taken to prevent their dangerous decomposition, transformation or polymerization during transport. To this end, care shall in particular be taken to ensure that shells do not contain any substances liable to promote these reactions.

4.2.1.4 The temperature of the outer surface of the shell, excluding openings and their closures, or of the thermal insulation shall not exceed 70°C during transport. When necessary, the shell shall be thermally insulated.

4.2.1.5 Empty portable tanks not cleaned and not gas-free shall comply with the same provisions as portable tanks filled with the previous substance.

4.2.1.6 Substances shall not be transported in adjoining compartments of shells when they may react dangerously with each other and cause:

.1 combustion and/or evolution of considerable heat;

.2 evolution of flammable, toxic or asphyxiant gases;

.3 the formation of corrosive substances;

.4 the formation of unstable substances;

.5 dangerous rise in pressure.

4.2.1.7 The design approval certificate, the test report and the certificate showing the results of the initial inspection and test for each portable tank issued by the competent authority or its authorized body shall be retained by the authority or body and the owner. Owners shall be able to provide this documentation upon the request of any competent authority.

4.2.1.8 Unless the name of the substance(s) being transported appears on the metal plate described in 6.7.2.20.2, a copy of the certificate specified in 6.7.2.18.1 shall be made available upon the request of a competent authority or its authorized body and readily provided by the consignor, consignee or agent, as appropriate.

4.2.1.9 Degree of filling

4.2.1.9.1 Prior to filling, the shipper shall ensure that the appropriate portable tank is used and that the portable tank is not loaded with substances which, in contact with the materials of the shell, gaskets, service equipment and any protective linings, are likely to react dangerously with them to form dangerous products or appreciably weaken these materials. The shipper may need to consult the manufacturer of the substance in conjunction with the competent authority for guidance on the compatibility of the substance with the portable tank materials.

4.2.1.9.1.1 Portable tanks shall not be filled in excess of the maximum degree of filling specified in 4.2.1.9.2 to 4.2.1.9.6. The applicability of 4.2.1.9.2, 4.2.1.9.3 or 4.2.1.9.5.1 to individual substances is specified in the applicable portable tank instructions or special provisions in 4.2.5.2.6 or 4.2.5.3 and columns 13 and 14 of the Dangerous Goods List.

4.2.1.9.2 The maximum degree of filling (in %) for general use is determined by the formula:

$$\text{Degree of filling} = \frac{97}{1 + \alpha(t_r - t_f)}$$

4.2.1.9.3 The maximum degree of filling (in %) for liquids of class 6.1 and class 8, in packing groups I and II, and liquids with an absolute vapour pressure of more than 175 kPa (1.75 bar) at 65°C, or for liquids identified as marine pollutants is determined by the formula:

$$\text{Degree of filling} = \frac{95}{1 + \alpha(t_r - t_f)}$$

4.2.1.9.4 In these formulae, α is the mean coefficient of cubical expansion of the liquid between the mean temperature of the liquid during filling (t_f) and the maximum mean bulk temperature during transport (t_r) (both in °C). For liquids transported under ambient conditions, α could be calculated by the formula:

$$\alpha = \frac{d_{15} - d_{50}}{35 \, d_{50}}$$

in which d_{15} and d_{50} are the densities of the liquid at 15°C and 50°C, respectively.

4.2.1.9.4.1 The maximum mean bulk temperature (t_r) shall be taken as 50°C except that, for journeys under temperate or extreme climatic conditions, the competent authorities concerned may agree to a lower or require a higher temperature, as appropriate.

4.2.1.9.5 The provisions of 4.2.1.9.2 to 4.2.1.9.4.1 do not apply to portable tanks which contain substances maintained at a temperature above 50°C during transport (such as by means of a heating device). For portable tanks equipped with a heating device, a temperature regulator shall be used to ensure the maximum degree of filling is not more than 95% full at any time during transport.

4.2.1.9.5.1 The maximum degree of filling (in %) for solids transported above their melting points and for elevated temperature liquids shall be determined by the following formula:

$$\text{Degree of filling} = 95 \frac{d_r}{d_f}$$

in which d_f and d_r are the densities of the liquid at the mean temperature of the liquid during filling and the maximum mean bulk temperature during transport respectively.

4.2.1.9.6 Portable tanks shall not be offered for transport:

.1 with a degree of filling, for liquids having a viscosity less than 2,680 mm^2/s at 20°C or at the maximum temperature of the substance during transport in the case of a heated substance, of more than 20% but less than 80% unless the shells of portable tanks are divided, by partitions or surge plates, into sections of not more than 7,500 L capacity;

.2 with residue of substances previously transported adhering to the outside of the shell or service equipment;

.3 when leaking or damaged to such an extent that the integrity of the portable tank or its lifting or securing arrangements may be affected; and

.4 unless the service equipment has been examined and found to be in good working order.

For certain dangerous substances, a lower degree of filling may be required.

4.2.1.9.7 Forklift pockets of portable tanks shall be closed off where the tank is filled. This provision does not apply to portable tanks which, according to 6.7.2.17.4, need not be provided with a means of closing off the forklift pockets.

4.2.1.9.8 Portable tanks shall not be filled or discharged while they remain on board.

4.2.1.10 Additional provisions applicable to the transport of class 3 substances in portable tanks

All portable tanks intended for the transport of flammable liquids shall be closed and be fitted with relief devices in accordance with 6.7.2.8 to 6.7.2.15.

4.2.1.11 Additional provisions applicable to the transport of class 4 substances (other than class 4.1 self-reactive substances) in portable tanks

[Reserved]

Note: For class 4.1 self-reactive substances, see 4.2.1.13.

4.2.1.12 Additional provisions applicable to the transport of class 5.1 substances in portable tanks

[Reserved]

4.2.1.13 Additional provisions applicable to the transport of class 5.2 substances and class 4.1 self-reactive substances in portable tanks

4.2.1.13.1 Each substance shall have been tested and a report submitted to the competent authority of the country of origin for approval. Notification thereof shall be sent to the competent authority of the country of destination.

The notification shall contain relevant transport information and the report with test results. The tests undertaken shall include those necessary:

.1 to prove the compatibility of all materials normally in contact with the substance during transport;

.2 to provide data for the design of the pressure and emergency relief devices, taking into account the design characteristics of the portable tank.

Any additional provisions necessary for safe transport of the substance shall be clearly described in the report.

4.2.1.13.2 The following provisions apply to portable tanks intended for the transport of type F organic peroxides or type F self-reactive substances with a self-accelerating decomposition temperature (SADT) of 55°C or more. In case of conflict, these provisions prevail over those specified in 6.7.2. Emergencies to be taken into account are self-accelerating decomposition of the substance and fire-engulfment as described in 4.2.1.13.8.

4.2.1.13.3 The additional provisions for transport of organic peroxides or self-reactive substances with an SADT less than 55°C in portable tanks shall be specified by the competent authority of the country of origin. Notification thereof shall be sent to the competent authority of the country of destination.

4.2.1.13.4 The portable tank shall be designed for a test pressure of at least 0.4 MPa (4 bar).

4.2.1.13.5 Portable tanks shall be fitted with temperature-sensing devices.

4.2.1.13.6 Portable tanks shall be fitted with pressure-relief devices and emergency relief devices. Vacuum-relief devices may also be used. Pressure-relief devices shall operate at pressures determined according to both the properties of the substance and the construction characteristics of the portable tank. Fusible elements are not allowed in the shell.

4.2.1.13.7 The pressure-relief devices shall consist of spring-loaded valves fitted to prevent significant build-up within the portable tank of the decomposition products and vapours released at a temperature of 50°C. The capacity and start-to-discharge pressure of the relief valves shall be based on the results of the tests specified in 4.2.1.13.1. The start-to-discharge pressure shall, however, in no case be such that liquid would escape from the valve(s) if the portable tank were overturned.

4.2.1.13.8 The emergency relief devices may be of the spring-loaded or frangible types, or a combination of the two, designed to vent all the decomposition products and vapours evolved during a period of not less than one hour of complete fire-engulfment as calculated by the following formula:

$$q = 70961FA^{0.82}$$

where:

q = heat absorption (W)

A = wetted area (m^2)

F = insulation factor;

$F = 1$ for non-insulated vessels, or

$F = \dfrac{U(923 - T)}{47032}$ for insulated shells

where:

K = heat conductivity of insulation layer		(W·m^{-1}·K^{-1})
L = thickness of insulation layer		(m)
$U = K/L$ = heat transfer coefficient of the insulation		(W·m^{-2}·K^{-1})
T = temperature of substance at relieving conditions		(K)

The start-to-discharge pressure of the emergency relief device(s) shall be higher than that specified in 4.2.1.13.7 and based on the results of the tests referred to in 4.2.1.13.1. The emergency relief devices shall be dimensioned in such a way that the maximum pressure in the tank never exceeds the test pressure of the portable tank.

Note: An example of a method to determine the size of emergency relief devices is given in appendix 5 of the Manual of Tests and Criteria.

4.2.1.13.9 For insulated portable tanks, the capacity and setting of emergency relief device(s) shall be determined assuming a loss of insulation from 1% of the surface area.

4.2.1.13.10 Vacuum-relief devices and spring-loaded valves shall be provided with flame arresters. Due attention shall be paid to the reduction of the relief capacity caused by the flame arrester.

4.2.1.13.11 Service equipment such as valves and external piping shall be so arranged that no substance remains in them after filling the portable tank.

4.2.1.13.12 Portable tanks may be either insulated or protected by a sunshield. If the SADT of the substance in the portable tank is 55°C or less, or the portable tank is constructed of aluminium, the portable tank shall be completely insulated. The outer surface shall be finished in white or bright metal.

4.2.1.13.13 The degree of filling shall not exceed 90% at 15°C.

△ **4.2.1.13.14** The mark as required in 6.7.2.20.2 shall include the UN number and the technical name with the approved concentration of the substance concerned.

4.2.1.13.15 Organic peroxides and self-reactive substances specifically listed in portable tank instruction T23 in 4.2.5.2.6 may be transported in portable tanks.

4.2.1.14 **Additional provisions applicable to the transport of class 6.1 substances in portable tanks**

[Reserved]

4.2.1.15 **Additional provisions applicable to the transport of class 6.2 substances in portable tanks**

[Reserved]

4.2.1.16 **Additional provisions applicable to the transport of class 7 substances in portable tanks**

4.2.1.16.1 Portable tanks used for the transport of radioactive material shall not be used for the transport of other goods.

4.2.1.16.2 The degree of filling for portable tanks shall not exceed 90% or, alternatively, any other value approved by the competent authority.

4.2.1.17 **Additional provisions applicable to the transport of class 8 substances in portable tanks**

4.2.1.17.1 Pressure-relief devices of portable tanks used for the transport of class 8 substances shall be inspected at intervals not exceeding one year.

4.2.1.18 **Additional provisions applicable to the transport of class 9 substances in portable tanks**

[Reserved]

4.2.1.19 **Additional provisions applicable to the transport of solid substances transported above their melting point**

4.2.1.19.1 Solid substances transported or offered for transport above their melting point which are not assigned a portable tank instruction in column 13 of the Dangerous Goods List of chapter 3.2 or when the assigned portable tank instruction does not apply to transport at temperatures above their melting point may be transported in portable tanks provided that the solid substances are classified in classes 4.1, 4.2, 4.3, 5.1, 6.1, 8 or 9 and have no subsidiary risk other than that of class 6.1 or class 8 and are in packing group II or III.

4.2.1.19.2 Unless otherwise indicated in the Dangerous Goods List, portable tanks used for the transport of these solid substances above their melting point shall conform to the provisions of portable tank instruction T4 for solid substances of packing group III or T7 for solid substances of packing group II. A portable tank that affords an equivalent or greater level of safety may be selected in accordance with 4.2.5.2.5. The maximum degree of filling (in %) shall be determined according to 4.2.1.9.5 (TP3).

4.2.2 **General provisions for the use of portable tanks for the transport of non-refrigerated liquefied gases and chemicals under pressure**

4.2.2.1 This section provides general provisions applicable to the use of portable tanks for the transport of non-refrigerated liquefied gases of class 2 and chemicals under pressure.

4.2.2.2 Portable tanks shall conform to the design, construction, inspection and testing provisions detailed in 6.7.3. Non-refrigerated liquefied gases and chemicals under pressure shall be transported in portable tanks conforming to portable tank instruction T50 as described in 4.2.5.2.6 and any portable tank special provisions assigned to specific non-refrigerated liquefied gases in the Dangerous Goods List and described in 4.2.5.3.

4.2.2.3 During transport, portable tanks shall be adequately protected against damage to the shell and service equipment resulting from lateral and longitudinal impact and overturning. If the shell and service equipment are so constructed as to withstand impact or overturning, it need not be protected in this way. Examples of such protection are given in 6.7.3.13.5.

4.2.2.4   Certain non-refrigerated liquefied gases are chemically unstable. They are accepted for transport only when the necessary steps have been taken to prevent their dangerous decomposition, transformation or polymerization during transport. To this end, care shall be taken to ensure that portable tanks do not contain any non-refrigerated liquefied gases liable to promote these reactions.

4.2.2.5   Unless the name of the gas(es) being transported appears on the metal plate described in 6.7.3.16.2, a copy of the certificate specified in 6.7.3.14.1 shall be made available upon a competent authority request and readily provided by the consignor, consignee or agent, as appropriate.

4.2.2.6   Empty portable tanks not cleaned and not gas-free shall comply with the same provisions as portable tanks filled with the previous non-refrigerated liquefied gas.

4.2.2.7   Filling

4.2.2.7.1   Prior to filling, the shipper shall ensure that the portable tank is approved for the non-refrigerated liquefied gas or the propellant of the chemical under pressure to be transported and that the portable tank is not loaded with non-refrigerated liquefied gases, or with chemicals under pressure which, in contact with the materials of the shell, gaskets and service equipment, are likely to react dangerously with them to form dangerous products or appreciably weaken these materials. During filling, the temperature of the non-refrigerated liquefied gas or propellant of chemicals under pressure shall fall within the limits of the design temperature range.

4.2.2.7.2   The maximum mass of non-refrigerated liquefied gas per litre of shell capacity (kg/L) shall not exceed the density of the non-refrigerated liquefied gas at 50°C multiplied by 0.95. Furthermore, the shell shall not be liquid-full at 60°C.

4.2.2.7.3   Portable tanks shall not be filled above their maximum permissible gross mass and the maximum permissible load mass specified for each gas to be transported.

4.2.2.7.4   Portable tanks shall not be filled or discharged while they remain on board.

4.2.2.8   Portable tanks shall not be offered for transport:

.1   in an ullage condition liable to produce an unacceptable hydraulic force due to surge within the portable tank;

.2   when leaking;

.3   when damaged to such an extent that the integrity of the tank or its lifting or securing arrangements may be affected; and

.4   unless the service equipment has been examined and found to be in good working order.

4.2.2.9   Forklift pockets of portable tanks shall be closed off when the tank is filled. This provision does not apply to portable tanks which, according to 6.7.3.13.4, need not be provided with a means of closing off the forklift pockets.

4.2.3   General provisions for the use of portable tanks for the transport of refrigerated liquefied gases of class 2

4.2.3.1   This section provides general provisions applicable to the use of portable tanks for the transport of refrigerated liquefied gases.

4.2.3.2   Portable tanks shall conform to the design, construction, inspection and testing provisions detailed in 6.7.4. Refrigerated liquefied gases shall be transported in portable tanks conforming to portable tank instruction T75 as described in 4.2.5.2.6 and the portable tank special provisions assigned to each substance in column 14 of the Dangerous Goods List and described in 4.2.5.3.

4.2.3.3   During transport, portable tanks shall be adequately protected against damage to the shell and service equipment resulting from lateral and longitudinal impact and overturning. If the shell and service equipment are so constructed as to withstand impact or overturning, it need not be protected in this way. Examples of such protection are provided in 6.7.4.12.5.

4.2.3.4   Unless the name of the gas(es) being transported appears on the metal plate described in 6.7.4.15.2, a copy of the certificate specified in 6.7.4.13.1 shall be made available upon a competent authority request and readily provided by the consignor, consignee or agent, as appropriate.

4.2.3.5   Empty portable tanks not cleaned and not gas-free shall comply with the same provisions as portable tanks filled with the previous substance.

4.2.3.6 **Filling**

4.2.3.6.1 Prior to filling, the shipper shall ensure that the portable tank is approved for the refrigerated liquefied gas to be transported and that the portable tank is not loaded with refrigerated liquefied gases which, in contact with the materials of the shell, gaskets and service equipment, are likely to react dangerously with them to form dangerous products or appreciably weaken these materials. During filling, the temperature of the refrigerated liquefied gas shall be within the limits of the design temperature range.

4.2.3.6.2 In estimating the initial degree of filling, the necessary holding time for the intended journey, including any delays which might be encountered, shall be taken into consideration. The initial degree of filling of the shell, except as provided for in 4.2.3.6.3 and 4.2.3.6.4, shall be such that if the contents, except helium, were to be raised to a temperature at which the vapour pressure is equal to the maximum allowable working pressure (MAWP) the volume occupied by liquid would not exceed 98%.

4.2.3.6.3 Shells intended for the transport of helium can be filled up to but not above the inlet of the pressure-relief device.

4.2.3.6.4 A higher initial degree of filling may be allowed, subject to approval by the competent authority, when the intended duration of transport is considerably shorter than the holding time.

4.2.3.6.5 Portable tanks shall not be filled or discharged while they remain on board.

4.2.3.7 **Actual holding time**

4.2.3.7.1 The actual holding time shall be calculated for each journey in accordance with a procedure recognized by the competent authority, on the basis of the following:

  .1 the reference holding time for the refrigerated liquefied gas to be transported (see 6.7.4.2.8.1) (as indicated on the plate referred to in 6.7.4.15.1);

  .2 the actual filling density;

  .3 the actual filling pressure;

  .4 the lowest set pressure of the pressure-limiting device(s).

4.2.3.7.2 The actual holding time shall be marked either on the portable tank itself or on a metal plate firmly secured to the portable tank, in accordance with 6.7.4.15.2.

4.2.3.8 Portable tanks shall not be offered for transport:

  .1 in an ullage condition liable to produce an unacceptable hydraulic force due to surge within the shell;

  .2 when leaking;

  .3 when damaged to such an extent that the integrity of the portable tank or its lifting or securing arrangements may be affected;

  .4 unless the service equipment has been examined and found to be in good working order;

  .5 unless the actual holding time for the refrigerated liquefied gas being transported has been determined in accordance with 4.2.3.7 and the portable tank is marked in accordance with 6.7.4.15.2; and

  .6 unless the duration of transport, after taking into consideration any delays which might be encountered, does not exceed the actual holding time.

4.2.3.9 Forklift pockets of portable tanks shall be closed off when the tank is filled. This provision does not apply to portable tanks which, according to 6.7.4.12.4, need not be provided with a means of closing off the forklift pockets.

4.2.4 General provisions for the use of multiple-element gas containers (MEGCs)

4.2.4.1 This section provides general requirements applicable to the use of multiple-element gas containers (MEGCs) for the transport of non-refrigerated gases.

4.2.4.2 MEGCs shall conform to the design, construction, inspection and testing requirements detailed in 6.7.5. The elements of MEGCs shall be periodically inspected according to the provisions set out in packing instruction P200 and in 6.2.1.6.

4.2.4.3 During transport, MEGCs shall be protected against damage to the elements and service equipment resulting from lateral and longitudinal impact and overturning. If the elements and service equipment are so constructed as to withstand impact or overturning, they need not be protected in this way. Examples of such protection are given in 6.7.5.10.4.

4

4.2.4.4 The periodic testing and inspection requirements for MEGCs are specified in 6.7.5.12. MEGCs or their elements shall not be charged or filled after they become due for periodic inspection but may be transported after the expiry of the time limit.

4.2.4.5 Filling

4.2.4.5.1 Prior to filling, the MEGC shall be inspected to ensure that it is authorized for the gas to be transported and that the applicable provisions of this Code have been met.

4.2.4.5.2 Elements of MEGCs shall be filled according to the working pressures, filling ratios and filling provisions specified in packing instruction P200 for the specific gas being filled into each element. In no case shall an MEGC or group of elements be filled as a unit in excess of the lowest working pressure of any given element.

4.2.4.5.3 MEGCs shall not be filled above their maximum permissible gross mass.

4.2.4.5.4 Isolation valves shall be closed after filling and remain closed during transport. Toxic gases of class 2.3 shall only be transported in MEGCs where each element is equipped with an isolation valve.

4.2.4.5.5 The opening(s) for filling shall be closed by caps or plugs. The leakproofness of the closures and equipment shall be verified by the shipper after filling.

4.2.4.5.6 MEGCs shall not be offered for filling:

   .1 when damaged to such an extent that the integrity of the pressure receptacles or their structural or service equipment may be affected;

   .2 unless the pressure receptacles and their structural and service equipment have been examined and found to be in good working order; and

△ .3 unless the required certification, retest, and filling marks are legible.

4.2.4.6 Filled MEGCs shall not be offered for transport;

   .1 when leaking;

   .2 when damaged to such an extent that the integrity of the pressure receptacles or their structural or service equipment may be affected;

   .3 unless the pressure receptacles and their structural and service equipment have been examined and found to be in good working order; and

△ .4 unless the required certification, retest, and filling marks are legible.

4.2.4.7 Empty MEGCs that have not been cleaned and purged shall comply with the same requirements as MEGCs filled with the previous substance.

4.2.5 Portable tank instructions and special provisions

4.2.5.1 General

4.2.5.1.1 This section includes the portable tank instructions and special provisions applicable to dangerous goods authorized to be transported in portable tanks. Each portable tank instruction is identified by an alpha-numeric designation (T1 to T75). The Dangerous Goods List in chapter 3.2 indicates the portable tank instruction that shall be used for each substance permitted for transport in a portable tank. When no portable tank instruction appears in the Dangerous Goods List, transport of the substance in portable tanks is not permitted unless a competent authority approval is granted as set out in 6.7.1.3. Portable tank special provisions are assigned to specific dangerous goods in the Dangerous Goods List in chapter 3.2. Each portable tank special provision is identified by an alpha-numeric designation (such as TP1). A listing of the portable tank special provisions is provided in 4.2.5.3.

Note: The gases authorized for transport in MEGCs are indicated in the column "MEGC" in Tables 1 and 2 of packing instruction P200 in 4.1.4.1.

4.2.5.2 Portable tank instructions

4.2.5.2.1 Portable tank instructions apply to dangerous goods of classes 1 to 9. Portable tank instructions provide specific information relevant to portable tank provisions applicable to specific substances. These provisions shall be met in addition to the general provisions in this chapter and chapter 6.7.

4.2.5.2.2 For substances of class 1 and classes 3 to 9, the portable tank instructions indicate the applicable minimum test pressure, the minimum shell thickness (in reference steel), bottom opening provisions and pressure-relief provisions. In T23, self-reactive substances of class 4.1 and class 5.2 organic peroxides permitted to be transported in portable tanks are listed along with applicable control and emergency temperatures.

4.2.5.2.3   Non-refrigerated liquefied gases are assigned to portable tank instruction T50. T50 provides the maximum allowable working pressures, bottom opening provisions, pressure-relief provisions and degree of filling provisions for non-refrigerated liquefied gases permitted for transport in portable tanks.

4.2.5.2.4   Refrigerated liquefied gases are assigned to portable tank instruction T75.

4.2.5.2.5   *Determination of the appropriate portable tank instructions*

When a specific portable tank instruction is specified in the Dangerous Goods List, additional portable tanks which possess higher test pressures, greater shell thicknesses, more stringent bottom opening and pressure-relief device arrangements may be used. The following guidelines apply to determining the appropriate portable tanks which may be used for transport of particular substances:

Portable tank instruction specified	Portable tank instructions also permitted
T1	T2, T3, T4, T5, T6, T7, T8, T9, T10, T11, T12, T13, T14, T15, T16, T17, T18, T19, T20, T21, T22
T2	T4, T5, T7, T8, T9, T10, T11, T12, T13, T14, T15, T16, T17, T18, T19, T20, T21, T22
T3	T4, T5, T6, T7, T8, T9, T10, T11, T12, T13, T14, T15, T16, T17, T18, T19, T20, T21, T22
T4	T5, T7, T8, T9, T10, T11, T12, T13, T14, T15, T16, T17, T18, T19, T20, T21, T22
T5	T10, T14, T19, T20, T22
T6	T7, T8, T9, T10, T11, T12, T13, T14, T15, T16, T17, T18, T19, T20, T21, T22
T7	T8, T9, T10, T11, T12, T13, T14, T15, T16, T17, T18, T19, T20, T21, T22
T8	T9, T10, T13, T14, T19, T20, T21, T22
T9	T10, T13, T14, T19, T20, T21, T22
T10	T14, T19, T20, T22
T11	T12, T13, T14, T15, T16, T17, T18, T19, T20, T21, T22
T12	T14, T16, T18, T19, T20, T22
T13	T14, T19, T20, T21, T22
T14	T19, T20, T22
T15	T16, T17, T18, T19, T20, T21, T22
T16	T18, T19, T20, T22
T17	T18 , T19, T20, T21, T22
T18	T19, T20, T22
T19	T20, T22
T20	T22
T21	T22
T22	None
T23	None
T50	None

4.2.5.2.6 *Portable tank instructions*

Portable tank instructions specify the provisions applicable to a portable tank when used for the transport of specific substances. Portable tank instructions T1 to T22 specify the applicable minimum test pressure, the minimum shell thickness (in mm of reference steel), and the pressure relief and bottom-opening provisions.

T1 – T22	PORTABLE TANK INSTRUCTIONS			T1 – T22
These portable tank instructions apply to liquid and solid substances of class 1 and classes 3 to 9. The general provisions of section 4.2.1 and the requirements of section 6.7.2 shall be met.				
Portable tank instruction	Minimum test pressure (bar)	Minimum shell thickness (in mm – reference steel) (see 6.7.2.4)	Pressure relief provisions[a] (see 6.7.2.8)	Bottom opening provisions[b] (see 6.7.2.6)
T1	1.5	See 6.7.2.4.2	Normal	See 6.7.2.6.2
T2	1.5	See 6.7.2.4.2	Normal	See 6.7.2.6.3
T3	2.65	See 6.7.2.4.2	Normal	See 6.7.2.6.2
T4	2.65	See 6.7.2.4.2	Normal	See 6.7.2.6.3
T5	2.65	See 6.7.2.4.2	See 6.7.2.8.3	Not allowed
T6	4	See 6.7.2.4.2	Normal	See 6.7.2.6.2
T7	4	See 6.7.2.4.2	Normal	See 6.7.2.6.3
T8	4	See 6.7.2.4.2	Normal	Not allowed
T9	4	6 mm	Normal	Not allowed
T10	4	6 mm	See 6.7.2.8.3	Not allowed
T11	6	See 6.7.2.4.2	Normal	See 6.7.2.6.3
T12	6	See 6.7.2.4.2	See 6.7.2.8.3	See 6.7.2.6.3
T13	6	6 mm	Normal	Not allowed
T14	6	6 mm	See 6.7.2.8.3	Not allowed
T15	10	See 6.7.2.4.2	Normal	See 6.7.2.6.3
T16	10	See 6.7.2.4.2	See 6.7.2.8.3	See 6.7.2.6.3
T17	10	6 mm	Normal	See 6.7.2.6.3
T18	10	6 mm	See 6.7.2.8.3	See 6.7.2.6.3
T19	10	6 mm	See 6.7.2.8.3	Not allowed
T20	10	8 mm	See 6.7.2.8.3	Not allowed
T21	10	10 mm	Normal	Not allowed
T22	10	10 mm	See 6.7.2.8.3	Not allowed

[a] When the word "Normal" is indicated, all the provisions of 6.7.2.8 apply except for 6.7.2.8.3.

[b] When this column indicates "not allowed", bottom openings are not permitted when the substance to be transported is a liquid (see 6.7.2.6.1). When the substance to be transported is a solid at all temperatures encountered under normal conditions of transport, bottom openings conforming to the provisions of 6.7.2.6.2 are authorized.

T23	PORTABLE TANK INSTRUCTION						T23
This portable tank instruction applies to self-reactive substances of class 4.1 and organic peroxides of class 5.2. The general provisions of 4.2.1 and the provisions of 6.7.2 shall be met. The provisions specific to self-reactive substances of class 4.1 and organic peroxides of class 5.2 in 4.2.1.13 shall also be met.							
UN No.	Substance	Minimum test pressure (bar)	Minimum shell thickness (mm – reference steel)	Bottom opening requirements	Pressure relief requirements	Degree of filling	Control temperature	Emergency temperature
3109	ORGANIC PEROXIDE TYPE F, LIQUID tert-Butyl hydroperoxide,* not more than 72% with water Cumyl hydroperoxide, not more than 90% in diluent type A Di-tert-butyl peroxide, not more than 32% in diluent type A Isopropyl cumyl hydroperoxide, not more than 72% in diluent type A p-Menthyl hydroperoxide, not more than 72% in diluent type A Pinanyl hydroperoxide, not more than 56% in diluent type A	4	See 6.7.2.4.2	See 6.7.2.6.3	See 6.7.2.8.2, 4.2.1.13.6, 4.2.1.13.7, 4.2.1.13.8	See 4.2.1.13.13		
3110	ORGANIC PEROXIDE TYPE F, SOLID Dicumyl peroxide†	4	See 6.7.2.4.2	See 6.7.2.6.3	See 6.7.2.8.2, 4.2.1.13.6, 4.2.1.13.7, 4.2.1.13.8	See 4.2.1.13.13		
3119	ORGANIC PEROXIDE TYPE F, LIQUID, TEMPERATURE CONTROLLED	4	See 6.7.2.4.2	See 6.7.2.6.3	See 6.7.2.8.2, 4.2.1.13.6, 4.2.1.13.7, 4.2.1.13.8	See 4.2.1.13.13	‡	‡
	tert-Amyl peroxyneodecanoate, not more than 47% in diluent type A						−10°C	−5°C
	tert-Butyl peroxyacetate, not more than 32% in diluent type B						+30°C	+35°C
	tert-Butyl peroxy-2-ethyl-hexanoate, not more than 32% in diluent type B						+15°C	+20°C
	tert-Butyl peroxypivalate, not more than 27% in diluent type B						+5°C	+10°C
	tert-Butyl peroxy-3,5,5-trimethylhexanoate, not more than 32% in diluent type B						+35°C	+40°C
	Di-(3,5,5-trimethylhexanoyl) peroxide, not more than 38% in diluent type A or type B						0°C	+5°C
	Peroxyacetic acid, distilled, stabilized§						+30°C	+35°C
3120	ORGANIC PEROXIDE TYPE F, SOLID, TEMPERATURE CONTROLLED	4	See 6.7.2.4.2	See 6.7.2.6.3	See 6.7.2.8.2, 4.2.1.13.6, 4.2.1.13.7, 4.2.1.13.8	See 4.2.1.13.13	‡	‡

* Provided that steps have been taken to achieve the safety equivalence of 65% tert-butyl hydroperoxide and 35% water.

† Maximum quantity per portable tank: 2000 kg.

‡ As approved by the competent authority.

§ Formulation derived from distillation of peroxyacetic acid originating from peroxyacetic acid in concentration of not more than 41% with water, total active oxygen (peroxyacetic acid + H_2O_2) ≤ 9.5%, which fulfils the criteria of 2.5.3.3.2.6. "CORROSIVE" subsidiary risk placard required (Model No. 8, see 5.2.2.2.2).

T23	PORTABLE TANK INSTRUCTION *(continued)*							T23
UN No.	Substance	Minimum test pressure (bar)	Minimum shell thickness (mm – reference steel)	Bottom opening require-ments	Pressure relief require-ments	Degree of filling	Control temper-ature	Emergency temperature
3229	SELF-REACTIVE LIQUID TYPE F	4	See 6.7.2.4.2	See 6.7.2.6.3	See 6.7.2.8.2, 4.2.1.13.6, 4.2.1.13.7, 4.2.1.13.8	See 4.2.1.13.13		
3230	SELF-REACTIVE SOLID TYPE F	4	See 6.7.2.4.2	See 6.7.2.6.3	See 6.7.2.8.2, 4.2.1.13.6, 4.2.1.13.7, 4.2.1.13.8	See 4.2.1.13.13		
3239	SELF-REACTIVE LIQUID TYPE F, TEMPERATURE CONTROLLED	4	See 6.7.2.4.2	See 6.7.2.6.3	See 6.7.2.8.2, 4.2.1.13.6, 4.2.1.13.7, 4.2.1.13.8	See 4.2.1.13.13	*	*
3240	SELF-REACTIVE SOLID TYPE F, TEMPERATURE CONTROLLED	4	See 6.7.2.4.2	See 6.7.2.6.3	See 6.7.2.8.2, 4.2.1.13.6, 4.2.1.13.7, 4.2.1.13.8	See 4.2.1.13.13	*	*

* As approved by the competent authority.

T50	PORTABLE TANK INSTRUCTION				T50
This portable tank instruction applies to non-refrigerated liquefied gases and chemicals under pressure (UN Nos. 3500, 3501, 3502, 3503, 3504 and 3505). The general provisions of 4.2.2 and the provisions of 6.7.3 shall be met.					
UN No.	Non-refrigerated liquefied gases	Maximum allowable working pressure (bar) Small; Bare; Sunshield; Insulated respectively[a]	Openings below liquid level	Pressure relief provisions[b] (see 6.7.3.7)	Maximum filling ratio (kg/L)
1005	Ammonia, anhydrous	29.0 25.7 22.0 19.7	Allowed	See 6.7.3.7.3	0.53
1009	Bromotrifluoromethane (Refrigerant gas R 13B1)	38.0 34.0 30.0 27.5	Allowed	Normal	1.13
1010	Butadienes, stabilized	7.5 7.0 7.0 7.0	Allowed	Normal	0.55
1010	Butadienes and hydrocarbon mixture, stabilized with more than 40% butadienes	See MAWP definition in 6.7.3.1	Allowed	Normal	See 4.2.2.7
1011	Butane	7.0 7.0 7.0 7.0	Allowed	Normal	0.51
1012	Butylene	8.0 7.0 7.0 7.0	Allowed	Normal	0.53

[a] "Small" means tanks having a shell with a diameter of 1.5 metres or less; "Bare" means tanks having a shell with a diameter of more than 1.5 metres without insulation or sun shield (see 6.7.3.2.12); "Sunshield" means tanks having a shell with a diameter of more than 1.5 metres with sun shield (see 6.7.3.2.12); "Insulated" means tanks having a shell with a diameter of more than 1.5 metres with insulation (see 6.7.3.2.12); (See definition of "Design reference temperature" in 6.7.3.1).

[b] The word "Normal" in the pressure relief column indicates that a frangible disc as specified in 6.7.3.7.3 is not required.

T50		PORTABLE TANK INSTRUCTION *(continued)*			T50
UN No.	Non-refrigerated liquefied gases	Maximum allowable working pressure (bar) Small; Bare; Sunshield; Insulated respectively[a]	Openings below liquid level	Pressure relief provisions[b] (see 6.7.3.7)	Maximum filling ratio (kg/L)
1017	Chlorine	19.0 17.0 15.0 13.5	Not allowed	See 6.7.3.7.3	1.25
1018	Chlorodifluoromethane (Refrigerant gas R 22)	26.0 24.0 21.0 19.0	Allowed	Normal	1.03
1020	Chloropentafluoroethane (Refrigerant gas R 115)	23.0 20.0 18.0 16.0	Allowed	Normal	1.06
1021	1-Chloro-1,2,2,2-tetrafluoroethane (Refrigerant gas R 124)	10.3 9.8 7.9 7.0	Allowed	Normal	1.20
1027	Cyclopropane	18.0 16.0 14.5 13.0	Allowed	Normal	0.53
1028	Dichlorodifluoromethane (Refrigerant gas R 12)	16.0 15.0 13.0 11.5	Allowed	Normal	1.15
1029	Dichlorofluoromethane (Refrigerant gas R 21)	7.0 7.0 7.0 7.0	Allowed	Normal	1.23
1030	1,1-Difluoroethane (Refrigerant gas R 152a)	16.0 14.0 12.4 11.0	Allowed	Normal	0.79
1032	Dimethylamine, anhydrous	7.0 7.0 7.0 7.0	Allowed	Normal	0.59
1033	Dimethyl ether	15.5 13.8 12.0 10.6	Allowed	Normal	0.58
1036	Ethylamine	7.0 7.0 7.0 7.0	Allowed	Normal	0.61
1037	Ethyl chloride	7.0 7.0 7.0 7.0	Allowed	Normal	0.80
1040	Ethylene oxide with nitrogen up to a total pressure of 1 MPa (10 bar) at 50°C	– – – 10.0	Not allowed	See 6.7.3.7.3	0.78
1041	Ethylene oxide and carbon dioxide mixture with more than 9% but not more than 87% ethylene oxide	See MAWP definition in 6.7.3.1	Allowed	Normal	See 4.2.2.7

[a] "Small" means tanks having a shell with a diameter of 1.5 metres or less; "Bare" means tanks having a shell with a diameter of more than 1.5 metres without insulation or sun shield (see 6.7.3.2.12); "Sunshield" means tanks having a shell with a diameter of more than 1.5 metres with sun shield (see 6.7.3.2.12); "Insulated" means tanks having a shell with a diameter of more than 1.5 metres with insulation (see 6.7.3.2.12); (See definition of "Design reference temperature" in 6.7.3.1).

[b] The word "Normal" in the pressure relief column indicates that a frangible disc as specified in 6.7.3.7.3 is not required.

T50		PORTABLE TANK INSTRUCTION *(continued)*			T50
UN No.	Non-refrigerated liquefied gases	Maximum allowable working pressure (bar) Small; Bare; Sunshield; Insulated respectively[a]	Openings below liquid level	Pressure relief provisions[b] (see 6.7.3.7)	Maximum filling ratio (kg/L)
1055	Isobutylene	8.1 7.0 7.0 7.0	Allowed	Normal	0.52
1060	Methylacetylene and propadiene mixture, stabilized	28.0 24.5 22.0 20.0	Allowed	Normal	0.43
1061	Methylamine, anhydrous	10.8 9.6 7.8 7.0	Allowed	Normal	0.58
1062	Methyl bromide with not more than 2% chloropicrin	7.0 7.0 7.0 7.0	Not allowed	See 6.7.3.7.3	1.51
1063	Methyl chloride (Refrigerant gas R40)	14.5 12.7 11.3 10.0	Allowed	Normal	0.81
1064	Methyl mercaptan	7.0 7.0 7.0 7.0	Not allowed	See 6.7.3.7.3	0.78
1067	Dinitrogen tetroxide	7.0 7.0 7.0 7.0	Not allowed	See 6.7.3.7.3	1.30
1075	Petroleum gas, liquefied	See MAWP definition in 6.7.3.1	Allowed	Normal	See 4.2.2.7
1077	Propylene	28.0 24.5 22.0 20.0	Allowed	Normal	0.43
1078	Refrigerant gas, N.O.S.	See MAWP definition in 6.7.3.1	Allowed	Normal	See 4.2.2.7
1079	Sulphur dioxide	11.6 10.3 8.5 7.6	Not allowed	See 6.7.3.7.3	1.23
1082	Trifluorochloroethylene, stabilized (Refrigerant gas R 1113)	17.0 15.0 13.1 11.6	Not allowed	See 6.7.3.7.3	1.13
1083	Trimethylamine, anhydrous	7.0 7.0 7.0 7.0	Allowed	Normal	0.56
1085	Vinyl bromide, stabilized	7.0 7.0 7.0 7.0	Allowed	Normal	1.37
1086	Vinyl chloride, stabilized	10.6 9.3 8.0 7.0	Allowed	Normal	0.81

[a] "Small" means tanks having a shell with a diameter of 1.5 metres or less; "Bare" means tanks having a shell with a diameter of more than 1.5 metres without insulation or sun shield (see 6.7.3.2.12); "Sunshield" means tanks having a shell with a diameter of more than 1.5 metres with sun shield (see 6.7.3.2.12); "Insulated" means tanks having a shell with a diameter of more than 1.5 metres with insulation (see 6.7.3.2.12); (See definition of "Design reference temperature" in 6.7.3.1).

[b] The word "Normal" in the pressure relief column indicates that a frangible disc as specified in 6.7.3.7.3 is not required.

IMDG Code (amendment 38-16)

T50		PORTABLE TANK INSTRUCTION *(continued)*			T50
UN No.	Non-refrigerated liquefied gases	Maximum allowable working pressure (bar) Small; Bare; Sunshield; Insulated respectively[a]	Openings below liquid level	Pressure relief provisions[b] (see 6.7.3.7)	Maximum filling ratio (kg/L)
1087	Vinyl methyl ether, stabilized	7.0 7.0 7.0 7.0	Allowed	Normal	0.67
1581	Chloropicrin and methyl bromide mixture with more than 2% chloropicrin	7.0 7.0 7.0 7.0	Not allowed	See 6.7.3.7.3	1.51
1582	Chloropicrin and methyl chloride mixture	19.2 16.9 15.1 13.1	Not allowed	See 6.7.3.7.3	0.81
1858	Hexafluoropropylene (Refrigerant gas R 1216)	19.2 16.9 15.1 13.1	Allowed	Normal	1.11
1912	Methyl chloride and methylene chloride mixture	15.2 13.0 11.6 10.1	Allowed	Normal	0.81
1958	1,2-Dichloro-1,1,2,2-tetrafluoroethane (Refrigerant gas R 114)	7.0 7.0 7.0 7.0	Allowed	Normal	1.30
1965	Hydrocarbon gas, mixture liquefied, N.O.S.	See MAWP definition in 6.7.3.1	Allowed	Normal	See 4.2.2.7
1969	Isobutane	8.5 7.5 7.0 7.0	Allowed	Normal	0.49
1973	Chlorodifluoromethane and chloropentafluoroethane mixture with fixed boiling point, with approximately 49% chlorodifluoromethane (Refrigerant gas R 502)	28.3 25.3 22.8 20.3	Allowed	Normal	1.05
1974	Chlorodifluorobromomethane (Refrigerant gas R 12B1)	7.4 7.0 7.0 7.0	Allowed	Normal	1.61
1976	Octafluorocyclobutane (Refrigerant gas RC 318)	8.8 7.8 7.0 7.0	Allowed	Normal	1.34
1978	Propane	22.5 20.4 18.0 16.5	Allowed	Normal	0.42
1983	1-Chloro-2,2,2-trifluoroethane (Refrigerant gas R 133a)	7.0 7.0 7.0 7.0	Allowed	Normal	1.18
2035	1,1,1-Trifluoroethane (Refrigerant gas R 143a)	31.0 27.5 24.2 21.8	Allowed	Normal	0.76

[a] "Small" means tanks having a shell with a diameter of 1.5 metres or less; "Bare" means tanks having a shell with a diameter of more than 1.5 metres without insulation or sun shield (see 6.7.3.2.12); "Sunshield" means tanks having a shell with a diameter of more than 1.5 metres with sun shield (see 6.7.3.2.12); "Insulated" means tanks having a shell with a diameter of more than 1.5 metres with insulation (see 6.7.3.2.12); (See definition of "Design reference temperature" in 6.7.3.1).

[b] The word "Normal" in the pressure relief column indicates that a frangible disc as specified in 6.7.3.7.3 is not required.

4

T50		PORTABLE TANK INSTRUCTION *(continued)*			T50
UN No.	Non-refrigerated liquefied gases	Maximum allowable working pressure (bar) Small; Bare; Sunshield; Insulated respectively[a]	Openings below liquid level	Pressure relief provisions[b] (see 6.7.3.7)	Maximum filling ratio (kg/L)
2424	Octafluoropropane (Refrigerant gas R 218)	23.1 20.8 18.6 16.6	Allowed	Normal	1.07
2517	1-Chloro-1,1-difluoroethane (Refrigerant gas R 142b)	8.9 7.8 7.0 7.0	Allowed	Normal	0.99
2602	Dichlorodifluoromethane and difluoroethane azeotropic mixture with approximately 74% dichlorodifluoromethane (Refrigerant gas R 500)	20.0 18.0 16.0 14.5	Allowed	Normal	1.01
3057	Trifluoroacetyl chloride	14.6 12.9 11.3 9.9	Not allowed	See 6.7.3.7.3	1.17
3070	Ethylene oxide and dichlorodifluoromethane mixture, with not more than 12.5% ethylene oxide	14.0 12.0 11.0 9.0	Allowed	See 6.7.3.7.3	1.09
3153	Perfluoro(methyl vinyl ether)	14.3 13.4 11.2 10.2	Allowed	Normal	1.14
3159	1,1,1,2-Tetrafluoroethane (Refrigerant gas R 134a)	17.7 15.7 13.8 12.1	Allowed	Normal	1.04
3161	Liquefied gas, flammable, N.O.S.	See MAWP definition in 6.7.3.1	Allowed	Normal	See 4.2.2.7
3163	Liquefied gas, N.O.S.	See MAWP definition in 6.7.3.1	Allowed	Normal	See 4.2.2.7
3220	Pentafluoroethane (Refrigerant gas R 125)	34.4 30.8 27.5 24.5	Allowed	Normal	0.87
3252	Difluoromethane (Refrigerant gas R 32)	43.0 39.0 34.4 30.5	Allowed	Normal	0.78
3296	Heptafluoropropane (Refrigerant gas R 227)	16.0 14.0 12.5 11.0	Allowed	Normal	1.20
3297	Ethylene oxide and chlorotetrafluoroethane mixture, with not more than 8.8% ethylene oxide	8.1 7.0 7.0 7.0	Allowed	Normal	1.16
3298	Ethylene oxide and pentafluoroethane mixture, with not more than 7.9% ethylene oxide	25.9 23.4 20.9 18.6	Allowed	Normal	1.02
3299	Ethylene oxide and tetrafluoroethane mixture, with not more than 5.6% ethylene oxide	16.7 14.7 12.9 11.2	Allowed	Normal	1.03

[a] "Small" means tanks having a shell with a diameter of 1.5 metres or less; "Bare" means tanks having a shell with a diameter of more than 1.5 metres without insulation or sun shield (see 6.7.3.2.12); "Sunshield" means tanks having a shell with a diameter of more than 1.5 metres with sun shield (see 6.7.3.2.12); "Insulated" means tanks having a shell with a diameter of more than 1.5 metres with insulation (see 6.7.3.2.12); (See definition of "Design reference temperature" in 6.7.3.1).

[b] The word "Normal" in the pressure relief column indicates that a frangible disc as specified in 6.7.3.7.3 is not required.

T50	PORTABLE TANK INSTRUCTION *(continued)*				T50
UN No.	Non-refrigerated liquefied gases	Maximum allowable working pressure (bar) Small; Bare; Sunshield; Insulated respectively[a]	Openings below liquid level	Pressure relief provisions[b] (see 6.7.3.7)	Maximum filling ratio (kg/L)
3318	Ammonia solution, relative density less than 0.880 at 15°C in water, with more than 50% ammonia	See MAWP definition in 6.7.3.1	Allowed	See 6.7.3.7.3	See 4.2.2.7
3337	Refrigerant gas R 404A	31.6 28.3 25.3 22.5	Allowed	Normal	0.82
3338	Refrigerant gas R 407A	31.3 28.1 25.1 22.4	Allowed	Normal	0.94
3339	Refrigerant gas R 407B	33.0 29.6 26.5 23.6	Allowed	Normal	0.93
3340	Refrigerant gas R 407C	29.9 26.8 23.9 21.3	Allowed	Normal	0.95
3500	Chemical under pressure, n.o.s.	See MAWP definition in 6.7.3.1	Allowed	See 6.7.3.7.3	TP4[c]
3501	Chemical under pressure, flammable, n.o.s.	See MAWP definition in 6.7.3.1	Allowed	See 6.7.3.7.3	TP4[c]
3502	Chemical under pressure, toxic, n.o.s.	See MAWP definition in 6.7.3.1	Allowed	See 6.7.3.7.3	TP4[c]
3503	Chemical under pressure, corrosive, n.o.s.	See MAWP definition in 6.7.3.1	Allowed	See 6.7.3.7.3	TP4[c]
3504	Chemical under pressure, flammable, toxic, n.o.s.	See MAWP definition in 6.7.3.1	Allowed	See 6.7.3.7.3	TP4[c]
3505	Chemical under pressure, flammable, corrosive, n.o.s.	See MAWP definition in 6.7.3.1	Allowed	See 6.7.3.7.3	TP4[c]

[a] "Small" means tanks having a shell with a diameter of 1.5 metres or less; "Bare" means tanks having a shell with a diameter of more than 1.5 metres without insulation or sun shield (see 6.7.3.2.12); "Sunshield" means tanks having a shell with a diameter of more than 1.5 metres with sun shield (see 6.7.3.2.12); "Insulated" means tanks having a shell with a diameter of more than 1.5 metres with insulation (see 6.7.3.2.12); (See definition of "Design reference temperature" in 6.7.3.1).

[b] The word "Normal" in the pressure relief column indicates that a frangible disc as specified in 6.7.3.7.3 is not required.

[c] For UN Nos. 3500, 3501, 3502, 3503, 3504 and 3505, the degree of filling shall be considered instead of the maximum filling ratio.

T75	PORTABLE TANK INSTRUCTION	T75
	This portable tank instruction applies to refrigerated liquefied gases. The general provisions of 4.2.3 and 6.7.4 shall be met.	

4.2.5.3 Portable tank special provisions

Portable tank special provisions are assigned to certain substances to indicate provisions which are in addition to or in lieu of those provided by the portable tank instructions or the provisions in chapter 6.7. Portable tank special provisions are identified by an alpha-numeric designation beginning with the letters "TP" (tank provision) and are assigned to specific substances in column 14 of the Dangerous Goods List in chapter 3.2. The following is a list of the portable tank special provisions:

TP1   The degree of filling prescribed in 4.2.1.9.2 shall not be exceeded.

TP2   The degree of filling prescribed in 4.2.1.9.3 shall not be exceeded.

TP3   The maximum degree of filling (in %) for solids transported above their melting points and for elevated temperature liquids shall be determined in accordance with 4.2.1.9.5.

TP4   The degree of filling shall not exceed 90% or, alternatively, any other value approved by the competent authority (see 4.2.1.16.2).

TP5   The degree of filling prescribed in 4.2.3.6 shall be met.

TP6   To prevent the tank bursting in any event, including fire engulfment, it shall be provided with pressure-relief devices which are adequate in relation to the capacity of the tank and to the nature of the substance transported. The device shall also be compatible with the substance.

TP7   Air shall be eliminated from the vapour space by nitrogen or other means.

TP8   The test pressure for the portable tank may be reduced to 1.5 bar when the flashpoint of the substances transported is greater than 0°C.

TP9   A substance under this description shall only be transported in a portable tank under an approval granted by the competent authority.

TP10   A lead lining, not less than 5 mm thick, which shall be tested annually, or another suitable lining material approved by the competent authority is required.

TP11   [Reserved]

TP12   [Reserved]

TP13   Self-contained breathing apparatus shall be provided when this substance is transported, unless no self-contained breathing apparatus, as required by SOLAS regulation II-2/19 (II-2/54), is on board.

TP14   [Reserved]

TP15   [Reserved]

TP16   The tank shall be fitted with a special device to prevent under-pressure and excess pressure during normal transport conditions. This device shall be approved by the competent authority. Pressure-relief provisions are as indicated in 6.7.2.8.3 to prevent crystallization of the product in the pressure-relief valve.

TP17   Only inorganic non-combustible materials shall be used for thermal insulation of the tank.

TP18   Temperature shall be maintained between 18°C and 40°C. Portable tanks containing solidified methacrylic acid shall not be reheated during transport.

TP19   The calculated shell thickness shall be increased by 3 mm. Shell thickness shall be verified ultrasonically at intervals midway between periodic hydraulic tests.

TP20   This substance shall only be transported in insulated tanks under a nitrogen blanket.

TP21   The shell thickness shall be not less than 8 mm. Tanks shall be hydraulically tested and internally inspected at intervals not exceeding 2.5 years.

TP22   Lubricant for joints or other devices shall be oxygen-compatible.

△ TP23   [Reserved]

TP24   The portable tank may be fitted with a device located, under maximum filling conditions, in the vapour space of the shell to prevent the build-up of excess pressure due to the slow decomposition of the substance transported. This device shall also prevent an unacceptable amount of leakage of liquid in the case of overturning or entry of foreign matter into the tank. This device shall be approved by the competent authority or its authorized body.

TP25   Sulphur trioxide 99.95% pure and above may be transported in tanks without an inhibitor provided that it is maintained at a temperature equal to or above 32.5°C.

TP26   When transported under heated conditions, the heating device shall be fitted outside the shell. For UN 3176, this provision only applies when the substance reacts dangerously with water.

TP27   A portable tank having a minimum test pressure of 4 bar may be used if it is shown that a test pressure of 4 bar or less is acceptable according to the test pressure definition in 6.7.2.1.

TP28   A portable tank having a minimum test pressure of 2.65 bar may be used if it is shown that a test pressure of 2.65 bar or less is acceptable according to the test pressure definition in 6.7.2.1.

TP29   A portable tank having a minimum test pressure of 1.5 bar may be used if it is shown that a test pressure of 1.5 bar or less is acceptable according to the test pressure definition in 6.7.2.1.

TP30   This substance shall be transported in insulated tanks.

TP31   This substance shall be transported in tanks in solid state.

TP32   For UN Nos. 0331, 0332 and 3375, portable tanks may be used subject to the following conditions:

   .1   To avoid unnecessary confinement, each portable tank constructed of metal shall be fitted with a pressure relief device that may be of the re-closing spring-loaded type, a frangible disc or a fusible element. The set-to-discharge or burst pressure, as applicable, shall not be greater than 2.65 bar for portable tanks with minimum test pressures greater than 4 bar.

   .2   For UN 3375 only, suitability for transport in tanks shall be demonstrated. One method to evaluate this suitability is test 8 (d) in Test Series 8 (see Manual of Tests and Criteria, part 1, subsection 18.7).

.3 Substances shall not be allowed to remain in the portable tank for any period that could result in caking. Appropriate measures shall be taken to avoid accumulation and packing of substances in the tank (e.g. cleaning, etc).

TP33 The portable tank instruction assigned for this substance applies for granular and powdered solids and for solids which are filled and discharged at temperatures above their melting point and which are cooled and transported as a solid mass. For solids which are transported above their melting point, see 4.2.1.19.

TP34 Portable tanks need not be subjected to the impact test in 6.7.4.14.1 if the portable tank is marked "NOT FOR RAIL TRANSPORT" on the plate specified in 6.7.4.15.1 and also in letters at least 10 cm high on both sides of the outer jacket.

TP35 Portable tank instruction T14 may continue to be applied until 31 December 2014.

TP36 Fusible elements in the vapour space may be used on portable tanks.

TP37 Portable tank instruction T14 may continue to be applied until 31 December 2016 except that until that date:

.1 for UN Nos. 1810, 2474 and 2668, T7 may be applied;

.2 for UN 2486, T8 may be applied; and

.3 for UN 1838, T10 may be applied.

TP38 The portable tank instruction T9 may continue to be applied until 31 December 2018.

TP39 The portable tank instruction T4 may continue to be applied until 31 December 2018.

TP40 Portable tanks shall not be transported when connected with spray application equipment.

TP41 The 2.5 year internal examination may be waived or substituted by other test methods or inspection procedures specified by the competent authority or its authorized body, provided that the portable tank is dedicated to the transport of the organometallic substances to which this tank special provision is assigned. However, this examination is required when the conditions of 6.7.2.19.7 are met.

TP90 Tanks with bottom openings may be used on short international voyages.

TP91 Portable tanks with bottom openings may also be used on long international voyages.

4.2.6 Additional provisions for the use of road tank vehicles

4.2.6.1 The tank of a road tank vehicle shall be attached to the vehicle during normal operations of filling, discharge and transport. IMO type 4 tanks shall be attached to the chassis when transported on board ships. Road tank vehicles shall not be filled or discharged while they remain on board. A road tank vehicle shall be driven on board on its own wheels and be fitted with permanent tie-down attachments for securing on board the ship.

4.2.6.2 Road tank vehicles shall comply with the provisions of chapter 6.8. IMO type 4, 6 and 8 tanks may be used according to the provisions of chapter 6.8 for short international voyages only.

Chapter 4.3

Use of bulk containers

Note: Sheeted bulk containers (BK1) shall not be used for sea transport, except as indicated in 4.3.3.

4.3.1   General provisions

4.3.1.1   This section provides general requirements applicable to the use of containers for the transport of solid substances in bulk. Substances shall be transported in bulk containers conforming to the applicable bulk container instruction identified by the letters BK in column 13 of the Dangerous Goods List, with the following meaning:

BK1: the transport in sheeted bulk containers is permitted;

BK2: the transport in closed bulk containers is permitted;

BK3: the transport in flexible bulk containers is permitted.

The bulk container used shall conform to the provisions of chapter 6.9.

4.3.1.2   Except as provided in 4.3.1.3, bulk containers shall only be used when a substance is assigned a bulk container code in column 13 of the Dangerous Goods List.

4.3.1.3   When a substance is not assigned BK2 or BK3 in column 13 of the Dangerous Goods List, interim approval for transport may be issued by the competent authority of the country of origin. The approval shall be included in the documentation of the consignment and contain, as a minimum, the information normally provided in the bulk container instruction and the conditions under which the substance shall be transported. Appropriate measures should be initiated by the competent authority to have the assignment included in the Dangerous Goods List. When a substance is not permitted in a BK1 bulk container, an exemption may be issued in accordance with 7.9.1.

4.3.1.4   Substances which may become liquid at temperatures likely to be encountered during transport are not permitted in bulk containers.

4.3.1.5   Bulk containers shall be siftproof and shall be so closed that none of the contents can escape under normal conditions of transport, including the effect of vibration, or by changes of temperature, humidity or pressure.

4.3.1.6   Bulk solids shall be loaded into bulk containers and evenly distributed in a manner that minimizes movement that could result in damage to the container or leakage of the dangerous goods.

4.3.1.7   Where venting devices are fitted, they shall be kept clear and operable.

4.3.1.8   Bulk solids shall not react dangerously with the material of the bulk container, gaskets, equipment including lids and tarpaulins, or with protective coatings which are in contact with the contents, or significantly weaken them. Bulk containers shall be so constructed or adapted that the goods cannot penetrate between wooden floor coverings or come into contact with those parts of the bulk containers that may be affected by the dangerous goods or residues thereof.

4.3.1.9   Before being filled and offered for transport, each bulk container shall be inspected and cleaned to ensure that it does not contain any residue on the interior or exterior that could:

–   cause a dangerous reaction with the substance intended for transport;

–   detrimentally affect the structural integrity of the bulk container; or

–   affect the dangerous goods retention capabilities of the bulk container.

4.3.1.10   During transport, no dangerous residues shall adhere to the outer surfaces of a bulk container.

4.3.1.11   If several closure systems are fitted in series, the system which is located nearest to the dangerous goods to be transported shall be closed first before filling.

4.3.1.12   Empty bulk containers that have contained dangerous goods shall be treated in the same manner as is prescribed in this Code for a filled bulk container, unless adequate measures have been taken to nullify any hazard.

4.3.1.13 If bulk containers are used for the carriage of bulk goods liable to cause a dust explosion, or evolve flammable vapours (e.g. for certain wastes), measures shall be taken to exclude sources of ignition and to prevent dangerous electrostatic discharge during transport, loading or unloading of the goods.

4.3.1.14 Substances, for example wastes, which may react dangerously with one another and substances of different classes and goods not subject to this Code, which are liable to react dangerously with one another, shall not be mixed together in the same bulk container. Dangerous reactions are:

.1 combustion and/or evolution of considerable heat;

.2 emission of flammable and/or toxic gases;

.3 formation of corrosive liquids; or

.4 formation of unstable substances.

4.3.1.15 Before a bulk container is filled, it shall be visually examined to ensure it is structurally serviceable, its interior walls, ceiling and floors are free from protrusions or damage and that any inner liners or substance retaining equipment are free from rips, tears or any damage that would compromise its cargo retention capabilities. "Structurally serviceable" means the bulk container does not have major defects in its structural components, such as top and bottom side rails, top and bottom end rails, door sill and header, floor cross members, corner posts, and corner fittings in a freight container. Major defects include:

.1 bends, cracks or breaks in the structural or supporting members that affect the integrity of the container;

.2 more than one splice or an improper splice (such as a lapped splice) in top or bottom end rails or door headers;

.3 more than two splices in any one top or bottom side rail;

.4 any splice in a door sill or corner post;

.5 door hinges and hardware that are seized, twisted, broken, missing, or otherwise inoperative;

.6 gaskets and seals that do not seal;

.7 any distortion of the overall configuration great enough to prevent proper alignment of handling equipment, mounting and securing chassis or vehicle, or insertion into ships' cargo spaces;

.8 any damage to lifting attachments or handling equipment interface features; or

.9 any damage to service or operational equipment.

4.3.1.16 Before a flexible bulk container is filled it shall be visually examined to ensure it is structurally serviceable, its textile slings, load-bearing structure straps, body fabric, lock device parts including metal and textile parts are free from protrusions or damage and that inner liners are free from rips, tears or any damage.

4.3.1.16.1 For flexible bulk containers, the period of use permitted for the transport of dangerous goods shall be two years from the date of manufacture of the flexible bulk container.

△ **4.3.1.16.2** A venting device shall be fitted if a dangerous accumulation of gases may develop within the flexible bulk container. The vent shall be so designed that the penetration of foreign substances or the ingress of water is prevented under normal conditions of transport.

4.3.2 Additional provisions applicable to bulk goods of classes 4.2, 4.3, 5.1, 6.2, 7 and 8

4.3.2.1 **Bulk goods of class 4.2**

Only closed bulk containers (BK2) may be used. The total mass carried in a bulk container shall be such that its spontaneous ignition temperature is greater than 55°C.

4.3.2.2 **Bulk goods of class 4.3**

Only closed bulk containers (BK2) may be used. These goods shall be transported in bulk containers which are waterproof.

4.3.2.3 **Bulk goods of class 5.1**

Bulk containers shall be so constructed or adapted that the goods cannot come into contact with wood or any other incompatible material.

4.3.2.4   **Bulk goods of class 6.2**

4.3.2.4.1   *Transport in bulk containers of animal material of class 6.2*

Animal material containing infectious substances (UN Nos. 2814, 2900 and 3373) is authorized for transport in bulk containers provided the following conditions are met:

.1   Closed bulk containers, and their openings, shall be leakproof by design or by the fitting of a suitable liner.

.2   The animal material shall be thoroughly treated with an appropriate disinfectant before loading prior to transport.

.3   Closed bulk containers shall not be re-used until they have been thoroughly cleaned and disinfected.

Note: Additional provisions may be required by appropriate national health authorities.

4.3.2.4.2   *Bulk wastes of class 6.2 (UN 3291)*

.1   only closed bulk containers (BK2) shall be permitted;

.2   closed bulk containers, and their openings, shall be leakproof by design. These bulk containers shall have non-porous interior surfaces and shall be free from cracks or other features that could damage packagings inside, impede disinfection or permit inadvertent release;

.3   wastes of UN 3291 shall be contained within the closed bulk container in UN type tested and approved sealed leakproof plastics bags tested for solids of packing group II and marked in accordance with 6.1.3.1. Such plastics bags shall be capable of passing the tests for tear and impact resistance according to ISO 7765-1:1988, *Plastics film and sheeting – Determination of impact resistance by the free-falling dart method – Part 1: Staircase methods,* and ISO 6383-2:1983, *Plastics – Film and sheeting – Determination of tear resistance – Part 2: Elmendorf method.* Each bag shall have an impact resistance of at least 165 g and a tear resistance of at least 480 g in both parallel and perpendicular planes with respect to the length of the bag. The maximum net mass of each plastics bag shall be 30 kg;

.4   single articles exceeding 30 kg such as soiled mattresses may be transported without the need for a plastics bag when authorized by the competent authority;

.5   wastes of UN 3291 which contain liquids shall only be transported in plastics bags containing sufficient absorbent material to absorb the entire amount of liquid without it spilling in the bulk container;

.6   wastes of UN 3291 containing sharp objects shall only be transported in UN type tested and approved rigid packagings meeting the provisions of packing instructions P621, IBC620 or LP621;

.7   rigid packagings specified in packing instructions P621, IBC620 or LP621 may also be used. They shall be properly secured to prevent damage during normal conditions of transport. Wastes transported in rigid packagings and plastics bags together in the same closed bulk container shall be adequately segregated from each other, e.g. by suitable rigid barriers or dividers, mesh nets or otherwise securing the packagings, such that they prevent damage to the packagings during normal conditions of transport;

.8   wastes of UN 3291 in plastics bags shall not be compressed in a closed bulk container in such a way that bags may be rendered no longer leakproof;

.9   the closed bulk container shall be inspected for leakage or spillage after each journey. If any wastes of UN 3291 have leaked or been spilled in the closed bulk container, it shall not be re-used until after it has been thoroughly cleaned and, if necessary, disinfected or decontaminated with an appropriate agent. No other goods shall be transported together with UN 3291 other than medical or veterinary wastes. Any such other wastes transported in the same closed bulk container shall be inspected for possible contamination.

4.3.2.5   **Bulk material of class 7**

For the transport of unpackaged radioactive material, see 4.1.9.2.4.

4.3.2.6   **Bulk goods of class 8**

Only closed bulk containers (BK2) may be used. These goods shall be transported in bulk containers which are watertight.

4.3.3   Additional provisions for the use of sheeted bulk containers (BK1)

4.3.3.1   Sheeted bulk containers (BK1) shall not be used for sea transport, except for UN 3077 not meeting the criteria of 2.9.3 transported on short international voyages.

4.3.4   Additional provisions for the use of flexible bulk containers (BK3)

4.3.4.1   Flexible bulk containers are only allowed in the holds of general cargo ships. They are not allowed to be transported in cargo transport units.

PART 5

CONSIGNMENT PROCEDURES

5

Chapter 5.1

General provisions

5.1.1　Application and general provisions

5.1.1.1　This part sets forth the provisions for dangerous goods consignments relative to authorization of consignments and advance notifications, marking, labelling, documentation (by manual, electronic data processing (EDP) or electronic data interchange (EDI) techniques) and placarding.

5.1.1.2　Except as otherwise provided in this Code, no person may offer dangerous goods for transport unless those goods are properly marked, labelled, placarded, described and certified on a transport document, and otherwise in a condition for transport as required by this part.

5.1.1.3.1　A carrier shall not accept dangerous goods for transport unless:

　　.1　A copy of the dangerous goods transport document and other documents or information as required by the provisions of this Code are provided; or

　　.2　The information applicable to the dangerous goods is provided in electronic form.

5.1.1.3.2　The information applicable to the dangerous goods shall accompany the dangerous goods to final destination. This information may be on the dangerous goods transport document or may be on another document. This information shall be given to the consignee when the dangerous goods are delivered.

5.1.1.3.3　When the information applicable to the dangerous goods is given to the carrier in electronic form, the information shall be available to the carrier at all times during transport to final destination. The information shall be able to be produced without delay as a paper document.

5.1.1.4　The purpose of indicating the proper shipping name (see 3.1.2.1 and 3.1.2.2) and the UN number of a substance, material or article offered for transport and, in the case of a marine pollutant, of the addition of "marine pollutant" on documentation accompanying the consignment, and of marking the proper shipping name in accordance with 5.2.1 on the package, including IBCs containing the goods, is to ensure that the substance, material or article can be readily identified during transport. This ready identification is particularly important in the case of an accident involving these goods, in order to determine what emergency procedures are necessary to deal properly with the situation and, in the case of marine pollutants, for the master to comply with the reporting requirements of Protocol I of MARPOL.

5.1.2　Use of overpacks and unit loads

5.1.2.1　An overpack and unit load shall be marked with the proper shipping name and the UN number and marked and labelled, as required for packages by chapter 5.2, for each item of dangerous goods contained in the overpack or unit load unless markings and labels representative of all dangerous goods in the overpack or unit load are visible. An overpack, in addition, shall be marked with the word "OVERPACK" unless markings and labels representative of all dangerous goods, as required by chapter 5.2, in the overpack are visible, except as required in 5.2.2.1.12. The lettering of the "OVERPACK" marking shall be at least 12 mm high.

⊗

△ **5.1.2.2**　The individual packages comprising a unit load or an overpack shall be marked and labelled in accordance with chapter 5.2. Each package of dangerous goods contained in the unit load or overpack shall comply with all applicable provisions of the Code. The "OVERPACK" mark on an overpack is an indication of compliance with this provision. The intended function of each package shall not be impaired by the unit load or overpack.

△ **5.1.2.3**　Each package bearing package orientation marks as prescribed in 5.2.1.7.1 of this Code and which is overpacked, placed in a unit load or used as an inner packaging in a large packaging shall be oriented in accordance with such marks.

5

5.1.3 Empty uncleaned packagings or units

5.1.3.1 Other than for class 7, a packaging, including an IBC, which previously contained dangerous goods shall be identified, marked, labelled and placarded as required for those dangerous goods unless steps such as cleaning, purging of vapours or refilling with a non-dangerous substance are taken to nullify any hazard.

5.1.3.2 Freight containers, tanks, IBCs, as well as other packagings and overpacks, used for the transport of radioactive material shall not be used for the transport of other goods unless decontaminated below the level of 0.4 Bq/cm^2 for beta and gamma emitters and low-toxicity alpha emitters and 0.04 Bq/cm^2 for all other alpha emitters.

5.1.3.3 Empty cargo transport units still containing residues of dangerous goods, or loaded with empty uncleaned packages or empty uncleaned bulk containers, shall comply with the provisions applicable to the goods last contained in the unit, packagings or bulk container.

5.1.4 Mixed packing

When two or more dangerous goods are packed within the same outer packaging, the package shall be labelled and marked as required for each substance. Subsidiary risk labels need not be applied if the hazard is already represented by a primary risk label.

5.1.5 General provisions for class 7

5.1.5.1 Approval of shipments and notification

5.1.5.1.1 *General*

In addition to the approval of package designs described in chapter 6.4, multilateral shipment approval is also required in certain circumstances (5.1.5.1.2 and 5.1.5.1.3). In some circumstances it is also necessary to notify competent authorities of a shipment (5.1.5.1.4).

5.1.5.1.2 *Shipment approvals*

Multilateral approval shall be required for:

.1 the shipment of Type B(M) packages not conforming with the provisions of 6.4.7.5 or designed to allow controlled intermittent venting;

.2 the shipment of Type B(M) packages containing radioactive material with an activity greater than 3,000A_1 or 3,000A_2, as appropriate, or 1,000 TBq, whichever is the lower;

.3 the shipment of packages containing fissile materials if the sum of the criticality safety indexes of the packages in a single freight container or in a single conveyance exceeds 50. Excluded from this requirement shall be shipments by seagoing vessels, if the sum of the criticality safety indexes does not exceed 50 for any hold, compartment or defined deck area and the distance of 6 m between groups of packages or overpacks as required in table 7.1.4.5.3.4 is met; and

.4 radiation protection programmes for shipments by special use vessels in accordance with 7.1.4.5.7

except that a competent authority may authorize transport into or through its country without shipment approval, by a specific provision in its design approval (see 5.1.5.2.1).

5.1.5.1.3 *Shipment approval by special arrangement*

Provisions may be approved by a competent authority under which a consignment which does not satisfy all of the applicable provisions of this Code may be transported under special arrangement (see 1.5.4).

5.1.5.1.4 *Notifications*

Notification to competent authorities is required as follows:

.1 Before the first shipment of any package requiring competent authority approval, the consignor shall ensure that copies of each applicable competent authority certificate applying to that package design have been submitted to the competent authority of the country of origin of the shipment and to the competent authority of each country through or into which the consignment is to be transported. The consignor is not required to await an acknowledgement from the competent authority, nor is the competent authority required to make such acknowledgement of receipt of the certificate.

.2 For each of the following types of shipments:

.1 Type C packages containing radioactive material with an activity greater than 3,000A_1 *or* 3,000A_2, as appropriate, or 1,000 TBq, whichever is the lower;

.2 Type B(U) packages containing radioactive material with an activity greater than $3,000A_1$ *or* $3,000A_2$, as appropriate, or 1,000 TBq, whichever is the lower;

.3 Type B(M) packages;

.4 shipment under special arrangement;

the consignor shall notify the competent authority of the country of origin of the shipment and the competent authority of each country through or into which the consignment is to be transported. This notification shall be in the hands of each competent authority prior to the commencement of the shipment, and preferably at least 7 days in advance.

.3 The consignor is not required to send a separate notification if the required information has been included in the application for approval of shipment (see 6.4.23.2).

.4 The consignment notification shall include:

.1 sufficient information to enable the identification of the package or packages, including all applicable certificate numbers and identification marks;

.2 information on the date of shipment, the expected date of arrival and proposed routeing;

.3 the names of the radioactive material or nuclides;

.4 descriptions of the physical and chemical forms of the radioactive material, or whether it is special form radioactive material or low dispersible radioactive material; and

.5 the maximum activity of the radioactive contents during transport, expressed in units of becquerels (Bq) with an appropriate SI prefix symbol (see 1.2.2.1). For fissile material, the mass of fissile material (or of each fissile nuclide for mixtures when appropriate) in units of grams (g), or multiples thereof, may be used in place of activity.

5.1.5.2 Certificates issued by competent authority

5.1.5.2.1 Certificates issued by the competent authority are required for the following:

.1 designs for:

.1 special form radioactive material;

.2 low dispersible radioactive material;

.3 fissile material excepted under 2.7.2.3.5.6;

.4 packages containing 0.1 kg or more of uranium hexafluoride;

.5 packages containing fissile material unless excepted by 2.7.2.3.5, 6.4.11.2 or 6.4.11.3;

.6 Type B(U) packages and Type B(M) packages;

.7 Type C packages;

.2 special arrangements;

.3 certain shipments (see 5.1.5.1.2);

.4 determination of the basic radionuclide values referred to in 2.7.2.2.1 for individual radionuclides which are not listed in table 2.7.2.2.1 (see 2.7.2.2.2.1);

.5 alternative activity limits for an exempt consignment of instruments or articles (see 2.7.2.2.2.2).

The certificates shall confirm that the applicable provisions are met, and for design approvals shall attribute to the design an identification mark.

The certificates of approval for the package design and the shipment may be combined into a single certificate.

Certificates and applications for these certificates shall be in accordance with the provisions in 6.4.23.

5.1.5.2.2 The consignor shall be in possession of a copy of each applicable certificate.

5.1.5.2.3 For package designs where it is not required that a competent authority issue a certificate of approval, the consignor shall, on request, make available, for inspection by the relevant competent authority, documentary evidence of the compliance of the package design with all the applicable provisions.

5.1.5.3 Determination of transport index (TI) and criticality safety index (CSI)

5.1.5.3.1 The transport index (TI) for a package, overpack or freight container, or for unpackaged LSA-I or SCO-I, shall be the number derived in accordance with the following procedure:

.1 determine the maximum radiation level in units of millisieverts per hour (mSv/h) at a distance of 1 m from the external surfaces of the package, overpack, freight container, or unpackaged LSA-I and SCO-I. The value determined shall be multiplied by 100 and the resulting number is the transport index. For uranium

5

and thorium ores and their concentrates, the maximum radiation level at any point 1 m from the external surface of the load may be taken as:

0.4 mSv/h   for ores and physical concentrates of uranium and thorium;

0.3 mSv/h   for chemical concentrates of thorium;

0.02 mSv/h   for chemical concentrates of uranium, other than uranium hexafluoride;

.2   for tanks, freight containers and unpackaged LSA-I and SCO-I, the value determined in 5.1.5.3.1.1 above shall be multiplied by the appropriate factor from table 5.1.5.3.1;

.3   the value obtained in 5.1.5.3.1.1 and 5.1.5.3.1.2 above shall be rounded up to the first decimal place (e.g. 1.13 becomes 1.2), except that a value of 0.05 or less may be considered as zero.

Table 5.1.5.3.1 – Multiplication factors for tanks, freight containers and unpackaged LSA-I and SCO-I

Size of load[a]	Multiplication factor
size of load ≤ 1 m^2	1
1 m$^2 <$ size of load ≤ 5 m^2	2
5 m$^2 <$ size of load ≤ 20 m^2	3
20 m$^2 <$ size of load	10

[a] Largest cross-sectional area of the load being measured.

5.1.5.3.2   The transport index for each overpack, freight container or conveyance shall be determined as either the sum of the TIs of all the packages contained, or by direct measurement of radiation level, except in the case of non-rigid overpacks for which the transport index shall be determined only as the sum of the TIs of all the packages.

5.1.5.3.3   The criticality safety index for each overpack or freight container shall be determined as the sum of the CSIs of all the packages contained. The same procedure shall be followed for determining the total sum of the CSIs in a consignment or aboard a conveyance.

5.1.5.3.4   Packages, overpacks and freight containers shall be assigned to either category I – WHITE, II – YELLOW or III – YELLOW in accordance with the conditions specified in table 5.1.5.3.4 and with the following requirements:

.1   for a package, overpack or freight container, both the transport index and the surface radiation level conditions shall be taken into account in determining which is the appropriate category. Where the transport index satisfies the condition for one category but the surface radiation level satisfies the condition for a different category, the package, overpack or freight container shall be assigned to the higher category. For this purpose, category I – WHITE shall be regarded as the lowest category;

.2   the transport index shall be determined following the procedures specified in 5.1.5.3.1 and 5.1.5.3.2;

.3   if the surface radiation level is greater than 2 mSv/h, the package or overpack shall be transported under exclusive use and under the provisions of 7.1.4.5.6 or 7.1.4.5.7, as appropriate;

.4   a package transported under a special arrangement shall be assigned to category III – YELLOW except under the provisions of 5.1.5.3.5;

.5   an overpack or freight container which contains packages transported under special arrangement shall be assigned to category III – YELLOW except under the provisions of 5.1.5.3.5.

Table 5.1.5.3.4 – Categories of packages, overpacks and freight containers

Conditions		Category
Transport index	Maximum radiation level at any point on external surface	
0[a]	Not more than 0.005 mSv/h	I – WHITE
More than 0 but not more than 1[a]	More than 0.005 mSv/h but not more than 0.5 mSv/h	II – YELLOW
More than 1 but not more than 10	More than 0.5 mSv/h but not more than 2 mSv/h	III – YELLOW
More than 10	More than 2 mSv/h but not more than 10 mSv/h	III – YELLOW[b]

[a] If the measured TI is not greater than 0.05, the value quoted may be zero in accordance with 5.1.5.3.1.3.
[b] Shall also be transported under "exclusive use" except for freight containers (see table 7.1.4.5.3).

5.1.5.3.5   In all cases of international transport of packages requiring competent authority approval of design or shipment, for which different approval types apply in the different countries concerned by the shipment, the categorization shall be in accordance with the certificate of the country of origin of design.

5.1.5.4   Specific provisions for excepted packages of radioactive material of class 7

5.1.5.4.1   Excepted packages of radioactive material of class 7 shall be legibly and durably marked on the outside of the packaging with:

.1   the UN number preceded by the letters "UN";

.2   an identification of either the consignor or consignee, or both; and

.3   the permissible gross mass if this exceeds 50 kg.

5.1.5.4.2   The documentation requirements of chapter 5.4 do not apply to excepted packages of radioactive material of class 7, except that:

.1   the UN number preceded by the letters "UN" and the name and address of the consignor and the consignee and, if relevant, the identification mark for each competent authority certificate of approval (see 5.4.1.5.7.1.7.) shall be shown on a transport document such as a bill of lading, air waybill or other similar document complying with the requirements of 5.4.1.2.1 to 5.4.1.2.4;

.2   the requirements of 5.4.1.6.2 and, if relevant, those of 5.4.1.5.7.1.7, 5.4.1.5.7.3 and 5.4.1.5.7.4 shall apply;

.3   the requirements of 5.4.2 and 5.4.4 shall apply.

5.1.5.4.3   The requirements of 5.2.1.5.8 and 5.2.2.1.12.5 shall apply if relevant.

5.1.5.5   Specific provisions for the consignment of fissile material

Fissile material meeting one of the provisions of 2.7.2.3.5.1 to 2.7.2.3.5.6 shall meet the following requirements:

.1   only one of the provisions of 2.7.2.3.5.1 to 2.7.2.3.5.6 is allowed per consignment;

.2   only one approved fissile material in packages classified in accordance with 2.7.2.3.5.6 is allowed per consignment unless multiple materials are authorized in the certificate of approval;

.3   fissile material in packages classified in accordance with 2.7.2.3.5.3 shall be transported in a consignment with no more than 45 g of fissile nuclides;

.4   fissile material in packages classified in accordance with 2.7.2.3.5.4 shall be transported in a consignment with no more than 15 g of fissile nuclides;

.5   unpackaged or packaged fissile material classified in accordance with 2.7.2.3.5.5 shall be transported under exclusive use on a conveyance with no more than 45 g of fissile nuclides.

5.1.6   Packages packed into a cargo transport unit

5.1.6.1   Regardless of the placarding and marking provisions for cargo transport units, each package containing dangerous goods packed into a cargo transport unit shall be marked and labelled in accordance with the requirements of chapter 5.2.

5

Chapter 5.2

Marking and labelling of packages including IBCs

Note: These provisions relate essentially to the marking and labelling of dangerous goods according to their properties. However, additional markings or symbols indicating precautions to be taken in handling or storing a package (such as a symbol representing an umbrella, indicating that a package shall be kept dry) may be displayed on a package if appropriate.

5.2.1 Marking of packages including IBCs

△ 5.2.1.1   Unless provided otherwise in this Code, the proper shipping name for the dangerous goods as determined in accordance with 3.1.2 and the corresponding UN number, preceded by the letters "UN", shall be displayed on each package. The UN number and the letters "UN" shall be at least 12 mm high, except for packages of 30 litres capacity or less or of 30 kg maximum net mass or less and for cylinders of 60 litres water capacity or less when they shall be at least 6 mm in height and except for packages of 5 litres or 5 kg or less when they shall be of an appropriate size. In the case of unpackaged articles, the mark shall be displayed on the article, on its cradle or on its handling, storage or launching device. For goods of division 1.4, compatibility group S, the division and compatibility group letter shall also be marked unless the label for 1.4S is displayed. A typical package mark is:

CORROSIVE LIQUID, ACIDIC, ORGANIC, N.O.S. (caprylyl chloride) UN 3265.

Note: Cylinders of 60 L water capacity or less marked with a UN number in accordance with the provisions of the IMDG Code up to 31 December 2013 and which do not conform to the provisions of 5.2.1.1 regarding the size of the UN number and of the letters "UN" applicable as from 1 January 2014 may continue to be used until the next periodic inspection but no later than 1 July 2018.

△ 5.2.1.2   All package marks required by 5.2.1.1:

    .1   shall be readily visible and legible;

    .2   shall be such that this information will still be identifiable on packages surviving at least three months' immersion in the sea. In considering suitable marking methods, account shall be taken of the durability of the packaging materials used and the surface of the package;

    .3   shall be displayed on a background of contrasting colour on the external surface of the package; and

    △ .4   shall not be located with other package marks that could substantially reduce their effectiveness.

△ 5.2.1.3   Salvage packagings and salvage pressure receptacles shall additionally be marked with the word "SALVAGE". The lettering of the "SALVAGE" mark shall be at least 12 mm high.

    ⊗

5.2.1.4   Intermediate bulk containers of more than 450 L capacity and large packagings shall be marked on two opposing sides.

5.2.1.5 Special marking provisions for radioactive material

△ 5.2.1.5.1   Each package shall be legibly and durably marked on the outside of the packaging with an identification of either the consignor or consignee, or both. Each overpack shall be legibly and durably marked on the outside of the overpack with an identification of either the consignor or consignee, or both unless these marks of all packages within the overpack are clearly visible.

5.2.1.5.2   The marking of excepted packages of radioactive material of class 7 shall be as required by 5.1.5.4.1.

5.2.1.5.3   Each package of gross mass exceeding 50 kg shall have its permissible gross mass legibly and durably marked on the outside of the packaging.

5.2.1.5.4   Each package which conforms to:

    .1   a Type IP-1 package, a Type IP-2 package or a Type IP-3 package design shall be legibly and durably marked on the outside of the packaging with "TYPE IP-1", "TYPE IP-2" or "TYPE IP-3" as appropriate;

.2 a Type A package design shall be legibly and durably marked on the outside of the packaging with "TYPE A";

.3 a Type IP-2 package, a Type IP-3 package or a Type A package design shall be legibly and durably marked on the outside of the packaging with the international vehicle registration code (VRI code) of the country of origin of design and either the name of the manufacturer or other identification of the packaging specified by the competent authority of the country of origin of design.

5.2.1.5.5 Each package which conforms to a design approved under one or more of paragraphs 5.1.5.2.1, 6.4.22.1 to 6.4.22.4, 6.4.23.4 to 6.4.23.7 and 6.4.24.2 shall be legibly and durably marked on the outside of the package with the following information:

.1 the identification mark allocated to that design by the competent authority;

.2 a serial number to uniquely identify each packaging which conforms to that design;

.3 "Type B(U)", "Type B(M)" or "Type C", in the case of a Type B(U), Type B(M) or Type C package design.

5.2.1.5.6 Each package which conforms to a Type B(U), Type B(M) or Type C package design shall have the outside of the outermost receptacle which is resistant to the effects of fire and water plainly marked by embossing, stamping or other means resistant to the effects of fire and water with the trefoil symbol shown below.

Basic trefoil symbol with proportions based on a central circle of radius *X*.
The minimum allowable size of *X* shall be 4 mm.

△ 5.2.1.5.7 Where LSA-I or SCO-I material is contained in receptacles or wrapping materials and is transported under exclusive use as permitted by 4.1.9.2.4, the outer surface of these receptacles or wrapping materials may bear the mark "RADIOACTIVE LSA-I" or "RADIOACTIVE SCO-I", as appropriate.

5.2.1.5.8 In all cases of international transport of packages requiring competent authority approval of design or shipment, for which different approval types apply in the different countries concerned by the shipment, marking shall be in accordance with the certificate of the country of origin of the design.

5.2.1.6 Special marking provisions for marine pollutants

5.2.1.6.1 Except as provided in 2.10.2.7, packages containing marine pollutants meeting the criteria of 2.9.3 shall be durably marked with the marine pollutant mark.

△ 5.2.1.6.2 The marine pollutant mark shall be located adjacent to the marks required by 5.2.1.1. The provisions of 5.2.1.2 and 5.2.1.4 shall be met.

5.2.1.6.3   The marine pollutant mark shall be as shown in the figure below.

Marine pollutant mark

△ The mark shall be in the form of a square set at an angle of 45° (diamond-shaped). The symbol (fish and tree) shall be black on white or a suitable contrasting background. The minimum dimensions shall be 100 mm × 100 mm and the minimum width of line forming the diamond shall be 2 mm. If the size of the package so requires, the dimensions/line thickness may be reduced, provided the mark remains clearly visible. Where dimensions are not specified, all features shall be in approximate proportion to those shown.

Note: The labelling provisions of 5.2.2 apply in addition to any requirement for packages to bear the marine pollutant mark.

⊗

■ **5.2.1.7**   **Orientation arrows**

△ **5.2.1.7.1**   Except as provided in 5.2.1.7.2:

–   combination packagings having inner packagings containing liquid dangerous goods;

–   single packagings fitted with vents; and

–   cryogenic receptacles intended for the transport of refrigerated liquefied gases

shall be legibly marked with package orientation arrows which are similar to the illustration shown below or with those meeting the specifications of ISO 780:1997. The orientation arrows shall appear on two opposite vertical sides of the package with the arrows pointing in the correct upright direction. They shall be rectangular and of a size that is clearly visible commensurate with the size of the package. Depicting a rectangular border around the arrows is optional.

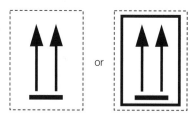

Two black or red arrows on white or suitable contrasting background.
The rectangular border is optional.
All features shall be in approximate proportion to those shown.

△ **5.2.1.7.2**   Orientation arrows are not required on:

.1   outer packagings containing pressure receptacles except cryogenic receptacles;

.2   outer packagings containing dangerous goods in inner packagings each containing not more than 120 mL, with sufficient absorbent material between the inner and outer packagings to completely absorb the liquid contents;

.3   outer packagings containing Division 6.2 infectious substances in primary receptacles each containing not more than 50 mL;

.4   type IP-2, type IP-3, type A, type B(U), type B(M) or type C packages containing class 7 radioactive material;

.5   outer packagings containing articles which are leak-tight in all orientations (e.g. alcohol or mercury in thermometers, aerosols, etc.); or

.6   outer packagings containing dangerous goods in hermetically sealed inner packagings each containing not more than 500 mL.

△ 5.2.1.7.3   Arrows for purposes other than indicating proper package orientation shall not be displayed on a package marked in accordance with this subsection.

5.2.1.8   Excepted quantity mark

5.2.1.8.1   Packages containing excepted quantities of dangerous goods shall be marked according to 3.5.4.

5.2.1.9   Limited quantity mark

5.2.1.9.1   Packages containing dangerous goods packed in limited quantities shall be marked according to 3.4.5.

■ 5.2.1.10   Lithium battery mark

■ 5.2.1.10.1   Packages containing lithium cells or batteries prepared in accordance with special provision 188 shall be marked as shown in Figure below.

■ 5.2.1.10.2   The mark shall indicate the UN number, preceded by the letters "UN", i.e. 'UN 3090' for lithium metal cells or batteries or 'UN 3480' for lithium ion cells or batteries. Where the lithium cells or batteries are contained in, or packed with, equipment, the UN number preceded by the letters "UN", i.e. 'UN 3091' or 'UN 3481' as appropriate shall be indicated. Where a package contains lithium cells or batteries assigned to different UN numbers, all applicable UN numbers shall be indicated on one or more marks.

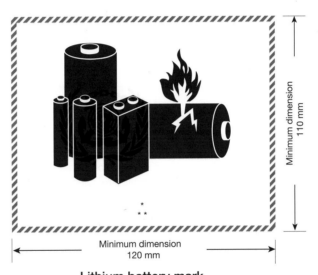

Lithium battery mark

* Place for UN number(s)

** Place for telephone number for additional information

■ The mark shall be in the form of a rectangle with hatched edging. The dimensions shall be a minimum of 120 mm wide × 110 mm high and the minimum width of the hatching shall be 5 mm. The symbol (group of batteries, one damaged and emitting flame, above the UN number for lithium ion or lithium metal batteries or cells) shall be black on white. The hatching shall be red. If the size of the package so requires, the dimensions/ line thickness may be reduced to not less than 105 mm wide × 74 mm high. Where dimensions are not specified, all features shall be in approximate proportion to those shown.

5.2.2   Labelling of packages including IBCs

△ 5.2.2.1   **Labelling provisions**

These provisions are related essentially to danger labels. However, additional marks or symbols indicating precautions to be taken in handling or storing a package (such as a symbol representing an umbrella, indicating that a package shall be kept dry) may be displayed on a package if appropriate.

5.2.2.1.1   Labels identifying primary and subsidiary risks shall conform to models Nos. 1 to 9 illustrated in 5.2.2.2.2. The "EXPLOSIVE" subsidiary risk label is model No. 1.

5.2.2.1.2   Where articles or substances are specifically listed in the Dangerous Goods List, a danger class label shall be affixed for the hazard shown in column 3. A subsidiary risk label shall also be affixed for any risk indicated by a class or division number in column 4 of the Dangerous Goods List. However, special provisions indicated in column 6 may also require a subsidiary risk label where no subsidiary risk is indicated in column 4 or may be exempt from the requirement for a subsidiary risk label where such a risk is indicated in the Dangerous Goods List.

5.2.2.1.2.1   A package containing a dangerous substance which has a low degree of danger may be exempt from these labelling requirements. In this case, a special provision specifying that no hazard label is required appears in column 6 of the Dangerous Goods List for the relevant substance. However, for certain substances the package shall be marked with the appropriate text as it appears in the special provision, for example:

Substance	UN No.	Class	Mark required on bales
Baled hay in cargo transport unit	1327	4.1	None
Baled hay not in cargo transport unit	1327	4.1	Class 4.1
Baled dry vegetable fibres in cargo transport unit	3360	4.1	None

Substance	UN No.	Class	Mark required on packages in addition to the proper shipping name and UN number
Fishmeal[*]	1374	4.2	Class 4.2[†]
Batteries, wet, non-spillable	2800	8	Class 8[‡]

[*] Only applicable to fishmeal in packing group III.

[†] Exempt from class marking when loaded in a cargo transport unit containing only fishmeal under UN 1374.

[‡] Exempt from class marking when loaded in a cargo transport unit containing only batteries under UN 2800.

5.2.2.1.3   Except as provided in 5.2.2.1.3.1, if a substance which meets the definition of more than one class is not specifically listed by name in the Dangerous Goods List in chapter 3.2, the provisions in chapter 2.0 shall be used to determine the primary risk class of the goods. In addition to the label required for that primary risk class, subsidiary risk labels shall also be applied as specified in the Dangerous Goods List.

5.2.2.1.3.1   Packagings containing substances of class 8 need not bear subsidiary risk label model No. 6.1 if the toxicity arises solely from the destructive effect on tissue. Substances of class 4.2 need not bear subsidiary risk label model No. 4.1.

5.2.2.1.4   *Labels for class 2 gases with subsidiary risk(s)*

Class	Subsidiary risk(s) shown in chapter 2.2	Primary risk label	Subsidiary risk label(s)
2.1	None	2.1	None
2.2	None	2.2	None
	5.1	2.2	5.1
2.3	None	2.3	None
	2.1	2.3	2.1
	5.1	2.3	5.1
	5.1, 8	2.3	5.1, 8
	8	2.3	8
	2.1, 8	2.3	2.1, 8

5.2.2.1.5   Three separate labels have been provided for class 2, one for flammable gases of class 2.1 (red), one for non-flammable, non-toxic gases of class 2.2 (green) and one for toxic gases of class 2.3 (white). Where the Dangerous Goods List indicates that a class 2 gas possesses single or multiple subsidiary risks, labels shall be used in accordance with the table in 5.2.2.1.4.

5.2.2.1.6   Except as provided in 5.2.2.2.1.2, each label shall:

△ .1   be located on the same surface of the package near the proper shipping name mark, if the package dimensions are adequate;

△ .2   be so placed on the packaging that it is not covered or obscured by any part or attachment to the packaging or any other label or mark; and

.3   when primary and subsidiary risk labels are required, be displayed next to each other.

Where a package is of such an irregular shape or small size that a label cannot be satisfactorily affixed, the label may be attached to the package by a securely affixed tag or other suitable means.

5.2.2.1.7   Intermediate bulk containers of more than 450 L capacity and large packagings shall be labelled on two opposing sides.

5.2.2.1.8   Labels shall be affixed on a surface of contrasting colour.

5.2.2.1.9   *Special provisions for the labelling of self-reactive substances*

An "EXPLOSIVE" subsidiary risk label (No. 1) shall be applied for type B self-reactive substances, unless the competent authority has permitted this label to be dispensed with for a specific packaging because test data have proved that the self-reactive substance in such a packaging does not exhibit explosive behaviour.

5.2.2.1.10   *Special provisions for the labelling of organic peroxides*

The class 5.2 label (model No. 5.2) shall be affixed to packages containing organic peroxides classified as types B, C, D, E or F. This label also implies that the product may be flammable and hence no "FLAMMABLE LIQUID" subsidiary risk label (model No. 3) is required. In addition, the following subsidiary risk labels shall be applied:

.1   An "EXPLOSIVE" subsidiary risk label (model No. 1) for organic peroxides type B, unless the competent authority has permitted this label to be dispensed with for a specific packaging because test data have proved that the organic peroxide in such a packaging does not exhibit explosive behaviour.

.2   A "CORROSIVE" subsidiary risk label (model No. 8) is required when packing group I or II criteria of class 8 are met.

5.2.2.1.11   *Special provisions for the labelling of infectious substances packages*

In addition to the primary risk label (model No. 6.2), infectious substances packages shall bear any other label required by the nature of the contents.

5.2.2.1.12   *Special provisions for the labelling of radioactive material*

△ **5.2.2.1.12.1**   Except when enlarged labels are used in accordance with 5.3.1.1.5.1, each package, overpack and freight container containing radioactive material shall bear the labels conforming to the applicable model Nos. 7A, 7B or 7C, according to the appropriate category. Labels shall be affixed to two opposite sides on the outside of the package or overpack or on the outside of all four sides of a freight container or tank. Each overpack containing radioactive material shall bear at least two labels on opposite sides of the outside of the overpack. In addition, each package, overpack and freight container containing fissile material, other than fissile material excepted under the provisions of 2.7.2.3.5, shall bear labels conforming to model No. 7E; such labels, where applicable, shall be affixed adjacent to the labels conforming to the applicable model Nos. 7A, 7B or 7C. Labels shall not cover the marks specified in this chapter. Any labels which do not relate to the contents shall be removed or covered.

5.2.2.1.12.2   Each label conforming to the applicable model No. 7A, 7B or 7C shall be completed with the following information:

.1   *Contents:*

    .1   Except for LSA-I material, the name(s) of the radionuclide(s) as taken from the table under 2.7.2.2.1, using the symbols prescribed therein. For mixtures of radionuclides, the most restrictive nuclides must be listed to the extent the space on the line permits. The group of LSA or SCO shall be shown following the name(s) of the radionuclide(s). The terms "LSA-II", "LSA-III", "SCO-I" and "SCO-II" shall be used for this purpose.

    .2   For LSA-I material, the term "LSA-I" is all that is necessary; the name of the radionuclide is not necessary.

.2   *Activity:* The maximum activity of the radioactive contents during transport, expressed in units of becquerels (Bq) with the appropriate SI prefix symbol (see 1.2.2.1). For fissile material, the total mass of fissile nuclides in units of grams (g), or multiples thereof, may be used in place of activity.

.3   For overpacks and freight containers, the "contents" and "activity" entries on the label shall bear the information required in 5.2.2.1.12.2.1 and 5.2.2.1.12.2.2, respectively, totalled together for the entire contents of the overpack or freight container except that, on labels for overpacks or freight containers containing mixed loads of packages containing different radionuclides, such entries may read "See transport documents".

.4 *Transport index:* The number determined in accordance with 5.1.5.3.1 and 5.1.5.3.2. (No transport index entry is required for category I – WHITE.)

5.2.2.1.12.3 Each label conforming to the model No. 7E shall be completed with the criticality safety index (CSI) as stated in the certificate of approval applicable in the countries through or into which the consignment is transported and issued by the competent authority or as specified in 6.4.11.2 or 6.4.11.3.

5.2.2.1.12.4 For overpacks and freight containers, the label conforming to model No. 7E shall bear the sum of the criticality safety indexes of all the packages contained therein.

5.2.2.1.12.5 In all cases of international transport of packages requiring competent authority approval of design or shipment, for which different approval types apply in the different countries concerned by the shipment, labelling shall be in accordance with the certificate of the country of origin of design.

5.2.2.2 Provisions for labels

5.2.2.2.1 Labels shall satisfy the provisions of this section and conform, in terms of colour, symbols, numbers and general format, to the specimen labels shown in 5.2.2.2.2.

Note: Where appropriate, labels in 5.2.2.2.2 are shown with a dotted outer boundary as provided for in 5.2.2.2.1.1. This is not required when the label is applied on a background of contrasting colour.

5.2.2.2.1.1 Labels shall be configured as shown in the figure below:

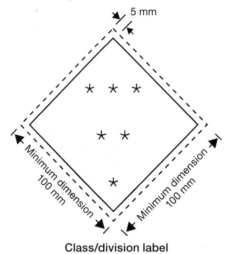

Class/division label

* The class or, for divisions 5.1 and 5.2, the division number shall be shown in the bottom corner.

△ ** Additional text/numbers/symbol/letters shall (if mandatory) or may (if optional) be shown in this bottom half.

*** The class or division symbol or, for divisions 1.4, 1.5 and 1.6, the division number, and for model No. 7E, the word "FISSILE" shall be shown in this top half.

5.2.2.2.1.1.1 Labels shall be displayed on a background of contrasting colour, or shall have either a dotted or solid outer boundary line.

5.2.2.2.1.1.2 The label shall be in the form of a square set at an angle of 45° (diamond-shaped). The minimum dimensions shall be 100 mm × 100 mm and the minimum width of the line inside the edge forming the diamond shall be 2 mm. The line inside the edge shall be parallel and 5 mm from the outside of that line to the edge of the label. The line inside the edge on the upper half of the label shall be the same colour as the symbol and the line inside the edge on the lower half of the label shall be the same colour as the class or division number in the bottom corner. Where dimensions are not specified, all features shall be in approximate proportion to those shown.

5.2.2.2.1.1.3 If the size of the package so requires the dimensions may be reduced, provided the symbols and other elements of the label remain clearly visible. The line inside the edge shall remain 5 mm to the edge of the label. The minimum width of the line inside the edge shall remain 2 mm. Dimensions for cylinders shall comply with 5.2.2.2.1.2.

⊗

5.2.2.2.1.2 Cylinders for class 2 may, on account of their shape, orientation and securing mechanisms for transport, bear labels representative of those specified in this section, which have been reduced in size, according to ISO 7225:2005, for display on the non-cylindrical part (shoulder) of such cylinders. Labels may overlap to the extent provided for by ISO 7225:2005, *Gas cylinders – Precautionary labels*; however, in all cases, the labels representing the primary hazard and the numbers appearing on any label shall remain fully visible and the symbols recognizable.

■ **Note:** When the diameter of the cylinder is too small to permit the display of the reduced size labels on the non-cylindrical upper part of the cylinder, the reduced sized labels may be displayed on the cylindrical part.

△ **5.2.2.2.1.3** With the exception of labels for divisions 1.4, 1.5 and 1.6 of class 1, the upper half of the label shall contain the pictorial symbol and the lower half shall contain the class number 1, 2, 3, 4, 5.1, 5.2, 6, 7, 8 or 9 as appropriate. The label may include text such as the UN number, or words describing the hazard class (e.g. "flammable") or for label No. 9A the symbol in accordance with 5.2.2.2.1.5 provided the text does not obscure or detract from the other required label elements.

5.2.2.2.1.4 In addition, except for divisions 1.4, 1.5 and 1.6, labels for class 1 shall show in the lower half, above the class number, the division number and compatibility group letter for the substance or article. Labels for divisions 1.4, 1.5 and 1.6 shall show in the upper half the division number and in the lower half the class number and the compatibility group letter. For division 1.4, compatibility group S, no label is generally required. However, in cases where a label is considered necessary for such goods, it shall be based on model No. 1.4.

△ **5.2.2.2.1.5** On labels other than those for material of class 7, the insertion of any text (other than the class or division number) in the space below the symbol shall be confined to particulars indicating the nature of the risk and precautions to be taken in handling. For label No. 9A, no text other than the class mark shall be included in the bottom part of the label.

5.2.2.2.1.6 The symbols, text and numbers shall be shown in black on all labels except for:

   .1   the class 8 label, where the text (if any) and class number shall appear in white;

   .2   labels with entirely green, red or blue backgrounds, where they may be shown in white;

   .3   the class 5.2 label, where the symbol may be shown in white; and

   .4   class 2.1 labels displayed on cylinders and gas cartridges for liquefied petroleum gases, where they may be shown in the background colour of the receptacle if adequate contrast is provided.

5.2.2.2.1.7 The method of affixing the label(s) or applying stencil(s) of label(s) on packages containing dangerous goods shall be such that the label(s) or stencil(s) will still be identifiable on packages surviving at least three months' immersion in the sea. In considering suitable labelling methods, account shall be taken of the durability of the packaging materials used and the surface of the package.

5

5.2.2.2.2 *Specimen labels*

Note: Labels shall satisfy the provisions below and conform, in terms of colour, symbols and general format, to the models shown in 5.2.2.2.2. Corresponding models required for other modes of transport, with minor variations which do not affect the obvious meaning of the label, are also acceptable.

Class 1 – Explosive substances or articles

(No. 1)
Divisions 1.1, 1.2 and 1.3
Symbol (exploding bomb): black. Background: orange. Figure '1' in bottom corner.

(No. 1.4)
Division 1.4

(No. 1.5)
Division 1.5

(No. 1.6)
Division 1.6

Background: orange. Figures: black. Numerals shall be about 30 mm in height and be about 5 mm thick (for a label measuring 100 mm × 100 mm). Figure '1' in bottom corner.

** Place for division – to be left blank if explosive is the subsidiary risk.
* Place for compatibility group – to be left blank if explosive is the subsidiary risk.

Class 2 – Gases

(No. 2.1)
Class 2.1
Flammable gases
Symbol (flame): black or white
(except as provided for in 5.2.2.2.1.6.4).
Background: red. Figure '2' in bottom corner.

(No. 2.2)
Class 2.2
Non-flammable, non-toxic gases
Symbol (gas cylinder): black or white.
Background: green. Figure '2' in bottom corner.

Class 3 – Flammable liquids

(No. 2.3)
Class 2.3
Toxic gases
Symbol (skull and crossbones): black.
Background: white. Figure '2' in bottom corner.

(No. 3)
Symbol (flame): black or white.
Background: red. Figure '3' in bottom corner.

Class 4

(No. 4.1)
Class 4.1
Flammable solids
Symbol (flame): black.
Background: white with
seven vertical red stripes.
Figure '4' in bottom corner.

(No. 4.2)
Class 4.2
*Substances liable to
spontaneous combustion*
Symbol (flame): black.
Background: upper half white,
lower half red.
Figure '4' in bottom corner.

(No. 4.3)
Class 4.3
*Substances which, in contact with water,
emit flammable gases*
Symbol (flame): black or white.
Background: blue.
Figure '4' in bottom corner.

Class 5

(No. 5.1)
Class 5.1
Oxidizing substances
Symbol (flame over circle): black;
Background: yellow.
Figure '**5.1**' in bottom corner.

(No. 5.2)
Class 5.2
Organic peroxides
Symbol (flame): black or white;
Background: upper half red; lower half yellow;
Figure '**5.2**' in bottom corner

Class 6

(No. 6.1)
Class 6.1
Toxic substances
Symbol (skull and crossbones): black.
Background: white. Figure '6' in bottom corner.

(No. 6.2)
Class 6.2
Infectious substances
The lower half of the label may bear the inscriptions **INFECTIOUS SUBSTANCE** and
In case of damage or leakage immediately notify Public Health Authority.
Symbol (three crescents superimposed on a circle) and inscriptions: black.
Background: white. Figure '6' in bottom corner.

Class 7 – Radioactive material

(No. 7A)
Category I – White

Symbol (trefoil): black.
Background: white.
Text (mandatory): black in
lower half of label:
RADIOACTIVE
CONTENTS ...
ACTIVITY ...
One red bar shall follow the word
RADIOACTIVE.
Figure '**7**' in bottom corner.

(No. 7B)
Category II – Yellow

(No. 7C)
Category III – Yellow

Symbol (trefoil): black.
Background: upper half yellow with white border, lower half white.
Text (mandatory): black in lower half of label:
RADIOACTIVE
CONTENTS ...
ACTIVITY ...
In a black outlined box: **TRANSPORT INDEX** ...

Two red vertical bars shall
follow the word **RADIOACTIVE**.

Three red vertical bars shall
follow the word **RADIOACTIVE**.

Figure '**7**' in bottom corner.

(No. 7E)
Class 7 fissile material
Background: white.
Text (mandatory): black in upper half of label: **FISSILE**.
In a black outlined box in the lower half of the label: **CRITICALITY SAFETY INDEX** ...
Figure '**7**' in bottom corner.

Class 8 – Corrosive substances

△ Class 9 – Miscellaneous dangerous substances and articles including environmentally hazardous substances

(No. 8)
Symbol (liquids, spilling from two glass vessels
and attacking a hand and a metal): black.
Background: upper half white;
lower half black with white border.
Figure '**8**' in bottom corner.[*]

[*] A class 8 label with a shaded hand may also be used.

(No. 9)
Symbol (seven vertical stripes
in upper half): black.
Background: white.
Figure '**9**' underlined in
bottom corner.

(No. 9A)
Symbol (seven vertical stripes
in upper half; battery group,
one broken and emitting flame
in lower half): black.
Background: white.
Figure '**9**' underlined in
bottom corner.

Chapter 5.3

Placarding and marking of cargo transport units

5.3.1 Placarding

5.3.1.1 Placarding provisions

5.3.1.1.1 *General provisions*

.1 Enlarged labels (placards) and marks and signs shall be affixed to the exterior surfaces of a cargo transport unit to provide a warning that the contents of the unit are dangerous goods and present risks, unless the labels and/or marks affixed to the packages are clearly visible from the exterior of the cargo transport unit.

.2 The methods of placarding and marking as required in 5.3.1.1.4 and 5.3.2 on cargo transport units shall be such that this information will still be identifiable on cargo transport units surviving at least three months' immersion in the sea. In considering suitable marking methods, account shall be taken of the ease with which the surface of the cargo transport unit can be marked.

.3 All placards, orange panels, marks and signs shall be removed from cargo transport units or masked as soon as both the dangerous goods or their residues which led to the application of those placards, orange panels, marks or signs are discharged.

5.3.1.1.2 Placards shall be affixed to the exterior surface of cargo transport units to provide a warning that the contents of the unit are dangerous goods and present risks. Placards shall correspond to the primary risk of the goods contained in the cargo transport unit except that:

.1 placards are not required on cargo transport units carrying any quantity of explosives of division 1.4, compatibility group S; and

.2 placards indicating the highest risk only need be affixed on cargo transport units carrying substances and articles of more than one division in class 1.

Placards shall be displayed on a background of contrasting colour, or shall have either a dotted or solid outer boundary line.

■ For dangerous goods of class 9 the placard shall correspond to the label model No. 9 as in 5.2.2.2.2; label model No. 9A shall not be used for placarding purposes.

5.3.1.1.3 Placards shall also be displayed for those subsidiary risks for which a subsidiary risk label is required according to 5.2.2.1.2. However, cargo transport units containing goods of more than one class need not bear a subsidiary risk placard if the hazard represented by that placard is already indicated by a primary risk placard.

5.3.1.1.4 *Placarding requirements*

5.3.1.1.4.1 A cargo transport unit containing dangerous goods or residues of dangerous goods shall clearly display placards as follows:

△ .1 *a freight container, semi-trailer or portable tank:* one on each side and one on each end of the unit. Portable tanks having a capacity of not more than 3,000 L may be placarded or, alternatively, may be labelled instead, on only two opposite sides;

.2 *a railway wagon:* at least on each side;

△ .3 *a multiple-compartment tank containing more than one dangerous substance or their residues:* along each side at the positions of the relevant compartments. If all compartments are required to display the same placards, these placards need to be displayed only once along each side of the cargo transport unit; and

.4 *any other cargo transport unit:* at least on both sides and on the back of the unit.

5.3.1.1.5 *Special provisions for class 7*

5.3.1.1.5.1 Large freight containers carrying packages other than excepted packages, and tanks, shall bear four placards which conform with the model No. 7D given in the figure. The placards shall be affixed in a vertical orientation

5

to each side wall and each end wall of the large freight container or tank. Any placards which do not relate to the contents shall be removed. Instead of using both labels and placards, it is permitted as an alternative to use enlarged labels only, as shown in label model Nos. 7A, 7B and 7C, except having the minimum size shown in the figure under 5.3.1.2.2.

5.3.1.1.5.2 Rail and road vehicles carrying packages, overpacks or freight containers labelled with any of the labels shown in 5.2.2.2.2 as model Nos. 7A, 7B, 7C and 7E, or carrying consignments under exclusive use, shall display the placard shown in the figure (model No. 7D) on each of:

.1   the two external lateral walls, in the case of a rail vehicle;

.2   the two external lateral walls and the external rear wall, in the case of a road vehicle.

In the case of a vehicle without sides, the placards may be affixed directly on the cargo-carrying unit provided that they are readily visible; in the case of physically large tanks or freight containers, the placards on the tanks or freight containers shall suffice. In the case of vehicles which have insufficient area to allow the fixing of larger placards, the dimensions of the placard as described in the figure may be reduced to 100 mm. Any placards which do not relate to the contents shall be removed.

5.3.1.2   Specifications for placards

5.3.1.2.1 Except as provided in 5.3.1.2.2 for the class 7 placard, and in 5.3.2.3.2 for the marine pollutant mark, a placard shall be configured as shown in the figure below.

Placard (except for class 7)

The placard shall be in the form of a square set at an angle of 45° (diamond-shaped). The minimum dimensions shall be 250 mm × 250 mm (to the edge of the placard). The line inside the edge shall be parallel and 12.5 mm from the outside of that line to the edge of the placard. The symbol and line inside the edge shall correspond in colour to the label for the class or division of the dangerous goods in question. The class or division symbol/numeral shall be positioned and sized in proportion to those prescribed in 5.2.2.2 for the corresponding class or division of the dangerous goods in question. The placard shall display the number of the class or division (and for goods in class 1, the compatibility group letter) of the dangerous goods in question in the manner prescribed in 5.2.2.2 for the corresponding label, in digits not less than 25 mm high. Where dimensions are not specified, all features shall be in approximate proportion to those shown.

Note: The provisions of 5.3.1.2.1 from the IMDG Code (amendment 36-12) may continue to be applied until 31 December 2016.

5.3.1.2.2 For class 7, the placard shall have minimum overall dimensions of 250 mm by 250 mm (except as permitted by 5.3.1.1.5.2) with a black line running 5 mm inside the edge and parallel with it, and shall be otherwise as shown in the figure below. When different dimensions are used, the relative proportions shall be maintained. The number "7" shall not be less than 25 mm high. The background colour of the upper half of the placard shall be yellow and of the lower half white; the colour of the trefoil and the printing shall be black. The use of the word "RADIOACTIVE" in the bottom half is optional to allow the use of this placard to display the appropriate United Nations Number for the consignment.

Placard for radioactive material of class 7

(No. 7D)

Symbol (trefoil): black.
Background: upper half yellow with white border, lower half white.
The lower half shall show the word **RADIOACTIVE** or
alternatively, when required (see 5.3.2.1), the appropriate UN number
and the figure '**7**' in the bottom corner.

5.3.2 Marking of cargo transport units

5.3.2.0 Display of proper shipping name

5.3.2.0.1 The proper shipping name of the contents shall be durably marked on at least both sides of:

.1 tank cargo transport units containing dangerous goods;

.2 bulk containers containing dangerous goods; or

.3 any other cargo transport unit containing packaged dangerous goods of a single commodity for which no placard, UN number or marine pollutant mark is required. Alternatively, the UN number may be displayed.

△ 5.3.2.0.2 The proper shipping name for the goods shall be displayed in characters not more than 65 mm high. The proper shipping name shall be of contrasting colour with the background. This may be reduced to 12 mm for portable tank containers with a capacity of less than 3,000 L.

5.3.2.1 Display of UN numbers

5.3.2.1.1 Except for goods of class 1, the UN number shall be displayed as required by this chapter on consignments of:

.1 solids, liquids or gases transported in tank cargo transport units, including on each compartment of a multi-compartment tank cargo transport unit;

.2 packaged dangerous goods loaded in excess of 4000 kg gross mass, to which only one UN number has been assigned and which are the only dangerous goods in the cargo transport unit;

.3 unpackaged LSA-I or SCO-I material of class 7 in or on a vehicle, or in a freight container, or in a tank;

.4 packaged radioactive material with a single UN number in or on a vehicle, or in a freight container, when required to be transported under exclusive use;

.5 solid dangerous goods in bulk containers.

5.3.2.1.2 The UN number for the goods shall be displayed in black digits not less than 65 mm high, either:

.1 against a white background in the area below the pictorial symbol and above the class number and the compatibility group letter in a manner that does not obscure or detract from the other required placard elements (see 5.3.2.1.3); or

△ .2 on an orange rectangular panel not less than 120 mm high and 300 mm wide, with a 10 mm black border, to be placed immediately adjacent to each placard or marine pollutant mark (see 5.3.2.1.3). For portable tanks with a capacity of not more than 3,000 litres, the UN number may be displayed on an orange rectangular panel of appropriately reduced size on the external surface of the tank in characters not less than 25 mm high. When no placard or marine pollutant mark is required, the UN number shall be displayed immediately adjacent to the proper shipping name.

5.3.2.1.3 *Examples of display of UN numbers*

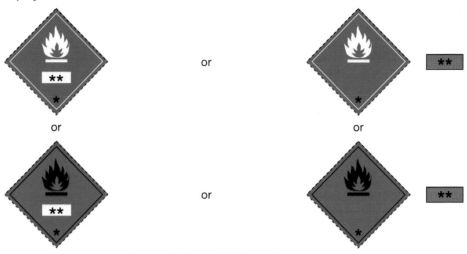

or

or

or

or

* location of class or division number
** location of UN number

5.3.2.2 **Elevated temperature substance mark**

5.3.2.2.1 Cargo transport units containing a substance that is transported or offered for transport in a liquid state at a temperature equal to or exceeding 100°C or in a solid state at a temperature equal to or exceeding 240°C shall bear on each side and on each end the mark shown in the figure below.

Mark for transport at elevated temperature

△ The mark shall be an equilateral triangle. The colour of the mark shall be red. The minimum dimension of the sides shall be 250 mm except for portable tanks with a capacity of not more than 3,000 L where the sides may be reduced to 100 mm. Where dimensions are not specified, all features shall be in approximate proportion to those shown.

⊗

5.3.2.2.2 In addition to the elevated temperature mark, the maximum temperature of the substance expected to be reached during transport shall be durably marked on both sides of the portable tank or insulation jacket, immediately adjacent to the elevated temperature mark, in characters at least 100 mm high.

5.3.2.3 **Marine pollutant mark**

5.3.2.3.1 Except as provided in 2.10.2.7, cargo transport units containing marine pollutants shall clearly display the marine pollutant mark in locations indicated in 5.3.1.1.4.1.

△ **5.3.2.3.2** The marine pollutant mark for cargo transport units shall be as described in 5.2.1.6.3, except that the minimum dimensions shall be 250 mm × 250 mm. For portable tanks with a capacity of not more than 3,000 L, the dimensions may be reduced to 100 mm × 100 mm.

5.3.2.4 **Limited quantities**

Cargo transport units containing dangerous goods packed in limited quantities shall be placarded and marked according to 3.4.5.5.

Chapter 5.4

Documentation

Note 1   The provisions of this Code do not preclude the use of electronic data processing (EDP) and electronic data interchange (EDI) transmission techniques as an alternative to paper documentation. All references to "dangerous goods transport document" in this chapter also include provision of the required information by use of EDP and EDI transmission techniques.

Note 2   When dangerous goods are offered for transport, similar documents to those required for other categories of goods have to be prepared. The form of these documents, the particulars to be entered on them and the obligations they entail may be fixed by international conventions applying to certain modes of transport and by national legislation.

Note 3   One of the primary requirements of a transport document for dangerous goods is to convey the fundamental information relative to the hazards of the goods. It is, therefore, necessary to include certain basic information on the document for a consignment of dangerous goods unless otherwise exempted or required in this Code.

Note 4   In addition to the provisions of this chapter, other elements of information may be required by the competent authority.

Note 5   In addition to the provisions of this chapter other additional information may be included. However, this information shall not:

    .1   divert attention from the safety information required by this chapter or by the competent authority;

    .2   contradict the safety information required by this chapter or by the competent authority; or

    .3   duplicate information already provided.

5.4.1   Dangerous goods transport information

5.4.1.1   General

5.4.1.1.1   Except as otherwise provided, the consignor who offers dangerous goods for transport shall give to the carrier the information applicable to those dangerous goods, including any additional information and documentation as specified in this Code. This information may be provided on a dangerous goods transport document or, with the agreement of the carrier, by EDP or EDI techniques.

5.4.1.1.2   When the dangerous goods transport information is given to the carrier by EDP or EDI techniques, the consignor shall be able to produce the information without delay as a paper document, with the information in the sequence required by this chapter.

5.4.1.2   Form of the transport document

5.4.1.2.1   A dangerous goods transport document may be in any form, provided it contains all of the information required by the provisions of this Code.

5.4.1.2.2   If both dangerous and non-dangerous goods are listed in one document, the dangerous goods shall be listed first, or otherwise be emphasized.

5.4.1.2.3   *Continuation page*

     A dangerous goods transport document may consist of more than one page, provided pages are consecutively numbered.

5.4.1.2.4   The information on a dangerous goods transport document shall be easy to identify, legible and durable.

5.4.1.2.5 *Example of a dangerous goods transport document*

The form shown in figure 5.4.5 is an example of a dangerous goods transport document.[*]

5.4.1.3 **Consignor, consignee and date**

The name and address of the consignor and the consignee of the dangerous goods shall be included on the dangerous goods transport document. The date the dangerous goods transport document or an electronic copy of it was prepared or given to the initial carrier shall be included.

5.4.1.4 **Information required on the dangerous goods transport document**

5.4.1.4.1 *Dangerous goods description*

The dangerous goods transport document shall contain the following information for each dangerous substance, material or article offered for transport:

.1   the UN number preceded by the letters "UN";

.2   the proper shipping name, as determined according to 3.1.2, including the technical name enclosed in parenthesis, as applicable (see 3.1.2.8);

.3   the primary hazard class or, when assigned, the division of the goods, including, for class 1, the compatibility group letter. The words "Class" or "Division" may be included preceding the primary hazard class or division numbers;

.4   subsidiary hazard class or division number(s) corresponding to the subsidiary risk label(s) required to be applied, when assigned, shall be entered following the primary hazard class or division and shall be enclosed in parenthesis. The words "Class" or "Division" may be included preceding the subsidiary hazard class or division numbers;

.5   where assigned, the packing group for the substance or article, which may be preceded by "PG" (e.g."PG II").

5.4.1.4.2 *Sequence of the dangerous goods description*

The five elements of the dangerous goods description specified in 5.4.1.4.1 shall be shown in the order listed above (i.e. .1, .2, .3, .4, and .5) with no information interspersed, except as provided in this Code. Unless permitted or required by this Code, additional information shall be placed after the dangerous goods description.

5.4.1.4.3 *Information which supplements the proper shipping name in the dangerous goods description*

The proper shipping name (see 3.1.2) in the dangerous goods description shall be supplemented as follows:

.1   *Technical names for "n.o.s." and other generic descriptions*: proper shipping names that are assigned special provision 274 or 318 in column 6 of the Dangerous Goods List shall be supplemented with their technical or chemical group names as described in 3.1.2.8.

.2   *Empty uncleaned packagings, bulk containers and tanks*: Empty means of containment (including packagings, IBCs, bulk containers, portable tanks, road tank vehicles and railway tank wagons) which contain the residue of dangerous goods of classes other than class 7 shall be described as such by, for example, placing the words "EMPTY UNCLEANED" or "RESIDUE LAST CONTAINED" before or after the dangerous goods description specified in 5.4.1.4.1.1 to .5.

.3   *Wastes*: For waste dangerous goods (other than radioactive wastes) which are being transported for disposal, or for processing for disposal, the proper shipping name shall be preceded by the word "WASTE", unless this is already a part of the proper shipping name.

.4   *Elevated temperature substances*: If the proper shipping name of a substance which is transported or offered for transport in a liquid state at a temperature equal to or exceeding 100°C, or in a solid state at a temperature equal to or exceeding 240°C, does not convey the elevated temperature condition (for example, by using the term "MOLTEN" or "ELEVATED TEMPERATURE" as part of the proper shipping name), the word "HOT" shall immediately precede the proper shipping name.

---

[*] For standardized formats, see also the relevant recommendations of the UNECE United Nations Centre for Trade Facilitation and Electronic Business (UN/CEFACT), in particular Recommendation No. 1 (United Nations Layout Key for Trade Documents) (ECE/TRADE/137, edition 81.3), UN Layout Key for Trade Documents – Guidelines for Applications (ECE/TRADE/270, edition 2002), Revised Recommendation No. 11 (Documentary Aspects of the International Transport of Dangerous Goods) (ECE/TRADE/C/CEFACT/2008/8) and Recommendation No. 22 (Layout Key for Standard Consignment Instructions) (ECE/TRADE/168, edition 1989). Refer also to the UN/CEFACT Summary of Trade Facilitation Recommendations (ECE/TRADE/346, edition 2006) and the United Nations Trade Data Elements Directory (UNTDED) (ECE/TRADE/362, edition 2005).

.5   *Marine pollutants:* Except as provided in 2.10.2.7, if the goods to be transported are marine pollutants, the goods shall be identified as "MARINE POLLUTANT", and for generic or "not otherwise specified" (N.O.S.) entries the proper shipping name shall be supplemented with the recognized chemical name of the marine pollutant (see 3.1.2.9). The term "MARINE POLLUTANT" may be supplemented with the term "ENVIRONMENTALLY HAZARDOUS".

.6   *Flashpoint:* If the dangerous goods to be transported have a flashpoint of 60°C or below (in °C closed-cup (c.c.)), the minimum flashpoint shall be indicated. Because of the presence of impurities, the flashpoint may be lower or higher than the reference temperature indicated in the Dangerous Goods List for the substance. For class 5.2 organic peroxides which are also flammable, the flashpoint need not be declared.

5.4.1.4.4   *Examples of dangerous goods descriptions:*

UN 1098, ALLYL ALCOHOL 6.1 (3) I (21°C c.c.)

UN 1098, ALLYL ALCOHOL, class 6.1, (class 3), PG I, (21°C c.c.)

UN 1092, Acrolein, stabilized, class 6.1 (3), PG I, (–24°C c.c.), MARINE POLLUTANT/ENVIRONMENTALLY HAZARDOUS

UN 2761, Organochlorine pesticide, solid, toxic, (Aldrin 19%), class 6.1, PG III, MARINE POLLUTANT

5.4.1.5   **Information required in addition to the dangerous goods description**

In addition to the dangerous goods description, the following information shall be included after the dangerous goods description on the dangerous goods transport document.

5.4.1.5.1   *Total quantity of dangerous goods*

Except for empty uncleaned packagings, the total quantity of dangerous goods covered by the description (by volume or mass as appropriate) of each item of dangerous goods bearing a different proper shipping name, UN number or packing group shall be included. For class 1 dangerous goods, the quantity shall be the net explosive mass. For dangerous goods transported in salvage packagings, an estimate of the quantity of dangerous goods shall be given. The number and kind (e.g. drum, box, etc.) of packages shall also be indicated. UN packaging codes may only be used to supplement the description of the kind of package (e.g. one box (4G)). Abbreviations may be used to specify the unit of measurement for the total quantity.

Note: The number, type and capacity of each inner packaging within the outer packaging of a combination packaging is not required to be indicated.

5.4.1.5.2   *Limited quantities*

5.4.1.5.2.1   When dangerous goods are transported according to the exceptions for dangerous goods packed in limited quantities provided for in column 7a of the Dangerous Goods List and chapter 3.4, the words "limited quantity" or "LTD QTY" shall be included.

5.4.1.5.2.2   Where a shipment is offered in accordance with 3.4.4.1.2, the following statement shall be included in the transport document: "Transport in accordance with 3.4.4.1.2 of the IMDG Code".

5.4.1.5.3   *Salvage packagings and salvage pressure receptacles*

For dangerous goods transported in salvage packagings or salvage pressure receptacles, the words "SALVAGE PACKAGING" or "SALVAGE PRESSURE RECEPTACLE" shall be included.

5.4.1.5.4   *Substances stabilized by temperature control*

If the word "STABILIZED" is part of the proper shipping name (see also 3.1.2.6), when stabilization is by means of temperature control, the control and emergency temperatures (see 7.3.7.2) shall be indicated in the transport document, as follows:

"Control temperature: ... °C   Emergency temperature: ... °C".

△ **5.4.1.5.5**   *Self-reactive substances, polymerizing substances and organic peroxides*

For self-reactive substances and polymerizing substances of class 4.1 and for organic peroxides which require temperature control during transport, the control and emergency temperatures (see 7.3.7.2) shall be indicated on the dangerous goods transport document, as follows:

"Control temperature: ... °C   Emergency temperature: ... °C".

5.4.1.5.5.1   When, for certain self-reactive substances and polymerizing substances of class 4.1 and organic peroxides of class 5.2, the competent authority has permitted the "EXPLOSIVE" subsidiary risk label (model No. 1) to be dispensed with for the specific package, a statement to this effect shall be included.

5.4.1.5.5.2 When organic peroxides and self-reactive substances are transported under conditions where approval is required (for organic peroxides, see 2.5.3.2.5, 4.1.7.2.2, 4.2.1.13.1 and 4.2.1.13.3; for self-reactive substances, see 2.4.2.3.2.4 and 4.1.7.2.2), a statement to this effect shall be included in the dangerous goods transport document. A copy of the classification approval and conditions of transport for non-listed organic peroxides and self-reactive substances shall be attached to the dangerous goods transport document.

5.4.1.5.5.3 When a sample of an organic peroxide (see 2.5.3.2.5.1) or a self-reactive substance (see 2.4.2.3.2.4.2) is transported, a statement to this effect shall be included in the dangerous goods transport document.

5.4.1.5.6 *Infectious substances*

The full address of the consignee shall be shown on the document, together with the name of a responsible person and his telephone number.

5.4.1.5.7 *Radioactive material*

5.4.1.5.7.1 The following information shall be included for each consignment of class 7 material, as applicable, in the order given:

.1 the name or symbol of each radionuclide or, for mixtures of radionuclides, an appropriate general description or a list of the most restrictive nuclides;

.2 a description of the physical and chemical form of the material, or a notation that the material is special form radioactive material or low dispersible radioactive material. A generic chemical description is acceptable for chemical form;

.3 the maximum activity of the radioactive contents during transport expressed in units of becquerels (Bq) with an appropriate SI prefix symbol (see 1.2.2.1). For fissile material, the mass of fissile material (or mass of each fissile nuclide for mixtures when appropriate) in units of grams (g), or appropriate multiples thereof, may be used in place of activity;

.4 the category of the package, i.e. I – WHITE, II – YELLOW, III – YELLOW;

.5 the transport index (categories II – YELLOW and III – YELLOW only);

.6 for fissile material:

.1 shipped under one exception of 2.7.2.3.5.1 to 2.7.2.3.5.6, reference to that paragraph;

.2 shipped under 2.7.2.3.5.1 to 2.7.2.3.5.5, the total mass of fissile nuclides;

.3 contained in a package for which one of 6.4.11.2 (a) to (c) or 6.4.11.3 is applied, reference to that paragraph;

.4 the criticality safety index, where applicable.

.7 the identification mark for each competent authority certificate of approval (special form radioactive material, low dispersible radioactive material, fissile material excepted under 2.7.2.3.5.6, special arrangement, package design, or shipment) applicable to the consignment;

.8 for consignments of more than one package, the information contained in 5.4.1.4.1.1 to .3 and 5.4.1.5.7.1.1 to .7 shall be given for each package. For packages in an overpack, freight container, or conveyance, a detailed statement of the contents of each package within the overpack, freight container, or conveyance and, where appropriate, of each overpack, freight container, or conveyance shall be included. If packages are to be removed from the overpack, freight container, or conveyance at a point of intermediate unloading, appropriate transport documents shall be made available;

.9 where a consignment is required to be shipped under exclusive use, the statement "EXCLUSIVE USE SHIPMENT"; and

.10 for LSA-II, LSA-III, SCO-I and SCO-II, the total activity of the consignment as a multiple of A_2. For radioactive material for which the A_2 value is unlimited, the multiple of A_2 shall be zero.

5.4.1.5.7.2 The transport document shall include a statement regarding actions, if any, that are required to be taken by the carrier. The statement shall be in the languages deemed necessary by the carrier or the authorities concerned, and shall include at least the following points:

.1 supplementary requirements for loading, stowage, transport, handling and unloading of the package, overpack or freight container, including any special stowage provisions for the safe dissipation of heat (see 7.1.4.5.2), or a statement that no such requirements are necessary;

.2 restrictions on the mode of transport or conveyance and any necessary routeing instructions;

.3 emergency arrangements appropriate to the consignment.

5.4.1.5.7.3 In all cases of international transport of packages requiring competent authority approval of design or shipment, for which different approval types apply in the different countries concerned by the shipment, the UN number and proper shipping name required in 5.4.1.4.1 shall be in accordance with the certificate of the country of origin of design.

5.4.1.5.7.4 The applicable competent authority certificates need not necessarily accompany the consignment. The consignor shall make them available to the carrier(s) before loading and unloading.

5.4.1.5.8 *Aerosols*

If the capacity of an aerosol is above 1000 mL, this shall be declared in the transport document.

5.4.1.5.9 *Explosives*

The following information shall be included for each consignment of class 1 goods, as applicable:

.1 Entries have been included for "SUBSTANCES, EXPLOSIVE, N.O.S.", "ARTICLES, EXPLOSIVE, N.O.S.", and "COMPONENTS, EXPLOSIVE TRAIN, N.O.S.". When a specific entry does not exist, the competent authority of the country of origin shall use the entry appropriate to the hazard division and compatibility group. The transport document shall contain the statement: "Transport under this entry approved by the competent authority of ..." followed by the State's distinguishing sign for motor vehicles in international traffic of the country of the competent authority.

.2 The transport of explosive substances for which a minimum water or phlegmatizer content is specified in the individual entry is prohibited when containing less water or phlegmatizer than the specified minimum. Such substances shall only be transported with special authorization granted by the competent authority of the country of origin. The transport document shall contain the statement "Transport under this entry approved by the competent authority of ..." followed by the State's distinguishing sign for motor vehicles in international traffic of the country of the competent authority.

.3 When explosive substances or articles are packaged "as approved by the competent authority", the transport document shall contain the statement "Packaging approved by the competent authority of ..." followed by the State's distinguishing sign for motor vehicles in international traffic of the country of the competent authority.

.4 There are some hazards which are not indicated by the hazard division and compatibility group of a substance. The shipper shall provide an indication of any such hazards on the dangerous goods documentation.

5.4.1.5.10 *Viscous substances*

When viscous substances are transported in accordance with 2.3.2.5, the following statement shall be included in the transport document: "Transport in accordance with 2.3.2.5 of the IMDG Code.".

5.4.1.5.11 *Special provisions for segregation*

5.4.1.5.11.1 For substances, mixtures, solutions or preparations classified under N.O.S. entries not included in the segregation groups listed in 3.1.4.4 but belonging, in the opinion of the consignor, to one of these groups (see 3.1.4.2), the appropriate segregation group name preceded by the phrase "IMDG Code segregation group" shall be included in the transport document after the dangerous goods description. For example:

"UN 1760 CORROSIVE LIQUID, N.O.S. (Phosphoric acid, acetic acid) 8 III IMDG Code segregation group 1 – Acids".

5.4.1.5.11.2 When substances are loaded together in a cargo transport unit in accordance with 7.2.6.3, the following statement shall be included in the transport document: "Transport in accordance with 7.2.6.3 of the IMDG Code".

5.4.1.5.11.3 When acid and alkali substances of class 8 are transported in the same cargo transport unit, whether in the same packaging or not, in accordance with 7.2.6.4, the following statement shall be included in the transport document: "Transport in accordance with 7.2.6.4 of the IMDG Code".

5.4.1.5.12 *Transport of solid dangerous goods in bulk containers*

For bulk containers other than freight containers, the following statement shall be included on the transport document (see 6.9.4.6):

"Bulk container BK(*x*) approved by the competent authority of ..."

Note: "(*x*)" shall be replaced with "1" or "2", as appropriate.

5.4.1.5.13 *Transport of IBCs or portable tanks after the date of expiry of the last periodic test or inspection*

For transport in accordance with 4.1.2.2.2, 6.7.2.19.6.2, 6.7.3.15.6.2 or 6.7.4.14.6.2, a statement to this effect shall be included in the transport document, as follows: "Transport in accordance with 4.1.2.2.2", "Transport in accordance with 6.7.2.19.6.2", "Transport in accordance with 6.7.3.15.6.2" or "Transport in accordance with 6.7.4.14.6.2" as appropriate.

5.4.1.5.14 *Dangerous goods in excepted quantities*

5.4.1.5.14.1 When dangerous goods are transported according to the exceptions for dangerous goods packed in excepted quantities provided for in column 7b of the Dangerous Goods List and chapter 3.5, the words "dangerous goods in excepted quantities" shall be included.

5.4.1.5.15 *Firework classification reference*

When fireworks of UN Nos. 0333, 0334, 0335, 0336 and 0337 are transported, the dangerous goods transport document shall include a classification reference(s) issued by the competent authority.

The classification reference(s) shall consist of the competent authority's state, indicated by the distinguishing sign for motor vehicles in international traffic, the competent authority identification and a unique serial reference. Examples of such classification references are:

– GB/HSE123456

– D/BAM1234

– USA EX20091234.

■ **5.4.1.5.16** *Classification where new data is available (see 2.0.0.2)*

For transport in accordance with 2.0.0.2, a statement to this effect shall be included in the transport document, as follows "Classified in accordance with 2.0.0.2".

■ **5.4.1.5.17** *Transport of UN Nos. 3528, 3529 and 3530*

For transport of UN Nos. 3528, 3529 and 3530, the transport document shall contain the following additional statement "Transport in accordance with special provision 363".

5.4.1.6 Certification

5.4.1.6.1 The dangerous goods transport document shall include a certification or declaration that the consignment is acceptable for transport and that the goods are properly packaged, marked and labelled, and in proper condition for transport in accordance with the applicable regulations. The text for this certification is:

> "I hereby declare that the contents of this consignment are fully and accurately described above/below[*] by the proper shipping name, and are classified, packaged, marked and labelled/placarded, and are in all respects in proper condition for transport according to applicable international and national government regulations."

The certification shall be signed and dated by the consignor. Facsimile signatures are acceptable where applicable laws and regulations recognize the legal validity of facsimile signatures.

5.4.1.6.2 If the dangerous goods documentation is presented to the carrier by means of EDP or EDI transmission techniques, the signature(s) may be electronic signature(s) or may be replaced by the name(s) (in capitals) of the person authorized to sign.

5.4.1.6.3 When the dangerous goods transport information is given to a carrier by EDP or EDI techniques and subsequently the dangerous goods are transferred to a carrier that requires a paper dangerous goods transport document, the carrier shall ensure that the paper document indicates "Original received electronically" and the name of the signatory shall be shown in capital letters.

5.4.2 Container/vehicle packing certificate

5.4.2.1 When dangerous goods are packed or loaded into any container[†] or vehicle, those responsible for packing the container or vehicle shall provide a "container/vehicle packing certificate" specifying the container/vehicle identification number(s) and certifying that the operation has been carried out in accordance with the following conditions:

.1 The container/vehicle was clean, dry and apparently fit to receive the goods;

.2 Packages which need to be segregated in accordance with applicable segregation requirements have not been packed together onto or in the container/vehicle (unless approved by the competent authority concerned in accordance with 7.3.4.1);

.3 All packages have been externally inspected for damage, and only sound packages have been loaded;

---

[*] As appropriate.

[†] See definition of "freight container" in 1.2.1.

.4 Drums have been stowed in an upright position, unless otherwise authorized by the competent authority, and all goods have been properly loaded and, where necessary, adequately braced with securing material to suit the mode(s)* of transport for the intended journey;

.5 Goods loaded in bulk have been evenly distributed within the container/vehicle;

.6 For consignments including goods of class 1 other than division 1.4, the container/vehicle is structurally serviceable in accordance with 7.1.2;

.7 The container/vehicle and packages are properly marked, labelled and placarded, as appropriate;

.8 When substances presenting a risk of asphyxiation are used for cooling or conditioning purposes (such as dry ice (UN 1845) or nitrogen, refrigerated liquid (UN 1977) or argon, refrigerated liquid (UN 1951)), the container/vehicle is externally marked in accordance with 5.5.3.6; and

.9 A dangerous goods transport document, as indicated in 5.4.1, has been received for each dangerous goods consignment loaded in the container/vehicle.

Note: The container/vehicle packing certificate is not required for portable tanks.

5.4.2.2 The information required in the dangerous goods transport document and the container/vehicle packing certificate may be incorporated into a single document; if not, these documents shall be attached one to the other. If the information is incorporated into a single document, the document shall include a signed declaration such as "It is declared that the packing of the goods into the container/vehicle has been carried out in accordance with the applicable provisions". This declaration shall be dated and the person signing this declaration shall be identified on the document. Facsimile signatures are acceptable where applicable laws and regulations recognize the legal validity of facsimile signatures.

5.4.2.3 If the container/vehicle packing certificate is presented to the carrier by means of EDP or EDI transmission techniques, the signature(s) may be electronic signature(s) or may be replaced by the name(s) (in capitals) of the person authorized to sign.

5.4.2.4 When the container/vehicle packing certificate is given to a carrier by EDP or EDI techniques and subsequently the dangerous goods are transferred to a carrier that requires a paper container/vehicle packing certificate, the carrier shall ensure that the paper document indicates "Original received electronically" and the name of the signatory shall be shown in capital letters.

5.4.3 Documentation required aboard the ship

5.4.3.1 Each ship carrying dangerous goods and marine pollutants shall have a special list, manifest† or stowage plan setting out, in accordance with regulation VII/ 4.2 of SOLAS, as amended, and with regulation 4.2 of Annex III of MARPOL, the dangerous goods and marine pollutants and the location thereof. This special list or manifest shall be based on the documentation and certification required in this Code. It shall contain in addition to the information in 5.4.1.4, 5.4.1.5 and, for UN 3359, in 5.5.2.4.1.1, the stowage location and the total quantity of dangerous goods and marine pollutants. A detailed stowage plan, which identifies by class and sets out the location of all dangerous goods and marine pollutants, may be used in place of such special list or manifest. A copy of one of these documents shall be made available before departure to the person or organization designated by the port State authority.

5.4.3.2 Emergency response information

5.4.3.2.1 For consignments of dangerous goods, appropriate information shall be immediately available at all times for use in emergency response to accidents and incidents involving dangerous goods in transport. The information shall be available away from packages containing the dangerous goods and immediately accessible in the event of an incident. Methods of compliance include:

.1 appropriate entries in the special list, manifest or dangerous goods declaration; or

.2 provision of a separate document such as a safety data sheet; or

.3 provision of separate documentation, such as the *Emergency Response Procedures for Ships Carrying Dangerous Goods (EmS Guide)* for use in conjunction with the transport document and the *Medical First Aid Guide for Use in Accidents Involving Dangerous Goods* (MFAG).

5.4.4 Other required information and documentation

5.4.4.1 In certain circumstances, special certificates or other documents are required such as:

△ * See CTU Code.

† Refer to Amendments to the annex to the Convention on facilitation of international maritime traffic, 1965 (resolution FAL.10(35), adopted on 16 January 2009).

.1   a weathering certificate; as required in the individual entries of the Dangerous Goods List;

.2   a certificate exempting a substance, material or article from the provisions of the IMDG Code (such as, see individual entries for charcoal, fishmeal, seedcake);

.3   for new self-reactive substances and organic peroxides or new formulation of currently assigned self-reactive substances and organic peroxides, a statement by the competent authority of the country of origin of the approved classification and conditions of transport.

5.4.5   Multimodal Dangerous Goods Form

5.4.5.1   This form meets the requirements of SOLAS, chapter VII, regulation 4, MARPOL, Annex III, regulation 4 and the provisions of this chapter. The information required by the provisions of this chapter is mandatory; however, the layout of this form is not mandatory.

MULTIMODAL DANGEROUS GOODS FORM

This form may be used as a dangerous goods declaration as it meets the requirements of SOLAS, chapter VII, regulation 4; MARPOL, Annex III, regulation 4.

1 Shipper/Consignor/Sender	2 Transport document number		
	3 Page 1 of pages	4 Shipper's reference	
		5 Freight forwarder's reference	
6 Consignee	7 Carrier (to be completed by the carrier)		
	SHIPPER'S DECLARATION I hereby declare that the contents of this consignment are fully and accurately described below by the proper shipping name, and are classified, packaged, marked and labelled/placarded and are in all respects in proper condition for transport according to the applicable international and national governmental regulations.		

8 This shipment is within the limitations prescribed for: (Delete non-applicable)		9 Additional handling information
PASSENGER AND CARGO AIRCRAFT	CARGO AIRCRAFT ONLY	
10 Vessel/flight No. and date	11 Port/place of loading	
12 Port/place of discharge	13 Destination	

| 14 Shipping marks | Number and kind of packages; description of goods* | Gross mass (kg) | Net mass (kg) | Cube (m^3) |
| | | | | |

| 15 Container identification No./ vehicle registration No. | 16 Seal number(s) | 17 Container/vehicle size and type | 18 Tare mass (kg) | 19 Total gross mass (including tare) (kg) |
| | | | | |

CONTAINER/VEHICLE PACKING CERTIFICATE I hereby declare that the goods described above have been packed/loaded into the container/vehicle identified above in accordance with the applicable provisions.† **MUST BE COMPLETED AND SIGNED FOR ALL CONTAINER/VEHICLE LOADS BY PERSON RESPONSIBLE FOR PACKING/LOADING**	21 RECEIVING ORGANISATION RECEIPT Received the above number of packages/containers/trailers in apparent good order and condition, unless stated hereon: RECEIVING ORGANISATION REMARKS:	
20 Name of company	Haulier's name Vehicle registration No. Signature and date	22 Name of company (OF SHIPPER PREPARING THIS NOTE)
Name/status of declarant		Name/status of declarant
Place and date		Place and date
Signature of declarant	DRIVER'S SIGNATURE	Signature of declarant

* **DANGEROUS GOODS:**
You must specify: UN No., proper shipping name, hazard class, packing group (where assigned), marine pollutant and observe the mandatory requirements under applicable national and international governmental regulations. For the purposes of the IMDG Code, see 5.4.1.4.

† For the purposes of the IMDG Code, see 5.4.2.

Documentary Aspects of the International Transport of Dangerous Goods
Container/Vehicle Packing Certificate

The signature given overleaf in box 20 must be that of the person controlling the container/vehicle operation.

It is certified that:

The container/vehicle was clean, dry and apparently fit to receive the goods.

If the consignments include goods of class 1, other than division 1.4, the container is structurally serviceable.

No incompatible goods have been packed into the container/vehicle unless specially authorized by the competent authority.

All packages have been externally inspected for damage and only sound packages packed.

Drums have been stowed in an upright position unless otherwise authorized by the competent authority.

All packages have been properly packed and secured in the container/vehicle.

When materials are transported in bulk packagings, the cargo has been evenly distributed in the container/vehicle.

The packages and the container/vehicle have been properly marked, labelled and placarded. Any irrelevant mark, labels and placards have been removed.

When solid carbon dioxide (CO_2 – dry ice) is used for cooling purposes, the vehicle or freight container is externally marked in accordance with 5.5.3.6.

When this Dangerous Goods Form is used as a container/vehicle packing certificate only, not a combined document, a dangerous goods declaration signed by the shipper or supplier must have been issued/received to cover each dangerous goods consignment packed in the container.

Note: The container packing certificate is not required for tanks.

MULTIMODAL DANGEROUS GOODS FORM
Continuation sheet

1 Shipper/Consignor/Sender	2 Transport document number		
	3 Page of pages	4 Shipper's reference	
		5 Freight forwarder's reference	

14 Shipping marks	Number and kind of packages; description of goods*	Gross mass (kg)	Net mass (kg)	Cube (m³)

*DANGEROUS GOODS:
You must specify: UN No., proper shipping name, hazard class, packing group (where assigned), marine pollutant and observe the mandatory requirements under applicable national and international governmental regulations. For the purposes of the IMDG Code, see 5.4.1.4.

5.4.6 Retention of dangerous goods transport information

5.4.6.1   The consignor and the carrier shall retain a copy of the dangerous goods transport document and additional information and documentation as specified in this Code, for a minimum period of three months.

5.4.6.2   When the documents are kept electronically or in a computer system, the consignor and the carrier shall be able to reproduce them in a printed form.

5

Chapter 5.5

Special provisions

5.5.1 [Reserved]

5.5.2 **Special provisions applicable to fumigated cargo transport units (UN 3359)**

5.5.2.1 **General**

5.5.2.1.1 Fumigated cargo transport units (UN 3359) containing no other dangerous goods are not subject to any provisions of this Code other than those of this section.

5.5.2.1.2 When the fumigated cargo transport unit is loaded with dangerous goods in addition to the fumigant, any provision of this Code relevant to these goods (including placarding, marking and documentation) applies in addition to the provisions of this section.

5.5.2.1.3 Only cargo transport units that can be closed in such a way that the escape of gas is reduced to a minimum shall be used for the transport of cargo under fumigation.

5.5.2.1.4 The provisions of 3.2 and 5.4.3 apply to all fumigated cargo transport units (UN 3359).

5.5.2.2 **Training**

Persons engaged in the handling of fumigated cargo transport units shall be trained commensurate with their responsibilities.

5.5.2.3 **Marking and placarding**

5.5.2.3.1 A fumigated cargo transport unit shall be marked with a warning mark, as specified in 5.5.2.3.2, affixed at each access point in a location where it will be easily seen by persons opening or entering the cargo transport unit. This mark shall remain on the cargo transport unit until the following provisions are met:

.1 the fumigated cargo transport unit has been ventilated to remove harmful concentrations of fumigant gas; and

.2 the fumigated goods or materials have been unloaded.

5.5.2.3.2 The fumigation warning mark shall be as shown in the figure below.

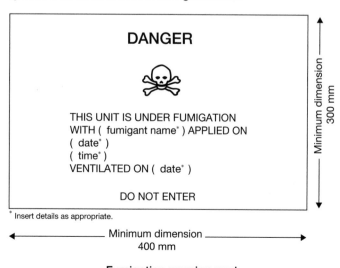

Fumigation warning mark

△ The mark shall be a rectangle. The minimum dimensions shall be 400 mm wide × 300 mm high and the minimum width of the outer line shall be 2 mm. The mark shall be in black print on a white background with lettering not less than 25 mm high. Where dimensions are not specified, all features shall be in approximate proportion to those shown.

△ The method of marking shall be such that this information will still be identifiable on cargo transport units surviving at least three months' immersion in the sea. In considering suitable marking methods, account shall be taken of the ease with which the surface of the cargo transport unit can be marked.

5.5.2.3.3 If the fumigated cargo transport unit has been completely ventilated either by opening the doors of the unit or by mechanical ventilation after fumigation, the date of ventilation shall be marked on the fumigation warning mark.

5.5.2.3.4 When the fumigated cargo transport unit has been ventilated and unloaded, the fumigation warning mark shall be removed.

5.5.2.3.5 Class 9 placards (Model No.9, see 5.2.2.2.2) shall not be affixed to a fumigated cargo transport unit except as required for other class 9 substances or articles packed therein.

5.5.2.4 Documentation

5.5.2.4.1 Documents associated with the transport of cargo transport units that have been fumigated and have not been completely ventilated before transport shall include the following information:

.1 UN 3359, fumigated cargo transport unit, 9, or UN 3359, fumigated cargo transport unit, class 9;

.2 The date and time of fumigation; and

.3 The type and amount of the fumigant used.

5.5.2.4.2 The transport document may be in any form, provided it contains the information required in 5.5.2.4.1. This information shall be easy to identify, legible and durable.

5.5.2.4.3 Instructions for disposal of any residual fumigant including fumigation devices (if used) shall be provided.

5.5.2.4.4 A document is not required when the fumigated cargo transport unit has been completely ventilated and the date of ventilation has been marked on the warning mark (see 5.5.2.3.3 and 5.5.2.3.4).

5.5.2.5 Additional provisions

5.5.2.5.1 Cargo transport units shall be fumigated and handled taking into account the provisions of the MSC.1/Circ.1361 on Revised Recommendations on the safe use of pesticides in ships applicable to the fumigation of cargo transport units.

5.5.2.5.2 When fumigated cargo transport units are stowed under deck, equipment for detecting fumigant gas(es) shall be carried on the ship with instructions for their use.

5.5.2.5.3 Fumigants shall not be applied to the contents of a cargo transport unit once it has been loaded aboard the ship.

5.5.2.5.4 A fumigated cargo transport unit shall not be allowed on board until a sufficient period has elapsed to attain a reasonable uniform gas concentration throughout the cargo in it. Because of variations due to types and amounts of fumigants and commodities and temperature levels, the period between fumigant application and loading of the fumigated cargo transport unit on board the ship shall be determined by the competent authority. Twenty-four hours is normally sufficient for this purpose. Unless the doors of a fumigated cargo transport unit have been opened to allow the fumigant gas(es) and residues to be completely ventilated or the unit has been mechanically ventilated, the shipment shall conform to the provisions of this Code concerning UN 3359. Ventilated cargo transport units shall be marked with the date of ventilation on the fumigation warning mark. When the fumigated goods or materials have been unloaded, the fumigation warning mark shall be removed.

5.5.2.5.5 The master shall be informed prior to the loading of a fumigated cargo transport unit.

5.5.3 Special provisions applicable to packages and cargo transport units containing substances presenting a risk of asphyxiation when used for cooling or conditioning purposes (such as dry ice (UN 1845) or nitrogen, refrigerated liquid (UN 1977) or argon, refrigerated liquid (UN 1951))

Note: See also 1.1.1.7.

5.5.3.1 Scope

5.5.3.1.1 This section is not applicable to substances which may be used for cooling or conditioning purposes when transported as a consignment of dangerous goods. When they are transported as a consignment, these substances shall be transported under the relevant entry of the Dangerous Goods List in chapter 3.2 in accordance with the associated conditions of transport.

5.5.3.1.2   This section is not applicable to gases in cooling cycles.

5.5.3.1.3   Dangerous goods used for cooling or conditioning portable tanks or MEGCs during transport are not subject to this section.

5.5.3.1.4   Cargo transport units containing substances used for cooling or conditioning purposes include cargo transport units containing substances used for cooling or conditioning purposes inside packages as well as cargo transport units with unpackaged substances used for cooling or conditioning purposes.

5.5.3.2   General

5.5.3.2.1   Cargo transport units containing substances used for cooling or conditioning purposes (other than fumigation) during transport are not subject to any provisions of this Code other than those of this section.

5.5.3.2.2   When dangerous goods are loaded in cargo transport units containing substances used for cooling or conditioning purposes, any provisions of this Code relevant to these dangerous goods apply in addition to the provisions of this section. For dangerous goods for which temperature control is required see also 7.3.7.

5.5.3.2.3   [Reserved]

5.5.3.2.4   Persons engaged in the handling or transport of cargo transport units containing substances used for cooling or conditioning purposes shall be trained commensurate with their responsibilities.

5.5.3.3   Packages containing a coolant or conditioner

5.5.3.3.1   Packaged dangerous goods requiring cooling or conditioning assigned to packing instructions P203, P620, P650, P800, P901 or P904 of 4.1.4.1 shall meet the appropriate requirements of that packing instruction.

5.5.3.3.2   For packaged dangerous goods requiring cooling or conditioning assigned to other packing instructions, the packages shall be capable of withstanding very low temperatures and shall not be affected or significantly weakened by the coolant or conditioner. Packages shall be designed and constructed to permit the release of gas to prevent a build-up of pressure that could rupture the packaging. The dangerous goods shall be packed in such a way to prevent movement after the dissipation of any coolant or conditioner.

5.5.3.3.3   Packages containing a coolant or conditioner shall be transported in well-ventilated cargo transport units.

5.5.3.4   Marking of packages containing a coolant or conditioner

5.5.3.4.1   Packages containing dangerous goods used for cooling or conditioning shall be marked with the proper shipping name of these dangerous goods followed by the words "AS COOLANT" or "AS CONDITIONER" as appropriate.

△ 5.5.3.4.2   The marks shall be durable, legible and placed in such a location and of such a size relative to the package as to be readily visible.

5.5.3.5   Cargo transport units containing unpackaged dry ice

5.5.3.5.1   If dry ice in unpackaged form is used, it shall not come into direct contact with the metal structure of a cargo transport unit to avoid embrittlement of the metal. Measures shall be taken to provide adequate insulation between the dry ice and the cargo transport unit by providing a minimum of 30 mm separation (e.g. by using suitable low heat conducting materials such as timber planks, pallets, etc.).

5.5.3.5.2   Where dry ice is placed around packages, measures shall be taken to ensure that packages remain in the original position during transport after the dry ice has dissipated.

5.5.3.6   Marking of cargo transport units

5.5.3.6.1   Cargo transport units containing dangerous goods used for cooling or conditioning purposes shall be marked with a warning mark, as specified in 5.5.3.6.2 affixed at each access point in a location where it will be easily seen by persons opening or entering the cargo transport unit. This mark shall remain on the cargo transport unit until the following provisions are met:

.1   the cargo transport unit has been ventilated to remove harmful concentrations of coolant or conditioner; and

.2   the cooled or conditioned goods have been unloaded.

5.5.3.6.2 The warning mark shall be as shown in the figure below.

Minimum dimension 250 mm

Minimum dimension 150 mm

Coolant/conditioning warning mark for cargo transport units

* Insert proper shipping name of the coolant/conditioner. The lettering shall be in capitals, all be on one line and shall be at least 25 mm high. If the length of the proper shipping name is too long to fit in the space provided, the lettering may be reduced to the maximum size possible to fit. For example: CARBON DIOXIDE, SOLID.

** Insert "AS COOLANT" or "AS CONDITIONER", as appropriate. The lettering shall be in capitals, all be on one line, and be at least 25 mm high.

△ The mark shall be a rectangle. The minimum dimensions shall be 150 mm wide × 250 mm high. The word "WARNING" shall be in red or white and be at least 25 mm high. Where dimensions are not specified, all features shall be in approximate proportion to those shown.

△ The method of marking shall be such that this information will still be identifiable on cargo transport units surviving at least three months' immersion in the sea. In considering suitable marking methods, account shall be taken of the ease with which the surface of the cargo transport unit can be marked.

5.5.3.7 **Documentation**

5.5.3.7.1 Documents associated with the transport of cargo transport units containing or having contained substances used for cooling or conditioning purposes and have not been completely ventilated before transport shall include the following information:

.1 the UN number preceded by the letters "UN"; and

.2 the proper shipping name followed by the words "AS COOLANT" or "AS CONDITIONER", as appropriate.

For example: UN 1845, CARBON DIOXIDE, SOLID, AS COOLANT.

5.5.3.7.2 The transport document may be in any form, provided it contains the information required in 5.5.3.7.1. This information shall be easy to identify, legible and durable.

PART 6

CONSTRUCTION AND TESTING OF PACKAGINGS,
INTERMEDIATE BULK CONTAINERS (IBCs),
LARGE PACKAGINGS, PORTABLE TANKS,
MULTIPLE-ELEMENT GAS CONTAINERS (MEGCs)
AND ROAD TANK VEHICLES

6

Chapter 6.1

Provisions for the construction and testing of packagings (other than for class 6.2 substances)

6.1.1 Applicability and general provisions

6.1.1.1 Applicability

The provisions in this chapter do not apply to:

.1 pressure receptacles;

.2 packages containing radioactive material, which shall comply with the Regulations of the International Atomic Energy Agency (IAEA), except that:

    (i) radioactive material possessing other dangerous properties (subsidiary risks) shall also comply with special provision 172 in chapter 3.3; and

    (ii) low specific activity (LSA) material and surface contaminated objects (SCO) may be carried in certain packagings defined in this Code provided that the supplementary provisions set out in the IAEA Regulations are also met;

.3 packages whose net mass exceeds 400 kg; and

.4 packagings for liquids, other than combination packagings, with capacity exceeding 450 L.

6.1.1.2 General provisions

6.1.1.2.1

The provisions for packagings in 6.1.4 are based on packagings currently used. In order to take into account progress in science and technology, there is no objection to the use of packagings having specifications different from those in 6.1.4, provided that they are equally effective, acceptable to the competent authority and able successfully to withstand the tests described in 6.1.1.2 and 6.1.5. Methods of testing other than those described in this chapter are acceptable, provided that they are equivalent.

△ 6.1.1.2.2

Every packaging intended to contain liquids shall successfully undergo a suitable leakproofness test. This test is part of a quality assurance programme as stipulated in 6.1.1.3 which shows the capability of meeting the appropriate test level indicated in 6.1.5.4.4:

.1 before it is first used for transport;

.2 after remanufacturing or reconditioning, before it is re-used for transport.

For this test, packagings need not have their own closures fitted.

The inner receptacle of a composite packaging may be tested without the outer packaging provided the test results are not affected. This test is not necessary for an inner packaging of a combination packaging.

6.1.1.2.3

Receptacles, parts of receptacles and closures (stoppers) made of plastics which may be directly in contact with a dangerous substance shall be resistant to it and shall not incorporate materials which may react dangerously or form hazardous compounds or lead to softening, weakening or failure of the receptacle or closure.

6.1.1.2.4

Plastics packagings shall be adequately resistant to ageing and to degradation caused either by the substance contained or by ultraviolet radiation. Any permeation of the substance contained shall not constitute a danger under normal conditions of transport.

6.1.1.3

Packagings shall be manufactured, reconditioned and tested under a quality-assurance programme which satisfies the competent authority in order to ensure that each packaging meets the provisions of this chapter.

Note: ISO 16106:2006, *Packaging – Transport packages for dangerous goods – Dangerous goods packagings, intermediate bulk containers (IBCs) and large packagings – Guidelines for the application of ISO 9001*, provides acceptable guidance on procedures which may be followed.

6.1.1.4

Manufacturers and subsequent distributors of packagings shall provide information regarding procedures to be followed and a description of the types and dimensions of closures (including required gaskets) and any other components needed to ensure that packages as presented for transport are capable of passing the applicable performance tests of this chapter.

6.1.2 Code for designating types of packagings

6.1.2.1 The code consists of:

.1 an Arabic numeral indicating the kind of packaging, such as drum, jerrican, etc., followed by

.2 one or more capital letters in Latin characters indicating the nature of the material, such as steel, wood, etc., followed where necessary by

.3 an Arabic numeral indicating the category of packaging within the type to which the packaging belongs.

6.1.2.2 In the case of composite packagings, two capital letters in Latin characters shall be used in sequence in the second position of the code. The first indicates the material of the inner receptacle and the second that of the outer packaging.

6.1.2.3 In the case of combination packagings, only the code number for the outer packaging shall be used.

6.1.2.4 The letters 'T', 'V' or 'W' may follow the packaging code. The letter 'T' signifies a salvage packaging conforming to the provisions of 6.1.5.1.11. The letter 'V' signifies a special packaging conforming to the provisions of 6.1.5.1.7. The letter 'W' signifies that the packaging, although of the same type as that indicated by the code, is manufactured to a specification different to that in 6.1.4 but is considered equivalent under the provisions of 6.1.1.2.

6.1.2.5 The following numerals shall be used for the kinds of packaging:

1 Drum

2 [Reserved]

3 Jerrican

4 Box

5 Bag

6 Composite packaging

6.1.2.6 The following capital letters shall be used for the types of material:

A Steel (all types and surface treatments)

B Aluminium

C Natural wood

D Plywood

F Reconstituted wood

G Fibreboard

H Plastics material

L Textile

M Paper, multiwall

N Metal (other than steel or aluminium)

P Glass, porcelain or stoneware

Note: "Plastics material" is taken to include other polymeric materials such as rubber.

6.1.2.7 The following table indicates the codes to be used for designating types of packagings depending on the kind of packagings, the material used for their construction and their category; it also refers to the paragraphs to be consulted for the appropriate provisions:

Kind	Material	Category	Code	Paragraph
1 Drums	A Steel	non-removable head	1A1	6.1.4.1
		removable head	1A2	
	B Aluminium	non-removable head	1B1	6.1.4.2
		removable head	1B2	
	D Plywood	–	1D	6.1.4.5
	G Fibre	–	1G	6.1.4.7
	H Plastics	non-removable head	1H1	6.1.4.8
		removable head	1H2	
	N Metal, other than steel or aluminium	non-removable head	1N1	6.1.4.3
		removable head	1N2	
2 [Reserved]				

Kind	Material	Category	Code	Paragraph
3 Jerricans	A Steel	non-removable head	3A1	6.1.4.4
		removable head	3A2	
	B Aluminium	non-removable head	3B1	6.1.4.4
		removable head	3B2	
	H Plastics	non-removable head	3H1	6.1.4.8
		removable head	3H2	
4 Boxes	A Steel	–	4A	6.1.4.14
	B Aluminium	–	4B	6.1.4.14
	C Natural wood	ordinary	4C1	6.1.4.9
		with sift-proof walls	4C2	
	D Plywood	–	4D	6.1.4.10
	F Reconstituted wood	–	4F	6.1.4.11
	G Fibreboard	–	4G	6.1.4.12
	H Plastics	expanded	4H1	6.1.4.13
		solid	4H2	
	N Metal, other than steel or aluminium	–	4N	6.1.4.14
5 Bags	H Woven plastics	without inner lining or coating	5H1	6.1.4.16
		sift-proof	5H2	
		water-resistant	5H3	
	H Plastics film	–	5H4	6.1.4.17
	L Textile	without inner lining or coating	5L1	6.1.4.15
		sift-proof	5L2	
		water-resistant	5L3	
	M Paper	multiwall	5M1	6.1.4.18
		multiwall, water-resistant	5M2	
6 Composite packagings	H Plastics receptacle	in steel drum	6HA1	6.1.4.19
		in steel crate or box	6HA2	6.1.4.19
		in aluminium drum	6HB1	6.1.4.19
		in aluminium crate or box	6HB2	6.1.4.19
		in wooden box	6HC	6.1.4.19
		in plywood drum	6HD1	6.1.4.19
		in plywood box	6HD2	6.1.4.19
		in fibre drum	6HG1	6.1.4.19
		in fibreboard box	6HG2	6.1.4.19
		in plastics drum	6HH1	6.1.4.19
		in solid plastics box	6HH2	6.1.4.19
	P Glass, porcelain or stoneware receptacle	in steel drum	6PA1	6.1.4.20
		in steel crate or box	6PA2	6.1.4.20
		in aluminium drum	6PB1	6.1.4.20
		in aluminium crate or box	6PB2	6.1.4.20
		in wooden box	6PC	6.1.4.20
		in plywood drum	6PD1	6.1.4.20
		in wickerwork hamper	6PD2	6.1.4.20
		in fibre drum	6PG1	6.1.4.20
		in fibreboard box	6PG2	6.1.4.20
		in expanded plastics packaging	6PH1	6.1.4.20
		in solid plastics packaging	6PH2	6.1.4.20

6.1.3   Marking

△ **Note 1:** The marks indicate that the packaging which bears them correspond to a successfully tested design type and that it complies with the provisions of this chapter which are related to the manufacture, but not to the use, of the packaging. In itself, therefore, the marks do not necessarily confirm that the packaging may be used for any substance. The type of packaging (such as steel drum), its maximum capacity or mass, and any special provisions are specified for each substance or article in part 3 of this Code.

△ **Note 2:** The marks are intended to be of assistance to packaging manufacturers, reconditioners, packaging users, carriers and regulatory authorities. In relation to the use of a new packaging, the original marks are a means for its manufacturer to identify the type and to indicate those performance test provisions that have been met.

△ **Note 3:** The marks do not always provide full details of the test levels, etc., and these may need to be taken further into account, such as by reference to a test certificate, test reports or register of successfully tested packagings. For example, a packaging having an X or Y mark may be used for substances to which a packing group having a lesser degree of danger has been assigned, with the relevant maximum permissible value of the relative density[*] determined by taking into account the factor 1.5 or 2.25 indicated in the packaging test provisions in 6.1.5 as appropriate, i.e. packing group I packaging tested for products of relative density 1.2 could be used as a packing group II packaging for products of relative density 1.8 or packing group III packaging of relative density 2.7, provided, of course, that all the performance criteria can still be met with the product having the higher relative density.

△ **6.1.3.1**   Each packaging intended for use according to this Code shall bear marks which are durable, legible and placed in such a location and of such a size relative to the packaging as to be readily visible. For packages with a gross mass of more than 30 kg, the marks or a duplicate thereof shall appear on the top or on a side of the packaging. Letters, numerals and symbols shall be at least 12 mm high, except for packagings of 30 L or 30 kg capacity or less, when they shall be at least 6 mm in height, and for packagings of 5 L or 5 kg or less, when they shall be of an appropriate size.

△ The marks shall show:

(a)   The United Nations packaging symbol:

This symbol shall not be used for any purpose other than certifying that a packaging, a flexible bulk container, a portable tank or a MEGC complies with the relevant requirements in chapters 6.1, 6.2, 6.3, 6.5, 6.6, 6.7 or 6.9. For embossed metal packagings the capital letters "UN" may be applied as the symbol.

(b)   The code designating the type of packaging according to 6.1.2.

(c)   A code in two parts:

    (i)   a letter designating the packing group or groups for which the design type has been successfully tested:

        "X" for packing groups I, II and III

        "Y" for packing groups II and III

        "Z" for packing group III only;

    (ii)   the relative density, rounded off to the first decimal, for which the design type has been tested for packagings, without inner packagings, intended to contain liquids; this may be omitted when the relative density does not exceed 1.2. For packagings intended to contain solids or inner packagings, the maximum gross mass in kilograms.

(d)   Either a letter "S", denoting that the packaging is intended for the transport of solids or inner packagings, or, for packagings (other than combination packagings) intended to contain liquids, the hydraulic test pressure which the packaging was shown to withstand in kilopascals, rounded down to the nearest 10 kPa.

---

[*] Relative density (*d*) is considered to be synonymous with specific gravity (SG) and will be used throughout this text.

△ (e) The last two digits of the year during which the packaging was manufactured. Packagings of types 1H and 3H shall also be appropriately marked with the month of manufacture; this may be marked on the packaging in a different place from the remainder of the marks. An appropriate method is:

△   * The last two digits of the year of manufacture may be displayed at that place. In such a case, the two digits of the year in the type approval mark and in the inner circle of the clock shall be identical.

Note: Other methods that provide the minimum required information in a durable, visible and legible form are also acceptable.

(f) The State authorizing the allocation of the mark, indicated by the distinguishing sign for motor vehicles in international traffic.

(g) The name of the manufacturer or other identification of the packaging specified by the competent authority.

△ **6.1.3.2** In addition to the durable marks prescribed in 6.1.3.1, every new metal drum of a capacity greater than 100 L shall bear the marks described in 6.1.3.1 (a) to (e) on the bottom, with an indication of the nominal thickness of at least the metal used in the body (in millimetres, to 0.1 mm), in permanent form (such as embossed). When the nominal thickness of either head of a metal drum is thinner than that of the body, the nominal thickness of the top head, body and bottom head shall be marked on the bottom in permanent form (such as embossed), for example '1.0 – 1.2 – 1.0' or '0.9 – 1.0 – 1.0'. Nominal thicknesses of metal shall be determined according to the appropriate ISO standard, e.g. ISO 3574:1999 for steel. The marks indicated in 6.1.3.1 (f) and (g) shall not be applied in a permanent form (such as embossed) except as provided in 6.1.3.5.

△ **6.1.3.3** Every packaging other than those referred to in 6.1.3.2 liable to undergo a reconditioning process shall bear the marks indicated in 6.1.3.1 (a) to (e) in a permanent form. Marks are permanent if they are able to withstand the reconditioning process (e.g. embossed). For packagings other than metal drums of a capacity greater than 100 L, these permanent marks may replace the corresponding durable markings prescribed in 6.1.3.1.

△ **6.1.3.4** For remanufactured metal drums, if there is no change to the packaging type and no replacement or removal of integral structural components, the required marks need not be permanent (such as embossed). Every other remanufactured metal drum shall bear the marks in 6.1.3.1 (a) to (e) in a permanent form (such as embossed) on the top head or side.

△ **6.1.3.5** Metal drums made from materials (such as stainless steel) designed to be re-used repeatedly may bear the marks indicated in 6.1.3.1 (f) and (g) in a permanent (such as embossed) form.

△ **6.1.3.6** Packagings manufactured with recycled plastics material as defined in 1.2.1 shall be marked "REC". This mark shall be placed near the marks prescribed in 6.1.3.1.

△ **6.1.3.7** Marks shall be applied in the sequence of the subparagraphs in 6.1.3.1; each mark required in these subparagraphs and when appropriate subparagraphs (h) to (j) of 6.1.3.8 shall be clearly separated, e.g. by a slash or space, so as to be easily identifiable. For examples, see 6.1.3.10. Any additional markings authorized by a competent authority shall still enable the other marks required in 6.1.3.1 to be correctly identified.

△ **6.1.3.8** After reconditioning a packaging, the reconditioner shall apply to it, in sequence, durable marks showing:

(h) the State in which the reconditioning was carried out, indicated by the distinguishing sign for motor vehicles in international traffic;

(i) the name of the reconditioner or other identification of the packaging specified by the competent authority;

(j) the year of reconditioning; the letter "R"; and, for every packaging successfully passing the leakproofness test in 6.1.1.2.2, the additional letter "L".

△ **6.1.3.9** When, after reconditioning, the marks required by 6.1.3.1 (a) to (d) no longer appear on the top head or the side of a metal drum, the reconditioner shall apply them in a durable form followed by those required by 6.1.3.8 (h), (i) and (j). These marks shall not identify a greater performance capability than that for which the original design type has been tested and marked.

△ 6.1.3.10   Examples for marking for NEW packagings

 4G/Y145/S/02   as in 6.1.3.1 (a), (b), (c), (d) and (e)   For a new fibreboard box

NL/VL823   as in 6.1.3.1 (f) and (g)

 1A1/Y1.4/150/98   as in 6.1.3.1 (a), (b), (c), (d) and (e)   For a new steel drum to contain liquids

NL/VL824   as in 6.1.3.1 (f) and (g)

 1A2/Y150/S/01   as in 6.1.3.1 (a), (b), (c), (d) and (e)   For a new steel drum to contain solids or inner packagings

NL/VL825   as in 6.1.3.1 (f) and (g)

 4HW/Y136/S/98   as in 6.1.3.1 (a), (b), (c), (d) and (e)   For a new plastics box of a specification equivalent to that indicated by the packaging code

NL/VL826   as in 6.1.3.1 (f) and (g)

 1A2/Y/100/01   as in 6.1.3.1 (a), (b), (c), (d) and (e)   For a remanufactured steel drum to contain liquids of relative density not exceeding 1.2

USA/MM5   as in 6.1.3.1 (f) and (g)

Note: For liquids, the marking of relative density not exceeding 1.2 is optional; see 6.1.3.1 (c)(ii)

△ 6.1.3.11   Examples for marking for RECONDITIONED packagings

 1A1/Y1.4/150/97   as in 6.1.3.1 (a), (b), (c), (d) and (e)

NL/RB/01 RL   as in 6.1.3.8 (h), (i) and (j)

 1A2/Y150/S/99   as in 6.1.3.1 (a), (b), (c), (d) and (e)

USA/RB/00 R   as in 6.1.3.8 (h), (i) and (j)

△ 6.1.3.12   Examples for marking for SALVAGE packagings

 1A2T/Y300/S/01   as in 6.1.3.1 (a), (b), (c), (d) and (e)

USA/abc   as in 6.1.3.1 (f) and (g)

△ **Note:** The marking, for which examples are given in 6.1.3.10, 6.1.3.11 and 6.1.3.12, may be applied in a single line or in multiple lines provided the correct sequence is respected.

6.1.4   Provisions for packagings

6.1.4.0   General provisions

Any permeation of the substance contained in the packaging shall not constitute a danger under normal conditions of transport.

6.1.4.1   Steel drums

1A1   non-removable head
1A2   removable head

6.1.4.1.1 Body and heads shall be constructed of steel sheet of suitable type and adequate thickness in relation to the capacity of the drum and the intended use.

Note: For carbon steel drums, "suitable" steels are identified in ISO 3573:1999, *Hot rolled carbon steel sheet of commercial and drawing qualities,* and ISO 3574:1999, *Cold-reduced carbon steel sheet of commercial and drawing qualities.*

For carbon steel drums below 100 L, "suitable" steels in addition to the above standards are also identified in ISO 11949:1995, *Cold-reduced electrolytic tinplate,* ISO 11950:1995, *Cold-reduced electrolytic chromium/chromium oxide-coated steel,* and ISO 11951:1995, *Cold-reduced blackplate in coil form for the production of tinplate or electrolytic chromium/chromium oxide-coated steel.*

6.1.4.1.2 Body seams of drums intended to contain more than 40 L of liquid shall be welded. Body seams of drums intended to contain solids or 40 L or less of liquids shall be mechanically seamed or welded.

6.1.4.1.3 Chimes shall be mechanically seamed or welded. Separate reinforcing rings may be applied.

6.1.4.1.4 The body of a drum of a capacity greater than 60 L shall, in general, have at least two expanded rolling hoops or, alternatively, at least two separate rolling hoops. If there are separate rolling hoops, they shall be fitted tightly on the body and so secured that they cannot shift. Rolling hoops shall not be spot-welded.

6.1.4.1.5 Openings for filling, emptying and venting in the bodies or heads of drums with a non-removable head (1A1) shall not exceed 7 cm in diameter. Drums with larger openings are considered to be of the removable-head type (1A2). Closures for openings in the bodies and heads of drums shall be so designed and applied that they will remain secure and leakproof under normal conditions of transport. Closure flanges may be mechanically seamed or welded in place. Gaskets or other sealing elements shall be used with closures, unless the closure is inherently leakproof.

6.1.4.1.6 Closure devices for removable-head drums shall be so designed and applied that they will remain secure and drums will remain leakproof under normal conditions of transport. Gaskets or other sealing elements shall be used with all removable heads.

6.1.4.1.7 If materials used for body, heads, closures and fittings are not in themselves compatible with the contents to be transported, suitable internal protective coatings or treatments shall be applied. These coatings or treatments shall retain their properties under normal conditions of transport.

6.1.4.1.8 Maximum capacity of drum: 450 L.

6.1.4.1.9 Maximum net mass: 400 kg.

6.1.4.2 **Aluminium drums**
>   1B1   non-removable head
>   1B2   removable head

6.1.4.2.1 Body and heads shall be constructed of aluminium at least 99% pure or of an aluminium-based alloy. Material shall be of a suitable type and of adequate thickness in relation to the capacity of the drum and the intended use.

6.1.4.2.2 All seams shall be welded. Chime seams, if any, shall be reinforced by the application of separate reinforcing rings.

6.1.4.2.3 The body of a drum of a capacity greater than 60 L shall, in general, have at least two expanded rolling hoops or, alternatively, at least two separate rolling hoops. If there are separate rolling hoops, they shall be fitted tightly on the body and so secured that they cannot shift. Rolling hoops shall not be spot-welded.

6.1.4.2.4 Openings for filling, emptying and venting in the bodies or heads of drums with a non-removable head (1B1) shall not exceed 7 cm in diameter. Drums with larger openings are considered to be of the removable-head type (1B2). Closures for openings in the bodies and heads of drums shall be so designed and applied that they will remain secure and leakproof under normal conditions of transport. Closure flanges shall be welded in place so that the weld provides a leakproof seam. Gaskets or other sealing elements shall be used with closures, unless the closure is inherently leakproof.

6.1.4.2.5 Closure devices for removable-head drums shall be so designed and applied that they will remain secure and drums will remain leakproof under normal conditions of transport. Gaskets or other sealing elements shall be used with all removable heads.

6.1.4.2.6 Maximum capacity of drum: 450 L.

6.1.4.2.7 Maximum net mass: 400 kg.

6.1.4.3 **Drums of metal other than aluminium or steel**
>   1N1   non-removable head
>   1N2   removable head

6.1.4.3.1 The body and heads shall be constructed of metal or metal alloy other than steel or aluminium. Material shall be of a suitable type and of adequate thickness in relation to the capacity of the drum and to its intended use.

6.1.4.3.2 Chime seams, if any, shall be reinforced by the application of separate reinforcing rings. All seams, if any, shall be joined (welded, soldered, etc.) in accordance with the technical state of the art for the used metal or metal alloy.

6.1.4.3.3 The body of a drum of a capacity greater than 60 L shall, in general, have at least two expanded rolling hoops or, alternatively, at least two separate rolling hoops. If there are separate rolling hoops, they shall be fitted tightly on the body and so secured that they cannot shift. Rolling hoops shall not be spot-welded.

6.1.4.3.4 Openings for filling, emptying and venting in the bodies or heads of non-removable-head (1N1) drums shall not exceed 7 cm in diameter. Drums with larger openings are considered to be of the removable-head type (1N2). Closures for openings in the bodies and heads of drums shall be so designed and applied that they will remain secure and leakproof under normal conditions of transport. Closure flanges shall be joined in place (welded, soldered, etc.) in accordance with the technical state of the art for the used metal or metal alloy so that the seam join is leakproof. Gaskets or other sealing elements shall be used with closures, unless the closure is inherently leakproof.

6.1.4.3.5 Closure devices for removable-head drums shall be so designed and applied that they will remain secure and drums will remain leakproof under normal conditions of transport. Gaskets or other sealing elements shall be used with all removable heads.

6.1.4.3.6 Maximum capacity of drum: 450 L.

6.1.4.3.7 Maximum net mass: 400 kg.

6.1.4.4 Steel or aluminium jerricans

      3A1   steel, non-removable head
      3A2   steel, removable head
      3B1   aluminium, non-removable head
      3B2   aluminium, removable head

6.1.4.4.1 Body and heads shall be constructed of steel sheet, of aluminium at least 99% pure or of an aluminium-based alloy. Material shall be of a suitable type and of adequate thickness in relation to the capacity of the jerrican and to its intended use.

6.1.4.4.2 Chimes of steel jerricans shall be mechanically seamed or welded. Body seams of steel jerricans intended to contain more than 40 L of liquid shall be welded. Body seams of steel jerricans intended to contain 40 L or less shall be mechanically seamed or welded. For aluminium jerricans, all seams shall be welded. Chime seams, if any, shall be reinforced by the application of a separate reinforcing ring.

6.1.4.4.3 Openings in jerricans (3A1 and 3B1) shall not exceed 7 cm in diameter. Jerricans with larger openings are considered to be of the removable-head type (3A2 and 3B2). Closures shall be so designed that they will remain secure and leakproof under normal conditions of transport. Gaskets or other sealing elements shall be used with closures, unless the closure is inherently leakproof.

6.1.4.4.4 If materials used for body, heads, closures and fittings are not in themselves compatible with the contents to be transported, suitable internal protective coatings or treatments shall be applied. These coatings or treatments shall retain their protective properties under normal conditions of transport.

6.1.4.4.5 Maximum capacity of jerrican: 60 L.

6.1.4.4.6 Maximum net mass: 120 kg.

6.1.4.5 Plywood drums

      1D

6.1.4.5.1 The wood used shall be well seasoned, commercially dry and free from any defect likely to lessen the effectiveness of the drum for the purpose intended. If a material other than plywood is used for the manufacture of the heads, it shall be of a quality equivalent to the plywood.

6.1.4.5.2 At least two-ply plywood shall be used for the body and at least three-ply plywood for the heads; the plies shall be firmly glued together by a water-resistant adhesive with their grain crosswise.

6.1.4.5.3 The body and heads of the drum and their joins shall be of a design appropriate to the capacity of the drum and its intended use.

6.1.4.5.4 In order to prevent sifting of the contents, lids shall be lined with kraft paper or some other equivalent material, which shall be securely fastened to the lid and extend to the outside along its full circumference.

6.1.4.5.5   Maximum capacity of drum: 250 L.

6.1.4.5.6   Maximum net mass: 400 kg.

6.1.4.6   [Reserved]

6.1.4.7   **Fibre drums**
                 1G

6.1.4.7.1   The body of the drum shall consist of multiple plies of heavy paper or fibreboard (without corrugations) firmly glued or laminated together and may include one or more protective layers of bitumen, waxed kraft paper, metal foil, plastics material, etc.

6.1.4.7.2   Heads shall be of natural wood, fibreboard, metal, plywood, plastics or other suitable material and may include one or more protective layers of bitumen, waxed kraft paper, metal foil, plastics material, etc.

6.1.4.7.3   The body and heads of the drum and their joins shall be of a design appropriate to the capacity of the drum and its intended use.

6.1.4.7.4   The assembled packaging shall be sufficiently water-resistant so as not to delaminate under normal conditions of transport.

6.1.4.7.5   Maximum capacity of drum: 450 L.

6.1.4.7.6   Maximum net mass: 400 kg.

6.1.4.8   **Plastics drums and jerricans**
                 1H1   drums, non-removable head
                 1H2   drums, removable head
                 3H1   jerricans, non-removable head
                 3H2   jerricans, removable head

6.1.4.8.1   The packaging shall be manufactured from suitable plastics material and be of adequate strength in relation to its capacity and intended use. Except for *recycled plastics material* as defined in 1.2.1, no used material other than production residues or regrind from the same manufacturing process may be used. The packaging shall be adequately resistant to ageing and to degradation caused by the substance contained or by ultraviolet radiation.

6.1.4.8.2   If protection against ultraviolet radiation is required, it shall be provided by the addition of carbon black or other suitable pigments or inhibitors. These additives shall be compatible with the contents and remain effective throughout the life of the packaging. Where use is made of carbon black, pigments or inhibitors other than those used in the manufacture of the tested design type, retesting may be waived if the carbon black content does not exceed 2% by mass or if the pigment content does not exceed 3% by mass; the content of inhibitors of ultraviolet radiation is not limited.

6.1.4.8.3   Additives serving purposes other than protection against ultraviolet radiation may be included in the composition of the plastics material, provided that they do not adversely affect the chemical and physical properties of the material of the packaging. In such circumstances, retesting may be waived.

6.1.4.8.4   The wall thickness at every point of the packaging shall be appropriate to its capacity and intended use, taking into account the stresses to which each point is liable to be exposed.

6.1.4.8.5   Openings for filling, emptying and venting in the bodies or heads of non-removable-head drums (1H1) and jerricans (3H1) shall not exceed 7 cm in diameter. Drums and jerricans with larger openings are considered to be of the removable-head type (1H2 and 3H2). Closures for openings in the bodies or heads of drums and jerricans shall be so designed and applied that they will remain secure and leakproof under normal conditions of transport. Gaskets or other sealing elements shall be used with closures, unless the closure is inherently leakproof.

6.1.4.8.6   Closure devices for removable-head drums and jerricans shall be so designed and applied that they will remain secure and leakproof under normal conditions of transport. Gaskets shall be used with all removable heads unless the drum or jerrican design is such that, where the removable head is properly secured, the drum or jerrican is inherently leakproof.

6.1.4.8.7   Maximum capacity of drums and jerricans: 1H1, 1H2: 450 L
                                                      3H1, 3H2: 60 L

6.1.4.8.8   Maximum net mass: 1H1, 1H2: 400 kg
                                    3H1, 3H2: 120 kg

6

6.1.4.9 **Boxes of natural wood**

4C1   ordinary

4C2   with sift-proof walls

6.1.4.9.1   The wood used shall be well seasoned, commercially dry and free from defects that would materially lessen the strength of any part of the box. The strength of the material used and the method of construction shall be appropriate to the capacity and intended use of the box. The tops and bottoms may be made of water-resistant reconstituted wood such as hardboard, particle board or other suitable type.

6.1.4.9.2   Fastenings shall be resistant to vibration experienced under normal conditions of transport. Nailing into the end shall be avoided whenever practicable. Joins which are likely to be highly stressed shall be made using clenched or annular ring nails or equivalent fastenings.

6.1.4.9.3   Box 4C2: each part shall consist of one piece or be equivalent thereto. Parts are considered equivalent to one piece when one of the following methods of glued assembly is used: Lindermann joint, tongue and groove joint, ship lap or rabbet joint or butt joint, all with at least two corrugated metal fasteners at each joint.

6.1.4.9.4   Maximum net mass: 400 kg.

6.1.4.10 **Plywood boxes**

4D

6.1.4.10.1   Plywood used shall be at least three-ply. It shall be made from well-seasoned rotary-cut, sliced or sawn veneer, commercially dry and free from defects that would materially lessen the strength of the box. The strength of the material used and the method of construction shall be appropriate to the capacity and intended use of the box. All adjacent plies shall be glued with water-resistant adhesive. Other suitable materials may be used together with plywood in the construction of boxes. Boxes shall be firmly nailed or secured to corner posts or ends or be assembled by equally suitable devices.

6.1.4.10.2   Maximum net mass: 400 kg.

6.1.4.11 **Reconstituted wood boxes**

4F

6.1.4.11.1   The walls of boxes shall be made of water-resistant reconstituted wood such as hardboard, particle board or other suitable type. The strength of the material used and the method of construction shall be appropriate to the capacity of the boxes and their intended use.

6.1.4.11.2   Other parts of the boxes may be made of other suitable material.

6.1.4.11.3   Boxes shall be securely assembled by means of suitable devices.

6.1.4.11.4   Maximum net mass: 400 kg.

6.1.4.12 **Fibreboard boxes**

4G

6.1.4.12.1   Strong and good-quality solid or double-faced corrugated fibreboard (single or multiwall) shall be used, appropriate to the capacity of the box and to its intended use. The water resistance of the outer surface shall be such that the increase in mass, as determined in a test carried out over a period of 30 minutes by the Cobb method of determining water absorption, is not greater than 155 g/m^2 – see ISO 535:1991. It shall have proper bending qualities. Fibreboard shall be cut, creased without scoring, and slotted so as to permit assembly without cracking, surface breaks or undue bending. The fluting of corrugated fibreboard shall be firmly glued to the facings.

6.1.4.12.2   The ends of boxes may have a wooden frame or be entirely of wood or other suitable material. Reinforcements of wooden battens or other suitable material may be used.

6.1.4.12.3   Manufacturing joins in the body of boxes shall be taped, lapped and glued or lapped and stitched with metal staples. Lapped joins shall have an appropriate overlap.

6.1.4.12.4   Where closing is effected by gluing or taping, a water-resistant adhesive shall be used.

6.1.4.12.5   Boxes shall be designed so as to provide a good fit to the contents.

6.1.4.12.6   Maximum net mass: 400 kg.

6.1.4.13 **Plastics boxes**

4H1   expanded plastics boxes

4H2   solid plastics boxes

6.1.4.13.1 The box shall be manufactured from suitable plastics material and be of adequate strength in relation to its capacity and intended use. The box shall be adequately resistant to ageing and to degradation caused either by the substance contained or by ultraviolet radiation.

6.1.4.13.2 An expanded plastics box shall comprise two parts made of a moulded expanded plastics material, a bottom section containing cavities for the inner packagings and a top section covering and interlocking with the bottom section. The top and bottom sections shall be designed so that the inner packagings fit snugly. The closure cap for any inner packaging shall not be in contact with the inside of the top section of this box.

6.1.4.13.3 For dispatch, an expanded plastics box shall be closed with a self-adhesive tape having sufficient tensile strength to prevent the box from opening. The adhesive tape shall be weather-resistant and its adhesive compatible with the expanded plastics material of the box. Other closing devices at least equally effective may be used.

6.1.4.13.4 For solid plastics boxes, protection against ultraviolet radiation, if required, shall be provided by the addition of carbon black or other suitable pigments or inhibitors. These additives shall be compatible with the contents and remain effective throughout the life of the box. Where use is made of carbon black, pigments or inhibitors other than those used in the manufacture of the tested design type, retesting may be waived if the carbon black content does not exceed 2% by mass or if the pigment content does not exceed 3% by mass; the content of inhibitors of ultraviolet radiation is not limited.

6.1.4.13.5 Additives serving purposes other than protection against ultraviolet radiation may be included in the composition of the plastics material provided that they do not adversely affect the chemical and physical properties of the material of the box. In such circumstances, retesting may be waived.

6.1.4.13.6 Solid plastics boxes shall have closure devices made of a suitable material of adequate strength and be so designed as to prevent the box from unintentional opening.

6.1.4.13.7 Maximum net mass: 4H1: 60 kg
4H2: 400 kg

6.1.4.14 **Steel, aluminium or other metal boxes**

4A steel boxes

4B aluminium boxes

4N metal, other than steel or aluminium, boxes

6.1.4.14.1 The strength of the metal and the construction of the box shall be appropriate to the capacity of the box and to its intended use.

6.1.4.14.2 Boxes shall be lined with fibreboard or felt packing pieces or shall have an inner liner or coating of suitable material, as required. If a double-seamed metal liner is used, steps shall be taken to prevent the ingress of substances, particularly explosives, into the recesses of the seams.

6.1.4.14.3 Closures may be of any suitable type; they shall remain secured under normal conditions of transport.

6.1.4.14.4 Maximum net mass: 400 kg.

6.1.4.15 **Textile bags**

5L1   without inner lining or coating

5L2   sift-proof

5L3   water-resistant

6.1.4.15.1 The textiles used shall be of good quality. The strength of the fabric and the construction of the bag shall be appropriate to the capacity of the bag and its intended use.

6.1.4.15.2 Bags, sift-proof, 5L2: the bag shall be made sift-proof, for example by the use of:

.1   paper bonded to the inner surface of the bag by a water-resistant adhesive such as bitumen; or

.2   plastics film bonded to the inner surface of the bag; or

.3   one or more inner liners made of paper or plastics material.

6.1.4.15.3 Bags, water-resistant, 5L3: to prevent the entry of moisture, the bag shall be made waterproof, for example by the use of:

.1   separate inner liners of water-resistant paper (such as waxed kraft paper, tarred paper or plastics-coated kraft paper); or

.2   plastics film bonded to the inner surface of the bag; or

.3   one or more inner liners made of plastics material.

6.1.4.15.4   Maximum net mass: 50 kg.

6.1.4.16   **Woven plastics bags**

   5H1   without inner liner or coating

   5H2   sift-proof

   5H3   water-resistant

6.1.4.16.1   Bags shall be made from stretched tapes or monofilaments of a suitable plastics material. The strength of the material used and the construction of the bag shall be appropriate to the capacity of the bag and its intended use.

6.1.4.16.2   If the fabric is woven flat, the bags shall be made by sewing or some other method ensuring closure of the bottom and one side. If the fabric is tubular, the bag shall be closed by sewing, weaving or some other equally strong method of closure.

6.1.4.16.3   Bags, sift-proof, 5H2: the bag shall be made sift-proof, for example by means of:

   .1   paper or a plastics film bonded to the inner surface of the bag; or

   .2   one or more separate inner liners made of paper or plastics material.

6.1.4.16.4   Bags, water-resistant, 5H3: to prevent the entry of moisture, the bag shall be made waterproof, for example by means of:

   .1   separate inner liners of water-resistant paper (such as waxed kraft paper, double-tarred kraft paper or plastics-coated kraft paper); or

   .2   plastics film bonded to the inner or outer surface of the bag; or

   .3   one or more inner plastics liners.

6.1.4.16.5   Maximum net mass: 50 kg.

6.1.4.17   **Plastics film bags**

   5H4

6.1.4.17.1   Bags shall be made of a suitable plastics material. The strength of the material used and the construction of the bag shall be appropriate to the capacity of the bag and its intended use. Joins and closures shall withstand pressures and impacts liable to occur under normal conditions of transport.

6.1.4.17.2   Maximum net mass: 50 kg.

6.1.4.18   **Paper bags**

   5M1   multiwall

   5M2   multiwall, water-resistant

6.1.4.18.1   Bags shall be made of a suitable kraft paper or of an equivalent paper with at least three plies, the middle ply of which may be net-cloth with adhesive bonding to the outermost ply. The strength of the paper and the construction of the bags shall be appropriate to the capacity of the bag and its intended use. Joins and closures shall be sift-proof.

6.1.4.18.2   Bags 5M2: to prevent the entry of moisture, a bag of four plies or more shall be made waterproof by the use of either a water-resistant ply as one of the two outermost plies or a water-resistant barrier made of a suitable protective material between the two outermost plies; a bag of three plies shall be made waterproof by the use of a water-resistant ply as the outermost ply. Where there is a danger of the substance contained reacting with moisture or where it is packed damp, a waterproof ply or barrier, such as double-tarred kraft paper, plastics-coated kraft paper, plastics film bonded to the inner surface of the bag, or one or more inner plastics liners, shall also be placed next to the substance. Joins and closures shall be waterproof.

6.1.4.18.3   Maximum net mass: 50 kg.

6.1.4.19   **Composite packagings (plastics material)**

   6HA1   plastics receptacle with outer steel drum

   6HA2   plastics receptacle with outer steel crate or box

   6HB1   plastics receptacle with outer aluminium drum

   6HB2   plastics receptacle with outer aluminium crate or box

   6HC   plastics receptacle with outer wooden box

   6HD1   plastics receptacle with outer plywood drum

   6HD2   plastics receptacle with outer plywood box

> 6HG1 plastics receptacle with outer fibre drum
> 6HG2 plastics receptacle with outer fibreboard box
> 6HH1 plastics receptacle with outer plastics drum
> 6HH2 plastics receptacle with outer solid plastics box

6.1.4.19.1 *Inner receptacle*

.1 The provisions of 6.1.4.8.1 and 6.1.4.8.3 to 6.1.4.8.6 shall apply to inner plastics receptacles.

.2 The inner plastics receptacle shall fit snugly inside the outer packaging, which shall be free of any projection that might abrade the plastics material.

.3 Maximum capacity of inner receptacle:
6HA1, 6HB1, 6HD1, 6HG1, 6HH1	250 L
6HA2, 6HB2, 6HC, 6HD2, 6HG2, 6HH2	60 L

.4 Maximum net mass:
6HA1, 6HB1, 6HD1, 6HG1, 6HH1	400 kg
6HA2, 6HB2, 6HC, 6HD2, 6HG2, 6HH2	75 kg

6.1.4.19.2 *Outer packaging*

.1 Plastics receptacle with outer steel or aluminium drum (6HA1 or 6HB1): the relevant provisions of 6.1.4.1 or 6.1.4.2, as appropriate, shall apply to the construction of the outer packaging.

.2 Plastics receptacle with outer steel or aluminium crate or box (6HA2 or 6HB2): the relevant provisions of 6.1.4.14 shall apply to the construction of the outer packaging.

.3 Plastics receptacle with outer wooden box 6HC: the relevant provisions of 6.1.4.9 shall apply to the construction of the outer packaging.

.4 Plastics receptacle with outer plywood drum 6HD1: the relevant provisions of 6.1.4.5 shall apply to the construction of the outer packaging.

.5 Plastics receptacle with outer plywood box 6HD2: the relevant provisions of 6.1.4.10 shall apply to the construction of the outer packaging.

.6 Plastics receptacle with outer fibre drum 6HG1: the provisions of 6.1.4.7.1 to 6.1.4.7.4 shall apply to the construction of the outer packaging.

.7 Plastics receptacle with outer fibreboard box 6HG2: the relevant provisions of 6.1.4.12 shall apply to the construction of the outer packaging.

.8 Plastics receptacle with outer plastics drum 6HH1: the provisions of 6.1.4.8.1 and 6.1.4.8.2 to 6.1.4.8.6 shall apply to the construction of the outer packaging.

.9 Plastics receptacle with outer solid plastics box (including corrugated plastics material) 6HH2: the provisions of 6.1.4.13.1 and 6.1.4.13.4 to 6.1.4.13.6 shall apply to the construction of the outer packaging.

6.1.4.20 **Composite packagings (glass, porcelain or stoneware)**

> 6PA1 receptacle with outer steel drum
> 6PA2 receptacle with outer steel crate or box
> 6PB1 receptacle with outer aluminium drum
> 6PB2 receptacle with outer aluminium crate or box
> 6PC receptacle with outer wooden box
> 6PD1 receptacle with outer plywood drum
> 6PD2 receptacle with outer wickerwork hamper
> 6PG1 receptacle with outer fibre drum
> 6PG2 receptacle with outer fibreboard box
> 6PH1 receptacle with outer expanded plastics packaging
> 6PH2 receptacle with outer solid plastics packaging

6.1.4.20.1 *Inner receptacle*

.1 Receptacles shall be of a suitable form (cylindrical or pear-shaped) and be made of good-quality material free from any defect that could impair their strength. The walls shall be sufficiently thick at every point.

.2 Screw-threaded plastics closures, ground glass stoppers or closures at least equally effective shall be used as closures for receptacles. Any part of the closure likely to come into contact with the contents of the receptacle shall be resistant to those contents. Care shall be taken to ensure that the closures are so fitted as to be leakproof and are suitably secured to prevent any loosening during transport. If vented closures are necessary, they shall comply with 4.1.1.8.

.3 The receptacle shall be firmly secured in the outer packaging by means of cushioning and/or absorbent materials.

.4 Maximum capacity of receptacle: 60 L.

.5 Maximum net mass: 75 kg.

6.1.4.20.2 *Outer packaging*

.1 Receptacle with outer steel drum 6PA1: the relevant provisions of 6.1.4.1 shall apply to the construction of the outer packaging. The removable lid required for this type of packaging may nevertheless be in the form of a cap.

.2 Receptacle with outer steel crate or box 6PA2: the relevant provisions of 6.1.4.14 shall apply to the construction of the outer packaging. For cylindrical receptacles, the outer packaging shall, when upright, rise above the receptacle and its closure. If the crate surrounds a pear-shaped receptacle and is of matching shape, the outer packaging shall be fitted with a protective cover (cap).

.3 Receptacle with outer aluminium drum 6PB1: the relevant provisions of 6.1.4.2 shall apply to the construction of the outer packaging.

.4 Receptacle with outer aluminium crate or box 6PB2: the relevant provisions of 6.1.4.14 shall apply to the construction of the outer packaging.

.5 Receptacle with outer wooden box 6PC: the relevant provisions of 6.1.4.9 shall apply to the construction of the outer packaging.

.6 Receptacle with outer plywood drum 6PD1: the relevant provisions of 6.1.4.5 shall apply to the construction of the outer packaging.

.7 Receptacle with outer wickerwork hamper 6PD2: the wickerwork hamper shall be properly made with material of good quality. It shall be fitted with a protective cover (cap) so as to prevent damage to the receptacle.

.8 Receptacle with outer fibre drum 6PG1: the relevant provisions of 6.1.4.7.1 to 6.1.4.7.4 shall apply to the body of the outer packaging.

.9 Receptacle with outer fibreboard box 6PG2: the relevant provisions of 6.1.4.12 shall apply to the construction of the outer packaging.

.10 Receptacle with outer expanded plastics or solid plastics packaging (6PH1 or 6PH2): the materials of both outer packagings shall meet the relevant provisions of 6.1.4.13. Solid plastics packaging shall be manufactured from high-density polyethylene or some other comparable plastics material. The removable lid for this type of packaging may nevertheless be in the form of a cap.

6.1.5 Test provisions for packagings

6.1.5.1 Performance and frequency of tests

6.1.5.1.1 The design type of each packaging shall be tested as provided in this section, in accordance with procedures established by the competent authority.

6.1.5.1.2 Each packaging design type shall successfully pass the tests prescribed in this chapter before being used. A packaging design type is defined by the design, size, material and thickness, manner of construction and packing, but may include various surface treatments. It also includes packagings which differ from the design type only in their lesser design height.

6.1.5.1.3 Tests shall be repeated on production samples at intervals established by the competent authority. For such tests on paper or fibreboard packagings, preparation at ambient conditions is considered equivalent to the provisions of 6.1.5.2.3.

6.1.5.1.4 Tests shall also be repeated after each modification which alters the design, material or manner of construction of a packaging.

6.1.5.1.5 The competent authority may permit the selective testing of packagings that differ only in minor respects from a tested type, such as smaller sizes of inner packagings or inner packagings of lower net mass; and packagings such as drums, bags and boxes which are produced with small reductions in external dimensions.

6.1.5.1.6 [Reserved]

△ **Note:** For the conditions for using different inner packagings in an outer packaging and permissible variations in inner packagings, see 4.1.1.5.1. These conditions do not limit the use of inner packagings when applying 6.1.5.1.7.

6.1.5.1.7 Articles or inner packagings of any type for solids or liquids may be assembled and transported without testing in an outer packaging under the following conditions:

.1 The outer packaging shall have been successfully tested in accordance with 6.1.5.3 with fragile (such as glass) inner packagings containing liquids, using the drop height for packing group I.

.2 The total combined gross mass of inner packagings shall not exceed one half the gross mass of inner packagings used for the drop test in .1 above.

.3 The thickness of the cushioning material between inner packagings and between inner packagings and the outside of the packaging shall not be reduced below the corresponding thicknesses in the originally tested packaging; and when a single inner packaging was used in the original test, the thicknesses of the cushioning between inner packagings shall not be less than the thickness of cushioning between the outside of the packaging and the inner packaging in the original test. When either fewer or smaller inner packagings are used (as compared to the inner packagings used in the drop test), sufficient additional cushioning material shall be used to take up void spaces.

.4 The outer packaging shall have successfully passed the stacking test in 6.1.5.6 while empty. The total mass of identical packages shall be based on the combined mass of inner packagings used in the drop test in .1 above.

.5 Inner packagings containing liquids shall be completely surrounded with a sufficient quantity of absorbent material to absorb the entire liquid contents of the inner packagings.

.6 When the outer packaging is intended to contain inner packagings for liquids and is not leakproof, or is intended to contain inner packagings for solids and is not sift-proof, a means of containing any liquid or solid contents in the event of leakage shall be provided in the form of a leakproof liner, plastics bag or other equally efficient means of containment. For packagings containing liquids, the absorbent material required in .5 above shall be placed inside the means of containing the liquid contents.

.7 Packagings shall be marked in accordance with section 6.1.3 as having been tested to packing group I performance for combination packagings. The marked gross mass, in kilograms, shall be the sum of the mass of the outer packaging plus one half of the mass of the inner packaging(s) as used for the drop test referred to in .1 above. Such a packaging mark shall also contain the letter 'V' as described in 6.1.2.4.

6.1.5.1.8 The competent authority may at any time require proof, by tests in accordance with this section, that serially produced packagings meet the provisions of the design type tests.

6.1.5.1.9 If an inner treatment or coating is required for safety reasons, it shall retain its protective properties after the tests.

6.1.5.1.10 Provided the validity of the test results is not affected, and with the approval of the competent authority, several tests may be made on one sample.

6.1.5.1.11 *Salvage packagings*

6.1.5.1.11.1 Salvage packagings (see 1.2.1) shall be tested and marked in accordance with the provisions applicable to packing group II packagings intended for the transport of solids or inner packagings, except as follows:

.1 The test substance used in performing the tests shall be water and the packagings shall be filled to not less than 98% of their maximum capacity. It is permissible to use additives, such as bags of lead shot, to achieve the requisite total package mass so long as they are placed in such a way that the test results are not affected. Alternatively, in performing the drop test, the drop height may be varied in accordance with 6.1.5.3.5(b);

.2 Packagings shall, in addition, have been successfully subjected to the leakproofness test at 30 kPa, with the results of this test reflected in the test report required by 6.1.5.7; and

.3 Packagings shall be marked with the letter 'T' as described in 6.1.2.4.

6.1.5.2 Preparation of packagings for testing

6.1.5.2.1 Tests shall be carried out on packagings prepared as for transport, including, with respect to combination packagings, the inner packagings used. Inner or single receptacles or packagings, other than bags, shall be filled to not less than 98% of their maximum capacity for liquids or 95% for solids. Bags shall be filled to the maximum mass at which they may be used. For combination packagings where the inner packaging is designed to carry liquids and solids, separate testing is required for both solid and liquid contents. The substances or articles to be transported in the packagings may be replaced by other substances or articles except where this would invalidate the results of the tests. For solids, when another substance is used, it shall have the same physical characteristics (mass, grain size, etc.) as the substance to be carried. It is permissible to use additives, such as bags of lead shot, to achieve the requisite total package mass, so long as they are placed so that the test results are not affected.

6.1.5.2.2 In the drop tests for liquids, when another substance is used, it shall be of similar relative density and viscosity to those of the substance being transported. Water may also be used for the liquid drop test under the conditions in 6.1.5.3.5.

6.1.5.2.3 Paper or fibreboard packagings shall be conditioned for at least 24 hours in an atmosphere having controlled temperature and relative humidity (r.h.). There are three options, one of which shall be chosen. The preferred atmosphere is 23°C ± 2°C and 50% ± 2% r.h. The two other options are 20°C ± 2°C and 65% ± 2% r.h. or 27°C ± 2°C and 65% ± 2% r.h.

Note: Average values shall fall within these limits. Short-term fluctuations and measurement limitations may cause individual measurements to vary by up to ± 5% relative humidity without significant impairment of test reproducibility.

6.1.5.2.4 Additional steps shall be taken to ascertain that the plastics material used in the manufacture of plastics drums, plastics jerricans and composite packagings (plastics material) intended to contain liquids complies with the provisions in 6.1.1.2, 6.1.4.8.1 and 6.1.4.8.3. This may be done, for example, by submitting sample receptacles or packagings to a preliminary test extending over a long period, for example six months, during which the samples would remain filled with the substances they are intended to contain and after which the samples shall be submitted to the applicable tests listed in 6.1.5.3, 6.1.5.4, 6.1.5.5, and 6.1.5.6. For substances which may cause stress cracking or weakening in plastics drums or jerricans, the sample, filled with the substance or another substance that is known to have at least as severe stress cracking influence on the plastics materials in question, shall be subjected to a superimposed load equivalent to the total mass of identical packages which might be stacked on it during transport. The minimum height of the stack including the test sample shall be 3 m.

6.1.5.3 Drop test

6.1.5.3.1 *Number of test samples (per design type and manufacturer) and drop orientation*

For other than flat drops, the centre of gravity shall be vertically over the point of impact.

Packaging	Number of test samples	Drop orientation
Steel drums Aluminium drums Metal drums, other than steel or aluminium drums Steel jerricans Aluminium jerricans Plywood drums Fibre drums Plastics drums and jerricans Composite packagings which are in the shape of a drum	Six (three for each drop)	*First drop* (using three samples): the packaging shall strike the target diagonally on the chime or, if the packaging has no chime, on a circumferential seam or an edge *Second drop* (using the other three samples): the packaging shall strike the target on the weakest part not tested by the first drop, for example a closure or, for some cylindrical drums, the welded longitudinal seam of the body
Boxes of natural wood Plywood boxes Reconstituted wood boxes Fibreboard boxes Plastics boxes Steel or aluminium boxes Composite packagings which are in the shape of a box	Five (one for each drop)	*First drop:* flat on the bottom *Second drop:* flat on the top *Third drop:* flat on the long side *Fourth drop:* flat on the short side *Fifth drop:* on a corner
Bags – single-ply with a side seam	Three (three drops per bag)	*First drop*: flat on a wide face *Second drop*: flat on a narrow face *Third drop*: on the end of the bag
Bags – single-ply without a side seam or multi-ply	Three (two drops per bag)	*First drop*: flat on a wide face *Second drop*: on an end of the bag

Where more than one orientation is possible for a given drop test, the orientation most likely to result in failure of the packaging shall be used.

6.1.5.3.2 *Special preparation of test samples for the drop test*

The temperature of the test sample and its contents shall be reduced to −18°C or lower for the following packagings:

.1 plastics drums (see 6.1.4.8);

.2   plastics jerricans (see 6.1.4.8);

.3   plastics boxes other than expanded plastics boxes (see 6.1.4.13);

.4   composite packagings (plastics material) (see 6.1.4.19); and

.5   combination packagings with plastics inner packagings, other than plastics bags intended to contain solids or articles.

Where the test samples are prepared in this way, the conditioning in 6.1.5.2.3 may be waived. Test liquids shall be kept in the liquid state by the addition of anti-freeze if necessary.

6.1.5.3.3   Removable head packagings for liquids shall not be dropped until at least 24 h after filling and closing to allow for any possible gasket relaxation.

6.1.5.3.4   *Target*

The target shall be a non-resilient and horizontal surface and shall be:

.1   integral and massive enough to be immovable;

.2   flat with a surface kept free from local defects capable of influencing the test results;

.3   rigid enough to be non-deformable under test conditions and not liable to become damaged by the tests; and

.4   sufficiently large to ensure that the test package falls entirely upon the surface.

6.1.5.3.5   *Drop height*

For solids and liquids, if the test is performed with the solid or liquid to be carried or with another substance having essentially the same physical characteristics:

Packing group I	Packing group II	Packing group III
1.8 m	1.2 m	0.8 m

For liquids in single packagings and for inner packagings of combination packagings, if the test is performed with water:

Note: The term "water" includes water/antifreeze solutions with a minimum specific gravity of 0.95 for testing at −18°C.

(a)   where the substances to be transported have a relative density not exceeding 1.2:

Packing group I	Packing group II	Packing group III
1.8 m	1.2 m	0.8 m

(b)   where the substances to be transported have a relative density exceeding 1.2, the drop height shall be calculated on the basis of the relative density (d) of the substance to be carried, rounded up to the first decimal, as follows:

Packing group I	Packing group II	Packing group III
$d \times 1.5$ m	$d \times 1.0$ m	$d \times 0.67$ m

6.1.5.3.6   *Criteria for passing the test*

.1   Each packaging containing liquid shall be leakproof when equilibrium has been reached between the internal and external pressures, except for inner packagings of combination packagings, when it is not necessary that the pressures be equalized.

.2   Where a packaging for solids undergoes a drop test and its upper face strikes the target, the test sample passes the test if the entire contents are retained by an inner packaging or inner receptacle (such as a plastics bag), even if the closure, while retaining its containment function, is no longer sift-proof.

.3   The packaging or outer packaging of a composite or combination packaging shall not exhibit any damage liable to affect safety during transport. Inner receptacles, inner packagings, or articles shall remain completely within the outer packaging and there shall be no leakage of the filling substance from the inner receptacles or inner packaging(s).

.4   Neither the outermost ply of a bag nor an outer packaging shall exhibit any damage liable to affect safety during transport.

.5   A slight discharge from the closures upon impact shall not be considered to be a failure of the packaging provided that no further leakage occurs.

6

.6   No rupture is permitted in packagings for goods of class 1 which would permit the spillage of loose explosive substances or articles from the outer packaging.

6.1.5.4   Leakproofness test

6.1.5.4.1   The leakproofness test shall be performed on all design types of packagings intended to contain liquids; however, this test is not required for the inner packagings of combination packagings.

6.1.5.4.2   Number of test samples: three test samples per design type and manufacturer.

6.1.5.4.3   Special preparation of test samples for the test: vented closures shall either be replaced by similar non-vented closures or the vent shall be sealed.

6.1.5.4.4   Test method and pressure to be applied: the packagings, including their closures, shall be restrained under water for 5 minutes while an internal air pressure is applied. The method of restraint shall not affect the results of the test.

The air pressure (gauge) to be applied shall be:

Packing group I	Packing group II	Packing group III
Not less than 30 kPa (0.3 bar)	Not less than 20 kPa (0.2 bar)	Not less than 20 kPa (0.2 bar)

Other methods at least equally as effective may be used.

6.1.5.4.5   Criterion for passing the test: there shall be no leakage.

6.1.5.5   Internal pressure (hydraulic) test

6.1.5.5.1   Packagings to be tested: the internal pressure (hydraulic) test shall be carried out on all design types of metal, plastics and composite packagings intended to contain liquids. This test is not required for inner packagings of combination packagings.

6.1.5.5.2   Number of test samples: three test samples per design type and manufacture.

6.1.5.5.3   Special preparation of packagings for testing: vented closures shall either be replaced by similar non-vented closures or the vent shall be sealed.

△ 6.1.5.5.4   Test method and pressure to be applied: metal packagings and composite packagings (glass, porcelain or stoneware), including their closures, shall be subjected to the test pressure for 5 minutes. Plastics packagings and composite packagings (plastics material), including their closures, shall be subjected to the test pressure for 30 minutes. This pressure is the one to be included in the mark required by 6.1.3.1(d). The manner in which the packagings are supported shall not invalidate the test. The test pressure shall be applied continuously and evenly; it shall be kept constant throughout the test period. The hydraulic pressure (gauge) applied, as determined by any one of the following methods, shall be:

.1   not less than the total gauge pressure measured in the packaging (i.e. the vapour pressure of the filling liquid and the partial pressure of the air or other inert gases, minus 100 kPa) at 55°C, multiplied by a safety factor of 1.5; this total gauge pressure shall be determined on the basis of a maximum degree of filling in accordance with 4.1.1.4 and a filling temperature of 15°C;

.2   not less than 1.75 times the vapour pressure at 50°C of the liquid to be transported, minus 100 kPa, but with a minimum test pressure of 100 kPa;

.3   not less than 1.5 times the vapour pressure at 55°C of the liquid to be transported minus 100 kPa, but with a minimum test pressure of 100 kPa.

6.1.5.5.5   In addition, packagings intended to contain liquids of packing group I shall be tested to a minimum test pressure of 250 kPa (gauge) for a test period of 5 or 30 minutes, depending upon the material of construction of the packaging.

6.1.5.5.6   Criterion for passing the test: no packaging shall leak.

6.1.5.6   Stacking test

All design types of packagings other than bags shall be subjected to a stacking test.

6.1.5.6.1   Number of test samples: three test samples per design type and manufacturer.

6.1.5.6.2   Test method: the test sample shall be subjected to a force applied to the top surface of the test sample equivalent to the total mass of identical packages which might be stacked on it during transport: where the contents of the test sample are liquids with relative density different from that of the liquid to be transported, the force shall be calculated in relation to the latter. The minimum height of the stack including the test sample shall be 3 m. The duration of the test shall be 24 hours except that plastics drums, jerricans, and composite packagings 6HH1 and 6HH2 intended for liquids shall be subjected to the stacking test for a period of 28 days at a temperature of not less than 40°C.

6.1.5.6.3   Criteria for passing the test: no test sample shall leak. In composite packagings or combination packagings, there shall be no leakage of the filling substance from the inner receptacle or inner packaging. No test sample shall show any deterioration which could adversely affect transport safety or any distortion liable to reduce its strength or cause instability in stacks of packages. Plastics packagings shall be cooled to ambient temperature before the assessment.

6.1.5.7   **Test report**

6.1.5.7.1   A test report containing at least the following particulars shall be drawn up and shall be available to the users of the packaging:

 .1   name and address of the test facility;

 .2   name and address of applicant (where applicable);

 .3   a unique test report identification;

 .4   date of the test report;

 .5   manufacturer of the packaging;

 .6   description of the packaging design type (such as dimensions, materials, closures, thickness, etc.), including method of manufacture (such as blow-moulding), and which may include drawing(s) and/or photograph(s);

 .7   maximum capacity;

 .8   characteristics of test contents, such as viscosity and relative density for liquids and particle size for solids;

 .9   test descriptions and results;

 .10 signature, with the name and status of the signatory.

6.1.5.7.2   The test report shall contain statements that the packaging prepared as for transport was tested in accordance with the appropriate provisions of this chapter and that the use of other packaging methods or components may render it invalid. A copy of the test report shall be available to the competent authority.

Chapter 6.2

Provisions for the construction and testing of pressure receptacles, aerosol dispensers, small receptacles containing gas (gas cartridges) and fuel cell cartridges containing liquefied flammable gas

Note:	Aerosol dispensers, small receptacles containing gas (gas cartridges) and fuel cell cartridges containing liquefied flammable gas are not subject to the provisions of 6.2.1 to 6.2.3.

6.2.1 General provisions

6.2.1.1 Design and construction

6.2.1.1.1 Pressure receptacles and their closures shall be designed, manufactured, tested and equipped in such a way as to withstand all conditions, including fatigue, to which they will be subjected during normal conditions of transport.

△ 6.2.1.1.2 In recognition of scientific and technological advances, and recognizing that pressure receptacles other than those that bear "UN" certification marks may be used on a national or regional basis, pressure receptacles conforming to requirements other than those specified in this Code may be used if approved by the competent authorities in the countries of transport and use.

6.2.1.1.3 In no case shall the minimum wall thickness be less than that specified in the design and construction technical standards.

6.2.1.1.4 For welded pressure receptacles, only metals of weldable quality shall be used.

6.2.1.1.5 The test pressure of cylinders, tubes, pressure drums and bundles of cylinders shall be in accordance with packing instruction P200, or, for a chemical under pressure, with packing instruction P206. The test pressure for closed cryogenic receptacles shall be in accordance with packing instruction P203. The test pressure of a metal hydride storage system shall be in accordance with packing instruction P205. The test pressure of a cylinder for an adsorbed gas shall be in accordance with packing instruction P208.

6.2.1.1.6 Pressure receptacles assembled in bundles shall be structurally supported and held together as a unit. Pressure receptacles shall be secured in a manner that prevents movement in relation to the structural assembly and movement that would result in the concentration of harmful local stresses. Manifold assemblies (e.g. manifold, valves, and pressure gauges) shall be designed and constructed such that they are protected from impact damage and forces normally encountered in transport. Manifolds shall have at least the same test pressure as the cylinders. For toxic liquefied gases, each pressure receptacle shall have an isolation valve to ensure that each pressure receptacle can be filled separately and that no interchange of pressure receptacle contents can occur during transport.

6.2.1.1.7 Contact between dissimilar metals which could result in damage by galvanic action shall be avoided.

6.2.1.1.8 The following additional provisions apply to the construction of closed cryogenic receptacles for refrigerated liquefied gases:

.1 The mechanical properties of the metal used shall be established for each pressure receptacle, including the impact strength and the bending coefficient;

.2 The pressure receptacles shall be thermally insulated. The thermal insulation shall be protected against impact by means of a jacket. If the space between the pressure receptacle and the jacket is evacuated of air (vacuum insulation), the jacket shall be designed to withstand, without permanent deformation, an external pressure of at least 100 kPa (1 bar) calculated in accordance with a recognized technical code or a calculated critical collapsing pressure of not less than 200 kPa (2 bar) gauge pressure. If the jacket is so closed as to be gas-tight (e.g. in the case of vacuum insulation), a device shall be provided to prevent any dangerous pressure from developing in the insulating layer in the event of inadequate gas-tightness of the pressure receptacle or its fittings. The device shall prevent moisture from penetrating into the insulation.

.3 Closed cryogenic receptacles intended for the transport of refrigerated liquefied gases having a boiling point below −182°C at atmospheric pressure shall not include materials which may react with oxygen or oxygen-enriched atmospheres in a dangerous manner, when located in parts of the thermal insulation where there is a risk of contact with oxygen or with oxygen-enriched liquid.

.4 Closed cryogenic receptacles shall be designed and constructed with suitable lifting and securing arrangements.

△ **6.2.1.1.9** *Additional requirements for the construction of pressure receptacle for acetylene*

Pressure receptacle for UN 1001 acetylene, dissolved, and UN 3374 acetylene, solvent free, shall be filled with a porous material, uniformly distributed, of a type that conforms to the requirements and testing specified by a standard or technical code recognized by the competent authority and which:

.1 is compatible with the pressure receptacle and does not form harmful or dangerous compounds either with the acetylene or with the solvent in the case of UN 1001; and

.2 is capable of preventing the spread of decomposition of the acetylene in the porous material.

In the case of UN 1001, the solvent shall be compatible with the pressure receptacle.

6.2.1.2 Materials

6.2.1.2.1 Construction materials of pressure receptacles and their closures which are in direct contact with dangerous goods shall not be affected or weakened by the dangerous goods intended to be transported and shall not cause a dangerous effect, e.g. catalysing a reaction or reacting with the dangerous goods.

6.2.1.2.2 Pressure receptacles and their closures shall be made of the materials specified in the design and construction technical standards and the applicable packing instruction for the substances intended for transport in the pressure receptacle. The materials shall be resistant to brittle fracture and to stress corrosion cracking as indicated in the design and construction technical standards.

6.2.1.3 Service equipment

6.2.1.3.1 Valves, piping and other fittings subjected to pressure, excluding pressure relief devices, shall be designed and constructed so that the burst pressure is at least 1.5 times the test pressure of the pressure receptacle.

6.2.1.3.2 Service equipment shall be configured or designed to prevent damage that could result in the release of the pressure receptacle contents during normal conditions of handling and transport. Manifold piping leading to shut-off valves shall be sufficiently flexible to protect the valves and the piping from shearing or releasing the pressure receptacle contents. The filling and discharge valves and any protective caps shall be capable of being secured against unintended opening. Valves shall be protected as specified in 4.1.6.1.8.

6.2.1.3.3 Pressure receptacles which are not capable of being handled manually or rolled shall be fitted with devices (skids, rings, straps) ensuring that they can be safely handled by mechanical means and so arranged as not to impair the strength of, nor cause undue stresses in, the pressure receptacle.

6.2.1.3.4 Individual pressure receptacles shall be equipped with pressure relief devices as specified in packing instruction P200(1), P205 or in 6.2.1.3.6.4 and 6.2.1.3.6.5. Pressure relief devices shall be designed to prevent the entry of foreign matter, the leakage of gas and the development of any dangerous excess pressure. When fitted, pressure relief devices on manifolded horizontal pressure receptacles filled with flammable gas shall be arranged to discharge freely to the open air in such a manner as to prevent any impingement of escaping gas upon the pressure receptacle itself under normal conditions of transport.

6.2.1.3.5 Pressure receptacles where filling is measured by volume shall be provided with a level indicator.

6.2.1.3.6 *Additional provisions for closed cryogenic receptacles*

6.2.1.3.6.1 Each filling and discharge opening in a closed cryogenic receptacle used for the transport of flammable refrigerated liquefied gases shall be fitted with at least two mutually independent shut-off devices in series, the first being a stop-valve, the second being a cap or equivalent device.

6.2.1.3.6.2 For sections of piping which can be closed at both ends and where liquid product can be trapped, a method of automatic pressure relief shall be provided to prevent excess pressure build-up within the piping.

6.2.1.3.6.3 Each connection on a closed cryogenic receptacle shall be clearly marked to indicate its function (e.g. vapour or liquid phase).

6.2.1.3.6.4 *Pressure relief devices*

6.2.1.3.6.4.1 Each closed cryogenic receptacle shall be provided with at least one pressure relief device. The pressure relief device shall be of the type that will resist dynamic forces, including surge.

6

6.2.1.3.6.4.2 Closed cryogenic receptacles may, in addition, have a frangible disc in parallel with the spring-loaded device(s) in order to meet the provisions of 6.2.1.3.6.5.

6.2.1.3.6.4.3 Connections to pressure relief devices shall be of sufficient size to enable the required discharge to pass unrestricted to the pressure relief device.

6.2.1.3.6.4.4 All pressure relief device inlets shall, under maximum filling conditions, be situated in the vapour space of the closed cryogenic receptacle and the devices shall be so arranged as to ensure that the escaping vapour is discharged unrestrictedly.

6.2.1.3.6.5 *Capacity and setting of pressure relief devices*

> **Note:** In relation to pressure relief devices of closed cryogenic receptacles, "MAWP" means the maximum effective gauge pressure permissible at the top of a loaded closed cryogenic receptacle in its operating position, including the highest effective pressure during filling and discharge.

6.2.1.3.6.5.1 The pressure relief device shall open automatically at a pressure not less than the MAWP and be fully open at a pressure equal to 110% of the MAWP. It shall, after discharge, close at a pressure not lower than 10% below the pressure at which discharge starts and shall remain closed at all lower pressures.

6.2.1.3.6.5.2 Frangible discs shall be set to rupture at a nominal pressure which is the lower of either the test pressure or 150% of the MAWP.

6.2.1.3.6.5.3 In the case of the loss of vacuum in a vacuum-insulated closed cryogenic receptacle, the combined capacity of all pressure relief devices installed shall be sufficient so that the pressure (including accumulation) inside the closed cryogenic receptacle does not exceed 120% of the MAWP.

6.2.1.3.6.5.4 The required capacity of the pressure relief devices shall be calculated in accordance with an established technical code recognized by the competent authority.[*]

6.2.1.4 Approval of pressure receptacles

6.2.1.4.1 The conformity of pressure receptacles shall be assessed at time of manufacture as required by the competent authority. Pressure receptacles shall be inspected, tested and approved by an inspection body. The technical documentation shall include full specifications on design and construction, and full documentation on the manufacturing and testing.

6.2.1.4.2 Quality assurance systems shall conform to the requirements of the competent authority.

6.2.1.5 Initial inspection and test

6.2.1.5.1 New pressure receptacles, other than closed cryogenic receptacles and metal hydride storage systems, shall be subjected to testing and inspection during and after manufacture in accordance with the applicable design standards including the following:

On an adequate sample of pressure receptacles:

.1 testing of the mechanical characteristics of the material of construction;

.2 verification of the minimum wall thickness;

.3 verification of the homogeneity of the material for each manufacturing batch;

.4 inspection of the external and internal conditions of the pressure receptacles;

.5 inspection of the neck threads;

.6 verification of the conformance with the design standard;

For all pressure receptacles:

△ .7 a hydraulic pressure test. Pressure receptacles shall meet the acceptance criteria specified in the design and construction technical standard or technical code;

> **Note:** With the agreement of the competent authority, the hydraulic pressure test may be replaced by a test using a gas, where such an operation does not entail any danger.

.8 inspection and assessment of manufacturing defects and either repairing them or rendering the pressure receptacles unserviceable. In the case of welded pressure receptacles, particular attention shall be paid to the quality of the welds;

△ .9 an inspection of the marks on the pressure receptacles;

---

[*] See, for example, CGA S-1.2-2003 "Pressure Relief Device Standards – Part 2 – Cargo and Portable Tanks for Compressed Gases" and S-1.1-2003 "Pressure Relief Device Standards – Part 1 – Cylinders for Compressed Gases".

.10 in addition, pressure receptacles intended for the transport of UN 1001 acetylene, dissolved and UN 3374 acetylene, solvent free shall be inspected to ensure proper installation and condition of the porous material and, if applicable, the quantity of solvent.

6.2.1.5.2 On an adequate sample of closed cryogenic receptacles, the inspections and tests specified in 6.2.1.5.1.1, .2, .4, and .6 shall be performed. In addition, welds shall be inspected by radiographic, ultrasonic or another suitable non-destructive test method on a sample of closed cryogenic receptacles, according to the applicable design and construction standard. This weld inspection does not apply to the jacket.

Additionally, all closed cryogenic receptacles shall undergo the inspections and tests specified in 6.2.1.5.1, .7, .8, and .9, as well as a leakproofness test and a test of the satisfactory operation of the service equipment after assembly.

6.2.1.5.3 For metal hydride storage systems, it shall be verified that the inspections and tests specified in 6.2.1.5.1.1, .2, .3, .4, .5 if applicable, .6, .7, .8 and .9 have been performed on an adequate sample of the receptacles used in the metal hydride storage system. In addition, on an adequate sample of metal hydride storage systems, the inspections and tests specified in 6.2.1.5.1.3 and .6 shall be performed, as well as 6.2.1.5.1.5, if applicable, and inspection of the external conditions of the metal hydride storage system.

Additionally, all metal hydride storage systems shall undergo the initial inspections and tests specified in 6.2.1.5.1.8 and .9, as well as a leakproofness test and a test of the satisfactory operation of the service equipment.

6.2.1.6 Periodic inspection and test

6.2.1.6.1 Refillable pressure receptacles, other than cryogenic receptacles, shall be subjected to periodic inspections and tests, by a body authorized by the competent authority, in accordance with the following:

△ .1 Check of the external conditions of the pressure receptacle and verification of the equipment and the external marks;

.2 Check of the internal conditions of the pressure receptacle (e.g. internal inspection, verification of minimum wall thickness);

.3 Check of the threads if there is evidence of corrosion or if the fittings are removed;

.4 A hydraulic pressure test and, if necessary, verification of the characteristics of the material by suitable tests;

Note 1: With the agreement of the competent authority, the hydraulic pressure test may be replaced by a test using a gas, where such an operation does not entail any danger.

Note 2: With the agreement of the competent authority, the hydraulic pressure test of cylinders or tubes may be replaced by an equivalent method based on acoustic emission testing or a combination of acoustic emission testing and ultrasonic examination. ISO 16148:2006 may be used as a guide for acoustic emission testing procedures.

Note 3: The hydraulic pressure test may be replaced by ultrasonic examination carried out in accordance with ISO 10461:2005+A1:2006 for seamless aluminium alloy gas cylinders and in accordance with ISO 6406:2005 for seamless steel gas cylinders.

.5 Check of service equipment, other accessories and pressure-relief devices, if to be reintroduced into service.

Note: For the periodic inspection and test frequencies, see packing instruction P200 or, for a chemical under pressure, packing instruction P206 of 4.1.4.1.

6.2.1.6.2 Pressure receptacles intended for the transport of UN 1001 acetylene, dissolved and UN 3374 acetylene, solvent free shall be examined only as specified in 6.2.1.6.1.1, 6.2.1.6.1.3 and 6.2.1.6.1.5. In addition, the condition of the porous material (e.g. cracks, top clearance, loosening, or settlement) shall be examined.

6.2.1.6.3 Pressure relief valves for closed cryogenic receptacles shall be subject to periodic inspections and tests.

6.2.1.7 Requirements for manufacturers

6.2.1.7.1 The manufacturer shall be technically able and shall possess all resources required for the satisfactory manufacture of pressure receptacles; this relates in particular to qualified personnel:

.1 to supervise the entire manufacturing process;

.2 to carry out joining of materials; and

.3 to carry out the relevant tests.

6.2.1.7.2 The proficiency test of a manufacturer shall in all instances be carried out by an inspection body approved by the competent authority of the country of approval.

6

6.2.1.8   **Requirements for inspection bodies**

6.2.1.8.1   Inspection bodies shall be independent from manufacturing enterprises and competent to perform the tests, inspections and approvals required.

6.2.2   Provisions for UN pressure receptacles

In addition to the general requirements of 6.2.1, UN pressure receptacles shall comply with the provisions of this section, including the standards, as applicable. Manufacture of new pressure receptacles or service equipment according to any particular standard in 6.2.2.1 and 6.2.2.3 is not permitted after the date shown in the right hand column of the tables.

Note 1: With the agreement of the competent authority, more recently published versions of the standards, if available, may be used.

Note 2: UN pressure receptacles and service equipment constructed according to standards applicable at the date of manufacture may continue in use subject to the periodic inspection provisions of this Code.

6.2.2.1   **Design, construction and initial inspection and test**

6.2.2.1.1   The following standards apply for the design, construction and initial inspection and test of UN cylinders, except that inspection requirements related to the conformity assessment system and approval shall be in accordance with 6.2.2.5:

	Reference	Title	Applicable for manufacture
	ISO 9809-1:1999	Gas cylinders – Refillable seamless steel gas cylinders – Design, construction and testing – Part 1: Quenched and tempered steel cylinders with tensile strength less than 1,100 MPa. **Note:** The note concerning the *F* factor in section 7.3 of this standard shall not be applied for UN cylinders.	Until 31 December 2018
	ISO 9809-1:2010	Gas cylinders – Refillable seamless steel gas cylinders – Design, construction and testing – Part 1: Quenched and tempered steel cylinders with tensile strength less than 1,100 MPa	Until further notice
	ISO 9809-2:2000	Gas cylinders – Refillable seamless steel gas cylinders – Design, construction and testing – Part 2: Quenched and tempered steel cylinders with tensile strength greater than or equal to 1,100 MPa	Until 31 December 2018
	ISO 9809-2:2010	Gas cylinders – Refillable seamless steel gas cylinders – Design, construction and testing – Part 2: Quenched and tempered steel cylinders with tensile strength greater than or equal to 1,100 MPa	Until further notice
	ISO 9809-3:2000	Gas cylinders – Refillable seamless steel gas cylinders – Design, construction and testing – Part 3: Normalized steel cylinders	Until 31 December 2018
	ISO 9809-3:2010	Gas cylinders – Refillable seamless steel gas cylinders – Design, construction and testing – Part 3: Normalized steel cylinders	Until further notice
■	ISO 9809-4:2014	Gas cylinders – Refillable seamless steel gas cylinders – Design, construction and testing – Part 4: Stainless steel cylinders with an Rm value of less than 1 100 MPa	Until further notice
△	ISO 7866:1999	Gas cylinders – Refillable seamless aluminium alloy gas cylinders – Design, construction and testing **Note:** The note concerning the *F* factor in section 7.2 of this standard shall not be applied for UN cylinders. Aluminium alloy 6351A-T6 or equivalent shall not be authorized.	Until 31 December 2020
■	ISO 7866:2012+ Cor 1:2014	Gas cylinders – Refillable seamless aluminium alloy gas cylinders – Design, construction and testing **Note:** Aluminium alloy 6351A or equivalent shall not be used.	Until further notice
	ISO 4706:2008	Gas cylinders – Refillable welded steel cylinders – Test pressure 60 bar and below	Until further notice
	ISO 18172-1:2007	Gas cylinders – Refillable welded stainless steel cylinders – Part 1: Test pressure 6 MPa and below	Until further notice
	ISO 20703:2006	Gas cylinders – Refillable welded aluminium-alloy cylinders – Design, construction and testing	Until further notice
	ISO 11118:1999	Gas cylinders – Non-refillable metallic gas cylinders – Specification and test methods	Until further notice

	Reference	Title	Applicable for manufacture
△	ISO 11119-1:2002	Gas cylinders of composite construction – Specification and test methods – Part 1: Hoop wrapped composite gas cylinders	Until 31 December 2020
■	ISO 11119-1:2012	Gas cylinders – Refillable composite gas cylinders and tubes – Design, construction and testing – Part 1: Hoop wrapped fibre reinforced composite gas cylinders and tubes up to 450 L	Until further notice
△	ISO 11119-2:2002	Gas cylinders of composite construction – Specification and test methods – Part 2: Fully wrapped fibre reinforced composite gas cylinders with load-sharing metal liners	Until 31 December 2020
■	ISO 11119-2:2012 + Amd 1:2014	Gas cylinders – Refillable composite gas cylinders and tubes – Design, construction and testing – Part 2: Fully wrapped fibre reinforced composite gas cylinders and tubes up to 450 L with load-sharing metal liners	Until further notice
△	ISO 11119-3:2002	Gas cylinders of composite construction – Specification and test methods – Part 3: Fully wrapped fibre reinforced composite gas cylinders with non-load-sharing metallic or non-metallic liners	Until 31 December 2020
■	ISO 11119-3:2013	Gas cylinders – Refillable composite gas cylinders and tubes – Design, construction and testing – Part 3: Fully wrapped fibre reinforced composite gas cylinders and tubes up to 450 L with non-load-sharing metallic or non-metallic liners	Until further notice

△ **Note 1:** In the above referenced standards, composite cylinders shall be designed for a design life of not less than 15 years.

△ **Note 2:** Composite cylinders with a design life longer than 15 years shall not be filled after 15 years from the date of manufacture, unless the design has successfully passed a service life test programme. The programme shall be part of the initial design type approval and shall specify inspections and tests to demonstrate that cylinders manufactured accordingly remain safe to the end of their design life. The service life test programme and the results shall be approved by the competent authority of the country of approval that is responsible for the initial approval of the cylinder design. The service life of a composite cylinder shall not be extended beyond its initial approved design life.

6.2.2.1.2   The following standards apply for the design, construction and initial inspection and test of UN tubes, except that inspection requirements related to the conformity assessment system and approval shall be in accordance with 6.2.2.5:

	Reference	Title	Applicable for manufacture
	ISO 11120:1999	Gas cylinders – Refillable seamless steel tubes for compressed gas transport, of water capacity between 150 L and 3,000 L – Design, construction and testing **Note:** The note concerning the *F* factor in section 7.1 of this standard shall not be applied for UN tubes.	Until further notice
■	ISO 11119-1:2012	Gas cylinders – Refillable composite gas cylinders and tubes – Design, construction and testing – Part 1: Hoop wrapped fibre reinforced composite gas cylinders and tubes up to 450 L	Until further notice
■	ISO 11119-2:2012 + Amd 1:2014	Gas cylinders – Refillable composite gas cylinders and tubes – Design, construction and testing – Part 2: Fully wrapped fibre reinforced composite gas cylinders and tubes up to 450 L with load-sharing metal liners	Until further notice
■	ISO 11119-3:2013	Gas cylinders – Refillable composite gas cylinders and tubes – Design, construction and testing – Part 3: Fully wrapped fibre reinforced composite gas cylinders and tubes up to 450 L with non-load-sharing metallic or non-metallic liners	Until further notice
■	ISO 11515: 2013	Gas cylinders – Refillable composite reinforced tubes of water capacity between 450 L and 3 000 L – Design, construction and testing	Until further notice

■ **Note 1:** In the above referenced standards composite tubes shall be designed for a design life of not less than 15 years.

■ **Note 2:** Composite tubes with a design life longer than 15 years shall not be filled after 15 years from the date of manufacture, unless the design has successfully passed a service life test programme. The programme shall be part of the initial design type approval and shall specify inspections and tests to demonstrate that tubes manufactured accordingly remain safe to the end of their design life. The service life test programme and the results shall be approved by the competent authority of the country of approval that is responsible for the initial approval of the tube design. The service life of a composite tube shall not be extended beyond its initial approved design life.

6

6.2.2.1.3 The following standards apply for the design, construction and initial inspection and test of UN acetylene cylinders, except that inspection requirements related to the conformity assessment system and approval shall be in accordance with 6.2.2.5:

For the cylinder shell:

Reference	Title	Applicable for manufacture
ISO 9809-1:1999	Gas cylinders – Refillable seamless steel gas cylinders – Design, construction and testing – Part 1: Quenched and tempered steel cylinders with tensile strength less than 1,100 MPa **Note:** The note concerning the *F* factor in section 7.3 of this standard shall not be applied for UN cylinders.	Until 31 December 2018
ISO 9809-1:2010	Gas cylinders – Refillable seamless steel gas cylinders – Design, construction and testing – Part 1: Quenched and tempered steel cylinders with tensile strength less than 1,100 MPa	Until further notice
ISO 9809-3:2000	Gas cylinders – Refillable seamless steel gas cylinders – Design, construction and testing – Part 3: Normalized steel cylinders	Until 31 December 2018
ISO 9809-3:2010	Gas cylinders – Refillable seamless steel gas cylinders – Design, construction and testing – Part 3: Normalized steel cylinders	Until further notice

For the porous material in the cylinder:

	Reference	Title	Applicable for manufacture
△	ISO 3807-1:2000	Cylinders for acetylene – Basic requirements – Part 1: Cylinders without fusible plugs	Until 31 December 2020
△	ISO 3807-2:2000	Cylinders for acetylene – Basic requirements – Part 2: Cylinders with fusible plugs	Until 31 December 2020
■	ISO 3807-2:2013	Gas cylinders – Acetylene cylinders – Basic requirements and type testing	Until further notice

6.2.2.1.4 The following standard applies for the design, construction and initial inspection and test of UN cryogenic receptacles, except that inspection requirements related to the conformity assessment system and approval shall be in accordance with 6.2.2.5:

Reference	Title	Applicable for manufacture
ISO 21029-1:2004	Cryogenic vessels – Transportable vacuum insulated vessels of not more than 1,000 L volume – Part 1: Design, fabrication, inspection and tests	Until further notice

6.2.2.1.5 The following standard applies for the design, construction and initial inspection and test of UN metal hydride storage systems, except that inspection requirements related to the conformity assessment system and approval shall be in accordance with 6.2.2.5:

Reference	Title	Applicable for manufacture
ISO 16111:2008	Transportable gas storage devices – Hydrogen absorbed in reversible metal hydride	Until further notice

6.2.2.1.6 The standard shown below applies for the design, construction and initial inspection and test of UN bundles of cylinders. Each cylinder in a UN bundle of cylinders shall be a UN cylinder complying with the requirements of 6.2.2. The inspection requirements related to the conformity assessment system and approval for UN bundles of cylinders shall be in accordance with 6.2.2.5.

Reference	Title	Applicable for manufacture
ISO 10961:2010	Gas cylinders – Cylinder bundles – Design, manufacture, testing and inspection	Until further notice

Note: Changing one or more cylinders of the same design type, including the same test pressure, in an existing UN bundle of cylinders does not require recertification of the existing bundle.

6.2.2.1.7   The following standards apply for the design, construction and initial inspection and test of UN cylinders for adsorbed gases except that the inspection requirements related to the conformity assessment system and approval shall be in accordance with 6.2.2.5.

Reference	Title	Applicable for manufacture
ISO 11513:2011	Gas cylinders – Refillable welded steel cylinders containing materials for sub-atmospheric gas packaging (excluding acetylene) – Design, construction, testing, use and periodic inspection	Until further notice
ISO 9809-1:2010	Gas cylinders – Refillable seamless steel gas cylinders – Design, construction and testing – Part 1: Quenched and tempered steel cylinders with tensile strength less than 1,100 MPa	Until further notice

6.2.2.2   Materials

In addition to the material requirements specified in the pressure receptacle design and construction standards, and any restrictions specified in the applicable packing instruction for the gas(es) to be transported (e.g. packing instruction P200 or P205), the following standards apply to material compatibility:

Reference	Title
ISO 11114-1:2012	Gas cylinders – Compatibility of cylinder and valve materials with gas contents – Part 1: Metallic materials
△ ISO 11114-2:2013	Gas cylinders – Compatibility of cylinder and valve materials with gas contents – Part 2: Non-metallic materials

6.2.2.3   Service equipment

The following standards apply to closures and their protection:

Reference	Title	Applicable for manufacture
ISO 11117:1998	Gas cylinders – Valve protection caps and valve guards for industrial and medical gas cylinders – Design, construction and tests	Until 31 December 2014
ISO 11117:2008 + Cor 1:2009	Gas cylinders – Valve protection caps and valve guards – Design, construction and tests	Until further notice
ISO 10297:1999	Gas cylinders – Refillable gas cylinder valves – Specification and type testing	Until 31 December 2008
△ ISO 10297:2006	Gas cylinders – Refillable gas cylinder valves – Specification and type testing	Until 31 December 2020
■ ISO 10297:2014	Gas cylinders – Cylinder valves – Specification and type testing	Until further notice
ISO 13340:2001	Transportable gas cylinders – Cylinder valves for non-refillable cylinders – Specification and prototype testing	Until further notice

For UN metal hydride storage systems, the requirements specified in the following standard apply to closures and their protection:

Reference	Title	Applicable for manufacture
ISO 16111:2008	Transportable gas storage devices – Hydrogen absorbed in reversible metal hydride	Until further notice

6.2.2.4   Periodic inspection and test

The following standards apply to the periodic inspection and testing of UN cylinders and UN metal hydride storage systems:

Reference	Title	Applicable
ISO 6406:2005	Seamless steel gas cylinders – Periodic inspection and testing	Until further notice
ISO 10461:2005/ Amd 1:2006	Seamless aluminium-alloy gas cylinders – Periodic inspection and testing	Until further notice

	Reference	Title	Applicable
△	ISO 10462:2005	Transportable cylinders for dissolved acetylene – Periodic inspection and maintenance	Until 31 December 2018
■	ISO 10462:2013	Gas cylinders – Acetylene cylinders – Periodic inspection and maintenance	Until further notice
	ISO 11513:2011	Gas cylinders – Refillable welded steel cylinders containing materials for sub-atmospheric gas packaging (excluding acetylene) – Design, construction, testing, use and periodic inspection	Until further notice
	ISO 11623:2002	Transportable gas cylinders – Periodic inspection and testing of composite gas cylinders	Until further notice
	ISO 16111:2008	Transportable gas storage devices – Hydrogen absorbed in reversible metal hydride	Until further notice
	ISO 10460:2005	Gas cylinders – Welded carbon-steel gas cylinders – Periodic inspection and testing **Note:** The repair of welds described in clause 12.1 of this standard shall not be permitted. Repairs described in clause 12.2 require the approval of the competent authority which approved the periodic inspection and test body in accordance with 6.2.2.6.	Until further notice

6.2.2.5 Conformity assessment system and approval for manufacture of pressure receptacles

6.2.2.5.1 *Definitions*

For the purposes of this section:

Conformity assessment system means a system for competent authority approval of a manufacturer, by pressure receptacle design type approval, approval of manufacturer's quality system and approval of inspection bodies;

Design type means a pressure receptacle design as specified by a particular pressure receptacle standard;

Verify means confirm by examination or provision of objective evidence that specified requirements have been fulfilled.

6.2.2.5.2 *General requirements*

Competent authority

△ 6.2.2.5.2.1 The competent authority that approves the pressure receptacle shall approve the conformity assessment system for the purpose of ensuring that pressure receptacles conform to the provisions of this Code. In instances where the competent authority that approves a pressure receptacle is not the competent authority in the country of manufacture, the marks of the approval country and the country of manufacture shall be indicated in the pressure receptacle marking (see 6.2.2.7 and 6.2.2.8).

The competent authority of the country of approval shall supply, upon request, evidence demonstrating compliance of this conformity assessment system to its counterpart in a country of use.

6.2.2.5.2.2 The competent authority may delegate its functions in this conformity assessment system in whole or in part.

6.2.2.5.2.3 The competent authority shall ensure that a current list of approved inspection bodies and their identity marks and approved manufacturers and their identity marks is available.

Inspection body

6.2.2.5.2.4 The inspection body shall be approved by the competent authority for the inspection of pressure receptacles and shall:

.1 have a staff with an organizational structure, capable, trained, competent, and skilled, to satisfactorily perform its technical functions;

.2 have access to suitable and adequate facilities and equipment;

.3 operate in an impartial manner and be free from any influence which could prevent it from doing so;

.4 ensure commercial confidentiality of the commercial and proprietary activities of the manufacturer and other bodies;

.5 maintain clear demarcation between actual inspection body functions and unrelated functions;

.6 operate a documented quality system;

.7 ensure that the tests and inspections specified in the relevant pressure receptacle standard and in this Code are performed; and

.8 maintain an effective and appropriate report and record system in accordance with 6.2.2.5.6.

6.2.2.5.2.5 The inspection body shall perform design type approval, pressure receptacle production testing and inspection, and certification to verify conformity with the relevant pressure receptacle standard (see 6.2.2.5.4 and 6.2.2.5.5).

Manufacturer

6.2.2.5.2.6 The manufacturer shall:

.1 operate a documented quality system in accordance with 6.2.2.5.3;

.2 apply for design type approvals in accordance with 6.2.2.5.4;

.3 select an inspection body from the list of approved inspection bodies maintained by the competent authority in the country of approval; and

.4 maintain records in accordance with 6.2.2.5.6.

Testing laboratory

6.2.2.5.2.7 The testing laboratory shall have:

.1 staff with an organizational structure, sufficient in number, competence and skill; and

.2 suitable and adequate facilities and equipment to perform the tests required by the manufacturing standard to the satisfaction of the inspection body.

6.2.2.5.3 *Manufacturer's quality system*

6.2.2.5.3.1 The quality system shall contain all the elements, requirements and provisions adopted by the manufacturer. It shall be documented in a systematic and orderly manner in the form of written policies, procedures and instructions.

The contents shall in particular include adequate descriptions of:

.1 the organizational structure and responsibilities of personnel with regard to design and product quality;

.2 the design control and design verification techniques, processes, and procedures that will be used when designing the pressure receptacles;

.3 the relevant pressure receptacle manufacturing, quality control, quality assurance and process operation instructions that will be used;

.4 quality records, such as inspection reports, test data and calibration data;

.5 management reviews to ensure the effective operation of the quality system arising from the audits in accordance with 6.2.2.5.3.2;

.6 the process describing how customer requirements are met;

.7 the process for control of documents and their revision;

.8 the means for control of non-conforming pressure receptacles, purchased components, in-process and final materials; and

.9 training programmes and qualification procedures for relevant personnel.

6.2.2.5.3.2 *Audit of the quality system*

The quality system shall be initially assessed to determine whether it meets the requirements in 6.2.2.5.3.1 to the satisfaction of the competent authority.

The manufacturer shall be notified of the results of the audit. The notification shall contain the conclusions of the audit and any corrective actions required.

Periodic audits shall be carried out, to the satisfaction of the competent authority, to ensure that the manufacturer maintains and applies the quality system. Reports of the periodic audits shall be provided to the manufacturer.

6.2.2.5.3.3 *Maintenance of the quality system*

The manufacturer shall maintain the quality system as approved in order that it remains adequate and efficient.

The manufacturer shall notify the competent authority that approved the quality system of any intended changes. The proposed changes shall be evaluated in order to determine whether the amended quality system will still satisfy the requirements in 6.2.2.5.3.1.

6.2.2.5.4 *Approval process*

Initial design type approval

6.2.2.5.4.1 The initial design type approval shall consist of approval of the manufacturer's quality system and approval of the pressure receptacle design to be produced. An application for an initial design type approval shall meet the requirements of 6.2.2.5.3, 6.2.2.5.4.2 to 6.2.2.5.4.6 and 6.2.2.5.4.9.

6.2.2.5.4.2 A manufacturer desiring to produce pressure receptacles in accordance with a pressure receptacle standard and this Code shall apply for, obtain, and retain a Design Type Approval Certificate issued by the competent authority in the country of approval for at least one pressure receptacle design type in accordance with the procedure given in 6.2.2.5.4.9. This certificate shall, on request, be submitted to the competent authority of the country of use.

6.2.2.5.4.3 An application shall be made for each manufacturing facility and shall include:

.1 the name and registered address of the manufacturer and in addition, if the application is submitted by an authorized representative, its name and address;

.2 the address of the manufacturing facility (if different from the above);

.3 the name and title of the person(s) responsible for the quality system;

.4 the designation of the pressure receptacle and the relevant pressure receptacle standard;

.5 details of any refusal of approval of a similar application by any other competent authority;

.6 the identity of the inspection body for design type approval;

.7 documentation on the manufacturing facility as specified under 6.2.2.5.3.1; and

.8 the technical documentation required for design type approval, which shall enable verification of the conformity of the pressure receptacles with the requirements of the relevant pressure receptacle design standard. The technical documentation shall cover the design and method of manufacture and shall contain, as far as is relevant for assessment, at least the following:

.1 pressure receptacle design standard, design and manufacturing drawings, showing components and sub-assemblies, if any;

.2 descriptions and explanations necessary for the understanding of the drawings and intended use of the pressure receptacles;

.3 a list of the standards necessary to fully define the manufacturing process;

.4 design calculations and material specifications; and

.5 design type approval test reports, describing the results of examinations and tests carried out in accordance with 6.2.2.5.4.9.

6.2.2.5.4.4 An initial audit in accordance with 6.2.2.5.3.2 shall be performed to the satisfaction of the competent authority.

6.2.2.5.4.5 If the manufacturer is denied approval, the competent authority shall provide written detailed reasons for such denial.

6.2.2.5.4.6 Following approval, changes to the information submitted under 6.2.2.5.4.3 relating to the initial approval shall be provided to the competent authority.

Subsequent design type approvals

6.2.2.5.4.7 An application for a subsequent design type approval shall encompass the requirements of 6.2.2.5.4.8 and 6.2.2.5.4.9, provided a manufacturer is in the possession of an initial design type approval. In such a case, the manufacturer's quality system according to 6.2.2.5.3 shall have been approved during the initial design type approval and shall be applicable for the new design.

6.2.2.5.4.8 The application shall include:

.1 the name and address of the manufacturer and in addition, if the application is submitted by an authorized representative, its name and address;

.2 details of any refusal of approval of a similar application by any other competent authority;

.3 evidence that initial design type approval has been granted; and

.4 the technical documentation, as described in 6.2.2.5.4.3.8.

Procedure for design type approval

6.2.2.5.4.9 The inspection body shall:

.1 examine the technical documentation to verify that:

.1 the design is in accordance with the relevant provisions of the standard, and

.2 the prototype lot has been manufactured in conformity with the technical documentation and is representative of the design;

.2 verify that the production inspections have been carried out as required in accordance with 6.2.2.5.5;

.3 select pressure receptacles from a prototype production lot and supervise the tests of these pressure receptacles as required for design type approval;

.4 perform or have performed the examinations and tests specified in the pressure receptacle standard to determine that:

.1 the standard has been applied and fulfilled, and

.2 the procedures adopted by the manufacturer meet the requirements of the standard; and

.5 ensure that the various type approval examinations and tests are correctly and competently carried out.

After prototype testing has been carried out with satisfactory results and all applicable requirements of 6.2.2.5.4 have been satisfied, a Design Type Approval Certificate shall be issued which shall include the name and address of the manufacturer, results and conclusions of the examination, and the necessary data for identification of the design type.

If the manufacturer is denied a design type approval, the competent authority shall provide written detailed reasons for such denial.

6.2.2.5.4.10 *Modifications to approved design types*

The manufacturer shall either:

(a) inform the issuing competent authority of modifications to the approved design type, where such modifications do not constitute a new design, as specified in the pressure receptacle standard; or

(b) request a subsequent design type approval where such modifications constitute a new design according to the relevant pressure receptacle standard. This additional approval shall be given in the form of an amendment to the original design type approval certificate.

6.2.2.5.4.11 Upon request, the competent authority shall communicate to any other competent authority information concerning design type approval, modifications of approvals, and withdrawn approvals.

6.2.2.5.5 *Production inspection and certification*

An inspection body, or its delegate, shall carry out the inspection and certification of each pressure receptacle. The inspection body selected by the manufacturer for inspection and testing during production may be different from the inspection body used for the design type approval testing.

Where it can be demonstrated to the satisfaction of the inspection body that the manufacturer has trained and competent inspectors, independent of the manufacturing operations, inspection may be performed by those inspectors. In such a case, the manufacturer shall maintain training records of the inspectors.

The inspection body shall verify that the inspections by the manufacturer and tests performed on those pressure receptacles fully conform to the standard and the provisions of this Code. Should non-conformance in conjunction with this inspection and testing be determined, the permission to have inspection performed by the manufacturer's inspectors may be withdrawn.

△ The manufacturer shall, after approval by the inspection body, make a declaration of conformity with the certified design type. The application of the pressure receptacle certification marks shall be considered a declaration that the pressure receptacle complies with the applicable pressure receptacle standards and the requirements of this conformity assessment system and with the provisions of this Code. The inspection body shall affix or delegate the manufacturer to affix the pressure receptacle certification marks and the registered mark of the inspection body to each approved pressure receptacle.

A certificate of compliance, signed by the inspection body and the manufacturer, shall be issued before the pressure receptacles are filled.

6.2.2.5.6 *Records*

Design type approval and certificate of compliance records shall be retained by the manufacturer and the inspection body for not less than 20 years.

6.2.2.6 **Approval system for periodic inspection and testing of pressure receptacles**

6.2.2.6.1 *Definitions*

For the purposes of this section:

Approval system means a system for competent authority approval of a body performing periodic inspection and testing of pressure receptacles (hereinafter referred to as "periodic inspection and testing body"), including approval of that body's quality system.

6.2.2.6.2   *General provisions*

Competent authority

△ **6.2.2.6.2.1**   The competent authority shall establish an approval system for the purpose of ensuring that the periodic inspection and testing of pressure receptacles conform to the provisions of this Code. In instances where the competent authority that approves a body performing periodic inspection and testing of a pressure receptacle is not the competent authority of the country approving the manufacture of the pressure receptacle, the marks of the approval country of periodic inspection and testing shall be indicated in the pressure receptacle mark (see 6.2.2.7). The competent authority of the country of approval for the periodic inspection and testing shall supply, upon request, evidence demonstrating compliance with this approval system, including the records of the periodic inspection and testing, to its counterpart in a country of use. The competent authority of the country of approval may terminate the Approval Certificate referred to in 6.2.2.6.4.1, upon evidence demonstrating non-compliance with the approval system.

6.2.2.6.2.2   The competent authority may delegate its functions in this approval system, in whole or in part.

6.2.2.6.2.3   The competent authority shall ensure that a current list of approved periodic inspection and testing bodies and their identity marks is available.

Periodic inspection and testing body

6.2.2.6.2.4   The periodic inspection and testing body shall be approved by the competent authority and shall:

.1   have a staff with an organizational structure, capable, trained, competent, and skilled, to perform its technical functions satisfactorily;

.2   have access to suitable and adequate facilities and equipment;

.3   operate in an impartial manner and be free from any influence which could prevent it from doing so;

.4   ensure commercial confidentiality;

.5   maintain clear demarcation between actual periodic inspection and testing body functions and unrelated functions;

.6   operate a documented quality system in accordance with 6.2.2.6.3;

.7   apply for approval in accordance with 6.2.2.6.4;

.8   ensure that the periodic inspections and tests are performed in accordance with 6.2.2.6.5; and

.9   maintain an effective and appropriate report and record system in accordance with 6.2.2.6.6.

6.2.2.6.3   *Quality system and audit of the periodic inspection and testing body*

6.2.2.6.3.1   *Quality system*. The quality system shall contain all the elements, requirements and provisions adopted by the periodic inspection and testing body. It shall be documented in a systematic and orderly manner in the form of written policies, procedures and instructions. The quality system shall include:

.1   a description of the organizational structure and responsibilities;

.2   the relevant inspection and test, quality control, quality assurance, and process operation instructions that will be used;

.3   quality records, such as inspection reports, test data, calibration data and certificates;

.4   management reviews to ensure the effective operation of the quality system arising from the audits performed in accordance with 6.2.2.6.3.2;

.5   a process for control of documents and their revision;

.6   a means for control of non-conforming pressure receptacles; and

.7   training programmes and qualification procedures for relevant personnel.

6.2.2.6.3.2   *Audit*. The periodic inspection and testing body and its quality system shall be audited in order to determine whether it meets the requirements of this Code to the satisfaction of the competent authority. An audit shall be conducted as part of the initial approval process (see 6.2.2.6.4.3). An audit may be required as part of the process to modify an approval (see 6.2.2.6.4.6). Periodic audits shall be conducted, to the satisfaction of the competent authority, to ensure that the periodic inspection and testing body continues to meet the provisions of this Code. The periodic inspection and testing body shall be notified of the results of any audit. The notification shall contain the conclusions of the audit and any corrective actions required.

6.2.2.6.3.3   *Maintenance of the quality system*. The periodic inspection and testing body shall maintain the quality system as approved in order that it remains adequate and efficient. The periodic inspection and testing body shall notify the competent authority that approved the quality system of any intended changes, in accordance with the process for modification of an approval in 6.2.2.6.4.6.

6.2.2.6.4 *Approval process for periodic inspection and testing bodies*

Initial approval

6.2.2.6.4.1 A body desiring to perform periodic inspection and testing of pressure receptacles in accordance with a pressure receptacle standard and with this Code shall apply for, obtain, and retain an Approval Certificate issued by the competent authority. This written approval shall, on request, be submitted to the competent authority of a country of use.

6.2.2.6.4.2 An application shall be made for each periodic inspection and testing body and shall include:

.1 the name and address of the periodic inspection and testing body and, if the application is submitted by an authorized representative, its name and address;

.2 the address of each facility performing periodic inspection and testing;

.3 the name and title of the person(s) responsible for the quality system;

.4 the designation of the pressure receptacles, the periodic inspection and test methods, and the relevant pressure receptacle standards met by the quality system;

.5 documentation on each facility, the equipment, and the quality system as specified under 6.2.2.6.3.1;

.6 the qualifications and training records of the periodic inspection and test personnel; and

.7 details of any refusal of approval of a similar application by any other competent authority.

6.2.2.6.4.3 The competent authority shall:

.1 examine the documentation to verify that the procedures are in accordance with the requirements of the relevant pressure receptacle standards and of this Code; and

.2 conduct an audit in accordance with 6.2.2.6.3.2 to verify that the inspections and tests are carried out as required by the relevant pressure receptacle standards and by this Code, to the satisfaction of the competent authority.

6.2.2.6.4.4 After the audit has been carried out with satisfactory results and all applicable requirements of 6.2.2.6.4 have been satisfied, an Approval Certificate shall be issued. It shall include the name of the periodic inspection and testing body, the registered mark, the address of each facility, and the necessary data for identification of its approved activities (e.g. designation of pressure receptacles, periodic inspection and test method and pressure receptacle standards).

6.2.2.6.4.5 If the periodic inspection and testing body is denied approval, the competent authority shall provide written detailed reasons for such denial.

Modifications to periodic inspection and testing body approvals

6.2.2.6.4.6 Following approval, the periodic inspection and testing body shall notify the issuing competent authority of any modifications to the information submitted under 6.2.2.6.4.2 relating to the initial approval. The modifications shall be evaluated in order to determine whether the requirements of the relevant pressure receptacle standards and of this Code will be satisfied. An audit in accordance with 6.2.2.6.3.2 may be required. The competent authority shall accept or reject these modifications in writing, and an amended Approval Certificate shall be issued as necessary.

6.2.2.6.4.7 Upon request, the competent authority shall communicate to any other competent authority, information concerning initial approvals, modifications of approvals, and withdrawn approvals.

△ **6.2.2.6.5** *Periodic inspection and test and certification*

The application of the periodic inspection and test marks to a pressure receptacle shall be considered a declaration that the pressure receptacle complies with the applicable pressure receptacle standards and with the provisions of this Code. The periodic inspection and testing body shall affix the periodic inspection and test marks, including its registered mark, to each approved pressure receptacle (see 6.2.2.7.7). A record certifying that a pressure receptacle has passed the periodic inspection and test shall be issued by the periodic inspection and testing body, before the pressure receptacle is filled.

6.2.2.6.6 *Records*

The periodic inspection and testing body shall retain records of pressure receptacle periodic inspection and tests (both passed and failed), including the location of the test facility, for not less than 15 years. The owner of the pressure receptacle shall retain an identical record until the next periodic inspection and test unless the pressure receptacle is permanently removed from service.

6.2.2.7 Marking of refillable UN pressure receptacles

Note: Marking requirements for UN metal hydride storage systems are given in 6.2.2.9 and marking requirements for UN bundles of cylinders are given in 6.2.2.10.

6

6.2.2.7.1 Refillable UN pressure receptacles shall be marked clearly and legibly with certification, operational and manufacturing marks. These marks shall be permanently affixed (e.g. stamped, engraved, or etched) on the pressure receptacle. The marks shall be on the shoulder, top end or neck of the pressure receptacle or on a permanently affixed component of the pressure receptacle (e.g. welded collar or corrosion-resistant plate welded on the outer jacket of a closed cryogenic receptacle). Except for the UN packaging symbol, the minimum size of the marks shall be 5 mm for pressure receptacles with a diameter greater than or equal to 140 mm and 2.5 mm for pressure receptacles with a diameter less than 140 mm. The minimum size of the UN packaging symbol shall be 10 mm for pressure receptacles with a diameter greater than or equal to 140 mm and 5 mm for pressure receptacles with a diameter less than 140 mm.

6.2.2.7.2 The following certification marks shall be applied:

(a) The UN packaging symbol:

This symbol shall not be used for any purpose other than certifying that a packaging, a flexible bulk container, a portable tank or a MEGC complies with the relevant requirements in chapters 6.1, 6.2, 6.3, 6.5, 6.6, 6.7 or 6.9.

(b) The technical standard (e.g. ISO 9809-1) used for design, construction and testing.

(c) The character(s) identifying the country of approval as indicated by the distinguishing signs of motor vehicles in international traffic.

(d) The identity mark or stamp of the inspection body that is registered with the competent authority of the country authorizing the marking.

(e) The date of the initial inspection, the year (four digits) followed by the month (two digits) separated by a slash (i.e. "/").

6.2.2.7.3 The following operational marks shall be applied:

(f) The test pressure in bar, preceded by the letters "PH" and followed by the letters "BAR".

(g) The mass of the empty pressure receptacle including all permanently attached integral parts (e.g. neck ring, foot ring, etc.) in kilograms, followed by the letters "KG". This mass shall not include the mass of valve, valve cap or valve guard, any coating, or porous mass for acetylene. The mass shall be expressed to three significant figures rounded up to the last digit. For cylinders of less than 1 kg, the mass shall be expressed to two significant figures rounded up to the last digit. In the case of pressure receptacles for UN 1001 acetylene, dissolved and UN 3374 acetylene, solvent free, at least one decimal shall be shown after the decimal point and two digits for pressure receptacles of less than 1 kg.

(h) The minimum guaranteed wall thickness of the pressure receptacle in millimetres followed by the letters "MM". This mark is not required for pressure receptacles with a water capacity less than or equal to 1 litre or for composite cylinders or for closed cryogenic receptacles.

(i) In the case of pressure receptacles for compressed gases, UN 1001 acetylene, dissolved, and UN 3374 acetylene, solvent free, the working pressure in bar, preceded by the letters "PW". In the case of closed cryogenic receptacles, the maximum allowable working pressure preceded by the letters "MAWP".

(j) In the case of pressure receptacles for liquefied gases and refrigerated liquefied gases, the water capacity in litres expressed to three significant figures rounded down to the last digit, followed by the letter "L". If the value of the minimum or nominal water capacity is an integer, the digits after the decimal point may be neglected.

(k) In the case of pressure receptacles for UN 1001 acetylene, dissolved, the total of the mass of the empty receptacle, the fittings and accessories not removed during filling, any coating, the porous material, the solvent and the saturation gas expressed to three significant figures rounded down to the last digit followed by the letters "KG". At least one decimal shall be shown after the decimal point. For pressure receptacles of less than 1 kg, the mass shall be expressed to two significant figures rounded down to the last digit.

(l) In the case of pressure receptacles for UN 3374 acetylene, solvent free, the total of the mass of the empty receptacle, the fittings and accessories not removed during filling, any coating and the porous material expressed to three significant figures rounded down to the last digit followed by the letters "KG". At least one decimal shall be shown after the decimal point. For pressure receptacles of less than 1 kg, the mass shall be expressed to two significant figures rounded down to the last digit.

6.2.2.7.4 The following manufacturing marks shall be applied:

(m) Identification of the cylinder thread (e.g. 25E). This mark is not required for closed cryogenic receptacles.

(n) The manufacturer's mark registered by the competent authority. When the country of manufacture is not the same as the country of approval, then the manufacturer's mark shall be preceded by the character(s) identifying the country of manufacture as indicated by the distinguishing signs of motor vehicles in international traffic. The country mark and the manufacturer's mark shall be separated by a space or slash.

(o)   The serial number assigned by the manufacturer.

(p)   In the case of steel pressure receptacles and composite pressure receptacles with steel liner intended for the transport of gases with a risk of hydrogen embrittlement, the letter "H" showing compatibility of the steel (see ISO 11114-1:2012).

■ (q)   For composite cylinders and tubes having a limited design life, the letters "FINAL" followed by the design life shown as the year (four digits) followed by the month (two digits) separated by a slash (i.e. "/").

■ (r)   For composite cylinders and tubes having a limited design life greater than 15 years and for composite cylinders and tubes having non-limited design life, the letters "SERVICE" followed by the date 15 years from the date of manufacture (initial inspection) shown as the year (four digits) followed by the month (two digits) separated by a slash (i.e. "/").

   ■ Note: Once the initial design type has passed the service life test programme requirements in accordance with 6.2.2.1.1 Note 2 or 6.2.2.1.2 Note 2, future production no longer requires this initial service life mark. The initial service life mark shall be made unreadable on cylinders and tubes of a design type that has met the service life test programme requirements.

6.2.2.7.5   The above marks shall be placed in three groups.

△   –   Manufacturing marks shall be the top grouping and shall appear consecutively in the sequence given in 6.2.2.7.4 except for the marks described in 6.2.2.7.4 (q) and (r) which shall be adjacent to the periodic inspection and test marks of 6.2.2.7.7.

   –   The operational marks in 6.2.2.7.3 shall be the middle grouping and the test pressure (f) shall be immediately preceded by the working pressure (i) when the latter is required.

   –   Certification marks shall be the bottom grouping and shall appear in the sequence given in 6.2.2.7.2.

△ The following is an example of marking a cylinder.

6.2.2.7.6   Other marks are allowed in areas other than the side wall, provided they are made in low-stress areas and are not of a size and depth that will create harmful stress concentrations. In the case of closed cryogenic receptacles, such marks may be on a separate plate attached to the outer jacket. Such marks shall not conflict with required marks.

6.2.2.7.7   In addition to the preceding marks, each refillable pressure receptacle that meets the periodic and test requirements of 6.2.2.4 shall be marked in sequence as follows:

△ (a)   the character(s) identifying the country authorizing the body performing the periodic inspection and test, as indicated by the distinguishing sign of motor vehicles in international traffic. This mark is not required if this body is approved by the competent authority of the country approving manufacture;

(b)   the registered mark of the body authorized by the competent authority for performing periodic inspection and test;

(c)   the date of the periodic inspection and test, the year (two digits) followed by the month (two digits) separated by a slash (i.e. "/"). Four digits may be used to indicate the year.

6.2.2.7.8   For acetylene cylinders, with the agreement of the competent authority, the date of the most recent periodic inspection and the stamp of the body performing the periodic inspection and test may be engraved on a ring held on the cylinder by the valve. The ring shall be configured so that it can only be removed by disconnecting the valve from the cylinder.

6.2.2.8 Marking of non-refillable UN pressure receptacles

6.2.2.8.1   Non-refillable UN pressure receptacles shall be marked clearly and legibly with certification and gas or pressure receptacle specific marks. These marks shall be permanently affixed (e.g. stencilled, stamped, engraved, or etched) on the pressure receptacle. Except when stencilled, the marks shall be on the shoulder, top end or neck of the pressure receptacle or on a permanently affixed component of the pressure receptacle (e.g. welded collar). Except for the "UN" mark and the "DO NOT REFILL" mark, the minimum size of the marks shall be 5 mm for pressure receptacles with a diameter greater than or equal to 140 mm and 2.5 mm for pressure receptacles with a diameter less than 140 mm. The minimum size of the "UN" mark shall be 10 mm for pressure receptacles with a diameter greater than or equal to 140 mm and 5 mm for pressure receptacles with a diameter less than 140 mm. The minimum size of the "DO NOT REFILL" mark shall be 5 mm.

6.2.2.8.2   The marks listed in 6.2.2.7.2 to 6.2.2.7.4 shall be applied with the exception of (g), (h) and (m). The serial number (o) may be replaced by the batch number. In addition, the words "DO NOT REFILL" in letters of at least 5 mm in height are required.

6.2.2.8.3   The requirements of 6.2.2.7.5 shall apply.

△ **Note:** Non-refillable pressure receptacles may, on account of their size, substitute a label for these permanent marks.

6.2.2.8.4   Other marks are allowed provided they are made in low-stress areas other than the side wall and are not of a size and depth that will create harmful stress concentrations. Such marks shall not conflict with required marks.

6.2.2.9 Marking of UN metal hydride storage systems

6.2.2.9.1   UN metal hydride storage systems shall be marked clearly and legibly with the marks listed below. These marks shall be permanently affixed (e.g. stamped, engraved, or etched) on the metal hydride storage system. The marks shall be on the shoulder, top end or neck of the metal hydride storage system or on a permanently affixed component of the metal hydride storage system. Except for the United Nations packaging symbol, the minimum size of the marks shall be 5 mm for metal hydride storage systems with a smallest overall dimension greater than or equal to 140 mm and 2.5 mm for metal hydride storage systems with a smallest overall dimension less than 140 mm. The minimum size of the United Nations packaging symbol shall be 10 mm for metal hydride storage systems with a smallest overall dimension greater than or equal to 140 mm and 5 mm for metal hydride storage systems with a smallest overall dimension less than 140 mm.

6.2.2.9.2   The following marks shall be applied:

(a)   The United Nations packaging symbol:

This symbol shall not be used for any purpose other than certifying that a packaging, a flexible bulk container, a portable tank or a MEGC complies with the relevant requirements in chapters 6.1, 6.2, 6.3, 6.5, 6.6, 6.7 or 6.9.

(b)   "ISO 16111" (the technical standard used for design, manufacture and testing).

(c)   The character(s) identifying the country of approval as indicated by the distinguishing signs of motor vehicles in international traffic.

(d)   The identity mark or stamp of the inspection body that is registered with the competent authority of the country authorizing the marking.

(e)   The date of the initial inspection, the year (four digits) followed by the month (two digits) separated by a slash (i.e. "/").

(f)   The test pressure of the receptacle in bar, preceded by the letters "PH" and followed by the letters "BAR".

(g)   The rated charging pressure of the metal hydride storage system in bar, preceded by the letters "RCP" and followed by the letters "BAR".

(h)   The manufacturer's mark registered by the competent authority. When the country of manufacture is not the same as the country of approval, then the manufacturer's mark shall be preceded by the character(s) identifying the country of manufacture as indicated by the distinguishing signs of motor vehicles in international traffic. The country mark and the manufacturer's mark shall be separated by a space or slash.

(i)   The serial number assigned by the manufacturer.

(j)   In the case of steel receptacles and composite receptacles with steel liner, the letter "H" showing compatibility of the steel (see ISO 11114-1:2012).

(k)   In the case of metal hydride storage systems having limited life, the date of expiry, denoted by the letters "FINAL" followed by the year (four digits) followed by the month (two digits) separated by a slash (i.e. "/").

The certification marks specified in (a) to (e) above shall appear consecutively in the sequence given. The test pressure (f) shall be immediately preceded by the rated charging pressure (g). The manufacturing marks specified in (h) to (k) above shall appear consecutively in the sequence given.

6.2.2.9.3   Other marks are allowed in areas other than the side wall, provided they are made in low stress areas and are not of a size and depth that will create harmful stress concentrations. Such marks shall not conflict with required marks.

6.2.2.9.4   In addition to the preceding marks, each metal hydride storage system that meets the periodic and test requirements of 6.2.2.4 shall be marked indicating:

△ (a)   The character(s) identifying the country authorizing the body performing the periodic inspection and test, as indicated by the distinguishing sign of motor vehicles in international traffic. This mark is not required if this body is approved by the competent authority of the country approving manufacture;

(b)   The registered mark of the body authorized by the competent authority for performing periodic inspection and test;

(c)   The date of the periodic inspection and test, the year (two digits) followed by the month (two digits) separated by a slash (i.e. "/"). Four digits may be used to indicate the year.

The above marks shall appear consecutively in the sequence given.

6.2.2.10   **Marking of UN bundles of cylinders**

6.2.2.10.1   Individual cylinders in a bundle of cylinders shall be marked in accordance with 6.2.2.7.

6.2.2.10.2   Refillable UN bundles of cylinders shall be marked clearly and legibly with certification, operational, and manufacturing marks. These marks shall be permanently affixed (e.g. stamped, engraved, or etched) on a plate permanently attached to the frame of the bundle of cylinders. Except for the UN packaging symbol, the minimum size of the marks shall be 5 mm. The minimum size of the UN packaging symbol shall be 10 mm.

6.2.2.10.3   The following marks shall be applied:

(a)   The certification marks specified in 6.2.2.7.2 (a), (b), (c), (d) and (e).

(b)   The operational marks specified in 6.2.2.7.3 (f), (i), (j) and the total of the mass of the frame of the bundle and all permanently attached parts (cylinders, manifold, fittings and valves). Bundles intended for the carriage of UN 1001 acetylene, dissolved and UN 3374 acetylene, solvent free shall bear the tare mass as specified in clause B.4.2 of ISO 10961:2010.

(c)   The manufacturing marks specified in 6.2.2.7.4 (n), (o) and, where applicable, (p).

6.2.2.10.4   The marks shall be placed in three groups:

(a)   The manufacturing marks shall be the top grouping and shall appear consecutively in the sequence given in 6.2.2.10.3 (c).

(b)   The operational marks in 6.2.2.10.3 (b) shall be the middle grouping and the operational mark specified in 6.2.2.7.3 (f) shall be immediately preceded by the operational mark specified in 6.2.2.7.3 (i) when the latter is required.

(c)   Certification marks shall be the bottom grouping and shall appear in the sequence given in 6.2.2.10.3 (a).

6.2.3   Provisions for non-UN pressure receptacles

6.2.3.1   Pressure receptacles not designed, constructed, inspected, tested and approved according to 6.2.2 shall be designed, constructed, inspected, tested and approved in accordance with a technical code recognized by the competent authority and the general provisions of 6.2.1.

6.2.3.2   Pressure receptacles designed, constructed, inspected, tested and approved under the provisions of this section shall not be marked with the UN packaging symbol.

6.2.3.3   For metallic cylinders, tubes, pressure drums, bundles of cylinders and salvage pressure receptacles, the construction shall be such that the minimum burst ratio (burst pressure divided by test pressure) is:

1.50   for refillable pressure receptacles;

2.00   for non-refillable pressure receptacles.

6.2.3.4   Marking shall be in accordance with the requirements of the competent authority of the country of use.

6

6.2.3.5 **Salvage pressure receptacles**

Note: These provisions of 6.2.3.5 for salvage pressure receptacles may be applied for new salvage pressure receptacles as from 1 January 2013, unless otherwise authorized, and shall be applied for all new salvage pressure receptacles as from 1 January 2014. Salvage pressure receptacles approved in accordance with national regulations may be used with the approval of the competent authorities of the countries of use.

6.2.3.5.1 To permit the safe handling and disposal of the pressure receptacles transported within the salvage pressure receptacle, the design may include equipment not otherwise used for cylinders or pressure drums such as flat heads, quick opening devices and openings in the cylindrical part.

6.2.3.5.2 Instructions on the safe handling and use of the salvage pressure receptacle shall be clearly shown in the documentation for the application to the competent authority and shall form part of the approval certificate. In the approval certificate, the pressure receptacles authorized to be transported in a salvage pressure receptacle shall be indicated. A list of the materials of construction of all parts likely to be in contact with the dangerous goods shall also be included.

6.2.3.5.3 A copy of the approval certificate shall be delivered by the manufacturer to the owner of a salvage pressure receptacle.

6.2.3.5.4 The marking of salvage pressure receptacles according to 6.2.3 shall be determined by the competent authority in taking into account suitable marking provisions of 6.2.2.7 as appropriate. The marking shall include the water capacity and test pressure of the salvage pressure receptacle.

6.2.4 Provisions for aerosol dispensers, small receptacles containing gas (gas cartridges) and fuel cell cartridges containing liquefied flammable gas

Each filled aerosol dispenser or gas cartridge or fuel cell cartridge shall be subjected to a test in a hot water bath in accordance with 6.2.4.1 or an approved water bath alternative in accordance with 6.2.4.2.

6.2.4.1 **Hot water bath test**

6.2.4.1.1 The temperature of the water bath and the duration of the test shall be such that the internal pressure reaches that which would be reached at 55°C (50°C if the liquid phase does not exceed 95% of the capacity of the aerosol dispenser, gas cartridge or fuel cell cartridge at 50°C). If the contents are sensitive to heat or if the aerosol dispensers, gas cartridges or fuel cell cartridges are made of plastics material which softens at this test temperature, the temperature of the bath shall be set at between 20°C and 30°C but, in addition, one aerosol dispenser, gas cartridge or fuel cell cartridge in 2,000 shall be tested at the higher temperature.

6.2.4.1.2 No leakage or permanent deformation of an aerosol dispenser, receptacle or fuel cell cartridge may occur, except that a plastic aerosol dispenser, gas cartridge or fuel cell cartridge may be deformed through softening provided that it does not leak.

6.2.4.2 **Alternative methods**

With the approval of the competent authority, alternative methods which provide an equivalent level of safety may be used provided that the requirements of 6.2.4.2.1 and, as appropriate, 6.2.4.2.2 or 6.2.4.2.3 are met.

6.2.4.2.1 *Quality system*

Aerosol dispenser, gas cartridge or fuel cell cartridge fillers and component manufacturers shall have a quality system. The quality system shall implement procedures to ensure that all aerosol dispensers, gas cartridges or fuel cell cartridges that leak or that are deformed are rejected and not offered for transport.

The quality system shall include:

(a) a description of the organizational structure and responsibilities;

(b) the relevant inspection and test, quality control, quality assurance, and process operation instructions that will be used;

(c) quality records, such as inspection reports, test data, calibration data and certificates;

(d) management reviews to ensure the effective operation of the quality system;

(e) a process for control of documents and their revision;

(f) a means for control of non-conforming aerosol dispensers, gas cartridges or fuel cell cartridges;

(g) training programmes and qualification procedures for relevant personnel; and

(h) procedures to ensure that there is no damage to the final product.

An initial audit and periodic audits shall be conducted to the satisfaction of the competent authority. These audits shall ensure the approved system is and remains adequate and efficient. Any proposed changes to the approved system shall be notified to the competent authority in advance.

6.2.4.2.2 *Aerosol dispensers*

6.2.4.2.2.1 *Pressure and leak testing of aerosol dispensers before filling*

Each empty aerosol dispenser shall be subjected to a pressure equal to or in excess of the maximum expected in the filled aerosol dispensers at 55°C (50°C if the liquid phase does not exceed 95% of the capacity of the receptacle at 50°C). This shall be at least two-thirds of the design pressure of the aerosol dispenser. If any aerosol dispenser shows evidence of leakage at a rate equal to or greater than 3.3×10^{-2} mbar·L·s^{-1} at the test pressure, distortion or other defect, it shall be rejected.

6.2.4.2.2.2 *Testing of the aerosol dispensers after filling*

Prior to filling, the filler shall ensure that the crimping equipment is set appropriately and the specified propellant is used.

Each filled aerosol dispenser shall be weighed and leak tested. The leak detection equipment shall be sufficiently sensitive to detect at least a leak rate of 2.0×10^{-3} mbar·L·s^{-1} at 20°C.

Any filled aerosol dispenser which shows evidence of leakage, deformation or excessive mass shall be rejected.

6.2.4.2.3 *Gas cartridges and fuel cell cartridges*

6.2.4.2.3.1 *Pressure testing of gas cartridges and fuel cell cartridges*

Each gas cartridge or fuel cell cartridge shall be subjected to a test pressure equal to or in excess of the maximum expected in the filled receptacle at 55°C (50°C if the liquid phase does not exceed 95% of the capacity of the receptacle at 50°C). This test pressure shall be that specified for the gas cartridge or fuel cell cartridge and shall not be less than two thirds the design pressure of the gas cartridge or fuel cell cartridge. If any gas cartridge or fuel cell cartridge shows evidence of leakage at a rate equal to or greater than 3.3×10^{-2} mbar·L·s^{-1} at the test pressure or distortion or any other defect, it shall be rejected.

6.2.4.2.3.2 *Leak testing gas cartridges and fuel cell cartridges*

Prior to filling and sealing, the filler shall ensure that the closures (if any), and the associated sealing equipment are closed appropriately and the specified gas is used.

Each filled gas cartridge or fuel cell cartridge shall be checked for the correct mass of gas and shall be leak tested. The leak detection equipment shall be sufficiently sensitive to detect at least a leak rate of 2.0×10^{-3} mbar·L·s^{-1} at 20°C.

Any gas cartridge or fuel cell cartridge that has gas masses not in conformity with the declared mass limits or shows evidence of leakage or deformation, shall be rejected.

6.2.4.3 With the approval of the competent authority, aerosols and receptacles, small, are not subject to 6.2.4.1 and 6.2.4.2, if they are required to be sterile but may be adversely affected by water bath testing, provided:

(a) They contain a non-flammable gas and either

    (i) contain other substances that are constituent parts of pharmaceutical products for medical, veterinary or similar purposes;

    (ii) contain other substances used in the production process for pharmaceutical products; or

    (iii) are used in medical, veterinary or similar applications;

(b) An equivalent level of safety is achieved by the manufacturer's use of alternative methods for leak detection and pressure resistance, such as helium detection and water bathing a statistical sample of at least 1 in 2,000 from each production batch; and

(c) For pharmaceutical products according to (a)(i) and (iii) above, they are manufactured under the authority of a national health administration. If required by the competent authority, the principles of Good Manufacturing Practice (GMP) established by the World Health Organization (WHO)[*] shall be followed.

---

[*] Refer to WHO publication: *Quality assurance of pharmaceuticals. A compendium of guidelines and related materials. Volume 2: Good manufacturing practices and inspection.*

6

Chapter 6.3

Provisions for the construction and testing of packagings for class 6.2 infectious substances of category A

6.3.1 General

6.3.1.1 The provisions of this chapter apply to packagings intended for the transport of infectious substances of category A.

6.3.2 Provisions for packagings

6.3.2.1 The provisions for packagings in this section are based on packagings, as specified in 6.1.4, currently used. In order to take into account progress in science and technology, there is no objection to the use of packagings having specifications different from those in this chapter provided that they are equally effective, acceptable to the competent authority and able successfully to withstand the tests described in 6.3.5. Methods of testing other than those described in the provisions of this Code are acceptable provided they are equivalent.

6.3.2.2 Packagings shall be manufactured and tested under a quality assurance programme which satisfies the competent authority in order to ensure that each packaging meets the provisions of this chapter.

Note: ISO 16106:2006, *Packaging – Transport packages for dangerous goods – Dangerous goods packagings, intermediate bulk containers (IBCs) and large packagings – Guidelines for the application of ISO 9001,* provides acceptable guidance on procedures which may be followed.

6.3.2.3 Manufacturers and subsequent distributors of packagings shall provide information regarding procedures to be followed and a description of the types and dimensions of closures (including required gaskets) and any other components needed to ensure that packages as presented for transport are capable of passing the applicable performance tests of this chapter.

6.3.3 Code for designating types of packagings

6.3.3.1 The codes for designating types of packagings are set out in 6.1.2.7.

6.3.3.2 The letters "U" or "W" may follow the packaging code. The letter "U" signifies a special packaging conforming to the provisions of 6.3.5.1.6. The letter "W" signifies that the packaging, although of the same type as indicated by the code, is manufactured to a specification different from that in 6.1.4 and is considered equivalent under the provisions of 6.3.2.1.

6.3.4 Marking

△ **Note 1:** The marks indicate that the packaging which bears them correspond to a successfully tested design type and that it complies with the provisions of this chapter which are related to the manufacture, but not to the use, of the packaging.

△ **Note 2:** The marks are intended to be of assistance to packaging manufacturers, reconditioners, packaging users, carriers and regulatory authorities.

△ **Note 3:** The marks do not always provide full details of the test levels, etc., and these may need to be taken further into account, e.g. by reference to a test certificate, to test reports or to a register of successfully tested packagings.

△ 6.3.4.1 Each packaging intended for use according to the provisions of this Code shall bear marks which are durable, legible and placed in a location and of such a size relative to the packaging as to be readily visible. For packages with a gross mass of more than 30 kg, the marks or a duplicate thereof shall appear on the top or on a side of the packaging. Letters, numerals and symbols shall be at least 12 mm high, except for packagings of 30 litres or 30 kg capacity or less, when they shall be at least 6 mm in height, and for packagings of 5 litres or 5 kg or less, when they shall be of an appropriate size.

6.3.4.2   A packaging that meets the provisions of this section and of 6.3.5 shall be marked with:

(a)   the United Nations packaging symbol:

    This symbol shall not be used for any purpose other than certifying that a packaging, a flexible bulk container, a portable tank or a MEGC complies with the relevant requirements in chapters 6.1, 6.2, 6.3, 6.5, 6.6, 6.7 or 6.9;

(b)   the code designating the type of packaging according to the provisions of 6.1.2;

(c)   the text "CLASS 6.2";

(d)   the last two digits of the year of manufacture of the packaging;

(e)   the State authorizing the allocation of the mark, indicated by the distinguishing sign for motor vehicles in international traffic;

(f)   the name of the manufacturer or other identification of the packaging specified by the competent authority;

△ (g)   for packagings meeting the provisions of 6.3.5.1.6, the letter "U" shall be inserted immediately following the mark required in (b) above; and

(h)   each element of the marking applied in accordance with subparagraphs (a) to (g).

△ 6.3.4.3   Marks shall be applied in the sequence shown in 6.3.4.2 (a) to (g); each mark required in these subparagraphs shall be clearly separated, e.g. by a slash or space, so as to be easily identifiable. For examples, see 6.3.4.4.

    Any additional markings authorized by a competent authority shall still enable the marks required in 6.3.4.1 to be correctly identified.

6.3.4.4   **Example of marking**

   4G/CLASS 6.2/06   as in 6.3.4.2 (a), (b), (c) and (d)

    S/SP-9989-ERIKSSON   as in 6.3.4.2 (e) and (f)

6.3.5   Test provisions for packagings

6.3.5.1   Performance and frequency of tests

6.3.5.1.1   The design type of each packaging shall be tested as provided in this section in accordance with procedures established by the competent authority.

6.3.5.1.2   Each packaging design type shall successfully pass the tests prescribed in this chapter before being used. A packaging design type is defined by the design, size, material and thickness, manner of construction and packing, but may include various surface treatments. It also includes packagings which differ from the design type only in their lesser design height.

6.3.5.1.3   Tests shall be repeated on production samples at intervals established by the competent authority.

6.3.5.1.4   Tests shall also be repeated after each modification which alters the design, material or manner of construction of a packaging.

6.3.5.1.5   The competent authority may permit the selective testing of packagings that differ only in minor respects from a tested type, such as smaller sizes or lower net mass of primary receptacles; and packagings such as drums and boxes which are produced with small reductions in external dimension(s).

6.3.5.1.6   Primary receptacles of any type may be assembled within a secondary packaging and transported without testing in the rigid outer packaging under the following conditions:

.1   the rigid outer packaging shall have been successfully tested in accordance with 6.3.5.2.2 with fragile (such as glass) primary receptacles;

.2   the total combined gross mass of primary receptacles shall not exceed one half of the gross mass of primary receptacles used for the drop test in .1 above;

.3   the thickness of cushioning between primary receptacles and between primary receptacles and the outside of the secondary packaging shall not be reduced below the corresponding thicknesses in the originally tested packaging; and if a single primary receptacle was used in the original test, the thickness of cushioning between primary receptacles shall not be less than the thickness of cushioning between the outside of the secondary packaging and the primary receptacle in the original test. When either fewer or smaller primary receptacles are used (as compared to the primary receptacles used in the drop test), sufficient additional cushioning material shall be used to take up the void spaces;

.4 the rigid outer packaging shall have successfully passed the stacking test in 6.1.5.6 while empty. The total mass of identical packages shall be based on the combined mass of packagings used in the drop test in .1 above;

.5 for primary receptacles containing liquids, an adequate quantity of absorbent material to absorb the entire liquid content of the primary receptacles shall be present;

.6 if the rigid outer packaging is intended to contain primary receptacles for liquids and is not leakproof, or is intended to contain primary receptacles for solids and is not sift-proof, a means of containing any liquid or solid contents in the event of leakage shall be provided in the form of a leakproof liner, plastics bag or other equally effective means of containment; and

△ .7 in addition to the marks prescribed in 6.3.4.2 (a) to (f), packagings shall be marked in accordance with 6.3,4.2(g).

6.3.5.1.7 The competent authority may at any time require proof, by tests in accordance with this section, that serially produced packagings meet the provisions of the design type tests.

6.3.5.1.8 Provided the validity of the test results is not affected and with the approval of the competent authority, several tests may be made on one sample.

6.3.5.2 Preparation of packagings for testing

6.3.5.2.1 Samples of each packaging shall be prepared as for transport except that a liquid or solid infectious substance shall be replaced by water or, where conditioning at −18°C is specified, by water containing antifreeze. Each primary receptacle shall be filled to not less than 98% of its capacity.

Note: The term "water" includes water/antifreeze solution with a minimum specific gravity of 0.95 for testing at −18°C.

6.3.5.2.2 *Tests and number of samples required*

Tests required for packaging types

Type of packaging[a]			Tests required					
Rigid outer packaging	Primary receptacle		Water spray 6.3.5.3.6.1	Cold conditioning 6.3.5.3.6.2	Drop 6.3.5.3	Additional drop 6.3.5.3.6.3	Puncture 6.3.5.4	Stack 6.1.5.6
	Plastics	Other	Number of samples	Number of samples	Number of samples	Number of samples	Number of samples	Number of samples
Fibreboard box	x		5	5	10	Required on one sample when the packaging is intended to contain dry ice.	2	Required on three samples when testing a "U"-marked packaging as defined in 6.3.5.1.6 for specific provisions.
		x	5	0	5		2	
Fibreboard drum	x		3	3	6		2	
		x	3	0	3		2	
Plastics box	x		0	5	5		2	
		x	0	5	5		2	
Plastics drum/ jerrican	x		0	3	3		2	
		x	0	3	3		2	
Boxes of other material	x		0	5	5		2	
		x	0	0	5		2	
Drums/jerricans of other material	x		0	3	3		2	
		x	0	0	3		2	

[a] "Type of packaging" categorizes packagings for test purposes according to the kind of packaging and its material characteristics.

Note 1: In instances where a primary receptacle is made of two or more materials, the material most liable to damage determines the appropriate test.

Note 2: The materials of the secondary packagings are not taken into consideration when selecting the test or conditioning for the test.

Explanation for use of the table:

If the packaging to be tested consists of a fibreboard outer box with a plastics primary receptacle, five samples must undergo the water spray test (see 6.3.5.3.6.1) prior to dropping and another five must be conditioned to −18°C (see 6.3.5.3.6.2) prior to dropping. If the packaging is to contain dry ice then one further single sample shall be dropped five times after conditioning in accordance with 6.3.5.3.6.3.

Packagings prepared as for transport shall be subjected to the tests in 6.3.5.3 and 6.3.5.4. For outer packagings, the headings in the table relate to fibreboard or similar materials whose performance may be rapidly affected by moisture; plastics which may embrittle at low temperature; and other materials such as metal whose performance is not affected by moisture or temperature.

6.3.5.3 Drop test

6.3.5.3.1 Samples shall be subjected to free-fall drops from a height of 9 m onto a non-resilient, horizontal, flat, massive and rigid surface in conformity with 6.1.5.3.4.

6.3.5.3.2 Where the samples are in the shape of a box, five shall be dropped, one in each of the following orientations:

.1 flat on the base;

.2 flat on the top;

.3 flat on the longest side;

.4 flat on the shortest side; and

.5 on a corner.

6.3.5.3.3 Where the samples are in the shape of a drum, three shall be dropped, one in each of the following orientations:

.1 diagonally on the top chime, with the centre of gravity directly above the point of impact;

.2 diagonally on the base chime; and

.3 flat on the side.

6.3.5.3.4 While the sample shall be released in the required orientation, it is accepted that, for aerodynamic reasons, the impact may not take place in that orientation.

6.3.5.3.5 Following the appropriate drop sequence, there shall be no leakage from the primary receptacle(s), which shall remain protected by cushioning/absorbent material in the secondary packaging.

6.3.5.3.6 *Special preparation of test sample for the drop test*

6.3.5.3.6.1 *Fibreboard – Water spray test*

Fibreboard outer packagings: The sample shall be subjected to a water spray that simulates exposure to rainfall of approximately 5 cm per hour for at least one hour. It shall then be subjected to the test described in 6.3.5.3.1.

6.3.5.3.6.2 *Plastics material – Cold conditioning*

Plastics primary receptacles or outer packagings: The temperature of the test sample and its contents shall be reduced to −18°C or lower for a period of at least 24 h and within 15 min of removal from that atmosphere the test sample shall be subjected to the test described in 6.3.5.3.1. Where the sample contains dry ice, the conditioning period shall be reduced to 4 hours.

6.3.5.3.6.3 *Packagings intended to contain dry ice – Additional drop test*

Where the packaging is intended to contain dry ice, a test additional to that specified in 6.3.5.3.1 and, when appropriate, in 6.3.5.3.6.1 or 6.3.5.3.6.2 shall be carried out. One sample shall be stored so that all the dry ice dissipates and then that sample shall be dropped in one of the orientations described in 6.3.5.3.2 which shall be that most likely to result in failure of the packaging.

6.3.5.4 Puncture test

6.3.5.4.1 *Packagings with a gross mass of 7 kg or less*

Samples shall be placed on a level hard surface. A cylindrical steel rod with a mass of at least 7 kg, a diameter of 38 mm and the impact end edges having a radius not exceeding 6 mm (see below) shall be dropped in a vertical free fall from a height of 1 m, measured from the impact to the impact surface of a sample. One sample shall be placed on its base. A second sample shall be placed in an orientation perpendicular to that used for the first. In each instance, the steel rod shall be aimed to impact the primary receptacle. Following each impact, penetration of the secondary packaging is acceptable, provided that there is no leakage from the primary receptacle(s).

6

6.3.5.4.2 *Packagings with a gross mass exceeding 7 kg*

Samples shall be dropped on to the end of a cylindrical steel rod. The rod shall be set vertically in a level hard surface. It shall have a diameter of 38 mm and the edges of the upper end a radius not exceeding 6 mm (see below). The rod shall protrude from the surface a distance at least equal to that between the centre of the primary receptacle(s) and the outer surface of the outer packaging with a minimum of 200 mm. One sample shall be dropped with its top face lowermost in a vertical free fall from a height of 1 m, measured from the top of the steel rod. A second sample shall be dropped from the same height in an orientation perpendicular to that used for the first. In each instance, the packaging shall be so orientated that the steel rod would be capable of penetrating the primary receptacle(s). Following each impact, penetration of the secondary packaging is acceptable, provided that there is no leakage from the primary receptacle(s).

6.3.5.5   **Test report**

6.3.5.5.1   A written test report containing at least the following particulars shall be drawn up and shall be available to the users of the packaging:

.1   Name and address of the test facility;

.2   Name and address of applicant (where appropriate);

.3   A unique test report identification;

.4   Date of the test and of the report;

.5   Manufacturer of the packaging;

.6   Description of the packaging design type (e.g. dimensions, materials, closures, thickness, etc.), including method of manufacture (e.g. blow moulding) and which may include drawing(s) and/or photograph(s);

.7   Maximum capacity;

.8   Test contents;

.9   Test descriptions and results;

.10   The test report shall be signed with the name and status of the signatory.

6.3.5.5.2   The test report shall contain statements that the packaging prepared as for transport was tested in accordance with the appropriate requirements of this chapter and that the use of other packaging methods or components may render it invalid. A copy of the test report shall be available to the competent authority.

Chapter 6.4

Provisions for the construction, testing and approval of packages for radioactive material and for the approval of such material

Note: This chapter includes provisions which apply to the construction, testing and approval of certain packages and material only when transported by air. Whilst these provisions do not apply to packages/material transported by sea, the provisions are reproduced for information/identification purposes, since such packages/material, designed, tested and approved for air transport, may also be transported by sea.

6.4.1 [Reserved]

6.4.2 General provisions

6.4.2.1 The package shall be so designed in relation to its mass, volume and shape that it can be easily and safely transported. In addition, the package shall be so designed that it can be properly secured in or on the conveyance during transport.

6.4.2.2 The design shall be such that any lifting attachments on the package will not fail when used in the intended manner and that, if failure of the attachments shall occur, the ability of the package to meet other provisions of this Code would not be impaired. The design shall take account of appropriate safety factors to cover snatch lifting.

6.4.2.3 Attachments and any other features on the outer surface of the package which could be used to lift it shall be designed either to support its mass in accordance with the provisions of 6.4.2.2 or shall be removable or otherwise rendered incapable of being used during transport.

6.4.2.4 As far as practicable, the packaging shall be so designed and finished that the external surfaces are free from protruding features and can be easily decontaminated.

6.4.2.5 As far as practicable, the outer layer of the package shall be so designed as to prevent the collection and the retention of water.

6.4.2.6 Any features added to the package at the time of transport which are not part of the package shall not reduce its safety.

6.4.2.7 The package shall be capable of withstanding the effects of any acceleration, vibration or vibration resonance which may arise under routine conditions of transport without any deterioration in the effectiveness of the closing devices on the various receptacles or in the integrity of the package as a whole. In particular, nuts, bolts and other securing devices shall be so designed as to prevent them from becoming loose or being released unintentionally, even after repeated use.

6.4.2.8 The materials of the packaging and any components or structures shall be physically and chemically compatible with each other and with the radioactive contents. Account shall be taken of their behaviour under irradiation.

6.4.2.9 All valves through which the radioactive contents could escape shall be protected against unauthorized operation.

6.4.2.10 The design of the package shall take into account ambient temperatures and pressures that are likely to be encountered in routine conditions of transport.

6.4.2.11 A package shall be so designed that it provides sufficient shielding to ensure that, under routine conditions of transport and with the maximum radioactive contents that the package is designed to contain, the radiation level at any point on the external surface of the package would not exceed the values specified in 2.7.2.4.1.2, 4.1.9.1.10 and 4.1.9.1.11, as applicable, with account taken of 7.1.4.5.3.3 and 7.1.4.5.5.

6.4.2.12   For radioactive material having other dangerous properties, the package design shall take into account those properties; see 4.1.9.1.5, 2.0.3.1 and 2.0.3.2.

6.4.2.13   Manufacturers and subsequent distributors of packagings shall provide information regarding procedures to be followed and a description of the types and dimensions of closures (including required gaskets) and any other components needed to ensure that packages as presented for transport are capable of passing the applicable performance tests of this chapter.

6.4.3   Additional provisions for packages transported by air

6.4.3.1   For packages to be transported by air, the temperature of the accessible surfaces shall not exceed 50°C at an ambient temperature of 38°C with no account taken for insolation.

6.4.3.2   Packages to be transported by air shall be so designed that, if they were exposed to ambient temperatures ranging from −40°C to +55°C, the integrity of containment would not be impaired.

6.4.3.3   Packages containing radioactive material, to be transported by air, shall be capable of withstanding, without loss or dispersal of radioactive contents from the containment system, an internal pressure which produces a pressure differential of not less than maximum normal operating pressure plus 95 kPa.

6.4.4   Provisions for excepted packages

An excepted package shall be designed to meet the provisions specified in 6.4.2 and, in addition, shall meet the provisions of 6.4.3 if carried by air.

6.4.5   Provisions for industrial packages

6.4.5.1   A Type IP-1 package shall be designed to meet the provisions specified in 6.4.2 and 6.4.7.2, and, in addition, shall meet the provisions of 6.4.3 if carried by air.

6.4.5.2   A package, to be qualified as a Type IP-2 package, shall be designed to meet the provisions for Type IP-1 as specified in 6.4.5.1 and, in addition, if it were subjected to the tests specified in 6.4.15.4 and 6.4.15.5, it would prevent:

.1   loss or dispersal of the radioactive contents, and

.2   more than a 20% increase in the maximum radiation level at any external surface of the package.

6.4.5.3   A package, to be qualified as a Type IP-3 package, shall be designed to meet the provisions for Type IP-1 as specified in 6.4.5.1 and, in addition, the provisions specified in 6.4.7.2–6.4.7.15.

6.4.5.4   Alternative provisions for Type IP-2 and Type IP-3 packages

6.4.5.4.1   Packages may be used as Type IP-2 package provided that:

.1   they satisfy the provisions for Type IP-1 specified in 6.4.5.1;

.2   they are designed to satisfy the provisions for packing group I or II in chapter 6.1 of this Code; and

.3   when subjected to the tests for UN packing group I or II in chapter 6.1, they would prevent:

(i) loss or dispersal of the radioactive contents; and

(ii) more than a 20% increase in the maximum radiation level at any external surface of the package.

6.4.5.4.2   Portable tanks may also be used as Type IP-2 or Type IP-3 packages provided that:

.1   they satisfy the provisions for Type IP-1 specified in 6.4.5.1;

.2   they are designed to satisfy the provisions of chapter 6.7 of this Code, and are capable of withstanding a test pressure of 265 kPa; and

.3   they are designed so that any shielding which is provided shall be capable of withstanding the static and dynamic stresses resulting from handling and routine conditions of transport and of preventing more than a 20% increase in the maximum radiation level at any external surface of the portable tanks.

6.4.5.4.3   Tanks, other than portable tanks, may also be used as Type IP-2 or Type IP-3 packages for transporting LSA-I and LSA-II liquids and gases as prescribed in the table under 4.1.9.2.5, provided that:

.1   they satisfy the provisions of 6.4.5.1;

.2   they are designed to satisfy the provisions prescribed in regional or national regulations for the transport of dangerous goods and are capable of withstanding a test pressure of 265 kPa; and

.3 they are designed so that any additional shielding which is provided shall be capable of withstanding the static and dynamic stresses resulting from handling and routine conditions of transport and of preventing more than a 20% increase in the maximum radiation level at any external surface of the tanks.

6.4.5.4.4 Freight containers with the characteristics of a permanent enclosure may also be used as Type IP-2 or Type IP-3 packages provided that:

.1 the radioactive contents are restricted to solid materials;

.2 they satisfy the provisions for Type IP-1 specified in 6.4.5.1; and

.3 they are designed to conform to the standards prescribed in ISO 1496-1:1990(E), *Series 1 Freight Containers – Specifications and Testing – Part 1: General Cargo Containers,* and subsequent amendments 1:1993, 2:1998, 3:2005, 4:2006 and 5:2006, excluding dimensions and ratings. They shall be designed such that, if subjected to the tests prescribed in that document and the accelerations occurring during routine conditions of transport, they would prevent:

.1 loss or dispersal of the radioactive contents; and

.2 more than a 20% increase in the maximum radiation level at any external surface of the package.

6.4.5.4.5 Metal intermediate bulk containers may also be used as Type IP-2 or Type IP-3 packages provided that:

.1 they satisfy the provisions for Type IP-1 specified in 6.4.5.1; and

.2 they are designed to satisfy the provisions of chapter 6.5 of this Code for packing group I or II, and if they were subjected to the tests prescribed in that chapter, but with the drop test conducted in the most damaging orientation, they would prevent:

.1 loss or dispersal of the radioactive contents; and

.2 more than a 20% increase in the maximum radiation level at any external surface of the package.

6.4.6 Provisions for packages containing uranium hexafluoride

6.4.6.1 Packages designed to contain uranium hexafluoride shall meet the requirements which pertain to the radioactive and fissile properties of the material prescribed elsewhere in this Code. Except as allowed in 6.4.6.4, uranium hexafluoride in quantities of 0.1 kg or more shall also be packaged and transported in accordance with ISO 7195:2005, *Nuclear energy – Packaging of uranium hexafluoride (UF6) for transport*, and the provisions of 6.4.6.2 to 6.4.6.3.

6.4.6.2 Each package designed to contain 0.1 kg or more of uranium hexafluoride shall be designed so that it would meet the following provisions:

.1 withstand, without leakage and without unacceptable stress, as specified in ISO 7195:2005, the structural test as specified in 6.4.21 except as allowed in 6.4.6.4;

.2 withstand, without loss or dispersal of the uranium hexafluoride, the free drop test specified in 6.4.15.4; and

.3 withstand, without rupture of the containment system, the thermal test specified in 6.4.17.3 except as allowed in 6.4.6.4.

6.4.6.3 Packages designed to contain 0.1 kg or more of uranium hexafluoride shall not be provided with pressure relief devices.

6.4.6.4 Subject to multilateral approval, packages designed to contain 0.1 kg or more of uranium hexafluoride may be transported if the packages are designed:

(a) to international or national standards other than ISO 7195:2005, provided an equivalent level of safety is maintained;

(b) to withstand, without leakage and without unacceptable stress, a test pressure of less than 2.76 MPa as specified in 6.4.21; and/or

(c) to contain 9000 kg or more of uranium hexafluoride and the packages do not meet the requirement of 6.4.6.2.3.

In all other respects, the provisions of 6.4.6.1 to 6.4.6.3 shall be satisfied.

6.4.7 Provisions for Type A packages

6.4.7.1 Type A packages shall be designed to meet the general provisions of 6.4.2, shall meet the provisions of 6.4.3 if carried by air, and shall meet the provisions of 6.4.7.2–6.4.7.17.

6.4.7.2 The smallest overall external dimension of the package shall not be less than 10 cm.

6.4.7.3   The outside of the package shall incorporate a feature, such as a seal, which is not readily breakable and which, while intact, will be evidence that it has not been opened.

6.4.7.4   Any tie-down attachments on the package shall be so designed that, under normal and accident conditions of transport, the forces in those attachments shall not impair the ability of the package to meet the provisions of this Code.

6.4.7.5   The design of the package shall take into account temperatures ranging from −40°C to +70°C for the components of the packaging. Attention shall be given to freezing temperatures for liquids and to the potential degradation of packaging materials within the given temperature range.

6.4.7.6   The design and manufacturing techniques shall be in accordance with national or international standards, or other provisions, acceptable to the competent authority.

6.4.7.7   The design shall include a containment system securely closed by a positive fastening device which cannot be opened unintentionally or by a pressure which may arise within the package.

6.4.7.8   Special form radioactive material may be considered as a component of the containment system.

6.4.7.9   If the containment system forms a separate unit of the package, it shall be capable of being securely closed by a positive fastening device which is independent of any other part of the packaging.

6.4.7.10   The design of any component of the containment system shall take into account, where applicable, the radiolytic decomposition of liquids and other vulnerable materials and the generation of gas by chemical reaction and radiolysis.

6.4.7.11   The containment system shall retain its radioactive contents under a reduction of ambient pressure to 60 kPa.

6.4.7.12   All valves, other than pressure relief valves, shall be provided with an enclosure to retain any leakage from the valve.

6.4.7.13   A radiation shield which encloses a component of the package specified as a part of the containment system shall be so designed as to prevent the unintentional release of that component from the shield. Where the radiation shield and such component within it form a separate unit, the radiation shield shall be capable of being securely closed by a positive fastening device which is independent of any other packaging structure.

6.4.7.14   A package shall be so designed that, if it were subjected to the tests specified in 6.4.15, it would prevent:

         (a)   loss or dispersal of the radioactive contents; and

         (b)   more than a 20% increase in the maximum radiation level at any external surface of the package.

6.4.7.15   The design of a package intended for liquid radioactive material shall make provision for ullage to accommodate variations in the temperature of the contents, dynamic effects and filling dynamics.

Type A packages to contain liquids

6.4.7.16   A Type A package designed to contain liquid radioactive material shall, in addition:

         .1   be adequate to meet the conditions specified in 6.4.7.14(a) above if the package is subjected to the tests specified in 6.4.16; and

         .2   either

             (i)   be provided with sufficient absorbent material to absorb twice the volume of the liquid contents. Such absorbent material must be suitably positioned so as to contact the liquid in the event of leakage; or

             (ii) be provided with a containment system composed of primary inner and secondary outer containment components designed to enclose the liquid contents completely and ensure their retention within the secondary outer containment components even if the primary inner components leak.

Type A packages to contain gas

6.4.7.17   A package designed for gases shall prevent loss or dispersal of the radioactive contents if the package were subjected to the tests specified in 6.4.16. A Type A package designed for tritium gas or for noble gases shall be excepted from this requirement.

6.4.8   Provisions for Type B(U) packages

6.4.8.1   Type B(U) packages shall be designed to meet the requirements specified in 6.4.2, the requirements specified in 6.4.3 if carried by air, and of 6.4.7.2 to 6.4.7.15, except as specified in 6.4.7.14(a), and, in addition, the requirements specified in 6.4.8.2 to 6.4.8.15.

6.4.8.2   A package shall be so designed that, under the ambient conditions specified in 6.4.8.5 and 6.4.8.6, heat generated within the package by the radioactive contents shall not, under normal conditions of transport, as demonstrated by the tests in 6.4.15, adversely affect the package in such a way that it would fail to meet the applicable provisions for containment and shielding if left unattended for a period of one week. Particular attention shall be paid to the effects of heat, which may cause one or more of the following:

   (a)   alter the arrangement, the geometrical form or the physical state of the radioactive contents or, if the radioactive material is enclosed in a can or receptacle (for example, clad fuel elements), cause the can, receptacle or radioactive material to deform or melt;

   (b)   lessen the efficiency of the packaging through differential thermal expansion or cracking or melting of the radiation shielding material;

   (c)   in combination with moisture, accelerate corrosion.

6.4.8.3   A package shall be so designed that, under the ambient condition specified in 6.4.8.5 and in the absence of insolation, the temperature of the accessible surfaces of a package shall not exceed 50°C, unless the package is transported under exclusive use.

6.4.8.4   Except as required in 6.4.3.1 for a package transported by air, the maximum temperature of any surface readily accessible during transport of a package under exclusive use shall not exceed 85°C in the absence of insolation under the ambient conditions specified in 6.4.8.5. Account may be taken of barriers or screens intended to give protection to persons without the need for the barriers or screens being subject to any test.

6.4.8.5   The ambient temperature shall be assumed to be 38°C.

6.4.8.6   The solar insolation conditions shall be assumed to be as specified in the table hereunder.

Insolation data

Case	Form and location of surface	Insolation for 12 hours per day (W/m^2)
1	Flat surfaces transported horizontally – downward facing	0
2	Flat surfaces transported horizontally – upward facing	800
3	Surfaces transported vertically	200[*]
4	Other downward-facing (not horizontal) surfaces	200[*]
5	All other surfaces	400[*]

[*] Alternatively, a sine function may be used, with an absorption coefficient adopted and the effects of possible reflection from neighbouring objects neglected.

6.4.8.7   A package which includes thermal protection for the purpose of satisfying the provisions of the thermal test specified in 6.4.17.3 shall be so designed that such protection will remain effective if the package is subjected to the tests specified in 6.4.15 and 6.4.17.2(a) and (b) or 6.4.17.2(b) and (c), as appropriate. Any such protection on the exterior of the package shall not be rendered ineffective by ripping, cutting, skidding, abrasion or rough handling.

6.4.8.8   A package shall be so designed that, if it were subjected to:

   .1   the tests specified in 6.4.15, it would restrict the loss of radioactive contents to not more than $10^{-6}A_2$ per hour; and

   .2   the tests specified in 6.4.17.1, 6.4.17.2(b), 6.4.17.3 and 6.4.17.4 and either the test in:

      (i)   6.4.17.2(c), when the package has a mass not greater than 500 kg, an overall density not greater than 1,000 kg/m^3 based on the external dimensions, and radioactive contents greater than 1,000A_2 not as special form radioactive material, or

      (ii)   6.4.17.2(a), for all other packages,

      it would meet the following provisions:

      –   retain sufficient shielding to ensure that the radiation level at 1 m from the surface of the package would not exceed 10 mSv/h with the maximum radioactive contents which the package is designed to contain; and

      –   restrict the accumulated loss of radioactive contents in a period of one week to not more than 10A_2 for krypton-85 and not more than A_2 for all other radionuclides.

   Where mixtures of different radionuclides are present, the provisions of 2.7.2.2.4–2.7.2.2.6 shall apply except that for krypton-85 an effective $A_2(i)$ value equal to 10A_2 may be used. For case .1 above, the assessment shall take into account the external contamination limits of 4.1.9.1.2.

6.4.8.9   A package for radioactive contents with activity greater than 10^5A_2 shall be so designed that, if it were subjected to the enhanced water immersion test specified in 6.4.18, there would be no rupture of the containment system.

6.4.8.10   Compliance with the permitted activity release limits shall depend neither upon filters nor upon a mechanical cooling system.

6.4.8.11   A package shall not include a pressure relief system from the containment system which would allow the release of radioactive material to the environment under the conditions of the tests specified in 6.4.15 and 6.4.17.

6.4.8.12   A package shall be so designed that, if it were at the maximum normal operating pressure and it were subjected to the tests specified in 6.4.15 and 6.4.17, the level of strains in the containment system would not attain values which would adversely affect the package in such a way that it would fail to meet the applicable provisions.

6.4.8.13   A package shall not have a maximum normal operating pressure in excess of a gauge pressure of 700 kPa.

6.4.8.14   A package containing low dispersible radioactive material shall be so designed that any features added to the low dispersible radioactive material that are not part of it, or any internal components of the packaging, shall not adversely affect the performance of the low dispersible radioactive material.

6.4.8.15   A package shall be designed for an ambient temperature range from $-40°C$ to $+38°C$.

6.4.9   Provisions for Type B(M) packages

△ 6.4.9.1   Type B(M) packages shall meet the provisions for Type B(U) packages specified in 6.4.8.1, except that, for packages to be transported solely within a specified country or solely between specified countries, conditions other than those given in 6.4.7.5, 6.4.8.4 to 6.4.8.6 and 6.4.8.9 to 6.4.8.15 above may be assumed, with the approval of the competent authorities of these countries. Notwithstanding, the provisions for Type B(U) packages specified in 6.4.8.4 and 6.4.8.9 to 6.4.8.15 shall be met as far as practicable.

6.4.9.2   Intermittent venting of Type B(M) packages may be permitted during transport, provided that the operational controls for venting are acceptable to the relevant competent authorities.

6.4.10   Provisions for Type C packages

6.4.10.1   Type C packages shall be designed to meet the provisions specified in 6.4.2 and 6.4.3, and of 6.4.7.2 to 6.4.7.15, except as specified in 6.4.7.14, and of the provisions specified in 6.4.8.2 to 6.4.8.6, 6.4.8.10 to 6.4.8.15, and, in addition, of 6.4.10.2–6.4.10.4.

6.4.10.2   A package shall be capable of meeting the assessment criteria prescribed for tests in 6.4.8.8.2 and 6.4.8.12 after burial in an environment defined by a thermal conductivity of 0.33 W/(m·K) and a temperature of 38°C in the steady state. Initial conditions for the assessment shall assume that any thermal insulation of the package remains intact, the package is at the maximum normal operating pressure and the ambient temperature is 38°C.

6.4.10.3   A package shall be so designed that, if it were at the maximum normal operating pressure and subjected to:

(a)   the tests specified in 6.4.15, it would restrict the loss of radioactive contents to not more than $10^{-6}A_2$ per hour; and

(b)   the test sequences in 6.4.20.1,

(i)   it would retain sufficient shielding to ensure that the radiation level at 1 m from the surface of the package would not exceed 10 mSv/h with the maximum radioactive contents which the package is designed to contain; and

(ii) it would restrict the accumulated loss of radioactive contents in a period of 1 week to not more than $10A_2$ for krypton-85 and not more than A_2 for all other radionuclides.

Where mixtures of different radionuclides are present, the provisions of 2.7.2.2.4 to 2.7.2.2.6 shall apply except that for krypton-85 an effective $A_2(i)$ value equal to $10A_2$ may be used. For case (a) above, the assessment shall take into account the external contamination limits of 4.1.9.1.2.

6.4.10.4   A package shall be so designed that there will be no rupture of the containment system following performance of the enhanced water immersion test specified in 6.4.18.

6.4.11   Provisions for packages containing fissile material

6.4.11.1   Fissile material shall be transported so as to:

(a)   maintain subcriticality during routine, normal and accident conditions of transport; in particular, the following contingencies shall be considered:

(i)   water leaking into or out of packages;

    (ii)   the loss of efficiency of built-in neutron absorbers or moderators;

    (iii) rearrangement of the contents either within the package or as a result of loss from the package;

    (iv) reduction of spaces within or between packages;

    (v)   packages becoming immersed in water or buried in snow; and

    (vi) temperature changes; and

(b) meet the provisions:

    (i)   of 6.4.7.2 except for unpackaged material when specifically allowed by 2.7.2.3.5.5;

    (ii)   prescribed elsewhere in this Code which pertain to the radioactive properties of the material;

    (iii) of 6.4.7.3 unless the material is excepted by 2.7.2.3.5;

    (iv) of 6.4.11.4 to 6.4.11.14, unless the material is excepted by 2.7.2.3.5, 6.4.11.2 or 6.4.11.3.

6.4.11.2   Packages containing fissile material that meet the provisions of subparagraph (d) and one of the provisions of (a) to (c) below are excepted from the requirements of 6.4.11.4 to 6.4.11.14.

(a) Packages containing fissile material in any form provided that:

    (i)   the smallest external dimension of the package is not less than 10 cm;

    (ii)   the criticality safety index (CSI) of the package is calculated using the following formula:

$$CSI = 50 \times 5 \times \left(\frac{Mass \text{ of U-235 in package (g)}}{Z} + \frac{Mass \text{ of other fissile nuclides}^{*} \text{ in package (g)}}{280} \right)$$

           * Plutonium may be of any isotopic composition provided that the amount of Pu-241 is less than that of Pu-240 in the package.

        where the values of *Z* are taken from table 6.4.11.2;

    (iii) the CSI of any package does not exceed 10.

(b) Packages containing fissile material in any form provided that:

    (i)   the smallest external dimension of the package is not less than 30 cm;

    (ii)   the package, after being subjected to the tests specified in 6.4.15.1 to 6.4.15.6:

        –   retains its fissile material contents;

        –   preserves the minimum overall outside dimensions of the package to at least 30 cm;

        –   prevents the entry of a 10 cm cube;

    (iii) the CSI of the package is calculated using the following formula:

$$CSI = 50 \times 2 \times \left(\frac{Mass \text{ of U-235 in package (g)}}{Z} + \frac{Mass \text{ of other fissile nuclides}^{*} \text{ in package (g)}}{280} \right)$$

           * Plutonium may be of any isotopic composition provided that the amount of Pu-241 is less than that of Pu-240 in the package.

        where the values of *Z* are taken from table 6.4.11.2.

    (iv) the CSI of any package does not exceed 10;

(c) Packages containing fissile material in any form provided that:

    (i)   the smallest external dimension of the package is not less than 10 cm;

    (ii)   the package, after being subjected to the tests specified in 6.4.15.1 to 6.4.15.6:

        –   retains its fissile material contents;

        –   preserves the minimum overall outside dimensions of the package to at least 10 cm;

        –   prevents the entry of a 10 cm cube.

    (iii) the CSI of the package is calculated using the following formula:

$$CSI = 50 \times 2 \times \left(\frac{Mass \text{ of U-235 in package (g)}}{450} + \frac{Mass \text{ of other fissile nuclides}^{*} \text{ in package (g)}}{280} \right)$$

           * Plutonium may be of any isotopic composition provided that the amount of Pu-241 is less than that of Pu-240 in the package.

    (iv) The maximum mass of fissile nuclides in any package does not exceed 15 g;

(d) The total mass of beryllium, hydrogenous material enriched in deuterium, graphite and other allotropic forms of carbon in an individual package shall not be greater than the mass of fissile nuclides in the package except where their total concentration does not exceed 1 g in any 1,000 g of material. Beryllium incorporated in copper alloys up to 4% in weight of the alloy does not need to be considered.

Table 6.4.11.2 – Values of *Z* for calculation of criticality safety index in accordance with 6.4.11.2

Enrichment[a]	*Z*
Uranium enriched up to 1.5%	2,200
Uranium enriched up to 5%	850
Uranium enriched up to 10%	660
Uranium enriched up to 20%	580
Uranium enriched up to 100%	450

[a] If a package contains uranium with varying enrichments of U-235, then the value corresponding to the highest enrichment shall be used for *Z*.

6.4.11.3 Packages containing not more than 1,000 g of plutonium are excepted from the application of 6.4.11.4 to 6.4.11.14 provided that:

(a) not more than 20% of the plutonium by mass is fissile nuclides;

(b) the criticality safety index of the package is calculated using the following formula:

$$CSI = 50 \times 2 \times \frac{\text{mass of plutonium (g)}}{1,000}$$

(c) if uranium is present with the plutonium, the mass of uranium shall be no more than 1% of the mass of the plutonium.

6.4.11.4 Where the chemical or physical form, isotopic composition, mass or concentration, moderation ratio or density, or geometric configuration is not known, the assessments of 6.4.11.8 to 6.4.11.13 shall be performed assuming that each parameter that is not known has the value which gives the maximum neutron multiplication consistent with the known conditions and parameters in these assessments.

6.4.11.5 For irradiated nuclear fuel, the assessments of 6.4.11.8 to 6.4.11.13 shall be based on an isotopic composition demonstrated to provide either:

(a) the maximum neutron multiplication during the irradiation history; or

(b) a conservative estimate of the neutron multiplication for the package assessments. After irradiation, but prior to shipment, a measurement shall be performed to confirm the conservatism of the isotopic composition.

6.4.11.6 The package, after being subjected to the tests specified in 6.4.15, shall:

(a) preserve the minimum overall outside dimensions of the package to at least 10 cm; and

(b) prevent the entry of a 10 cm cube.

6.4.11.7 The package shall be designed for an ambient temperature range of −40°C to +38°C unless the competent authority specifies otherwise in the certificate of approval for the package design.

6.4.11.8 For a package in isolation, it shall be assumed that water can leak into or out of all void spaces of the package, including those within the containment system. However, if the design incorporates special features to prevent such leakage of water into or out of certain void spaces, even as a result of error, absence of leakage may be assumed in respect of those void spaces. Special features shall include either of the following:

(a) multiple high-standard water barriers, not less than two of which would remain watertight if the package were subject to the tests prescribed in 6.4.11.13(b), a high degree of quality control in the manufacture, maintenance and repair of packagings and tests to demonstrate the closure of each package before each shipment; or

(b) for packages containing uranium hexafluoride only, with maximum enrichment of 5 mass percent uranium-235:

(i) packages where, following the tests prescribed in 6.4.11.13(b), there is no physical contact between the valve and any other component of the packaging other than at its original point of attachment and where, in addition, following the test prescribed in 6.4.17.3, the valves remain leaktight; and

(ii) a high degree of quality control in the manufacture, maintenance and repair of packagings coupled with tests to demonstrate closure of each package before each shipment.

6.4.11.9 It shall be assumed that the confinement system is closely reflected by at least 20 cm of water or such greater reflection as may additionally be provided by the surrounding material of the packaging. However, when it can be demonstrated that the confinement system remains within the packaging following the tests prescribed in 6.4.11.13(b), close reflection of the package by at least 20 cm of water may be assumed in 6.4.11.10(c).

6.4.11.10 The package shall be subcritical under the conditions of 6.4.11.8 and 6.4.11.9 and with the package conditions that result in the maximum neutron multiplication consistent with:

(a) routine conditions of transport (incident-free);

(b) the tests specified in 6.4.11.12(b);

(c) the tests specified in 6.4.11.13(b).

6.4.11.11 For packages to be transported by air:

(a) the package shall be subcritical under conditions consistent with the Type C package tests specified in 6.4.20.1 assuming reflection by at least 20 cm of water but no water in-leakage; and

(b) in the assessment of 6.4.11.10, allowance shall not be made for special features of 6.4.11.8 unless, following the Type C package tests specified in 6.4.20.1 and, subsequently, the water in-leakage test of 6.4.19.3, leakage of water into or out of the void spaces is prevented.

6.4.11.12 A number "*N*" shall be derived, such that five times "*N*" packages shall be subcritical for the arrangement and package conditions that provide the maximum neutron multiplication consistent with the following:

(a) there shall not be anything between the packages, and the package arrangement shall be reflected on all sides by at least 20 cm of water; and

(b) the state of the packages shall be their assessed or demonstrated condition if they had been subjected to the tests specified in 6.4.15.

6.4.11.13 A number "*N*" shall be derived, such that two times "*N*" packages shall be subcritical for the arrangement and package conditions that provide the maximum neutron multiplication consistent with the following:

(a) hydrogenous moderation between packages, and the package arrangement reflected on all sides by at least 20 cm of water; and

(b) the tests specified in 6.4.15 followed by whichever of the following is the more limiting:

(i) the tests specified in 6.4.17.2(b) and either 6.4.17.2(c), for packages having a mass not greater than 500 kg and an overall density not greater than 1000 kg/m^3 based on the external dimensions, or 6.4.17.2(a), for all other packages; followed by the test specified in 6.4.17.3 and completed by the tests specified in 6.4.19.1–6.4.19.3; or

(ii) the test specified in 6.4.17.4; and

(c) where any part of the fissile material escapes from the containment system following the tests specified in 6.4.11.13(b), it shall be assumed that fissile material escapes from each package in the array and all of the fissile material shall be arranged in the configuration and moderation that results in the maximum neutron multiplication with close reflection by at least 20 cm of water.

6.4.11.14 The criticality safety index (CSI) for packages containing fissile material shall be obtained by dividing the number 50 by the smaller of the two values of *N* derived in 6.4.11.12 and 6.4.11.13 (i.e. CSI = 50/*N*). The value of the criticality safety index may be zero, provided that an unlimited number of packages is subcritical (i.e. *N* is effectively equal to infinity in both cases).

6.4.12 Test procedures and demonstration of compliance

6.4.12.1 Demonstration of compliance with the performance standards required in 2.7.2.3.1.3, 2.7.2.3.1.4, 2.7.2.3.3.1, 2.7.2.3.3.2, 2.7.2.3.4.1, 2.7.2.3.4.2 and 6.4.2–6.4.11 shall be accomplished by any of the methods listed below or by a combination thereof.

(a) Performance of tests with specimens representing LSA-III material, or special form radioactive material, or low dispersible radioactive material or with prototypes or samples of the packaging, where the contents of the specimen or the packaging for the tests shall simulate as closely as practicable the expected range of radioactive contents and the specimen or packaging to be tested shall be prepared as presented for transport.

(b) Reference to previous satisfactory demonstrations of a sufficiently similar nature.

(c) Performance of tests with models of appropriate scale incorporating those features which are significant with respect to the item under investigation when engineering experience has shown results of such tests to be suitable for design purposes. When a scale model is used, the need for adjusting certain test parameters, such as penetrator diameter or compressive load, shall be taken into account.

(d) Calculation, or reasoned argument, when the calculation procedures and parameters are generally agreed to be reliable or conservative.

6.4.12.2 After the specimen, prototype or sample has been subjected to the tests, appropriate methods of assessment shall be used to assure that the provisions of this chapter have been fulfilled in compliance with the performance and acceptance standards prescribed in this chapter (see 2.7.2.3.1.3, 2.7.2.3.1.4, 2.7.2.3.3.1, 2.7.2.3.3.2, 2.7.2.3.4.1, 2.7.2.3.4.2 and 6.4.2–6.4.11).

6

6.4.12.3 All specimens shall be inspected before testing in order to identify and record faults or damage, including the following:

(a) divergence from the design;

(b) defects in manufacture;

(c) corrosion or other deterioration; and

(d) distortion of features.

The containment system of the package shall be clearly specified. The external features of the specimen shall be clearly identified so that reference may be made simply and clearly to any part of such specimen.

6.4.13 Testing the integrity of the containment system and shielding and evaluating criticality safety

After each of the applicable tests specified in 6.4.15 to 6.4.21:

(a) faults and damage shall be identified and recorded;

(b) it shall be determined whether the integrity of the containment system and shielding has been retained to the extent required in this chapter for the package under test; and

(c) for packages containing fissile material, it shall be determined whether the assumptions and conditions used in the assessments required by 6.4.11.1 to 6.4.11.14 for one or more packages are valid.

6.4.14 Target for drop tests

The target for the drop tests specified in 2.7.2.3.3.5, 6.4.15.4, 6.4.16(a), 6.4.17.2 and 6.4.20.2 shall be a flat, horizontal surface of such a character that any increase in its resistance to displacement or deformation upon impact by the specimen would not significantly increase the damage to the specimen.

6.4.15 Test for demonstrating ability to withstand normal conditions of transport

6.4.15.1 The tests are: the water spray test, the free drop test, the stacking test and the penetration test. Specimens of the package shall be subjected to the free drop test, the stacking test and the penetration test, preceded in each case by the water spray test. One specimen may be used for all the tests, provided that the provisions of 6.4.15.2 are fulfilled.

6.4.15.2 The time interval between the conclusion of the water spray test and the succeeding test shall be such that the water has soaked in to the maximum extent, without appreciable drying of the exterior of the specimen. In the absence of any evidence to the contrary, this interval shall be taken to be two hours if the water spray is applied from four directions simultaneously. No time interval shall elapse, however, if the water spray is applied from each of the four directions consecutively.

6.4.15.3 Water spray test: The specimen shall be subjected to a water spray test that simulates exposure to rainfall of approximately 5 cm per hour for at least one hour.

6.4.15.4 Free drop test: The specimen shall drop onto the target so as to suffer maximum damage in respect of the safety features to be tested.

(a) The height of drop measured from the lowest point of the specimen to the upper surface of the target shall be not less than the distance specified in the table hereunder for the applicable mass. The target shall be as defined in 6.4.14.

(b) For rectangular fibreboard or wood packages not exceeding a mass of 50 kg, a separate specimen shall be subjected to a free drop onto each corner from a height of 0.3 m.

(c) For cylindrical fibreboard packages not exceeding a mass of 100 kg, a separate specimen shall be subjected to a free drop onto each of the quarters of each rim from a height of 0.3 m.

Free drop distance for testing packages to normal conditions of transport

Package mass (kg)	Free drop distance (m)
Package mass < 5,000	1.2
5000 ≤ Package mass < 10,000	0.9
10000 ≤ Package mass < 15,000	0.6
15000 ≤ Package mass	0.3

6.4.15.5 Stacking test: Unless the shape of the packaging effectively prevents stacking, the specimen shall be subjected, for a period of 24 hours, to a compressive load equal to the greater of the following:

(a) the equivalent of 5 times the maximum weight of the package; and

(b) the equivalent of 13 kPa multiplied by the vertically projected area of the package.

The load shall be applied uniformly to two opposite sides of the specimen, one of which shall be the base on which the package would typically rest.

6.4.15.6 Penetration test: The specimen shall be placed on a rigid, flat, horizontal surface which will not move significantly while the test is being carried out.

(a) A bar of 3.2 cm in diameter with a hemispherical end and a mass of 6 kg shall be dropped and directed to fall, with its longitudinal axis vertical, onto the centre of the weakest part of the specimen, so that, if it penetrates sufficiently far, it will hit the containment system. The bar shall not be significantly deformed by the test performance.

(b) The height of drop of the bar measured from its lower end to the intended point of impact on the upper surface of the specimen shall be 1 m.

6.4.16 Additional tests for Type A packages designed for liquids and gases

A specimen or separate specimens shall be subjected to each of the following tests unless it can be demonstrated that one test is more severe for the specimen in question than the other, in which case one specimen shall be subjected to the more severe test.

(a) Free drop test: The specimen shall drop onto the target so as to suffer the maximum damage in respect of containment. The height of the drop measured from the lowest part of the specimen to the upper surface of the target shall be 9 m. The target shall be as defined in 6.4.14.

(b) Penetration test: The specimen shall be subjected to the test specified in 6.4.15.6 except that the height of drop shall be increased to 1.7 m from the 1 m specified in 6.4.15.6(b).

6.4.17 Tests for demonstrating ability to withstand accident conditions of transport

6.4.17.1 The specimen shall be subjected to the cumulative effects of the tests specified in 6.4.17.2 and 6.4.17.3, in that order. Following these tests, either this specimen or a separate specimen shall be subjected to the effect(s) of the water immersion test(s) as specified in 6.4.17.4 and, if applicable, 6.4.18.

6.4.17.2 Mechanical test: The mechanical test consists of three different drop tests. Each specimen shall be subjected to the applicable drops as specified in 6.4.8.8 or 6.4.11.13. The order in which the specimen is subjected to the drops shall be such that, on completion of the mechanical test, the specimen shall have suffered such damage as will lead to the maximum damage in the thermal test which follows.

(a) For drop I, the specimen shall drop onto the target so as to suffer the maximum damage, and the height of the drop measured from the lowest point of the specimen to the upper surface of the target shall be 9 m. The target shall be as defined in 6.4.14.

(b) For drop II, the specimen shall drop onto a bar rigidly mounted perpendicularly on the target so as to suffer the maximum damage. The height of the drop measured from the intended point of impact of the specimen to the upper surface of the bar shall be 1 m. The bar shall be of solid mild steel of circular section, (15.0±0.5) cm in diameter and 20 cm long unless a longer bar would cause greater damage, in which case a bar of sufficient length to cause maximum damage shall be used. The upper end of the bar shall be flat and horizontal with its edge rounded off to a radius of not more than 6 mm. The target on which the bar is mounted shall be as described in 6.4.14.

(c) For drop III, the specimen shall be subjected to a dynamic crush test by positioning the specimen on the target so as to suffer maximum damage by the drop of a 500 kg mass from 9 m onto the specimen. The mass shall consist of a solid mild steel plate 1 m by 1 m and shall fall in a horizontal attitude. The lower face of the steel plate shall have its edges and corners rounded off to a radius of not more than 6 mm. The height of the drop shall be measured from the underside of the plate to the highest point of the specimen. The target on which the specimen rests shall be as defined in 6.4.14.

6.4.17.3 Thermal test: The specimen shall be in thermal equilibrium under conditions of an ambient temperature of 38°C, subject to the solar insolation conditions specified in the table under 6.4.8.6 and subject to the design maximum rate of internal heat generation within the package from the radioactive contents. Alternatively, any of these parameters are allowed to have different values prior to and during the test, providing due account is taken of them in the subsequent assessment of package response.

The thermal test shall then consist of:

(a) exposure of a specimen for a period of 30 minutes to a thermal environment which provides a heat flux at least equivalent to that of a hydrocarbon fuel/air fire in sufficiently quiescent ambient conditions to give a minimum average flame emissivity coefficient of 0.9 and an average temperature of at least 800°C, fully engulfing the specimen, with a surface absorptivity coefficient of 0.8 or that value which the package may be demonstrated to possess if exposed to the fire specified, followed by:

(b) exposure of the specimen to an ambient temperature of 38°C, subject to the solar insolation conditions specified in the table under 6.4.8.6 and subject to the design maximum rate of internal heat generation within the package by the radioactive contents, for a sufficient period to ensure that temperatures in the specimen are everywhere decreasing and/or are approaching initial steady-state conditions. Alternatively, any of these parameters are allowed to have different values following cessation of heating, providing due account is taken of them in the subsequent assessment of package response.

During and following the test, the specimen shall not be artificially cooled and any combustion of materials of the specimen shall be permitted to proceed naturally.

6.4.17.4   Water immersion test: The specimen shall be immersed under a head of water of at least 15 m for a period of not less than eight hours in the attitude which will lead to maximum damage. For demonstration purposes, an external gauge pressure of at least 150 kPa shall be considered to meet these conditions.

6.4.18   Enhanced water immersion test for Type B(U) and Type B(M) packages containing more than 10^5A_2 and Type C packages

Enhanced water immersion test: The specimen shall be immersed under a head of water of at least 200 m for a period of not less than one hour. For demonstration purposes, an external gauge pressure of at least 2 MPa shall be considered to meet these conditions.

6.4.19   Water leakage test for packages containing fissile material

6.4.19.1   Packages for which water in-leakage or out-leakage to the extent which results in greatest reactivity has been assumed for purposes of assessment under 6.4.11.8 to 6.4.11.13 shall be excepted from the test.

6.4.19.2   Before the specimen is subjected to the water leakage test specified below, it shall be subjected to the tests in 6.4.17.2(b), and either 6.4.17.2(a) or (c) as required by 6.4.11.13, and the test specified in 6.4.17.3.

6.4.19.3   The specimen shall be immersed under a head of water of at least 0.9 m for a period of not less than eight hours and in the attitude for which maximum leakage is expected.

6.4.20   Tests for Type C packages

6.4.20.1   Specimens shall be subjected to the effects of each of the following test sequences in the orders specified:

(a) the tests specified in 6.4.17.2(a), 6.4.17.2(c), 6.4.20.2 and 6.4.20.3; and

(b) the test specified in 6.4.20.4.

Separate specimens are allowed to be used for each of the sequences (a) and (b).

6.4.20.2   Puncture/tearing test: The specimen shall be subjected to the damaging effects of a vertical, solid probe made of mild steel. The orientation of the package specimen and the impact point on the package surface shall be such as to cause maximum damage at the conclusion of the test sequence specified in 6.4.20.1(a).

(a) The specimen, representing a package having a mass less than 250 kg, shall be placed on a target and subjected to a probe having a mass of 250 kg falling from a height of 3 m above the intended impact point. For this test, the probe shall be a 20 cm diameter cylindrical bar with the striking end forming a frustum of a right circular cone with the following dimensions: 30 cm height and 2.5 cm in diameter at the top with its edge rounded off to a radius of not more than 6 mm. The target on which the specimen is placed shall be as specified in 6.4.14.

(b) For packages having a mass of 250 kg or more, the base of the probe shall be placed on a target and the specimen dropped onto the probe. The height of the drop, measured from the point of impact with the specimen to the upper surface of the probe, shall be 3 m. For this test, the probe shall have the same properties and dimensions as specified in (a) above, except that the length and mass of the probe shall be such as to incur maximum damage to the specimen. The target on which the base of the probe is placed shall be as specified in 6.4.14.

6.4.20.3   Enhanced thermal test: The conditions for this test shall be as specified in 6.4.17.3, except that the exposure to the thermal environment shall be for a period of 60 min.

6.4.20.4   Impact test: The specimen shall be subject to an impact on a target at a velocity of not less than 90 m/s, at such an orientation as to suffer maximum damage. The target shall be as defined in 6.4.14, except that the target surface may be at any orientation provided that the surface is normal to the specimen path.

6.4.21 Tests for packagings designed to contain uranium hexafluoride

Specimens that comprise or simulate packagings designed to contain 0.1 kg or more of uranium hexafluoride shall be tested hydraulically at an internal pressure of at least 1.38 MPa but, when the test pressure is less than 2.76 MPa, the design will require multilateral approval. For retesting packagings, any other equivalent non-destructive testing may be applied, subject to multilateral approval.

6.4.22 Approvals of package designs and materials

6.4.22.1 The approval of designs for packages containing 0.1 kg or more of uranium hexafluoride requires that:

(a) Each design that meets the provisions of 6.4.6.4 shall require multilateral approval;

(b) Each design that meets the provisions of 6.4.6.1 to 6.4.6.3 shall require unilateral approval by the competent authority of the country of origin of the design, unless multilateral approval is otherwise required by this Code.

6.4.22.2 Each Type B(U) and Type C package design will require unilateral approval, except that:

(a) a package design for fissile material which is also subject to 6.4.22.4, 6.4.23.7 and 5.1.5.2.1 will require multilateral approval; and

(b) a Type B(U) package design for low dispersible radioactive material will require multilateral approval.

6.4.22.3 Each Type B(M) package design, including those for fissile material which are also subject to 6.4.22.4, 6.4.23.7 and 5.1.5.2.1 and those for low dispersible radioactive material, will require multilateral approval.

6.4.22.4 Each package design for fissile material which is not excepted by any of the paragraphs 2.7.2.3.5.1 to 2.7.2.3.5.6, 6.4.11.2 and 6.4.11.3 shall require multilateral approval.

6.4.22.5 The design for special form radioactive material will require unilateral approval. The design for low dispersible radioactive material will require multilateral approval (see also 6.4.23.8).

6.4.22.6 The design for a fissile material excepted from "FISSILE" classification in accordance with 2.7.2.3.5.6 shall require multilateral approval.

6.4.22.7 Alternative activity limits for an exempt consignment of instruments or articles in accordance with 2.7.2.2.2.2 shall require multilateral approval.

6.4.23 Applications for approval and approvals for radioactive material transport

6.4.23.1 [Reserved]

6.4.23.2 An application for approval of shipment shall include:

(a) the period of time, related to the shipment, for which the approval is sought;

(b) the actual radioactive contents, the expected modes of transport, the type of conveyance, and the probable or proposed route; and

(c) the details of how the precautions and administrative or operational controls referred to in the certificate of approval for the package design, if applicable, issued under 5.1.5.2.1.1.3, 5.1.5.2.1.1.6 or 5.1.5.2.1.1.7, are to be put into effect.

6.4.23.3 An application for approval of shipments under special arrangement shall include all the information necessary to satisfy the competent authority that the overall level of safety in transport is at least equivalent to that which would be provided if all the applicable provisions of this Code had been met. The application shall also include:

(a) a statement of the respects in which, and of the reasons why, the shipment cannot be made in full accordance with the applicable provisions; and

(b) a statement of any special precautions or special administrative or operational controls which are to be employed during transport to compensate for the failure to meet the applicable provisions.

6.4.23.4 An application for approval of Type B(U) or Type C package design shall include:

(a) a detailed description of the proposed radioactive contents with reference to their physical and chemical states and the nature of the radiation emitted;

(b) a detailed statement of the design, including complete engineering drawings and schedules of materials and methods of manufacture;

(c) a statement of the tests which have been done and their results, or evidence based on calculative methods or other evidence that the design is adequate to meet the applicable provisions;

(d) the proposed operating and maintenance instructions for the use of the packaging;

6

(e) if the package is designed to have a maximum normal operating pressure in excess of 100 kPa gauge, a specification of the materials of manufacture of the containment system, the samples to be taken, and the tests to be made;

(f) where the proposed radioactive contents are irradiated nuclear fuel, a statement and a justification of any assumption in the safety analysis relating to the characteristics of the fuel and a description of any pre-shipment measurement required by 6.4.11.5(b);

(g) any special stowage provisions necessary to ensure the safe dissipation of heat from the package, considering the various modes of transport to be used and type of conveyance or freight container;

(h) a reproducible illustration, not larger than 21 cm by 30 cm, showing the make-up of the package; and

(i) a specification of the applicable management system as required in 1.5.3.1.

6.4.23.5 An application for approval of a Type B(M) package design shall include, in addition to the information required in 6.4.23.4 for Type B(U) packages:

(a) a list of the provisions specified in 6.4.7.5, 6.4.8.4 to 6.4.8.6 and 6.4.8.9 to 6.4.8.15 with which the package does not conform;

(b) any proposed supplementary operational controls to be applied during transport not regularly provided for in this Code, but which are necessary to ensure the safety of the package or to compensate for the deficiencies listed in (a) above;

(c) a statement relative to any restrictions on the mode of transport and to any special loading, carriage, unloading or handling procedures; and

(d) a statement of the range of ambient conditions (temperature, solar radiation) which are expected to be encountered during transport and which have been taken into account in the design.

6.4.23.6 The application for approval of designs for packages containing 0.1 kg or more of uranium hexafluoride shall include all information necessary to satisfy the competent authority that the design meets the provisions of 6.4.6.1, and a specification of the applicable management system as required in 1.5.3.1.

6.4.23.7 An application for a fissile package approval shall include all information necessary to satisfy the competent authority that the design meets the provisions of 6.4.11.1, and a specification of the applicable management system as required in 1.5.3.1.

6.4.23.8 An application for approval of design for special form radioactive material and design for low dispersible radioactive material shall include:

(a) a detailed description of the radioactive material or, if a capsule, the contents; particular reference shall be made to both physical and chemical states;

(b) a detailed statement of the design of any capsule to be used;

(c) a statement of the tests which have been done and their results, or evidence based on calculative methods to show that the radioactive material is capable of meeting the performance standards, or other evidence that the special form radioactive material or low dispersible radioactive material meets the applicable provisions of this Code;

(d) a specification of the applicable management system as required in 1.5.3.1; and

(e) any proposed pre-shipment actions for use in the consignment of special form radioactive material or low dispersible radioactive material.

6.4.23.9 An application for approval of design for fissile material excepted from "FISSILE" classification in accordance with table 2.7.2.1.1, under 2.7.2.3.5.6 shall include:

(a) a detailed description of the material; particular reference shall be made to both physical and chemical states;

(b) a statement of the tests that have been carried out and their results, or evidence based on calculation methods to show that the material is capable of meeting the requirements specified in 2.7.2.3.6;

(c) a specification of the applicable management system as required in 1.5.3.1;

(d) a statement of specific actions to be taken prior to shipment.

6.4.23.10 An application for approval of alternative activity limits for an exempt consignment of instruments or articles shall include:

(a) an identification and detailed description of the instrument or article, its intended uses and the radionuclide(s) incorporated;

(b) the maximum activity of the radionuclide(s) in the instrument or article;

(c) maximum external radiation levels arising from the instrument or article;

(d) the chemical and physical forms of the radionuclide(s) contained in the instrument or article;

(e) details of the construction and design of the instrument or article, particularly as related to the containment and shielding of the radionuclide in routine, normal and accident conditions of transport;

(f) the applicable management system, including the quality testing and verification procedures to be applied to radioactive sources, components and finished products to ensure that the maximum specified activity of radioactive material or the maximum radiation levels specified for the instrument or article are not exceeded, and that the instruments or articles are constructed according to the design specifications;

(g) the maximum number of instruments or articles expected to be shipped per consignment and annually;

(h) dose assessments in accordance with the principles and methodologies set out in the *International Basic Safety Standards for Protection against Ionizing Radiation and for the Safety of Radiation Sources*, Safety Series No.115, IAEA, Vienna (1996), including individual doses to transport workers and members of the public and, if appropriate, collective doses arising from routine, normal and accident conditions of transport, based on representative transport scenarios the consignments are subject to.

6.4.23.11 Each certificate of approval issued by a competent authority shall be assigned an identification mark. The mark shall be of the following generalized type:

VRI/number/type code

(a) Except as provided in 6.4.23.12(b), "VRI" represents the international vehicle registration identification code of the country issuing the certificate.[*]

(b) The number shall be assigned by the competent authority, and shall be unique and specific with regard to the particular design or shipment or alternative activity limit for exempt consignment. The identification mark of the approval of shipment shall be clearly related to the identification mark of the approval of design.

(c) The following type codes shall be used, in the order listed, to indicate the types of certificate of approval issued:

AF	Type A package design for fissile material
B(U)	Type B(U) package design ("B(U)F" if for fissile material)
B(M)	Type B(M) package design ("B(M)F" if for fissile material)
C	Type C package design ("CF" if for fissile material)
IF	industrial package design for fissile material
S	special form radioactive material
LD	low dispersible radioactive material
FE	fissile material complying with the requirements of 2.7.2.3.6
T	shipment
X	special arrangement
AL	alternative activity limits for an exempt consignment of instruments or articles.

In the case of package designs for non-fissile or fissile-excepted uranium hexafluoride, where none of the above codes apply, then the following type codes shall be used:

H(U)	unilateral approval
H(M)	multilateral approval.

(d) For certificates of approval of package design and special form radioactive material, other than those issued under the provisions of 6.4.24.2 to 6.4.24.5, and for low dispersible radioactive material, the symbols "-96" shall be added to the type code.

6.4.23.12 These identification marks shall be applied as follows:

△ (a) each certificate and each package shall bear the appropriate identification marks, comprising the symbols prescribed in 6.4.23.11(a), (b), (c) and (d) above, except that, for packages, only the applicable design type codes, including, if applicable, the symbols "-96", shall appear following the second stroke; that is, the "T" or "X" shall not appear in the identification marking on the package. Where the approval of design and the approval of shipment are combined, the applicable type codes do not need to be repeated. For example:

A/132/B(M)F-96: a Type B(M) package design approved for fissile material, requiring multilateral approval, for which the competent authority of Austria has assigned the design number 132 (to be marked on both the package and on the certificate of approval for the package design);

A/132/B(M)F-96T: the approval of shipment issued for a package bearing the identification mark elaborated above (to be marked on the certificate only);

A/137/X: an approval of special arrangement issued by the competent authority of Austria, to which the number 137 has been assigned (to be marked on the certificate only);

---

[*] Refer to Convention on Road Traffic, Vienna, 1968.

A/139/IF-96: an industrial package design for fissile material approved by the competent authority of Austria, to which package design number 139 has been assigned (to be marked on both the package and on the certificate of approval for the package design); and

A/145/H(U)-96: a package design for fissile-excepted uranium hexafluoride approved by the competent authority of Austria, to which package design number 145 has been assigned (to be marked on both the package and on the certificate of approval for the package design);

(b) where multilateral approval is effected by validation in accordance with 6.4.23.20, only the identification mark issued by the country of origin of the design or shipment shall be used. Where multilateral approval is effected by issue of certificates by successive countries, each certificate shall bear the appropriate identification mark and the package whose design was so approved shall bear all appropriate identification marks. For example:

A/132/B(M)F-96

CH/28/B(M)F-96

would be the identification mark of a package which was originally approved by Austria and was subsequently approved, by separate certificate, by Switzerland. Additional identification marks would be tabulated in a similar manner on the package;

(c) the revision of a certificate shall be indicated by a parenthetical expression following the identification mark on the certificate. For example, **A/132/B(M)F-96(Rev.2)** would indicate revision 2 of the Austrian certificate of approval for the package design; or **A/132/B(M)F-96(Rev.0)** would indicate the original issuance of the Austrian certificate of approval for the package design. For original issuances, the parenthetical entry is optional and other words such as 'original issuance' may also be used in place of 'Rev.0'. Certificate revision numbers may only be issued by the country issuing the original certificate of approval;

(d) additional symbols (as may be necessitated by national provisions) may be added in parentheses to the end of the identification mark. For example, **A/132/B(M)F-96(SP503)**; and

(e) it is not necessary to alter the identification mark on the packaging each time that a revision to the design certificate is made. Such re-marking shall be required only in those cases where the revision to the package design certificate involves a change in the letter type codes for the package design following the second stroke.

6.4.23.13 Each certificate of approval issued by a competent authority for special form radioactive material or low dispersible radioactive material shall include the following information:

(a) Type of certificate.

(b) The competent authority identification mark.

(c) The issue date and an expiry date.

(d) List of applicable national and international regulations, including the edition of the IAEA *Regulations for the Safe Transport of Radioactive Material* under which the special form radioactive material or low dispersible radioactive material is approved.

(e) The identification of the special form radioactive material or low dispersible radioactive material.

(f) A description of the special form radioactive material or low dispersible radioactive material.

(g) Design specifications for the special form radioactive material or low dispersible radioactive material, which may include references to drawings.

(h) A specification of the radioactive contents which includes the activities involved and which may include the physical and chemical form.

(i) A specification of the applicable management system as required in 1.5.3.1.

(j) Reference to information provided by the applicant relating to specific actions to be taken prior to shipment.

(k) If deemed appropriate by the competent authority, reference to the identity of the applicant.

(l) Signature and identification of the certifying official.

6.4.23.14 Each certificate of approval issued by a competent authority for material excepted from classification as "FISSILE" shall include the following information:

(a) Type of certificate.

(b) The competent authority identification mark.

(c) The issue date and an expiry date.

(d) List of applicable national and international regulations, including the edition of the IAEA *Regulations for the Safe Transport of Radioactive Material* under which the exception is approved.

(e) A description of the excepted material.

(f) Limiting specifications for the excepted material.

(g) A specification of the applicable management system as required in 1.5.3.1.

(h) Reference to information provided by the applicant relating to specific actions to be taken prior to shipment.

(i) If deemed appropriate by the competent authority, reference to the identity of the applicant.

(j) Signature and identification of the certifying official.

(k) Reference to documentation that demonstrates compliance with 2.7.2.3.6.

6.4.23.15   Each certificate of approval issued by a competent authority for a special arrangement shall include the following information:

(a) Type of certificate.

(b) The competent authority identification mark.

(c) The issue date and an expiry date.

(d) Mode(s) of transport.

(e) Any restrictions on the modes of transport, type of conveyance, freight container, and any necessary routeing instructions.

(f) List of applicable national and international regulations, including the edition of the IAEA *Regulations for the Safe Transport of Radioactive Material* under which the special arrangement is approved.

(g) The following statement: "This certificate does not relieve the consignor from compliance with any requirement of the government of any country through or into which the package will be transported."

(h) References to certificates for alternative radioactive contents, other competent authority validation, or additional technical data or information, as deemed appropriate by the competent authority.

(i) Description of the packaging by a reference to the drawings or a specification of the design. If deemed appropriate by the competent authority, a reproducible illustration, not larger than 21 cm by 30 cm, showing the make-up of the package shall also be provided, accompanied by a brief description of the packaging, including materials of manufacture, gross mass, general outside dimensions and appearance.

(j) A specification of the authorized radioactive contents, including any restrictions on the radioactive contents which might not be obvious from the nature of the packaging. This shall include the physical and chemical forms, the activities involved (including those of the various isotopes, if appropriate), mass in grams (for fissile material or for each fissile nuclide when appropriate), and whether special form radioactive material, low dispersible radioactive material or fissile material excepted under 2.7.2.3.5.6, if applicable.

(k) Additionally, for packages containing fissile material:

    (i) a detailed description of the authorized radioactive contents;

    (ii) the value of the criticality safety index;

    (iii) reference to the documentation that demonstrates the criticality safety of the contents;

    (iv) any special features, on the basis of which the absence of water from certain void spaces has been assumed in the criticality assessment;

    (v) any allowance (based on 6.4.11.5(b)) for a change in neutron multiplication assumed in the criticality assessment as a result of actual irradiation experience; and

    (vi) the ambient temperature range for which the special arrangement has been approved.

(l) A detailed listing of any supplementary operational controls required for preparation, loading, carriage, unloading and handling of the consignment, including any special stowage provisions for the safe dissipation of heat.

(m) If deemed appropriate by the competent authority, reasons for the special arrangement.

(n) Description of the compensatory measures to be applied as a result of the shipment being under special arrangement.

(o) Reference to information provided by the applicant relating to the use of the packaging or specific actions to be taken prior to the shipment.

(p) A statement regarding the ambient conditions assumed for purposes of design if these are not in accordance with those specified in 6.4.8.5, 6.4.8.6 and 6.4.8.15, as applicable.

(q) Any emergency arrangements deemed necessary by the competent authority.

(r) A specification of the applicable management system as required in 1.5.3.1.

(s) If deemed appropriate by the competent authority, reference to the identity of the applicant and to the identity of the carrier.

(t) Signature and identification of the certifying official.

6

6.4.23.16   Each certificate of approval for a shipment issued by a competent authority shall include the following information:

(a)   Type of certificate.

(b)   The competent authority identification mark(s).

(c)   The issue date and an expiry date.

(d)   List of applicable national and international regulations, including the edition of the IAEA *Regulations for the Safe Transport of Radioactive Material* under which the shipment is approved.

(e)   Any restrictions on the modes of transport, type of conveyance, freight container, and any necessary routeing instructions.

(f)   The following statement: "This certificate does not relieve the consignor from compliance with any requirement of the government of any country through or into which the package will be transported."

(g)   A detailed listing of any supplementary operational controls required for preparation, loading, carriage, unloading and handling of the consignment, including any special stowage provisions for the safe dissipation of heat or maintenance of criticality safety.

(h)   Reference to information provided by the applicant relating to specific actions to be taken prior to shipment.

(i)   Reference to the applicable certificate(s) of approval of design.

(j)   A specification of the actual radioactive contents, including any restrictions on the radioactive contents which might not be obvious from the nature of the packaging. This shall include the physical and chemical forms, the total activities involved (including those of the various isotopes, if appropriate), mass in grams (for fissile material or for each fissile nuclide when appropriate), and whether special form radioactive material, low dispersible radioactive material or fissile material excepted under 2.7.2.3.5.6, if applicable.

(k)   Any emergency arrangements deemed necessary by the competent authority.

(l)   A specification of the applicable management system as required in 1.5.3.1.

(m)   If deemed appropriate by the competent authority, reference to the identity of the applicant.

(n)   Signature and identification of the certifying official.

6.4.23.17   Each certificate of approval of the design of a package issued by a competent authority shall include the following information:

(a)   Type of certificate.

(b)   The competent authority identification mark.

(c)   The issue date and an expiry date.

(d)   Any restriction on the modes of transport, if appropriate.

(e)   List of applicable national and international regulations, including the edition of the IAEA *Regulations for the Safe Transport of Radioactive Material* under which the design is approved.

(f)   The following statement: "This certificate does not relieve the consignor from compliance with any requirement of the government of any country through or into which the package will be transported."

(g)   References to certificates for alternative radioactive contents, other competent authority validation, or additional technical data or information, as deemed appropriate by the competent authority.

(h)   A statement authorizing shipment where approval of shipment is required under 5.1.5.1.2, if deemed appropriate.

(i)   Identification of the packaging.

(j)   Description of the packaging by a reference to the drawings or specification of the design. If deemed appropriate by the competent authority, a reproducible illustration, not larger than 21 cm by 30 cm, showing the make-up of the package shall also be provided, accompanied by a brief description of the packaging, including materials of manufacture, gross mass, general outside dimensions and appearance.

(k)   Specification of the design by reference to the drawings.

(l)   A specification of the authorized radioactive content, including any restrictions on the radioactive contents which might not be obvious from the nature of the packaging. This shall include the physical and chemical forms, the activities involved (including those of the various isotopes, if appropriate), mass in grams (for fissile material the total mass of fissile nuclides or the mass for each fissile nuclide, when appropriate) and whether special form radioactive material, low dispersible radioactive material or fissile material excepted under 2.7.2.3.5.6, if applicable.

(m)   A description of the containment system;

(n)   For package designs containing fissile material which require multilateral approval of the package design in accordance with 6.4.22.4:

(i)   a detailed description of the authorized radioactive contents;

(ii)   a description of the confinement system;

    (iii) the value of the criticality safety index;

    (iv) reference to the documentation that demonstrates the criticality safety of the contents;

    (v) any special features, on the basis of which the absence of water from certain void spaces has been assumed in the criticality assessment;

    (vi) any allowance (based on 6.4.11.5(b)) for a change in neutron multiplication assumed in the criticality assessment as a result of actual irradiation experience; and

    (vii) the ambient temperature range for which the package design has been approved.

(o) For Type B(M) packages, a statement specifying those prescriptions of 6.4.7.5, 6.4.8.4, 6.4.8.5, 6.4.8.6 and 6.4.8.9–6.4.8.15 with which the package does not conform and any amplifying information which may be useful to other competent authorities.

(p) For packages containing more than 0.1 kg of uranium hexafluoride, a statement specifying those prescriptions of 6.4.6.4 that apply, if any, and any amplifying information which may be useful to other competent authorities.

(q) A detailed listing of any supplementary operational controls required for preparation, loading, carriage, unloading and handling of the consignment, including any special stowage provisions for the safe dissipation of heat.

(r) Reference to information provided by the applicant relating to the use of the packaging or specific actions to be taken prior to shipment.

(s) A statement regarding the ambient conditions assumed for purposes of design if these are not in accordance with those specified in 6.4.8.5, 6.4.8.6 and 6.4.8.15, as applicable.

(t) A specification of the applicable management system as required in 1.5.3.1.

(u) Any emergency arrangements deemed necessary by the competent authority.

(v) If deemed appropriate by the competent authority, reference to the identity of the applicant.

(w) Signature and identification of the certifying official.

6.4.23.18   Each certificate issued by a competent authority for alternative activity limits for an exempt consignment of instruments or articles according to 5.1.5.2.1.4 shall include the following information:

(a) Type of certificate.

(b) The competent authority identification mark.

(c) The issue date and an expiry date.

(d) List of applicable national and international regulations, including the edition of the IAEA *Regulations for the Safe Transport of Radioactive Material* under which the exemption is approved.

(e) The identification of the instrument or article.

(f) A description of the instrument or article.

(g) Design specifications for the instrument or article.

(h) A specification of the radionuclide(s), the approved alternative activity limit(s) for the exempt consignment(s) of the instrument(s) or article(s).

(i) Reference to documentation that demonstrates compliance with 2.7.2.2.2.2.

(j) If deemed appropriate by the competent authority, reference to the identity of the applicant.

(k) Signature and identification of the certifying official.

6.4.23.19   The competent authority shall be informed of the serial number of each packaging manufactured to a design approved under 6.4.22.2, 6.4.22.3, 6.4.22.4, 6.4.24.2 and 6.4.24.3.

6.4.23.20   Multilateral approval may be by validation of the original certificate issued by the competent authority of the country of origin of the design or shipment. Such validation may take the form of an endorsement on the original certificate or the issuance of a separate endorsement, annex, supplement, etc., by the competent authority of the country through or into which the shipment is made.

6.4.24   Transitional measures for class 7

Packages not requiring competent authority approval of design under the 1985 and 1985 (as amended 1990) editions of IAEA Safety Series No. 6

6.4.24.1   Packages not requiring competent authority approval of design (excepted packages, Type IP-1, Type IP-2, Type IP-3 and Type A packages) shall meet the provisions of this Code in full, except that packages that meet the requirements of the 1985 or 1985 (as amended 1990) editions of IAEA *Regulations for the Safe Transport of Radioactive Material* (IAEA Safety Series No. 6):

(a) may continue in transport provided that they were prepared for transport prior to 31 December 2003, and subject to the requirements of 6.4.24.4, if applicable;

6

(b)   may continue to be used provided that:

    (i)   they were not designed to contain uranium hexafluoride;

    (ii)   the applicable requirements of 1.5.3.1 of this Code are applied;

    (iii)   the activity limits and classification in chapter 2.7 of this Code are applied;

    (iv)   the requirements and controls for transport in parts 1, 3, 4, 5 and 7 of this Code are applied;

    (v)   the packaging was not manufactured or modified after 31 December 2003.

Packages approved under the 1973, 1973 (as amended), 1985 and 1985 (as amended 1990) editions of IAEA Safety Series No. 6

6.4.24.2   Packages requiring competent authority approval of the design shall meet the provisions of this Code in full unless the following conditions are met:

(a)   the packagings were manufactured to a package design approved by the competent authority under the provisions of the 1973 or 1973 (as amended) or the 1985 or 1985 (as amended 1990) editions of IAEA *Regulations for the Safe Transport of Radioactive Material* (IAEA Safety Series No. 6);

(b)   the package design is subject to multilateral approval;

(c)   the applicable requirements of 1.5.3.1 of this Code are applied;

(d)   the activity limits and classification in chapter 2.7 of this Code are applied;

(e)   the requirements and controls for transport in in parts 1, 3, 4, 5 and 7 of this Code are applied;

(f)   for a package containing fissile material and transported by air, the requirement of 6.4.11.11 is met;

(g)   for packages that meet the requirements of the 1973 or 1973 (as amended) editions of IAEA Safety Series No. 6:

    (i)   the packages retain sufficient shielding to ensure that the radiation level at 1 m from the surface of the package would not exceed 10 mSv/h in the accident conditions of transport defined in the 1973 Revised or 1973 revised (as amended) editions of IAEA Safety Series No. 6 with the maximum radioactive contents which the package is authorized to contain;

    (ii)   the packages do not utilize continuous venting;

    (iii)   a serial number in accordance with the provision of 5.2.1.5.5 is assigned to and marked on the outside of each packaging.

6.4.24.3   No new manufacture of packagings to a package design meeting the provisions of the 1973, 1973 (as amended), 1985, and 1985 (as amended 1990) editions of IAEA Safety Series No. 6 shall be permitted to commence.

Packages excepted from the requirements for fissile materials under the Regulations annexed to the 16th revised edition or the 17th revised edition of the United Nations Recommendations on the Transport of Dangerous Goods (2009 edition of IAEA Safety Standard Series No. TS-R-1)

6.4.24.4   Packages containing fissile material that is excepted from classification as "FISSILE" according to 2.7.2.3.5.1(i) or (iii) of the IMDG Code amendments 35-10 or 36-12 (paragraphs 417(a)(i) or (iii) of the 2009 edition of IAEA *Regulations for the Safe Transport of Radioactive Material*) prepared for transport before 31 December 2014 may continue in transport and may continue to be classified as non-fissile or fissile-excepted except that the consignment limits in table 2.7.2.3.5 of these editions shall apply to the conveyance. The consignment shall be transported under exclusive use.

Special form radioactive material approved under the 1973, 1973 (as amended), 1985 and 1985 (as amended 1990) editions of IAEA Safety Series No. 6

6.4.24.5   Special form radioactive material manufactured to a design which had received unilateral approval by the competent authority under the 1973, 1973 (as amended), 1985 or 1985 (as amended 1990) editions of IAEA Safety Series No. 6 may continue to be used when in compliance with the mandatory management system in accordance with the applicable provisions of 1.5.3.1. No new manufacture of such special form radioactive material shall be permitted to commence.

Chapter 6.5

Provisions for the construction and testing of intermediate bulk containers (IBCs)

6.5.1　General requirements

6.5.1.1　Scope

6.5.1.1.1　The provisions of this chapter apply to IBCs intended for the transport of certain dangerous substances and materials.

6.5.1.1.2　IBCs and their service equipment not conforming strictly to the provisions herein, but conforming to acceptable alternatives, may be considered by the competent authority concerned for approval. In order to take into account progress in science and technology, the use of alternative arrangements which offer at least an equivalent degree of safety in transport in respect of compatibility with the substances to be loaded therein and an equivalent or superior resistance to handling impact, and fire, may be considered by the competent authority concerned.

6.5.1.1.3　The construction, equipment, testing, marking and operation of IBCs shall be subject to acceptance by the competent authority of the country in which the IBCs are approved.

6.5.1.1.4　Manufacturers and subsequent distributors of IBCs shall provide information regarding procedures to be followed and a description of the types and dimensions of closures (including required gaskets) and any other components needed to ensure that IBCs as presented for transport are capable of passing the applicable performance tests of this chapter.

6.5.1.2　Definitions

Body (for all categories of IBCs other than composite IBCs) means the receptacle proper, including openings and their closures, but does not include service equipment.

Handling device (for flexible IBCs) means any sling, loop, eye or frame attached to the body of the IBC or formed from a continuation of the IBC body material.

Maximum permissible gross mass means the mass of the IBC and any service or structural equipment together with the maximum net mass.

Plastics material, when used in connection with inner receptacles for composite IBCs, is taken to include other polymeric materials such as rubber.

Protected (for metal IBCs) means the IBC being provided with additional protection against impact, the protection taking the form of, for example, a multi-layer (sandwich) or double-wall construction or a frame with a metal latticework packaging.

Service equipment means filling and discharge devices and, according to the category of IBC, pressure relief or venting, safety, heating and heat-insulating devices and measuring instruments.

Structural equipment (for all categories of IBCs other than flexible IBCs) means the reinforcing, fastening, handling, protective or stabilizing members of the body, including the base pallet for composite IBCs with plastics inner receptacle, fibreboard and wooden IBCs.

Woven plastics (for flexible IBCs) means a material made from stretched tapes or monofilaments of a suitable plastics material.

6.5.1.3　Categories of IBCs

6.5.1.3.1　*Metal* IBCs consist of a metal body together with appropriate service and structural equipment.

6.5.1.3.2　*Flexible* IBCs consist of a body constituted of film, woven fabric or any other flexible material or combinations thereof, and if necessary an inner coating or liner, together with any appropriate service equipment and handling devices.

6.5.1.3.3　*Rigid plastics* IBCs consist of a rigid plastics body, which may have structural equipment together with appropriate service equipment.

6

6.5.1.3.4 *Composite* IBCs consist of structural equipment in the form of a rigid outer packaging enclosing a plastics inner receptacle together with any service or other structural equipment. The IBC is so constructed that the inner receptacle and outer packaging, once assembled, form, and are used as, an integrated single unit to be filled, stored, transported or emptied as such.

6.5.1.3.5 *Fibreboard* IBCs consist of a fibreboard body with or without separate top and bottom caps, if necessary, an inner liner (but no inner packagings) and appropriate service and structural equipment.

6.5.1.3.6 *Wooden* IBCs consist of a rigid or collapsible wooden body together with an inner liner (but no inner packagings) and appropriate service and structural equipment.

6.5.1.4 Designatory code system for IBCs

6.5.1.4.1 The code shall consist of two Arabic numerals as specified in .1 followed by one or more capital letters as specified in .2; followed, when specified in an individual section, by an Arabic numeral indicating the category of IBC.

.1

Type	For solids, filled or discharged		For liquids
	by gravity	under pressure of more than 10 kPa (0.1 bar)	
Rigid	11	21	31
Flexible	13	–	–

.2 Materials

A	Steel (all types and surface treatments)
B	Aluminium
C	Natural wood
D	Plywood
F	Reconstituted wood
G	Fibreboard
H	Plastics material
L	Textile
M	Paper, multiwall
N	Metal (other than steel or aluminium)

6.5.1.4.2 For a composite IBC, two capital letters in Latin characters shall be used in sequence in the second position of the code. The first shall indicate the material of the inner receptacle of the IBC and the second that of the outer packaging of the IBC.

6.5.1.4.3 The following types and codes of IBCs are assigned:

Material	Category	Code	Paragraph
Metal A Steel	for solids, filled or discharged by gravity for solids, filled or discharged under pressure for liquids	11A 21A 31A	6.5.5.1
B Aluminium	for solids, filled or discharged by gravity for solids, filled or discharged under pressure for liquids	11B 21B 31B	
N Other than steel or aluminium	for solids, filled or discharged by gravity for solids, filled or discharged under pressure for liquids	11N 21N 31N	
Flexible H Plastics	woven plastics without coating or liner woven plastics, coated woven plastics with liner woven plastics, coated and with liner plastics film	13H1 13H2 13H3 13H4 13H5	6.5.5.2
L Textile	without coating or liner coated with liner coated and with liner	13L1 13L2 13L3 13L4	

Material	Category	Code	Paragraph
Flexible (continued) M Paper	multiwall multiwall, water-resistant	13M1 13M2	6.5.5.2
H Rigid plastics	for solids, filled or discharged by gravity, fitted with structural equipment	11H1	6.5.5.3
	for solids, filled or discharged by gravity, freestanding	11H2	
	for solids, filled or discharged under pressure, fitted with structural equipment	21H1	
	for solids, filled or discharged under pressure, freestanding	21H2	
	for liquids, fitted with structural equipment	31H1	
	for liquids, freestanding	31H2	
HZ Composite with plastics inner receptacle*	for solids, filled or discharged by gravity, with rigid plastics inner receptacle	11HZ1	6.5.5.4
	for solids, filled or discharged by gravity, with flexible plastics inner receptacle	11HZ2	
	for solids, filled or discharged under pressure, with rigid plastics inner receptacle	21HZ1	
	for solids, filled or discharged under pressure, with flexible plastics inner receptacle	21HZ2	
	for liquids, with rigid plastics inner receptacle	31HZ1	
	for liquids, with flexible plastics inner receptacle	31HZ2	
G Fibreboard	for solids, filled or discharged by gravity	11G	6.5.5.5
Wooden C Natural wood	for solids, filled or discharged by gravity, with inner liner	11C	6.5.5.6
D Plywood	for solids, filled or discharged by gravity, with inner liner	11D	
F Reconstituted wood	for solids, filled or discharged by gravity, with inner liner	11F	

* The code shall be completed by replacing the letter 'Z' by a capital letter in accordance with 6.5.1.4.1.2 to indicate the nature of the material used for the outer packaging.

6.5.1.4.4 The letter 'W' may follow the IBC code. The letter 'W' signifies that the IBC, although of the same type as indicated by the code, is manufactured to a specification different from those in section 6.5.3 and is considered equivalent in accordance with the provisions in 6.5.1.1.2.

6.5.2   Marking

6.5.2.1   Primary marking

△ **6.5.2.1.1** Each IBC manufactured and intended for use according to these provisions shall bear durable marks which are legible and placed in a location so as to be readily visible. Letters, numbers and symbols shall be at least 12 mm high and shall show:

.1   the United Nations packaging symbol:

△   This symbol shall not be used for any purpose other than certifying that a packaging, a flexible bulk container, a portable tank or a MEGC complies with the relevant requirements in chapters 6.1, 6.2, 6.3, 6.5, 6.6, 6.7 or 6.9. For metal IBCs on which the mark is stamped or embossed, the capital letters "UN" may be applied instead of the symbol;

.2   the code designating the type of IBC according to 6.5.1.4;

.3   a capital letter designating the packing group(s) for which the design type has been approved:

"X" for packing groups I, II and III (IBCs for solids only);

"Y" for packing groups II and III; or

"Z" for packing group III only;

.4   the month and year (last two digits) of manufacture;

.5   the State authorizing the allocation of the mark, indicated by the distinguishing sign for motor vehicles in international traffic;

.6   the name or symbol of the manufacturer and other identifications of the IBC as specified by the competent authority;

.7   the stacking test load* in kilograms. For IBCs not designed for stacking, the figure "0" shall be shown;

△ .8   the maximum permissible gross mass in kilograms.

The primary marks required above shall be applied in the sequence of the subparagraphs above. The marks required by 6.5.2.2 and any further mark authorized by a competent authority shall still enable the primary marks to be correctly identified.

Each mark applied in accordance with .1 to .8 and with 6.5.2.2 shall be clearly separated, e.g. by a slash or space, so as to be easily identifiable.

△ **6.5.2.1.2**   Examples of marks for various types of IBCs in accordance with .1 to .8 above:

 11A/Y/02 99/
NL/...* 007/
5500/1500

For a metal IBC for solids discharged by gravity and made from steel/ for packing groups II and III/ manufactured in February 1999/ authorized by the Netherlands/ manufactured by . . . *(name of manufacturer) and of a design type to which the competent authority has allocated serial number 007/ the stacking test load in kilograms/ and the maximum permissible gross mass in kilograms.

 13H3/Z/03 01/
F/...* 1713/
0/1500

For a flexible IBC for solids discharged by gravity and made from woven plastics with a liner/ not designed to be stacked.

 31H1/Y/04 99/
GB/...* 9099/
10800/1200

For a rigid plastics IBC for liquids made from plastics with structural equipment withstanding the stack load.

 31HA1/Y/05 01/
D/...* 1683/
10800/1200

For a composite IBC for liquids with a rigid plastics inner receptacle and steel outer packaging.

 11C/X/01 02/
S/...* 9876/
3000/910

For a wooden IBC for solids with an inner liner and authorized for packing group I solids.

 11G/Z/06 02/
I/...* 962/
0/500

For a fibreboard IBC/ not designed to be stacked.

 11D/Y/07 02/
E/...* 261/
3240/600

For a plywood IBC with inner liner.

Each element of the marking applied in accordance with subparagraphs .1 to .8 and with 6.5.2.2 shall be clearly separated, such as by a slash or space, so as to be easily identifiable.

---

* The stacking test load in kilograms to be placed on the IBC shall be 1.8 times the combined maximum permissible gross mass of the number of similar IBC that may be stacked on top of the IBC during transport (see 6.5.6.6.4).

6.5.2.2 Additional marking

△ **6.5.2.2.1** Each IBC shall bear the marks required in 6.5.2.1 and, in addition, the following information, which may appear on a corrosion-resistant plate permanently attached in a place readily accessible for inspection:

Note: For metal IBCs, this plate shall be a corrosion-resistant metal plate.

Additional marks	Category of IBC				
	Metal	Rigid plastics	Composite	Fibreboard	Wooden
Capacity in litres[a] at 20°C	X	X	X		
Tare mass in kg[a]	X	X	X	X	X
Test (gauge) pressure, in kPa or bar,[a] if applicable		X	X		
Maximum filling/discharge pressure in kPa or bar,[a] if applicable	X	X	X		
Body material and its minimum thickness in mm	X				
Date of last leakproofness test, if applicable (month and year)	X	X	X		
Date of last inspection (month and year)	X	X	X		
Serial number of the manufacturer	X				
Maximum permitted stacking load[b]	X	X	X	X	X

[a] The unit used shall be indicated.

△ [b] See 6.5.2.2.2. This additional mark shall apply to all IBCs manufactured, repaired or remanufactured as from 1 January 2011.

6.5.2.2.2 The maximum permitted stacking load applicable when the IBC is in use shall be displayed on a symbol as shown in the figures below. The symbol shall be durable and clearly visible.

IBCs capable of being stacked

IBCs NOT capable of being stacked

The minimum dimensions shall be 100 mm x 100 mm. The letters and numbers indicating the mass shall be at least 12 mm high. The area within the printer's marks indicated by the dimensional arrows shall be square. Where dimensions are not specified, all features shall be in approximate proportion to those shown. The mass marked above the symbol shall not exceed the load imposed during the design type test (see 6.5.6.6.4) divided by 1.8.

Note: The provisions of 6.5.2.2.2 shall apply to all IBCs manufactured, repaired or remanufactured as from 1 January 2011. The provisions of 6.5.2.2.2 of the IMDG Code (amendment 36-12) may continue to be applied to all IBCs manufactured, repaired or remanufactured between 1 January 2011 and 31 December 2016.

6.5.2.2.3 Each flexible IBC may also bear a pictogram or pictograms indicating the recommended lifting methods.

△ **6.5.2.2.4** Inner receptacles that are of composite IBC design type shall be identified by the application of the marks indicated in 6.5.2.1.1.2, .3, .4 where this date is that of the manufacture of the plastics inner receptacle, .5 and .6. The UN packaging symbol shall not be applied. The marks shall be applied in the sequence shown in 6.5.2.1.1. It shall be durable, legible and placed in a location so as to be readily visible when the inner receptacle is placed in the outer casing.

6

The date of the manufacture of the plastics inner receptacle may alternatively be marked on the inner receptacle adjacent to the remainder of the marks. In such a case, the two digits of the year in the mark and in the inner circle of the clock shall be identical. An example of an appropriate marking method is:

△ **Note 1**: Other methods that provide the minimum required information in a durable, visible and legible form are also acceptable.

■ **Note 2:** The date of manufacture of the inner receptacle may be different from the marked date of manufacture (see 6.5.2.1), repair (see 6.5.4.5.3) or remanufacture (see 6.5.2.4) of the composite IBC.

6.5.2.2.5 Where a composite IBC is designed in such a manner that the outer packaging is intended to be dismantled for transport when empty (such as for return of the IBC for re-use to the original consignor), each of the parts intended to be detached when so dismantled shall be marked with the month and year of manufacture and the name or symbol of the manufacturer and other identification of the IBC as specified by the competent authority (see 6.5.2.1.1.6).

6.5.2.3 **Conformity to design type**

△ The marks indicate that the IBCs correspond to a successfully tested design type and that the provisions referred to in the certificate have been met.

6.5.2.4 **Marking of remanufactured composite IBCs (31HZ1)**

△ The marks specified in 6.5.2.1.1 and 6.5.2.2 shall be removed from the original IBC or made permanently illegible and new marks shall be applied to an IBC remanufactured in accordance with these provisions of this Code.

6.5.3 Construction requirements

6.5.3.1 General requirements

6.5.3.1.1 IBCs shall be resistant to or adequately protected from deterioration due to the external environment.

6.5.3.1.2 IBCs shall be so constructed and closed that none of the contents can escape under normal conditions of transport, including the effects of vibration, or by changes in temperature, humidity or pressure.

6.5.3.1.3 IBCs and their closures shall be constructed of materials compatible with their contents, or be protected internally, so that they are not liable:

.1 to be attacked by the contents so as to make their use dangerous;

.2 to cause the contents to react or decompose, or form harmful or dangerous compounds with the IBCs.

6.5.3.1.4 Gaskets, where used, shall be made of materials not subject to attack by the contents of an IBC.

6.5.3.1.5 All service equipment shall be so positioned or protected as to minimize the risk of escape of the contents owing to damage during handling and transport.

6.5.3.1.6 IBCs, their attachments and their service and structural equipment shall be designed to withstand, without loss of contents, the internal pressure of the contents and the stresses of normal handling and transport. IBCs intended for stacking shall be designed for stacking. Any lifting or securing features of IBCs shall be of sufficient strength to withstand the normal conditions of handling and transport without gross distortion or failure and shall be so positioned that no undue stress is caused in any part of the IBC.

6.5.3.1.7 Where an IBC consists of a body within a framework, it shall be so constructed that:

.1 the body does not chafe or rub against the framework so as to cause material damage to the body,

.2 the body is retained within the framework at all times,

.3 the items of equipment are fixed in such a way that they cannot be damaged if the connections between body and frame allow relative expansion or movement.

6.5.3.1.8   Where a bottom discharge valve is fitted, it shall be capable of being made secure in the closed position and the whole discharge system shall be suitably protected from damage. Valves having lever closures shall be able to be secured against accidental opening and the open or closed position shall be readily apparent. For IBCs containing liquids, a secondary means of sealing the discharge aperture shall also be provided, such as by a blank flange or equivalent device.

6.5.4   Testing, certification and inspection

6.5.4.1   Quality assurance

IBCs shall be manufactured, remanufactured, repaired and tested under a quality assurance programme which satisfies the competent authority, in order to ensure that each manufactured, remanufactured or repaired IBC meets the provisions of this chapter.

Note: ISO 16106:2006, *Packaging – Transport packages for dangerous goods – Dangerous goods packagings, intermediate bulk containers (IBCs) and large packagings – Guidelines for the application of ISO 9001,* provides acceptable guidance on procedures which may be followed.

6.5.4.2   Test provisions

IBCs shall be subjected to design type tests and, if applicable, to initial and periodic inspections and tests in accordance with 6.5.4.4.

6.5.4.3   Certification

In respect of each design type of IBC, a certificate and mark (as in 6.5.2) shall be issued attesting that the design type, including its equipment, meets the test provisions.

6.5.4.4   Inspection and testing

Note: See also 6.5.4.5 for tests and inspections on repaired IBCs.

6.5.4.4.1   Every metal, rigid plastics and composite IBC shall be inspected to the satisfaction of the competent authority:

    .1   before it is put into service (including after remanufactured), and thereafter at intervals not exceeding five years, with regard to:

       △ **.1**   conformity to the design type, including marks;

          .2   internal and external condition; and

          .3   proper functioning of service equipment.

        Thermal insulation, if any, need be removed only to the extent necessary for a proper examination of the body of the IBC.

    .2   at intervals of not more than two and a half years with regard to:

          .1   external condition; and

          .2   proper functioning of service equipment.

        Thermal insulation, if any, need be removed only to the extent necessary for a proper examination of the body of the IBC.

    Each IBC shall correspond in all respects to its design type.

△ **6.5.4.4.2**   Every metal, rigid plastics and composite IBC for liquids, or for solids which are filled or discharged under pressure, shall undergo a suitable leakproofness test. This test is part of a quality assurance programme as stipulated in 6.5.4.1 which shows the capability of meeting the appropriate test level indicated in 6.5.6.7.3:

    (a)   before it is first used for transport;

    (b)   at intervals of not more than two and a half years.

For this test the IBC shall be fitted with the primary bottom closure. The inner receptacle of a composite IBC may be tested without the outer casing, provided the test results are not affected.

6.5.4.4.3   A report of each inspection and test shall be kept by the owner of the IBC at least until the next inspection or test. The report shall include the results of the inspection and test and shall identify the party performing the inspection and test (see also the marking requirements in 6.5.2.2.1).

6.5.4.4.4   The competent authority may at any time require proof, by tests in accordance with this chapter, that the IBCs meet the provisions of the design type tests.

6.5.4.5 **Repaired IBCs**

6.5.4.5.1 When an IBC is impaired as a result of impact (e.g. accident) or any other cause, it shall be repaired or otherwise maintained (see definition of "Routine maintenance of IBCs" in 1.2.1), so as to conform to the design type. The bodies of rigid plastics IBCs and the inner receptacles of composite IBCs that are impaired shall be replaced.

6.5.4.5.2 In addition to any other testing and inspection requirements in this Code, an IBC shall be subjected to the full testing and inspection requirements set out in 6.5.4.4, and the required reports shall be prepared, whenever it is repaired.

△ **6.5.4.5.3** The party performing the tests and inspections after the repair shall durably mark the IBC near the manufacturer's UN design type marks to show:

.1 the State in which the tests and inspections were carried out;

.2 the name or authorized symbol of the party performing the tests and inspections; and

.3 the date (month, year) of the tests and inspections.

6.5.4.5.4 Tests and inspections performed in accordance with 6.5.4.5.2 may be considered to satisfy the requirements for the 2.5- and 5-year periodic tests and inspections.

6.5.5 Specific provisions for IBCs

6.5.5.1 **Specific provisions for metal IBCs**

6.5.5.1.1 These provisions apply to metal IBCs for the transport of liquids and solids. There are three categories of metal IBCs:

those for solids which are filled and discharged by gravity (11A, 11B, 11N);

those for solids which are filled and discharged at a gauge pressure greater than 10 kPa (21A, 21B, 21N); and

those for liquids (31A, 31B, 31N).

6.5.5.1.2 Bodies shall be made of suitable ductile metal in which the weldability has been fully demonstrated. Welds shall be skilfully made and afford complete safety. Low-temperature performance shall be taken into account when appropriate.

6.5.5.1.3 Care shall be taken to avoid damage by galvanic action due to the juxtaposition of dissimilar metals.

6.5.5.1.4 Aluminium IBCs intended for the transport of flammable liquids shall have no movable parts, such as covers, closures, etc., made of unprotected steel liable to rust, which might cause a dangerous reaction by coming into frictional or percussive contact with the aluminium.

6.5.5.1.5 Metal IBCs shall be made of metals which meet the following provisions:

.1 For steel, the elongation at fracture, per cent, shall not be less than $10,000/R_m$ with an absolute minimum of 20%, where R_m = guaranteed minimum tensile strength of the reference steel to be used, in N/mm^2.

.2 For aluminium and aluminium alloys, the elongation at fracture, per cent, shall not be less than $10,000/6R_m$ with an absolute minimum of 8%.

Specimens used to determine the elongation at fracture shall be taken transversely to the direction of rolling and be so secured that:

$L_o = 5d$, or

$L_o = 5.65\sqrt{A}$

where :

L_o = gauge length of the specimen before the test;

d = diameter; and

A = cross-sectional area of the test specimen.

6.5.5.1.6 *Minimum wall thickness*

.1 For a reference steel having a product of $R_m \times A_o = 10{,}000$, the wall thickness shall not be less than:

Capacity (C) in litres	Wall thickness (T) in mm			
	Types 11A, 11B, 11N		Types 21A, 21B, 21N, 31A, 31B, 31N	
	Unprotected	Protected	Unprotected	Protected
$C \leq 1000$	2.0	1.5	2.5	2.0
$1000 < C \leq 2000$	$T = C/2000 + 1.5$	$T = C/2000 + 1.0$	$T = C/2000 + 2.0$	$T = C/2000 + 1.5$
$2000 < C \leq 3000$	$T = C/2000 + 1.5$	$T = C/2000 + 1.0$	$T = C/1000 + 1.0$	$T = C/2000 + 1.5$

where: A_o = minimum elongation (as a percentage) of the reference steel to be used on fracture under tensile stress (see 6.5.5.1.5).

.2 For metals other than the reference steel described in .1, the minimum wall thickness is given by the following equivalence formula:

$$e_1 = \frac{21.4 \times e_0}{\sqrt[3]{R_{m1} \times A_1}}$$

where:

e_1 = required equivalent wall thickness of the metal to be used (in mm);

e_0 = required minimum wall thickness for the reference steel (in mm);

R_{m1} = guaranteed minimum tensile strength of the metal to be used (in N/mm^2) (see .3); and

A_1 = minimum elongation (as a percentage) of the metal to be used on fracture under tensile stress (see 6.5.5.1.5).

However, in no case shall the wall thickness be less than 1.5 mm.

.3 For purposes of the calculation described in .2, the guaranteed minimum tensile strength of the metal to be used (R_{m1}) shall be the minimum value according to national or international material standards.

However, for austenitic steels, the specified minimum value for R_m according to the material standards may be increased by up to 15% when a greater value is attested in the material inspection certificate. When no material standard exists for the material in question, the value of R_m shall be the minimum value attested in the material inspection certificate.

6.5.5.1.7 *Pressure relief provisions*

IBCs for liquids shall be capable of releasing a sufficient amount of vapour in the event of fire engulfment to ensure that no rupture of the shell will occur. This can be achieved by conventional pressure relief devices or by other constructional means. The start-to-discharge pressure shall not be higher than 65 kPa and no lower than the total gauge pressure experienced in the IBC (i.e. the vapour pressure of the filling substance plus the partial pressure of the air or other inert gases, minus 100 kPa) at 55°C, determined on the basis of a maximum degree of filling as defined in 4.1.1.4. The pressure relief devices shall be fitted in the vapour space.

6.5.5.2 **Specific provisions for flexible IBCs**

6.5.5.2.1 These provisions apply to flexible IBCs of the following types:

13H1 woven plastics without coating or liner
13H2 woven plastics, coated
13H3 woven plastics with liner
13H4 woven plastics, coated and with liner
13H5 plastics film
13L1 textile without coating or liner
13L2 textile, coated
13L3 textile with liner
13L4 textile, coated and with liner
13M1 paper, multiwall
13M2 paper, multiwall, water-resistant.

Flexible IBCs are intended for the transport of solids only.

6.5.5.2.2 Bodies of IBCs shall be manufactured from suitable materials. The strength of the material and the construction of a flexible IBC shall be appropriate to its capacity and its intended use.

6.5.5.2.3 All materials used in the construction of flexible IBCs of types 13M1 and 13M2 shall, after complete immersion in water for not less than 24 hours, retain at least 85% of the tensile strength as measured originally on the material conditioned to equilibrium at 67% relative humidity or less.

6.5.5.2.4 Seams of IBCs shall be formed by stitching, heat sealing, gluing or any equivalent method. All stitched seam-ends shall be secured.

6.5.5.2.5 Flexible IBCs shall provide adequate resistance to ageing and to degradation caused by ultraviolet radiation, by climatic conditions, or by the substance contained within which would thereby render them unsuitable for their intended use.

6.5.5.2.6 For plastics flexible IBCs where protection against ultraviolet radiation is required, it shall be provided by the addition of carbon black or other suitable pigments or inhibitors. These additives shall be compatible with the contents and remain effective throughout the life of the body of the IBC. Where use is made of carbon black, pigments or inhibitors other than those used in the manufacture of the tested design type, retesting may be waived if changes in the carbon black content, the pigment content or the inhibitor content do not adversely affect the physical properties of the material of construction.

6.5.5.2.7 Additives may be incorporated into the material of the body to improve the resistance to ageing or to serve other purposes, provided that these do not adversely affect the physical or chemical properties of the material.

6.5.5.2.8 No material recovered from used receptacles shall be used in the manufacture of IBC bodies. Production residues or scrap from the same manufacturing process may, however, be used. Component parts such as fittings and pallet bases may also be used provided such components have not in any way been damaged in previous use.

6.5.5.2.9 When filled, the ratio of height to width shall be not more than 2:1.

6.5.5.2.10 The liner shall be made of a suitable material. The strength of the material used and the construction of the liner shall be appropriate to the capacity of the IBC and the intended use. Joints and closures shall be sift-proof and capable of withstanding pressures and impacts liable to occur under normal conditions of handling and transport.

6.5.5.3 Specific provisions for rigid plastics IBCs

6.5.5.3.1 These provisions apply to rigid plastics IBCs for the transport of solids or liquids. Rigid plastics IBCs are of the following types:

11H1	fitted with structural equipment designed to withstand the whole load when IBCs are stacked, for solids which are filled or discharged by gravity
11H2	freestanding, for solids which are filled or discharged by gravity
21H1	fitted with structural equipment designed to withstand the whole load when IBCs are stacked, for solids which are filled or discharged under pressure
21H2	freestanding, for solids which are filled or discharged under pressure
31H1	fitted with structural equipment designed to withstand the whole load when IBCs are stacked, for liquids
31H2	freestanding, for liquids.

6.5.5.3.2 The body shall be manufactured from suitable plastics material of known specifications and be of adequate strength in relation to its capacity and to the service it is required to perform. The material shall be adequately resistant to ageing and to degradation caused by the substance contained within or, where relevant, by ultraviolet radiation. Low-temperature performance shall be taken into account when appropriate. Any permeation of the substance contained within shall not constitute a danger under normal conditions of transport.

6.5.5.3.3 Where protection against ultraviolet radiation is required, it shall be provided by the addition of carbon black or other suitable pigments or inhibitors. These additives shall be compatible with the contents and remain effective throughout the life of the body of the IBC. Where use is made of carbon black, pigments or inhibitors other than those used in the manufacture of the tested design type, retesting may be waived if changes in the carbon black content, the pigment content or the inhibitor content do not adversely affect the physical properties of the material of construction.

6.5.5.3.4 Additives may be incorporated in the material of the body to improve the resistance to ageing or to serve other purposes, provided that these do not adversely affect the physical or chemical properties of the material.

6.5.5.3.5 No used material other than production residues or regrind from the same manufacturing process may be used in the manufacturing of rigid plastics IBCs.

6.5.5.4   Specific provisions for composite IBCs with plastics inner receptacles

6.5.5.4.1   These provisions apply to composite IBCs for the transport of solids or liquids of the following types:

11HZ1	composite IBCs with a rigid plastics inner receptacle, for solids filled or discharged by gravity
11HZ2	composite IBCs with a flexible plastics inner receptacle, for solids filled or discharged by gravity
21HZ1	composite IBCs with a rigid plastics inner receptacle, for solids filled or discharged under pressure
21HZ2	composite IBCs with a flexible plastics inner receptacle, for solids filled or discharged under pressure
31HZ1	composite IBCs with a rigid plastics inner receptacle, for liquids
31HZ2	composite IBCs with a flexible plastics inner receptacle, for liquids.

This code shall be completed by replacing the letter 'Z' by a capital letter in accordance with 6.5.1.4.1.2 to indicate the nature of the material used for the outer packaging.

6.5.5.4.2   The inner receptacle is not intended to perform a containment function without its outer packaging. A "rigid" inner receptacle is a receptacle which retains its general shape when empty without closures in place and without the benefit of the outer packaging. Any inner receptacle that is not "rigid" is considered to be "flexible".

6.5.5.4.3   The outer packaging normally consists of rigid material formed so as to protect the inner receptacle from physical damage during handling and transport, but is not intended to perform the containment function. It includes the base pallet where appropriate.

6.5.5.4.4   A composite IBC with a fully enclosing outer packaging shall be so designed that the integrity of the inner receptacle may be readily assessed following the leakproofness and hydraulic tests.

6.5.5.4.5   IBCs of type 31HZ2 shall be limited to a capacity of not more than 1250 L.

6.5.5.4.6   The inner receptacle shall be manufactured from suitable plastics material of known specifications and be of adequate strength in relation to its capacity and to the service it is required to perform. The material shall be adequately resistant to ageing and to degradation caused by the substance contained and, where relevant, by ultraviolet radiation. Low-temperature performance shall be taken into account when appropriate. Any permeation of the substance contained shall not constitute a danger under normal conditions of transport.

6.5.5.4.7   Where protection against ultraviolet radiation is required, it shall be provided by the addition of carbon black or other suitable pigments or inhibitors. These additives shall be compatible with the contents and remain effective throughout the life of the inner receptacle. Where use is made of carbon black, pigments or inhibitors other than those used in the manufacture of the tested design type, re-testing may be waived if changes in carbon black content, the pigment content or the inhibitor content do not adversely affect the physical properties of the material of construction.

6.5.5.4.8   Additives may be incorporated in the material of the inner receptacle to improve the resistance to ageing or to serve other purposes, provided that these do not adversely affect the physical or chemical properties of the material.

6.5.5.4.9   No used material other than production residues or regrind from the same manufacturing process may be used in the manufacture of inner receptacles.

6.5.5.4.10   The inner receptacle of IBCs of type 31HZ2 shall consist of at least three plies of film.

6.5.5.4.11   The strength of the material and the construction of the outer packaging shall be appropriate to the capacity of the composite IBC and its intended use.

6.5.5.4.12   The outer packaging shall be free of any projection that might damage the inner receptacle.

6.5.5.4.13   Outer packagings of steel or aluminium shall be constructed of a suitable metal of adequate thickness.

6.5.5.4.14   Outer packagings of natural wood shall be of well-seasoned wood, commercially dry and free from defects that would materially lessen the strength of any part of the packaging. The tops and bottoms may be made of water-resistant reconstituted wood such as hardboard, particle board or other suitable type.

6.5.5.4.15   Outer packagings of plywood shall be made of well-seasoned rotary-cut, sliced or sawn veneer plywood, commercially dry and free from defects that would materially lessen the strength of the packaging. All adjacent plies shall be glued with water-resistant adhesive. Other suitable materials may be used in conjunction with plywood for the construction of packagings. Packagings shall be firmly nailed or secured to corner posts or ends or be assembled by equally suitable devices.

6.5.5.4.16   The walls of outer packagings of reconstituted wood shall be made of water-resistant reconstituted wood such as hardboard, particle board or other suitable type. Other parts of the packagings may be made of other suitable material.

6

6.5.5.4.17   For fibreboard outer packagings, strong and good-quality solid or double-faced corrugated fibreboard (single or multiwall) shall be used appropriate to the capacity of the packaging and to its intended use. The water resistance of the outer surface shall be such that the increase in mass, as determined in a test carried out over 30 minutes by the Cobb method of determining water absorption, is not greater than 155 g/m^2 – see ISO 535:1991. It shall have proper bending qualities. Fibreboard shall be cut, creased without scoring, and slotted so as to permit assembly without cracking, surface breaks or undue bending. The fluting of corrugated fibreboard shall be firmly glued by water-resistant adhesive to the facings.

6.5.5.4.18   The ends of fibreboard outer packagings may have a wooden frame or be entirely of wood. Reinforcements of wooden battens may be used.

6.5.5.4.19   Manufacturing joins in the fibreboard outer packagings shall be taped, lapped and glued, or lapped and stitched with metal staples. Lapped joins shall have an appropriate overlap. Where closing is effected by gluing or taping, a water-resistant adhesive shall be used.

6.5.5.4.20   Where the outer packagings are of plastics material, the relevant provisions of 6.5.5.4.6 to 6.5.5.4.9 shall apply.

6.5.5.4.21   The outer packagings of IBCs of type 31HZ2 shall enclose the inner receptacle on all sides.

6.5.5.4.22   Any integral pallet base forming part of the IBC or a detachable pallet shall be suitable for mechanical handling with the IBC filled to its maximum permissible gross mass.

6.5.5.4.23   The pallet or integral base shall be designed so as to avoid any protrusion of the base of the IBC that might be liable to damage in handling.

6.5.5.4.24   The outer packagings shall be secured to a detachable pallet to ensure stability in handling and transport. Where a detachable pallet is used, its top surface shall be free from sharp protrusions that might damage the IBC.

6.5.5.4.25   Strengthening devices such as timber supports to increase stacking performance may be used but shall be external to the inner receptacle.

6.5.5.4.26   Where IBCs are intended for stacking, the bearing surfaces shall be such as to distribute the load in a safe manner. Such IBCs shall be designed so that the load is not supported by the inner receptacle.

6.5.5.5   **Specific provisions for fibreboard IBCs**

6.5.5.5.1   These provisions apply to fibreboard IBCs for the transport of solids which are filled or discharged by gravity. Fibreboard IBCs are of the following type: 11G.

6.5.5.5.2   Fibreboard IBCs shall not incorporate top lifting devices.

6.5.5.5.3   The body shall be made of strong and good-quality solid or double-faced corrugated fibreboard (single or multiwall), appropriate to the capacity of the IBC and to its intended use. The water resistance of the outer surface shall be such that the increase in mass, as determined in a test carried out over a period of 30 minutes by the Cobb method of determining water absorption, is not greater than 155 g/m^2 – see ISO 535:1991. It shall have proper bending qualities. Fibreboard shall be cut, creased without scoring, and slotted so as to permit assembly without cracking, surface breaks or undue bending. The fluting or corrugated fibreboard shall be firmly glued to the facings.

6.5.5.5.4   The walls, including top and bottom, shall have a minimum puncture resistance of 15 J, measured according to ISO 3036:1975.

6.5.5.5.5   Manufacturing joins in the body of IBCs shall be made with an appropriate overlap and shall be taped, glued, stitched with metal staples or fastened by other means at least equally effective. Where joins are effected by gluing or taping, a water-resistant adhesive shall be used. Metal staples shall pass completely through all pieces to be fastened and be formed or protected so that any inner liner cannot be abraded or punctured by them.

6.5.5.5.6   The liner shall be made of suitable material. The strength of the material used and the construction of the liner shall be appropriate to the capacity of the IBC and its intended use. Joins and closures shall be sift-proof and capable of withstanding pressure and impacts liable to occur under normal conditions of handling and transport.

6.5.5.5.7   Any integral pallet base forming part of the IBC or any detachable pallet shall be suitable for mechanical handling with the IBC filled to its maximum permissible gross mass.

6.5.5.5.8   The pallet or integral base shall be designed so as to avoid any protrusion of the base of the IBC that might be liable to damage in handling.

6.5.5.5.9   The body shall be secured to any detachable pallet to ensure stability in handling and transport. Where a detachable pallet is used, its top surface shall be free from sharp protrusions that might damage the IBC.

6.5.5.5.10   Strengthening devices such as timber supports to increase stacking performance may be used but shall be external to the liner.

6.5.5.5.11   Where IBCs are intended for stacking, the bearing surface shall be such as to distribute the load in a safe manner.

6.5.5.6   Specific provisions for wooden IBCs

6.5.5.6.1   These provisions apply to wooden IBCs for the transport of solids which are filled or discharged by gravity. Wooden IBCs are of the following types:

    11C   natural wood with inner liner
    11D   plywood with inner liner
    11F   reconstituted wood with inner liner.

6.5.5.6.2   Wooden IBCs shall not incorporate top lifting devices.

6.5.5.6.3   The strength of the materials used and the method of construction shall be appropriate to the capacity and intended use of the IBC.

6.5.5.6.4   Natural wood shall be well seasoned, commercially dry and free from defects that would materially lessen the strength of any part of the IBC. Each part of the IBC shall consist of one piece or be equivalent thereto. Parts are considered equivalent to one piece when a suitable method of glued assembly is used (as for instance Lindermann joint, tongue and groove joint, ship lap or rabbet joint, or butt joint), with at least two corrugated metal fasteners at each joint, or when other methods at least equally effective are used.

6.5.5.6.5   Bodies of plywood shall be at least three-ply. It shall be made of well-seasoned rotary-cut, sliced or sawn veneer, commercially dry and free from defects that would materially lessen the strength of the body. All adjacent plies shall be glued with water-resistant adhesive. Other suitable materials may be used with plywood for the construction of the body.

6.5.5.6.6   Bodies of reconstituted wood shall be made of water-resistant reconstituted wood such as hardboard, particle board or other suitable type.

6.5.5.6.7   IBCs shall be firmly nailed or secured to corner posts or ends or be assembled by equally suitable devices.

6.5.5.6.8   The liner shall be made of a suitable material. The strength of the material used and the construction of the liner shall be appropriate to the capacity of the IBC and its intended use. Joins and closures shall be sift-proof and capable of withstanding pressure and impacts liable to occur under normal conditions of handling and transport.

6.5.5.6.9   Any integral pallet base forming part of the IBC or any detachable pallet shall be suitable for mechanical handling with the IBC filled to its maximum permissible gross mass.

6.5.5.6.10   The pallet or integral base shall be designed so as to avoid any protrusion of the base of the IBC that might be liable to damage in handling.

6.5.5.6.11   The body shall be secured to any detachable pallet to ensure stability in handling and transport. Where a detachable pallet is used, its top surface shall be free from sharp protrusions that might damage the IBC.

6.5.5.6.12   Strengthening devices such as timber supports to increase stacking performance may be used but shall be external to the liner.

6.5.5.6.13   Where IBCs are intended for stacking, the bearing surface shall be such as to distribute the load in a safe manner.

6.5.6   Test provisions for IBCs

6.5.6.1   Performance and frequency of tests

6.5.6.1.1   Each IBC design type shall successfully pass the tests prescribed in this chapter before being used. An IBC design type is defined by the design, size and material and thickness, manner of construction and means of filling and discharging, but may include various surface treatments; it also includes IBCs which differ from the design type only in their lesser external dimensions.

6.5.6.1.2   Tests shall be carried out on IBCs as prepared for transport. IBCs shall be filled as indicated in the relevant section. The substances to be transported in the IBCs may be replaced by other substances except where this would invalidate the results of the tests. For solids, when another substance is used, it shall have the same physical characteristics (mass, grain size, etc.) as the substance to be transported. It is permissible to use additives, such as bags of lead shot, to achieve the requisite total package gross mass, so long as they are placed so that the test results are not affected.

6.5.6.2 Design type tests

6.5.6.2.1 One IBC of each design type, size, wall thickness and manner of construction shall be submitted to the tests in the order shown in 6.5.6.3.5 and as set out in 6.5.6.4 to 6.5.6.13. These design type tests shall be carried out as required by the competent authority.

6.5.6.2.2 The competent authority may permit the selective testing of IBCs which differ only in minor respects from the tested type, such as with small reductions in external dimensions.

6.5.6.2.3 If detachable pallets are used in the tests, the test report issued in accordance with 6.5.6.14 shall include a technical description of the pallets to be used.

6.5.6.3 Preparation of IBC for testing

6.5.6.3.1 Paper and fibreboard IBCs and composite IBCs with fibreboard outer packagings shall be conditioned for at least 24 hours in an atmosphere having a controlled temperature and relative humidity (r.h.). There are three options, one of which shall be chosen. The preferred atmosphere is 23°C±2°C and 50%±2% r.h. The two other options are 20°C±2°C and 65%±2% r.h. or 27°C±2°C and 65%±2% r.h.

Note: Average values shall fall within these limits. Short-term fluctuations and measurement limitations may cause individual measurements to vary by up to ±5% relative humidity without significant impairment of test reproducibility.

6.5.6.3.2 Additional steps shall be taken to ascertain that the plastics material used in the manufacture of rigid plastics IBCs of types 31H1 and 31H2 and composite IBCs of type 31HZ1 and 31HZ2 complies with the provisions of 6.5.5.3.2 to 6.5.5.3.4 and 6.5.5.4.6 to 6.5.5.4.9.

6.5.6.3.3 This may be done, for example, by submitting sample IBCs to a preliminary test extending over a long period, for example six months, during which the samples would remain filled with the substances they are intended to contain or with substances which are known to have at least as severe a stress-cracking, weakening or molecular degradation influence on the plastics materials in question, and after which the samples shall be submitted to the applicable tests listed in the table in 6.5.6.3.5.

6.5.6.3.4 Where the behaviour of the plastics material has been established by other means, the above compatibility test may be dispensed with.

6.5.6.3.5 Design type tests required in sequential order:

Type of IBC	Vibration[f]	Bottom lift	Top lift[a]	Stacking[b]	Leak-proofness	Hydraulic pressure	Drop	Tear	Topple	Righting[c]
Metal:										
11A, 11B, 11N	–	1st[a]	2nd	3rd	–	–	4th[e]	–	–	–
21A, 21B, 21N	–	1st[a]	2nd	3rd	4th	5th	6th[e]	–	–	–
31A, 31B, 31N	1st	2nd[a]	3rd	4th	5th	6th	7th[e]	–	–	–
Flexible[d]	–	–	x[c]	x	–	–	x	x	x	x
Rigid plastics:										
11H1, 11H2	–	1st[a]	2nd	3rd	–	–	4th	–	–	–
21H1, 21H2	–	1st[a]	2nd	3rd	4th	5th	6th	–	–	–
31H1, 31H2	1st	2nd[a]	3rd	4th	5th	6th	7th	–	–	–
Composite:										
11HZ1, 11HZ2	–	1st[a]	2nd	3rd	–	–	4th[e]	–	–	–
21HZ1, 21HZ2	–	1st[a]	2nd	3rd	4th	5th	6th[e]	–	–	–
31HZ1, 31HZ2	1st	2nd[a]	3rd	4th	5th	6th	7th[e]	–	–	–
Fibreboard	–	1st	–	2nd	–	–	3rd	–	–	–
Wooden	–	1st	–	2nd	–	–	3rd	–	–	–

[a] When IBCs are designed for this method of handling.

[b] When IBCs are designed to be stacked.

[c] When IBCs are designed to be lifted from the top or the side.

[d] Required test indicated by "x"; an IBC which has passed one test may be used for other tests, in any order.

[e] Another IBC of the same design may be used for the drop test.

[f] Another IBC of the same design may be used for the vibration test.

6.5.6.4   Bottom lift test

6.5.6.4.1   *Applicability*

For all fibreboard and wooden IBCs and for all types of IBCs which are fitted with means for lifting from the base, as a design type test.

6.5.6.4.2   *Preparation of the IBC for test*

The IBC shall be filled. A load shall be added and evenly distributed. The mass of filled IBC and the load shall be 1.25 times its maximum permissible gross mass.

6.5.6.4.3   *Method of testing*

The IBC shall be raised and lowered twice by a forklift truck with the forks centrally positioned so that the space between them is three quarters of the length of the side of entry (unless the points of entry are fixed). The forks shall penetrate to three quarters of the depth in the direction of entry. The test shall be repeated from each possible direction of entry.

6.5.6.4.4   *Criteria for passing the test*

No permanent deformation which renders the IBC, including the base pallet, if any, unsafe for transport and no loss of contents.

6.5.6.5   Top lift test

6.5.6.5.1   *Applicability*

For all types of IBCs which are designed to be lifted from the top, and for flexible IBCs designed to be lifted from the top or the side, as a design type test.

6.5.6.5.2   *Preparation of the IBC for test*

Metal, rigid plastics and composite IBCs shall be filled. A load shall be added and evenly distributed. The mass of filled IBC and the load shall be twice the maximum permissible gross mass. Flexible IBCs shall be filled with a representative material and then shall be loaded to six times their maximum permissible gross mass, the load being evenly distributed.

6.5.6.5.3   *Method of testing*

Metal and flexible IBCs shall be lifted in the manner for which they are designed until clear of the floor and maintained in that position for a period of five minutes.

Rigid plastics and composite IBCs shall be lifted:

   .1   by each pair of diagonally opposite lifting devices, so that the hoisting forces are applied vertically, for a period of five minutes; and

   .2   by each pair of diagonally opposite lifting devices, so that the hoisting forces are applied towards the centre at 45° to the vertical, for a period of five minutes.

6.5.6.5.4   Other methods of top-lift testing and preparation at least equally effective may be used for flexible IBCs.

6.5.6.5.5   *Criteria for passing the test*

   .1   Metal, rigid plastics and composite IBCs: the IBC remains safe for normal conditions of transport, there is no observable permanent deformation of the IBC, including the base pallet, if any, and no loss of contents.

   .2   Flexible IBCs: no damage to the IBC or its lifting devices which renders the IBC unsafe for transport or handling and no loss of contents.

6.5.6.6   Stacking test

6.5.6.6.1   *Applicability*

For all types of IBCs which are designed to be stacked on each other, as a design type test.

6.5.6.6.2   *Preparation of the IBC for test*

The IBC shall be filled to its maximum permissible gross mass. If the specific gravity of the product being used for testing makes this impracticable, the IBC shall additionally be loaded so that it is tested at its maximum permissible gross mass, the load being evenly distributed.

6

6.5.6.6.3 *Method of testing*

    .1   The IBC shall be placed on its base on level hard ground and subjected to a uniformly distributed superimposed test load (see 6.5.6.6.4). IBCs shall be subjected to the test load for a period of at least:

- 5 minutes, for metal IBCs;

- 28 days at 40°C, for rigid plastics IBCs of types 11H2, 21H2 and 31H2 and for composite IBCs with outer packagings of plastics material which bear the stacking load (i.e. types 11HH1, 11HH2, 21HH1, 21HH2, 31HH1 and 31HH2);

- 24 hours, for all other types of IBCs.

    .2   The load shall be applied by one of the following methods:

- one or more IBCs of the same type, filled to the maximum permissible gross mass, stacked on the test IBC;

- appropriate mass loaded on to either a flat plate or a reproduction of the base of the IBC, which is stacked on the test IBC.

6.5.6.6.4 *Calculation of superimposed test load*

The load to be placed on the IBC shall be 1.8 times the combined maximum permissible gross mass of the number of similar IBCs that may be stacked on top of the IBC during transport.

6.5.6.6.5 *Criteria for passing the test*

    .1   All types of IBCs other than flexible IBCs: no permanent deformation which renders the IBC, including the base pallet, if any, unsafe for transport and no loss of contents.

    .2   Flexible IBCs: no deterioration of the body which renders the IBC unsafe for transport and no loss of contents.

6.5.6.7   **Leakproofness test**

6.5.6.7.1 *Applicability*

For those types of IBCs used for liquids, or for solids filled or discharged under pressure, as a design type test and a periodic test.

6.5.6.7.2 *Preparation of the IBC for test*

The test shall be carried out before the fitting of any thermal insulation equipment. Vented closures shall either be replaced by similar non-vented closures or the vent shall be sealed.

6.5.6.7.3 *Method of testing and pressure to be applied*

The test shall be carried out for a period of at least 10 minutes, using air at a gauge pressure of not less than 20 kPa (0.2 bar). The airtightness of the IBC shall be determined by a suitable method such as air-pressure differential test or by immersing the IBC in water, or for metal IBCs, by coating the seams and joints with a soap solution. In the latter case, a correction factor shall be applied for the hydrostatic pressure.

6.5.6.7.4 *Criterion for passing the test*

No leakage of air.

6.5.6.8   **Hydraulic pressure test**

6.5.6.8.1 *Applicability*

For those types of IBCs used for liquids or for solids filled or discharged under pressure, as a design type test.

6.5.6.8.2 *Preparation of the IBC for test*

The test shall be carried out before the fitting of any thermal insulation equipment. Pressure relief devices shall be removed and their apertures plugged, or shall be rendered inoperative.

6.5.6.8.3 *Method of testing*

The test shall be carried out for a period of at least ten minutes, applying a hydraulic pressure of not less than that indicated in 6.5.6.8.4. The IBC shall not be mechanically restrained during the test.

6.5.6.8.4 *Pressures to be applied*

6.5.6.8.4.1 Metal IBCs:

    .1   For IBCs of types 21A, 21B and 21N, for packing group I solids, a 250 kPa (2.5 bar) gauge pressure;

    .2   For IBCs of types 21A, 21B, 21N, 31A, 31B and 31N, for packing groups II or III substances, a 200 kPa (2 bar) gauge pressure;

    .3   In addition, for IBCs of types 31A, 31B and 31N, a 65 kPa (0.65 bar) gauge pressure. This test shall be performed before the 200 kPa (2 bar) test.

6.5.6.8.4.2 Rigid plastics and composite IBCs:

    .1   For IBCs of types 21H1, 21H2, 21HZ1 and 21HZ2: 75 kPa (0.75 bar) gauge;

    .2   For IBCs of types 31H1, 31H2, 31HZ1 and 31HZ2: whichever is the greater of two values, the first as determined by one of the following methods:

        –   the total gauge pressure measured in the IBC (i.e. the vapour pressure of the filling substance and the partial pressure of the air or other inert gases, minus 100 kPa) at 55°C multiplied by a safety factor of 1.5; this total gauge pressure shall be determined on the basis of a maximum degree of filling in accordance with 4.1.1.4 and a filling temperature of 15°C; or

        –   1.75 times the vapour pressure at 50°C of the substance to be transported minus 100 kPa, but with a minimum test pressure of 100 kPa; or

        –   1.5 times the vapour pressure at 55°C of the substance to be transported minus 100 kPa, but with a minimum test pressure of 100 kPa;

    and the second as determined by the following method:

        –   twice the static pressure of the substance to be transported, with a minimum of twice the static pressure of water.

6.5.6.8.5 *Criteria for passing the test(s)*

    .1   For IBCs of types 21A, 21B, 21N, 31A, 31B and 31N, when subjected to the test pressure specified in 6.5.6.8.4.1.1 or .2: no leakage;

    .2   For IBCs of types 31A, 31B and 31N, when subjected to the test pressure specified in 6.5.6.8.4.1.3: neither permanent deformation which would render the IBC unsafe for transport nor leakage; and

    .3   For rigid plastics and composite IBCs: no permanent deformation which would render the IBC unsafe for transport and no leakage.

6.5.6.9 Drop test

6.5.6.9.1 *Applicability*

For all types of IBCs, as a design type test.

6.5.6.9.2 *Preparation of the IBC for test*

    .1   Metal IBCs: the IBC shall be filled to not less than 95% of its maximum capacity for solids or 98% of its maximum capacity for liquids. Pressure relief devices shall be rendered inoperative or shall be removed and their apertures sealed.

    .2   Flexible IBCs: the IBC shall be filled to the maximum permissible gross mass, the contents being evenly distributed.

    .3   Rigid plastics and composite IBCs: the IBC shall be filled to not less than 95% of its maximum capacity for solids or 98% of its maximum capacity for liquids. Arrangements provided for pressure relief may be removed and sealed or rendered inoperative. Testing of IBCs shall be carried out when the temperature of the test sample and its contents has been reduced to −18°C or lower. Where test samples of composite IBCs are prepared in this way, the conditioning specified in 6.5.6.3.1 may be waived. Test liquids shall be kept in the liquid state, if necessary by the addition of anti-freeze. This conditioning may be disregarded if the materials in question are of sufficient ductility and tensile strength at low temperatures.

    .4   Fibreboard and wooden IBCs: the IBC shall be filled to not less than 95% of its maximum capacity.

6.5.6.9.3 *Method of testing*

The IBC shall be dropped on its base onto a non-resilient, horizontal, flat, massive and rigid surface in conformity with the requirements of 6.1.5.3.4, in such a manner as to ensure that the point of impact is that part of the base of the IBC considered to be the most vulnerable. IBCs of 0.45 m^3 or less capacity shall also be dropped:

    .1   Metal IBCs: on the most vulnerable part other than the part of the base of the IBC tested in the first drop;

    .2   Flexible IBCs: on the most vulnerable side;

6

.3   Rigid plastics, composite, fibreboard and wooden IBCs: flat on a side, flat on the top and on a corner.

The same or different IBCs may be used for each drop.

6.5.6.9.4   *Drop height*

For solids and liquids, if the test is performed with the solid or liquid to be transported or with another substance having essentially the same physical characteristics:

Packing group I	Packing group II	Packing group III
1.8 m	1.2 m	0.8 m

For liquids, if the test is performed with water:

(a)   where the substances to be transported have a relative density not exceeding 1.2:

Packing group II	Packing group III
1.2 m	0.8 m

(b)   where the substances to be transported have a relative density exceeding 1.2, the drop heights shall be calculated on the basis of the relative density (d) of the substance to be transported rounded up to the first decimal as follows:

Packing group II	Packing group III
$d \times 1.0$ m	$d \times 0.67$ m

6.5.6.9.5   *Criteria for passing the test(s)*

.1   Metal IBCs: no loss of contents.

.2   Flexible IBCs: no loss of contents. A slight discharge, such as from closures or stitch holes, upon impact shall not be considered to be a failure of the IBC provided that no further leakage occurs after the IBC has been raised clear of the ground.

.3   Rigid plastics, composite, fibreboard and wooden IBCs: no loss of contents. A slight discharge from a closure upon impact shall not be considered to be a failure of the IBC provided that no further leakage occurs.

.4   All IBCs: no damage which renders the IBC unsafe to be transported for salvage or for disposal, and no loss of contents. In addition, the IBC shall be capable of being lifted by an appropriate means until clear of the floor for five minutes.

Note: The criterion in 6.5.6.9.5.4 applies to design types for IBCs manufactured as from 1 January 2011.

6.5.6.10   Tear test

6.5.6.10.1   *Applicability*

For all types of flexible IBCs, as a design type test.

6.5.6.10.2   *Preparation of the IBC for test*

The IBC shall be filled to not less than 95% of its capacity and to its maximum permissible gross mass, the contents being evenly distributed.

6.5.6.10.3   *Method of testing*

Once the IBC is placed on the ground, a 100 mm knife score, completely penetrating the wall of a wide face, is made at a 45° angle to the principal axis of the IBC, halfway between the bottom surface and the top level of the contents. The IBC shall then be subjected to a uniformly distributed superimposed load equivalent to twice the maximum permissible gross mass. The load shall be applied for at least five minutes. An IBC which is designed to be lifted from the top or the side shall then, after removal of the superimposed load, be lifted until it is clear of the floor and maintained in that position for a period of five minutes.

6.5.6.10.4   *Criterion for passing the test*

The cut shall not propagate more than 25% of its original length.

6.5.6.11 **Topple test**

6.5.6.11.1 *Applicability*

For all types of flexible IBCs, as a design type test.

6.5.6.11.2 *Preparation of the IBC for test*

The IBC shall be filled to not less than 95% of its capacity and to its maximum permissible gross mass, the contents being evenly distributed.

6.5.6.11.3 *Method of testing*

The IBC shall be caused to topple onto any part of its top onto a rigid, non-resilient, smooth, flat and horizontal surface.

6.5.6.11.4 *Topple height*

Packing group I	Packing group II	Packing group III
1.8 m	1.2 m	0.8 m

6.5.6.11.5 *Criterion for passing the test*

No loss of contents. A slight discharge, such as from closures or stitch holes, upon impact shall not be considered to be a failure of the IBC provided that no further leakage occurs.

6.5.6.12 **Righting test**

6.5.6.12.1 *Applicability*

For all flexible IBCs designed to be lifted from the top or side, as a design type test.

6.5.6.12.2 *Preparation of the IBC for test*

The IBC shall be filled to not less than 95% of its capacity and its maximum permissible gross mass, the contents being evenly distributed.

6.5.6.12.3 *Method of testing*

The IBC, lying on its side, shall be lifted at a speed of 0.1 m/s to an upright position, clear of the floor, by one lifting device or by two lifting devices when four are provided.

6.5.6.12.4 *Criterion for passing the test*

No damage to the IBC or its lifting devices which renders the IBC unsafe for transport or handling.

6.5.6.13 **Vibration test**

6.5.6.13.1 *Applicability*

For all IBCs used for liquids, as a design type test.

Note: This test applies to design types for IBCs manufactured as from 1 January 2011.

6.5.6.13.2 *Preparation of the IBC for test*

A sample IBC shall be selected at random and shall be fitted and closed as for transport. The IBC shall be filled with water to not less than 98% of its maximum capacity.

6.5.6.13.3 *Test method and duration*

6.5.6.13.3.1 The IBC shall be placed in the centre of the test machine platform with a vertical sinusoidal, double amplitude (peak-to-peak displacement) of 25 mm ± 5%. If necessary, restraining devices shall be attached to the platform to prevent the specimen from moving horizontally off the platform without restricting vertical movement.

6.5.6.13.3.2 The test shall be conducted for one hour at a frequency that causes part of the base of the IBC to be momentarily raised from the vibrating platform for part of each cycle to such a degree that a metal shim can be completely inserted intermittently at, at least, one point between the base of the IBC and the test platform. The frequency may need to be adjusted after the initial set point to prevent the packaging from going into resonance. Nevertheless, the test frequency shall continue to allow placement of the metal shim under the IBC as described in this paragraph. The continuing ability to insert the metal shim is essential to passing the test. The metal shim used for this test shall be at least 1.6 mm thick, 50 mm wide, and be of sufficient length to be inserted between the IBC and the test platform a minimum of 100 mm to perform the test.

6.5.6.13.4 *Criteria for passing the test*

No leakage or rupture shall be observed. In addition, no breakage or failure of structural components, such as broken welds or failed fastenings, shall be observed.

6.5.6.14 **Test report**

6.5.6.14.1 A test report containing at least the following particulars shall be drawn up and shall be available to the users of the IBC:

.1   name and address of the test facility;

.2   name and address of applicant (where appropriate);

.3   a unique test report identification;

.4   date of the test report;

.5   manufacturer of the IBC;

.6   description of the IBC design type (such as dimensions, materials, closures, thickness, etc.), including method of manufacture (such as blow-moulding), and which may include drawing(s) and/or photograph(s);

.7   maximum capacity;

.8   characteristics of test contents, such as viscosity and relative density for liquids and particle size for solids;

.9   test descriptions and results; and

.10 signature, with the name and status of the signatory.

6.5.6.14.2 The test report shall contain statements that the IBC, prepared as for transport, was tested in accordance with the appropriate provisions of this chapter and that the use of other packaging methods or components may render it invalid. A copy of the test report shall be available to the competent authority.

Chapter 6.6

Provisions for the construction and testing of large packagings

6.6.1 General

6.6.1.1 The provisions of this chapter do not apply to:
- class 2, except articles including aerosols;
- class 6.2, except clinical waste of UN 3291;
- class 7 packages containing radioactive material.

6.6.1.2 Large packagings shall be manufactured, tested and remanufactured under a quality-assurance programme which satisfies the competent authority in order to ensure that each manufactured or remanufactured large packaging meets the provisions of this chapter.

Note: ISO 16106:2006, *Packaging – Transport packages for dangerous goods – Dangerous goods packagings, intermediate bulk containers (IBCs) and large packagings – Guidelines for the application of ISO 9001*, provides acceptable guidance on procedures which may be followed.

6.6.1.3 The specific requirements for large packagings in 6.6.4 are based on large packagings currently used. In order to take into account progress in science and technology, there is no objection to the use of large packagings having specifications different from those in 6.6.4 provided they are equally effective, acceptable to the competent authority and able successfully to withstand the tests described in 6.6.5. Methods of testing other than those prescribed in this Code are acceptable provided they are equivalent.

6.6.1.4 Manufacturers and subsequent distributors of packagings shall provide information regarding procedures to be followed and a description of the types and dimensions of closures (including required gaskets) and any other components needed to ensure that packages as presented for transport are capable of passing the applicable performance tests of this chapter.

6.6.2 Code for designating types of large packagings

6.6.2.1 The code used for large packagings consists of:

(a) two Arabic numerals:

"50" for rigid large packagings; or

"51" for flexible large packagings; and

(b) capital letters in Latin characters indicating the nature of the material, such as wood, steel, etc. The capital letters used shall be those shown in 6.1.2.6.

6.6.2.2 The letters "T" or "W" may follow the large packaging code. The letter "T" signifies a large salvage packaging conforming to the requirements of 6.6.5.1.9. The letter "W" signifies that the large packaging, although of the same type as indicated by the code, is manufactured to a specification different from those in 6.6.4 and is considered equivalent in accordance with the requirements in 6.6.1.3.

6.6.3 Marking

6.6.3.1 **Primary marking**

△ Each large packaging manufactured and intended for the use according to this Code shall bear marks which are durable, legible and placed in a location so as to be readily visible. Letters, numerals and symbols shall be at least 12 mm high and shall show:

(a) The United Nations packaging symbol:

△ This symbol shall not be used for any purpose other than certifying that a packaging, a flexible bulk container, a portable tank or a MEGC complies with the relevant requirements in chapters 6.1, 6.2, 6.3, 6.5, 6.6, 6.7 or 6.9. For metal large packagings on which the marks are stamped or embossed, the capital letters "UN" may apply instead of the symbol.

    (b)   The code "50" designating a large rigid packaging or "51" for flexible large packagings, followed by the material type in accordance with 6.5.1.4.1.2.

    (c)   A capital letter designating the packing group(s) for which the design type has been approved:

        "X" for packing groups I, II and III

        "Y" for packing groups II and III

        "Z" for packing group III only.

    (d)   The month and year (last two digits) of manufacture.

    (e)   The State authorizing the allocation of the marks, indicated by the distinguishing sign for motor vehicles in international traffic.

    (f)   The name or symbol of the manufacturer and other identification of the large packagings as specified by the competent authority.

    (g)   The stacking test load[*] in kilograms. For large packagings not designed for stacking, the figure "0" shall be shown.

    (h)   The maximum permissible gross mass in kilograms.

△ The primary mark required above shall be applied in the sequence of the subparagraphs. Each mark applied in accordance with subparagraphs (a) to (h) shall be clearly separated, such as by a slash or space, so as to be easily identifiable.

⊗

△ **6.6.3.2**   **Examples of marking**

 50A/X/05 01/N/PQRS 2500/1000 — For a large steel packaging suitable for stacking; stacking load: 2,500 kg; maximum gross mass: 1,000 kg.

 50AT/Y/05/01/B/PQRS 2500/1000 — For a large steel salvage packaging suitable for stacking; stacking load: 2,500 kg; maximum gross mass: 1,000 kg.

50H/Y/04 02/D/ABCD 987 0/800 — For a large plastics packaging not suitable for stacking; maximum gross mass: 800 kg.

 51H/Z/06 01/S/1999 0/500 — For a large flexible packaging not suitable for stacking; maximum gross mass: 500 kg.

6.6.3.3   The maximum permitted stacking load applicable when the large packaging is in use shall be displayed on a symbol as shown in the figures below. The symbol shall be durable and clearly visible.

Large packagings capable of being stacked   **Large packagings NOT capable of being stacked**

The minimum dimensions shall be 100 mm × 100 mm. The letters and numbers indicating the mass shall be at least 12 mm high. The area within the printer's marks indicated by the dimensional arrows shall be square. Where dimensions are not specified, all features shall be in approximate proportion to those shown. The mass marked above the symbol shall not exceed the load imposed during the design type test (see 6.6.5.3.3.4) divided by 1.8.

---

[*] The stacking test load in kilograms to be placed on the large packaging shall be 1.8 times the combined maximum permissible gross mass of the number of similar large packagings that may be stacked on top of the large packaging during transport (see 6.6.5.3.3.4).

Note: The provisions of 6.6.3.3 shall apply to all large packagings manufactured, repaired or remanufactured as from 1 January 2015. The provisions of 6.6.3.3 of the IMDG Code (amendment 36-12) may continue to be applied to all large packagings manufactured, repaired or remanufactured between 1 January 2015 and 31 December 2016.

6.6.4 Specific provisions for large packagings

6.6.4.1 Specific provisions for metal large packagings

    50A   steel

    50B   aluminium

    50N   metal (other than steel or aluminium)

6.6.4.1.1 The large packaging shall be made of suitable ductile metal in which the weldability has been fully demonstrated. Welds shall be skillfully made and afford complete safety. Low-temperature performance shall be taken into account when appropriate.

6.6.4.1.2 Care shall be taken to avoid damage by galvanic action due to the juxtaposition of dissimilar metals.

6.6.4.2 Specific provisions for flexible material large packagings

    51H   flexible plastics

    51M   flexible paper

6.6.4.2.1 The large packaging shall be manufactured from suitable materials. The strength of the material and the construction of the flexible large packaging shall be appropriate to its capacity and its intended use.

6.6.4.2.2 All materials used in the construction of flexible large packagings of types 51M shall, after complete immersion in water for not less than 24 hours, retain at least 85% of the tensile strength as measured originally on the material conditioned to equilibrium at 67% relative humidity or less.

6.6.4.2.3 Seams shall be formed by stitching, heat sealing, gluing or any equivalent method. All stitched seam-ends shall be secured.

6.6.4.2.4 Flexible large packagings shall provide adequate resistance to ageing and to degradation caused by ultraviolet radiation or the climatic conditions, or by the substance contained, thereby rendering them appropriate to their intended use.

6.6.4.2.5 For plastics flexible large packagings where protection against ultraviolet radiation is required, it shall be provided by the addition of carbon black or other suitable pigments or inhibitors. These additives shall be compatible with the contents and remain effective throughout the life of the large packaging. Where use is made of carbon black, pigments or inhibitors other than those used in the manufacture of the tested design type, re-testing may be waived if changes in the carbon black content, the pigment content or the inhibitor content do not adversely affect the physical properties of the material of construction.

6.6.4.2.6 Additives may be incorporated into the material of the large packaging to improve the resistance to ageing or to serve other purposes, provided that these do not adversely affect the physical or chemical properties of the material.

6.6.4.2.7 When filled, the ratio of height to width shall be not more than 2:1.

6.6.4.3 Specific provisions for plastics large packagings

    50H   rigid plastics

6.6.4.3.1 The large packaging shall be manufactured from suitable plastics material of known specifications and be of adequate strength in relation to its capacity and its intended use. The material shall be adequately resistant to ageing and to degradation caused by the substance contained or, where relevant, by ultraviolet radiation. Low-temperature performance shall be taken into account when appropriate. Any permeation of the substance contained shall not constitute a danger under normal conditions of transport.

6.6.4.3.2 Where protection against ultraviolet radiation is required, it shall be provided by the addition of carbon black or other suitable pigments or inhibitors. These additives shall be compatible with the contents and remain effective throughout the life of the outer packaging. Where use is made of carbon black, pigments or inhibitors other than those used in the manufacture of the tested design type, re-testing may be waived if changes in the carbon black content, the pigment content or the inhibitor content do not adversely affect the physical properties of the material of construction.

6.6.4.3.3 Additives may be incorporated into the material of the large packaging to improve the resistance to ageing or to serve other purposes, provided that these do not adversely affect the physical or chemical properties of the material.

6.6.4.4 Specific provisions for fibreboard large packagings

50G rigid fibreboard

6.6.4.4.1 Strong and good-quality solid or double-faced corrugated fibreboard (single or multiwall) shall be used, appropriate to the capacity of the large packagings and to their intended use. The water resistance of the outer surface shall be such that the increase in mass, as determined in a test carried out over a period of 30 minutes by the Cobb method of determining water absorption, is not greater than 155 g/m^2 – see ISO 535:1991. It shall have proper bending qualities. Fibreboard shall be cut, creased without scoring, and slotted so as to permit assembly without cracking, surface breaks or undue bending. The fluting of corrugated fibreboard shall be firmly glued to the facings.

6.6.4.4.2 The walls, including top and bottom, shall have a minimum puncture resistance of 15 J, measured according to ISO 3036:1975.

6.6.4.4.3 Manufacturing joins in the outer packaging of large packagings shall be made with an appropriate overlap and shall be taped, glued, stitched with metal staples or fastened by other means at least equally effective. Where joins are effected by gluing or taping, a water-resistant adhesive shall be used. Metal staples shall pass completely through all pieces to be fastened and be formed or protected so that any inner liner cannot be abraded or punctured by them.

6.6.4.4.4 Any integral pallet base forming part of a large packaging or any detachable pallet shall be suitable for mechanical handling with the large packaging filled to its maximum permissible gross mass.

6.6.4.4.5 The pallet or integral base shall be designed so as to avoid any protrusion of the base of the large packaging that might be liable to damage in handling.

6.6.4.4.6 The body shall be secured to any detachable pallet to ensure stability in handling and transport. Where a detachable pallet is used, its top surface shall be free from sharp protrusions that might damage the large packaging.

6.6.4.4.7 Strengthening devices such as timber supports to increase stacking performance may be used but shall be external to the liner.

6.6.4.4.8 Where large packagings are intended for stacking, the bearing surface shall be such as to distribute the load in a safe manner.

6.6.4.5 Specific provisions for wooden large packagings

50C natural wood

50D plywood

50F reconstituted wood

6.6.4.5.1 The strength of the materials used and the method of construction shall be appropriate to the capacity and intended use of the large packagings.

6.6.4.5.2 Natural wood shall be well seasoned, commercially dry and free from defects that would materially lessen the strength of any part of the large packaging. Each part of the large packaging shall consist of one piece or be equivalent thereto. Parts are considered equivalent to one piece when a suitable method of glued assembly is used, as for instance Lindermann joint, tongue and groove joint, ship lap or rabbet joint, or butt joint with at least two corrugated metal fasteners at each joint, or when other methods at least equally effective are used.

6.6.4.5.3 Large packagings of plywood shall be at least three-ply. They shall be made of well-seasoned rotary-cut, sliced or sawn veneer, commercially dry and free from defects that would materially lessen the strength of the large packaging. All adjacent plies shall be glued with water-resistant adhesive. Other suitable materials may be used with plywood for the construction of the large packaging.

6.6.4.5.4 Large packagings of reconstituted wood shall be made of water-resistant reconstituted wood such as hardboard, particle board or other suitable type.

6.6.4.5.5 Large packagings shall be firmly nailed or secured to corner posts or ends or be assembled by equally suitable devices.

6.6.4.5.6 Any integral pallet base forming part of a large packaging or any detachable pallet shall be suitable for mechanical handling with the large packaging filled to its maximum permissible gross mass.

6.6.4.5.7 The pallet or integral base shall be designed so as to avoid any protrusion of the base of the large packaging that might be liable to damage in handling.

6.6.4.5.8 The body shall be secured to any detachable pallet to ensure stability in handling and transport. Where a detachable pallet is used, its top surface shall be free from sharp protrusions that might damage the large packaging.

6.6.4.5.9 Strengthening devices such as timber supports to increase stacking performance may be used but shall be external to the liner.

6.6.4.5.10 Where large packagings are intended for stacking, the bearing surface shall be such as to distribute the load in a safe manner.

6.6.5 Test provisions for large packagings

6.6.5.1 Performance and frequency of test

6.6.5.1.1 The design type of each large packaging shall be tested as provided in 6.6.5.3 in accordance with procedures established by the competent authority.

6.6.5.1.2 Each large packaging design type shall successfully pass the tests prescribed in this chapter before being used. A large packaging design type is defined by the design, size, material and thickness, manner of construction and packing, but may include various surface treatments. It also includes large packagings that differ from the design type only in their lesser design height.

6.6.5.1.3 Tests shall be repeated on production samples at intervals established by the competent authority. For such tests on fibreboard large packagings, preparation at ambient conditions is considered equivalent to the provisions of 6.6.5.2.4.

6.6.5.1.4 Tests shall also be repeated after each modification which alters the design, material or manner of construction of large packagings.

6.6.5.1.5 The competent authority may permit the selective testing of large packagings that differ only in minor respects from a tested type, such as smaller sizes of inner packagings or inner packagings of lower net mass, and large packagings which are produced with small reductions in external dimension(s).

6.6.5.1.6 [Reserved]

Note: For the conditions for assembling different inner packagings in a large packaging and permissible variations in inner packagings, see 4.1.1.5.1.

6.6.5.1.7 The competent authority may at any time require proof, by tests in accordance with this section, that serially produced large packagings meet the provisions of the design type tests.

6.6.5.1.8 Provided the validity of the test results is not affected, and with the approval of the competent authority, several tests may be made on one sample.

6.6.5.1.9 *Large salvage packagings*

Large salvage packagings shall be tested and marked in accordance with the provisions applicable to packing group II large packagings intended for the transport of solids or inner packagings, except as follows:

(a) The test substance used in performing the tests shall be water, and the large salvage packagings shall be filled to not less than 98% of their maximum capacity. It is permissible to use additives, such as bags of lead shot, to achieve the requisite total package mass so long as they are placed so that the test results are not affected. Alternatively, in performing the drop test, the drop height may be varied in accordance with 6.6.5.3.4.4.2(b);

(b) Large salvage packagings shall, in addition, have been successfully subjected to the leakproofness test at 30 kPa, with the results of this test reflected in the test report required by 6.6.5.4.

(c) Large salvage packagings shall be marked with the letter "T" as described in 6.6.2.2.

6.6.5.2 Preparation for testing

6.6.5.2.1 Tests shall be carried out on large packagings prepared as for transport, including the inner packagings or articles used. Inner packagings shall be filled to not less than 98% of their maximum capacity for liquids or 95% for solids. For large packagings where the inner packagings are designed to carry liquids and solids, separate testing is required for both liquid and solid contents. The substances in the inner packagings or the articles to be transported in the large packagings may be replaced by other material or articles except where this would invalidate the results of the tests. When other inner packagings or articles are used, they shall have the same physical characteristics (mass, etc.) as the inner packagings or articles to be carried. It is permissible to use additives, such as bags of lead shot, to achieve the requisite total package mass, so long as they are placed so that the test results are not affected.

6.6.5.2.2 In the drop tests for liquids, when another substance is used, it shall be of similar relative density and viscosity to those of the substance being transported. Water may also be used for the liquid drop test under the conditions in 6.6.5.3.4.4.

6.6.5.2.3 Large packagings made of plastics materials and large packagings containing inner packagings of plastic materials – other than bags intended to contain solids or articles – shall be drop tested when the temperature of the test sample and its contents has been reduced to −18°C or lower. This conditioning may be disregarded if the materials in question are of sufficient ductility and tensile strength at low temperatures. Where test samples are prepared in this way, the conditioning in 6.6.5.2.4 may be waived. Test liquids shall be kept in the liquid state by the addition of anti-freeze if necessary.

6.6.5.2.4 Large packagings of fibreboard shall be conditioned for at least 24 hours in an atmosphere having a controlled temperature and relative humidity (r.h.). There are three options, one of which shall be chosen. The preferred atmosphere is 23°C±2°C and 50%±2% r.h. The two other options are 20°C±2°C and 65%±2% r.h. or 27°C±2°C and 65%±2% r.h.

Note: Average values shall fall within these limits. Short-term fluctuation and measurement limitations may cause individual measurements to vary by up to ±5% relative humidity without significant impairment of test reproducibility.

6.6.5.3 **Test provisions**

6.6.5.3.1 *Bottom lift test*

6.6.5.3.1.1 *Applicability*

For all types of large packagings which are fitted with means of lifting from the base, as a design type test.

6.6.5.3.1.2 *Preparation of large packaging for test*

The large packaging shall be filled to 1.25 times its maximum permissible gross mass, the load being evenly distributed.

6.6.5.3.1.3 *Method of testing*

The large packaging shall be raised and lowered twice by a lift truck with the forks centrally positioned and spaced at three quarters of the dimension of the side of entry (unless the points of entry are fixed). The forks shall penetrate to three quarters of the depth in the direction of entry. The test shall be repeated from each possible direction of entry.

6.6.5.3.1.4 *Criteria for passing the test*

No permanent deformation which renders the large packaging unsafe for transport and no loss of contents.

6.6.5.3.2 *Top lift test*

6.6.5.3.2.1 *Applicability*

For types of large packaging which are intended to be lifted from the top and fitted with means of lifting, as a design type test.

6.6.5.3.2.2 *Preparation of large packaging for test*

The large packaging shall be loaded to twice its maximum permissible gross mass. A flexible large packaging shall be loaded to six times its maximum permissible gross mass, the load being evenly distributed.

6.6.5.3.2.3 *Method of testing*

The large packaging shall be lifted in the manner for which it is designed until clear of the floor and maintained in that position for a period of five minutes.

6.6.5.3.2.4 *Criteria for passing the test*

   .1   Metal, rigid plastics and composite large packagings: no permanent deformation which renders the large packaging, including the base pallet, if any, unsafe for transport and no loss of contents.

   .2   Flexible large packagings: no damage to the large packaging or its lifting devices which renders the large packaging unsafe for transport or handling and no loss of contents.

6.6.5.3.3 *Stacking test*

6.6.5.3.3.1 *Applicability*

For all types of large packaging which are designed to be stacked on each other, as a design type test.

6.6.5.3.3.2 *Preparation of large packaging for test*

The large packaging shall be filled to its maximum permissible gross mass.

6.6.5.3.3.3 *Method of testing*

The large packaging shall be placed on its base on level hard ground and subjected to a uniformly distributed superimposed test load (see 6.6.5.3.3.4) for a period of at least five minutes: for large packaging of wood, fibreboard and plastics materials for a period of 24 hours.

6.6.5.3.3.4 *Calculation of superimposed test load*

The load to be placed on the large packaging shall be 1.8 times the combined maximum permissible gross mass of the number of similar large packagings that may be stacked on top of the large packaging during transport.

6.6.5.3.3.5 *Criteria for passing the test*

.1 All types of large packagings other than flexible large packagings: no permanent deformation which renders the large packaging, including the base pallet, if any, unsafe for transport and no loss of contents.

.2 Flexible large packagings: no deterioration of the body which renders the large packaging unsafe for transport and no loss of contents.

6.6.5.3.4 *Drop test*

6.6.5.3.4.1 *Applicability*

For all types of large packaging, as a design type test.

6.6.5.3.4.2 *Preparation of large packaging for testing*

The large packaging shall be filled in accordance with 6.6.5.2.1.

6.6.5.3.4.3 *Method of testing*

The large packaging shall be dropped onto a non-resilient, horizontal, flat, massive and rigid surface in conformity with the requirements of 6.1.5.3.4, in such a manner as to ensure that the point of impact is that part of the base of the large packaging considered to be the most vulnerable.

6.6.5.3.4.4 *Drop height*

Note: Large packagings for substances and articles of class 1 shall be tested at the packing group II performance level.

6.6.5.3.4.4.1 For inner packagings containing solid or liquid substances or articles, if the test is performed with the solid, liquid or articles to be transported, or with another substance or article having essentially the same characteristics:

Packing group I	Packing group II	Packing group III
1.8 m	1.2 m	0.8 m

6.6.5.3.4.4.2 For inner packagings containing liquids if the test is performed with water:

(a) Where the substances to be transported have a relative density not exceeding 1.2:

Packing group I	Packing group II	Packing group III
1.8 m	1.2 m	0.8 m

(b) Where the substances to be transported have a relative density exceeding 1.2, the drop height shall be calculated on the basis of the relative density (*d*) of the substance to be carried, rounded up to the first decimal, as follows:

Packing group I	Packing group II	Packing group III
$d \times 1.5$ m	$d \times 1.0$ m	$d \times 0.67$ m

6.6.5.3.4.5 *Criteria for passing the test*

6.6.5.3.4.5.1 The large packaging shall not exhibit any damage liable to affect safety during transport. There shall be no leakage of the filling substance from inner packaging(s) or article(s).

6.6.5.3.4.5.2 No rupture is permitted in a large packaging for articles of class 1 which would permit the spillage of loose explosive substances or articles from the large packaging.

6.6.5.3.4.5.3 Where a large packaging undergoes a drop test, the sample passes the test if the entire contents are retained even if the closure is no longer sift-proof.

6.6.5.4 **Certification and test report**

6.6.5.4.1 In respect of each design type of large packaging, a certificate and mark (as in 6.6.3) shall be issued attesting that the design type, including its equipment, meets the test provisions.

6.6.5.4.2 A test report containing at least the following particulars shall be drawn up and shall be available to the users of the large packaging:

.1 name and address of the test facility;

.2 name and address of applicant (where appropriate);

.3 a unique test report identification;

.4 date of the test report;

.5 manufacturer of the large packaging;

.6 description of the large packaging design type (such as dimensions, materials, closures, thickness, etc.) and/or photograph(s);

.7 maximum capacity/maximum permissible gross mass;

.8 characteristics of test contents, such as types and descriptions of inner packaging or articles used;

.9 test descriptions and results;

.10 the test report shall be signed with the name and status of the signatory.

6.6.5.4.3 The test report shall contain statements that the large packaging prepared as for transport was tested in accordance with the appropriate provisions of this chapter and that the use of other packaging methods or components may render it invalid. A copy of the test report shall be available to the competent authority.

Chapter 6.7

Provisions for the design, construction, inspection and testing of portable tanks and multiple-element gas containers (MEGCs)

Note: The provisions of this chapter also apply to road tank vehicles to the extent indicated in chapter 6.8.

6.7.1 Application and general provisions

6.7.1.1 The provisions of this chapter apply to portable tanks intended for the transport of dangerous goods, and to MEGCs intended for the transport of non-refrigerated gases of class 2, by all modes of transport. In addition to the provisions of this chapter, unless otherwise specified, the applicable provisions of the International Convention for Safe Containers (CSC) 1972, as amended, shall be fulfilled by any multimodal portable tank or MEGC which meets the definition of a "container" within the terms of that Convention. Additional provisions may apply to offshore portable tanks that are handled in open seas.

6.7.1.1.1 The International Convention for Safe Containers does not apply to offshore tank-containers that are handled in open seas. The design and testing of offshore tank-containers shall take into account the dynamic lifting and impact forces that may occur when a tank is handled in open seas in adverse weather and sea conditions. The provisions for such tanks shall be determined by the approving competent authority (see also MSC/Circ.860 "Guidelines for the approval of offshore containers handled in open seas").

6.7.1.2 In recognition of scientific and technological advances, the technical provisions of this chapter may be varied by alternative arrangements. These alternative arrangements shall offer a level of safety not less than that given by the provisions of this chapter with respect to the compatibility with substances transported and the ability of the portable tank to withstand impact, loading and fire conditions. For international transport, alternative arrangement portable tanks or MEGCs shall be approved by the applicable competent authorities.

6.7.1.3 When a substance is not assigned a portable tank instruction (T1 to T75) in the Dangerous Goods List in chapter 3.2, interim approval for transport may be issued by the competent authority of the country of origin. The approval shall be included in the documentation of the consignment and contain, as a minimum, the information normally provided in the portable tank instructions and the conditions under which the substance shall be transported. Appropriate measures shall be initiated by the competent authority to include the assignment in the Dangerous Goods List.

6.7.2 Provisions for the design, construction, inspection and testing of portable tanks intended for the transport of substances of class 1 and classes 3 to 9

6.7.2.1 Definitions

For the purposes of this section:

Design pressure means the pressure to be used in calculations required by a recognized pressure-vessel code. The design pressure shall be not less than the highest of the following pressures:

   .1   the maximum effective gauge pressure allowed in the shell during filling or discharge; or

   .2   the sum of:

      .1   the absolute vapour pressure (in bar) of the substance at 65°C (or at the highest temperature during filling, discharge or transport for substances which are filled, discharged or transported over 65°C), minus 1 bar;

      .2   the partial pressure (in bar) of air or other gases in the ullage space, being determined by a maximum ullage temperature of 65°C and a liquid expansion due to an increase in mean bulk temperature of $t_r - t_f$ (t_f = filling temperature, usually 15°C; t_r = 50°C, maximum mean bulk temperature); and

      .3   a head pressure determined on the basis of the static forces specified in 6.7.2.2.12, but not less than 0.35 bar.

   .3   two thirds of the minimum test pressure specified in the applicable portable tank instruction in 4.2.5.2.6;

Design temperature range for the shell shall be −40°C to 50°C for substances transported under ambient conditions. For the other substances filled, discharged or transported above 50°C, the design temperature shall not be less than the maximum temperature of the substance during filling, discharge or transport. More severe design temperatures shall be considered for portable tanks subjected to severe climatic conditions;

Fine grain steel means steel which has a ferritic grain size of 6 or finer when determined in accordance with ASTM E 112-96 or as defined in EN 10028-3, Part 3;

Fusible element means a non-reclosable pressure relief device that is thermally actuated;

Leakproofness test means a test using gas, subjecting the shell and its service equipment to an effective internal pressure of not less than 25% of the MAWP;

Maximum allowable working pressure (MAWP) means a pressure that shall be not less than the highest of the following pressures measured at the top of the shell while in operating position:

.1 the maximum effective gauge pressure allowed in the shell during filling or discharge; or

.2 the maximum effective gauge pressure to which the shell is designed, which shall be not less than the sum of:

    .1 the absolute vapour pressure (in bar) of the substance at 65°C (or at the highest temperature during filling, discharge or transport for substances which are filled, discharged or transported over 65°C) minus 1 bar; and

    .2 the partial pressure (in bar) of air or other gases in the ullage space, being determined by a maximum ullage temperature of 65°C and a liquid expansion due to an increase in mean bulk temperature of $t_r - t_f$ (t_f = filling temperature, usually 15°C; t_r = 50°C, maximum mean bulk temperature);

Maximum permissible gross mass (MPGM) means the sum of the tare mass of the portable tank and the heaviest load authorized for transport;

Mild steel means a steel with a guaranteed minimum tensile strength of 360 N/mm^2 to 440 N/mm^2 and a guaranteed minimum elongation at fracture conforming to 6.7.2.3.3.3;

Offshore portable tank means a portable tank specially designed for repeated use for transport of dangerous goods to, from and between offshore facilities. An offshore portable tank is designed and constructed in accordance with MSC/Circ.860 "Guidelines for the approval of containers handled in open seas";

Portable tank means a multimodal tank used for the transport of substances of class 1 and classes 3 to 9. The portable tank includes a shell fitted with service equipment and structural equipment necessary for the transport of dangerous substances. The portable tank shall be capable of being filled and discharged without the removal of its structural equipment. It shall possess stabilizing members external to the shell, and shall be capable of being lifted when full. It shall be designed primarily to be loaded onto a vehicle or ship and shall be equipped with skids, mountings or accessories to facilitate mechanical handling. Road tank-vehicles, rail tank-wagons, non-metallic tanks and intermediate bulk containers (IBCs) are not considered to fall within the definition for portable tanks;

Reference steel means a steel with a tensile strength of 370 N/mm^2 and an elongation at fracture of 27%;

Service equipment means measuring instruments and filling, discharge, venting, safety, heating, cooling and insulating devices;

Shell means the part of the portable tank which retains the substance intended for transport (tank proper), including openings and their closures, but does not include service equipment or external structural equipment;

Structural equipment means the reinforcing, fastening, protective and stabilizing members external to the shell;

Test pressure means the maximum gauge pressure at the top of the shell during the hydraulic pressure test, equal to not less than 1.5 times the design pressure. The minimum test pressure for portable tanks intended for specific substances is specified in the applicable portable tank instruction in 4.2.5.2.6.

6.7.2.2	General design and construction provisions

6.7.2.2.1 Shells shall be designed and constructed in accordance with the provisions of a pressure-vessel code recognized by the competent authority. Shells shall be made of metallic materials suitable for forming. The materials shall, in principle, conform to national or international material standards. For welded shells, only a material whose weldability has been fully demonstrated shall be used. Welds shall be skillfully made and afford complete safety. When the manufacturing process or the materials make it necessary, the shells shall be suitably heat-treated to guarantee adequate toughness in the weld and in the heat-affected zones. In choosing the material, the design temperature range shall be taken into account with respect to risk of brittle fracture, to stress corrosion cracking and to resistance to impact. When fine grain-steel is used, the guaranteed value of the yield strength shall be not more than 460 N/mm^2 and the guaranteed value of the upper limit of the tensile strength shall be not more than 725 N/mm^2 according to the material specification. Aluminium may only be used as a construction material when indicated in a portable tank special provision assigned to a specific substance in the Dangerous Goods List or when approved by the competent authority. When aluminium is authorized, it shall be insulated to prevent significant loss of physical properties when subjected to a heat load of 110 kW/m^2 for a period of not less than 30 minutes. The insulation shall remain effective at all temperatures less than 649°C and shall be jacketed with a material with a melting point of not less than 700°C. Portable tank materials shall be suitable for the external environment in which they may be transported.

6.7.2.2.2   Portable tank shells, fittings, and pipework shall be constructed from materials which are:

.1   substantially immune to attack by the substance(s) intended to be transported; or

.2   properly passivated or neutralized by chemical reaction; or

.3   lined with corrosion-resistant material directly bonded to the shell or attached by equivalent means.

6.7.2.2.3   Gaskets shall be made of materials not subject to attack by the substance(s) intended to be transported.

6.7.2.2.4   When shells are lined, the lining shall be substantially immune to attack by the substance(s) intended to be transported, homogeneous, non-porous, free from perforations, sufficiently elastic and compatible with the thermal expansion characteristics of the shell. The lining of every shell, shell fittings and piping shall be continuous, and shall extend around the face of any flange. Where external fittings are welded to the tank, the lining shall be continuous through the fitting and around the face of external flanges.

6.7.2.2.5   Joints and seams in the lining shall be made by fusing the material together or by other equally effective means.

6.7.2.2.6   Contact between dissimilar metals which could result in damage by galvanic action shall be avoided.

6.7.2.2.7   The materials of the portable tank, including any devices, gaskets, linings and accessories, shall not adversely affect the substance(s) intended to be transported in the portable tank.

6.7.2.2.8   Portable tanks shall be designed and constructed with supports to provide a secure base during transport and with suitable lifting and tie-down attachments.

6.7.2.2.9   Portable tanks shall be designed to withstand, without loss of contents, at least the internal pressure due to the contents and the static, dynamic and thermal loads during normal conditions of handling and transport. The design shall demonstrate that the effects of fatigue, caused by repeated application of these loads through the expected life of the portable tank, have been taken into account.

6.7.2.2.9.1   For portable tanks that are intended for use as offshore tank-containers, the dynamic stresses imposed by handling in open seas shall be taken into account.

6.7.2.2.10   A shell which is to be equipped with a vacuum-relief device shall be designed to withstand, without permanent deformation, an external pressure of not less than 0.21 bar above the internal pressure. The vacuum-relief device shall be set to relieve at a vacuum setting not greater than −0.21 bar unless the shell is designed for a higher external overpressure, in which case the vacuum-relief pressure of the device to be fitted shall be not greater than the tank design vacuum pressure. A shell used for the transport of solid substances of packing groups II or III only which do not liquefy during transport may be designed for a lower external pressure, subject to competent authority's approval. In this case, the vacuum-relief device shall be set to relieve at this lower pressure. A shell that is not to be fitted with a vacuum-relief device shall be designed to withstand, without permanent deformation, an external pressure of not less than 0.4 bar above the internal pressure.

6.7.2.2.11   Vacuum-relief devices used on portable tanks intended for the transport of substances meeting the flashpoint criteria of class 3, including elevated-temperature substances transported at or above their flashpoint, shall prevent the immediate passage of flame into the shell, or the portable tank shall have a shell capable of withstanding, without leakage, an internal explosion resulting from the passage of flame into the shell.

6.7.2.2.12   Portable tanks and their fastenings shall, under the maximum permissible load, be capable of absorbing the following separately applied static forces:

.1   in the direction of travel: twice the MPGM multiplied by the acceleration due to gravity (*g*);[*]

.2   horizontally at right angles to the direction of travel: the MPGM (when the direction of travel is not clearly determined, the forces shall be equal to twice the MPGM) multiplied by the acceleration due to gravity (*g*);[*]

.3   vertically upwards: the MPGM multiplied by the acceleration due to gravity (*g*);[*] and

---

[*] For calculation purposes, $g = 9.81$ m/s^2.

.4   vertically downwards: twice the MPGM (total loading including the effect of gravity) multiplied by the acceleration due to gravity (*g*).[*]

6.7.2.2.13   Under each of the forces in 6.7.2.2.12, the safety factor to be observed shall be as follows:

.1   for metals having a clearly defined yield point, a safety factor of 1.5 in relation to the guaranteed yield strength; or

.2   for metals with no clearly defined yield point, a safety factor of 1.5 in relation to the guaranteed 0.2% proof strength and, for austenitic steels, the 1% proof strength.

6.7.2.2.14   The value of yield strength or proof strength shall be the value according to national or international material standards. When austenitic steels are used, the specified minimum values of yield strength or proof strength according to the material standards may be increased by up to 15% when these greater values are attested in the material inspection certificate. When no material standard exists for the metal in question, the value of yield strength or proof strength used shall be approved by the competent authority.

6.7.2.2.15   Portable tanks shall be capable of being electrically earthed when intended for the transport of substances meeting the flashpoint criteria of class 3, including elevated-temperature substances transported above their flashpoint. Measures shall be taken to prevent dangerous electrostatic discharge.

6.7.2.2.16   When required for certain substances by the applicable portable tank instruction indicated in column 13 of the Dangerous Goods List, or by a portable tank special provision indicated in column 14, portable tanks shall be provided with additional protection, which may take the form of additional shell thickness or a higher test pressure, the additional shell thickness or higher test pressure being determined in the light of the inherent risks associated with the transport of the substances concerned.

6.7.2.2.17   Thermal insulation directly in contact with the shell intended for substances transported at elevated temperature shall have an ignition temperature at least 50°C higher than the maximum design temperature of the tank.

6.7.2.3   Design criteria

6.7.2.3.1   Shells shall be of a design capable of being stress-analysed mathematically or experimentally by resistance strain gauges, or by other methods approved by the competent authority.

6.7.2.3.2   Shells shall be designed and constructed to withstand a hydraulic test pressure not less than 1.5 times the design pressure. Specific provisions are laid down for certain substances in the applicable portable tank instruction indicated in column 13 of the Dangerous Goods List and described in 4.2.5 or by a portable tank special provision indicated in column 14 of the Dangerous Goods List and described in 4.2.5.3. The minimum shell thickness shall not be less than that specified for these tanks in 6.7.2.4.1 to 6.7.2.4.10.

6.7.2.3.3   For metals exhibiting a clearly defined yield point or characterized by a guaranteed proof strength (0.2% proof strength, generally, or 1% proof strength for austenitic steels), the primary membrane stress σ (sigma) in the shell shall not exceed $0.75R_e$ or $0.50R_m$, whichever is lower, at the test pressure, where:

R_e = yield strength in N/mm², or 0.2% proof strength or, for austenitic steels, 1% proof strength;

R_m = minimum tensile strength in N/mm².

6.7.2.3.3.1   The values of R_e and R_m to be used shall be the specified minimum values according to national or international material standards. When austenitic steels are used, the specified minimum values for R_e and R_m according to the material standards may be increased by up to 15% when these greater values are attested in the material inspection certificate. When no material standard exists for the metal in question, the values of R_e and R_m used shall be approved by the competent authority or its authorized body.

6.7.2.3.3.2   Steels which have a R_e/R_m ratio of more than 0.85 are not allowed for the construction of welded shells. The values of R_e and R_m to be used in determining this ratio shall be the values specified in the material inspection certificate.

6.7.2.3.3.3   Steels used in the construction of shells shall have an elongation at fracture, in %, of not less than $10,000/R_m$ with an absolute minimum of 16% for fine-grain steels and 20% for other steels. Aluminium and aluminium alloys used in the construction of shells shall have an elongation at fracture, in %, of not less than $10,000/6R_m$ with an absolute minimum of 12%.

6.7.2.3.3.4   For the purpose of determining actual values for materials, it shall be noted that for sheet metal, the axis of the tensile test specimen shall be at right angles (transversely) to the direction of rolling. The permanent elongation at fracture shall be measured on test specimens of rectangular cross-section in accordance with ISO 6892:1998 using a 50 mm gauge length.

6.7.2.4   **Minimum shell thickness**

6.7.2.4.1   The minimum shell thickness shall be the greater thickness based on:

.1   the minimum thickness determined in accordance with the provisions of 6.7.2.4.2 to 6.7.2.4.10;

.2   the minimum thickness determined in accordance with the recognized pressure-vessel code, including the provisions in 6.7.2.3; and

.3   the minimum thickness specified in the applicable portable tank instruction indicated in column 13 of the Dangerous Goods List, or by a portable tank special provision indicated in column 14.

6.7.2.4.2   The cylindrical portions, ends (heads) and manhole covers of shells not more than 1.80 m in diameter shall be not less than 5 mm thick in the reference steel or of equivalent thickness in the metal to be used. Shells more than 1.80 m in diameter shall be not less than 6 mm thick in the reference steel or of equivalent thickness in the metal to be used, except that for powdered or granular solid substances of packing group II or III the minimum thickness requirement may be reduced to not less than 5 mm thick in the reference steel or of equivalent thickness in the metal to be used.

6.7.2.4.3   When additional protection against shell damage is provided, portable tanks with test pressures less than 2.65 bar may have the minimum shell thickness reduced, in proportion to the protection provided, as approved by the competent authority. However, shells not more than 1.80 m in diameter shall be not less than 3 mm thick in the reference steel or of equivalent thickness in the metal to be used. Shells more than 1.80 m in diameter shall be not less than 4 mm thick in the reference steel or of equivalent thickness in the metal to be used.

6.7.2.4.4   The cylindrical portions, ends (heads) and manhole covers of all shells shall be not less than 3 mm thick regardless of the material of construction.

6.7.2.4.5   The additional protection referred to in 6.7.2.4.3 may be provided by overall external structural protection, such as suitable "sandwich" construction with the outer sheathing (jacket) secured to the shell, double-wall construction or by enclosing the shell in a complete framework with longitudinal and transverse structural members.

6.7.2.4.6   The equivalent thickness of a metal other than the thickness prescribed for the reference steel in 6.7.2.4.3 shall be determined using the following equation:

$$e_1 = \frac{21.4 \times e_0}{\sqrt[3]{R_{m1} \times A_1}}$$

where:

e_1 =   required equivalent thickness (in mm) of the metal to be used;

e_0 =   minimum thickness (in mm) of the reference steel specified in the applicable portable tank instruction or by a portable tank special provision indicated in column 13 or 14 of the Dangerous Goods List;

R_{m1} =   guaranteed minimum tensile strength (in N/mm^2) of the metal to be used (see 6.7.2.3.3);

A_1 =   guaranteed minimum elongation at fracture (in %) of the metal to be used according to national or international standards.

6.7.2.4.7   When, in the applicable portable tank instruction in 4.2.5.2.6, a minimum thickness of 8 mm, 10 mm or 12 mm is specified, it shall be noted that these thicknesses are based on the properties of the reference steel and a shell diameter of 1.80 m. When a metal other than mild steel (see 6.7.2.1) is used or the shell has a diameter of more than 1.80 m, the thickness shall be determined using the following equation:

$$e_1 = \frac{21.4 \times e_0 d_1}{1.8 \sqrt[3]{R_{m1} \times A_1}}$$

where:

e_1 =   required equivalent thickness (in mm) of the metal to be used;

e_0 =   minimum thickness (in mm) of the reference steel specified in the applicable portable tank instruction or by a portable tank special provision indicated in column 13 or 14 of the Dangerous Goods List;

d_1 =   diameter of the shell (in m), but not less than 1.80 m;

R_{m1} =   guaranteed minimum tensile strength (in N/mm^2) of the metal to be used (see 6.7.2.3.3);

A_1 =   guaranteed minimum elongation at fracture (in %) of the metal to be used according to national or international standards.

6.7.2.4.8   In no case shall the wall thickness be less than that prescribed in 6.7.2.4.2, 6.7.2.4.3 and 6.7.2.4.4. All parts of the shell shall have a minimum thickness as determined by 6.7.2.4.2 to 6.7.2.4.4. This thickness shall be exclusive of any corrosion allowance.

6.7.2.4.9   When mild steel is used (see 6.7.2.1), calculation using the equation in 6.7.2.4.6 is not required.

6.7.2.4.10   There shall be no sudden change of plate thickness at the attachment of the ends (heads) to the cylindrical portion of the shell.

6

6.7.2.5   Service equipment

6.7.2.5.1   Service equipment shall be so arranged as to be protected against the risk of being wrenched off or damaged during handling and transport. When the connection between the frame and the shell allows relative movement between the sub-assemblies, the equipment shall be so fastened as to permit such movement without risk of damage to working parts. The external discharge fittings (pipe sockets, shut-off devices), the internal stop-valve and its seating shall be protected against the danger of being wrenched off by external forces (for example, by using shear sections). The filling and discharge devices (including flanges or threaded plugs) and any protective caps shall be capable of being secured against unintended opening.

6.7.2.5.1.1   For offshore tank-containers, where positioning of service equipment and the design and strength of protection for such equipment is concerned, the increased danger of impact damage when handling such tanks in open seas shall be taken into account.

6.7.2.5.2   All openings in the shell, intended for filling or discharging the portable tank, shall be fitted with a manually operated stop-valve located as close to the shell as reasonably practicable. Other openings, except for openings leading to venting or pressure relief devices, shall be equipped with either a stop-valve or another suitable means of closure located as close to the shell as reasonably practicable.

6.7.2.5.3   All portable tanks shall be fitted with a manhole or other inspection openings of a suitable size to allow for internal inspection and adequate access for maintenance and repair of the interior. Compartmented portable tanks shall have a manhole or other inspection openings for each compartment.

6.7.2.5.4   As far as reasonably practicable, external fittings shall be grouped together. For insulated portable tanks, top fittings shall be surrounded by a spill-collection reservoir with suitable drains.

6.7.2.5.5   Each connection to a portable tank shall be clearly marked to indicate its function.

6.7.2.5.6   Each stop-valve or other means of closure shall be designed and constructed to a rated pressure not less than the MAWP of the shell, taking into account the temperatures expected during transport. All stop-valves with screwed spindles shall close by a clockwise motion of the handwheel. For other stop-valves, the position (open and closed) and direction of closure shall be clearly indicated. All stop-valves shall be designed to prevent unintentional opening.

6.7.2.5.7   No moving parts, such as covers, components of closures, etc., shall be made of unprotected corrodible steel when they are liable to come into frictional or percussive contact with aluminium portable tanks intended for the transport of substances meeting the flashpoint criteria of class 3, including elevated-temperature substances transported above their flashpoint.

6.7.2.5.8   Piping shall be designed, constructed and installed so as to avoid the risk of damage due to thermal expansion and contraction, mechanical shock and vibration. All piping shall be of a suitable metallic material. Welded pipe joints shall be used wherever possible.

6.7.2.5.9   Joints in copper tubing shall be brazed or have an equally strong metal union. The melting point of brazing materials shall be no lower than 525°C. The joints shall not decrease the strength of the tubing, as may happen when cutting threads.

6.7.2.5.10   The burst pressure of all piping and pipe fittings shall be not less than the highest of four times the MAWP of the shell or four times the pressure to which it may be subjected in service by the action of a pump or other device (except pressure relief devices).

6.7.2.5.11   Ductile metals shall be used in the construction of valves and accessories.

6.7.2.5.12   The heating system shall be designed or controlled so that a substance cannot reach a temperature at which the pressure in the tank exceeds its MAWP or causes other hazards (e.g. dangerous thermal decomposition).

6.7.2.5.13   The heating system shall be designed or controlled so that power for internal heating elements is not available unless the heating elements are completely submerged. The temperature at the surface of the heating elements for internal heating equipment or the temperature at the shell for external heating equipment shall, in no case, exceed 80% of the auto-ignition temperature (in °C) of the substances carried.

6.7.2.5.14   If an electrical heating system is installed inside the tank, it shall be equipped with an earth leakage circuit breaker with a releasing current of less than 100 mA.

6.7.2.5.15   Electrical switch cabinets mounted to tanks shall not have a direct connection to the tank interior and shall provide protection of at least the equivalent of IP 56 according to IEC 144 or IEC 529.

6.7.2.6   Bottom openings

6.7.2.6.1   Certain substances shall not be transported in portable tanks with bottom openings. When the applicable portable tank instruction identified in the Dangerous Goods List and described in 4.2.5.2.6 indicates that bottom openings are prohibited, there shall be no openings below the liquid level of the shell when it is filled to its maximum permissible filling limit. When an existing opening is closed, it shall be accomplished by internally and externally welding one plate to the shell.

6.7.2.6.2　Bottom discharge outlets for portable tanks carrying certain solid, crystallizable or highly viscous substances shall be equipped with not less than two serially fitted and mutually independent shut-off devices. The design of the equipment shall be to the satisfaction of the competent authority or its authorized body and shall include:

.1　an external stop-valve, fitted as close to the shell as reasonably practicable, and so designed as to prevent any unintended opening through impact or other inadvertent act; and

.2　a liquid-tight closure at the end of the discharge pipe, which may be a bolted blank flange or a screw cap.

6.7.2.6.3　Every bottom discharge outlet, except as provided in 6.7.2.6.2, shall be equipped with three serially fitted and mutually independent shut-off devices. The design of the equipment shall be to the satisfaction of the competent authority or its authorized body and include:

.1　a self-closing internal stop-valve, that is a stop-valve within the shell or within a welded flange or its companion flange, such that:

.1　the control devices for the operation of the valve are designed so as to prevent any unintended opening through impact or other inadvertent act;

.2　the valve may be operable from above or below;

.3　if possible, the setting of the valve (open or closed) shall be capable of being verified from the ground;

.4　except for portable tanks having a capacity of not more than 1000 L, it shall be possible to close the valve from an accessible position of the portable tank that is remote from the valve itself; and

.5　the valve shall continue to be effective in the event of damage to the external device for controlling the operation of the valve;

.2　an external stop-valve fitted as close to the shell as reasonably practicable; and

.3　a liquid-tight closure at the end of the discharge pipe, which may be a bolted blank flange or a screw cap.

6.7.2.6.4　For a lined shell, the internal stop-valve required by 6.7.2.6.3.1 may be replaced by an additional external stop-valve. The manufacturer shall satisfy the provisions of the competent authority or its authorized body.

6.7.2.7　Safety relief devices

6.7.2.7.1　All portable tanks shall be fitted with at least one pressure relief device. All relief devices shall be designed, constructed and marked to the satisfaction of the competent authority or its authorized body.

6.7.2.8　Pressure relief devices

6.7.2.8.1　Every portable tank with a capacity not less than 1900 L and every independent compartment of a portable tank with a similar capacity shall be provided with one or more pressure relief devices of the spring-loaded type and may in addition have a frangible disc or fusible element in parallel with the spring-loaded devices except when prohibited by reference to 6.7.2.8.3 in the applicable portable tank instruction in 4.2.5.2.6. The pressure relief devices shall have sufficient capacity to prevent rupture of the shell due to over-pressurization or vacuum resulting from filling, from discharging, or from heating of the contents.

6.7.2.8.2　Pressure relief devices shall be designed to prevent the entry of foreign matter, the leakage of liquid and the development of any dangerous excess pressure.

6.7.2.8.3　When required for certain substances by the applicable portable tank instruction identified in the Dangerous Goods List and described in 4.2.5.2.6, portable tanks shall have a pressure relief device approved by the competent authority. Unless a portable tank in dedicated service is fitted with an approved relief device constructed of materials compatible with the load, the relief device shall comprise a frangible disc preceding a spring-loaded pressure relief device. When a frangible disc is inserted in series with the required pressure relief device, the space between the frangible disc and the pressure relief device shall be provided with a pressure gauge or suitable tell-tale indicator for the detection of disc rupture, pinholing, or leakage which could cause a malfunction of the pressure relief system. The frangible disc shall rupture at a nominal pressure 10% above the start-to-discharge pressure of the relief device.

6.7.2.8.4　Every portable tank with a capacity less than 1900 L shall be fitted with a pressure relief device, which may be a frangible disc when this disc complies with the provisions of 6.7.2.11.1. When no spring-loaded pressure relief device is used, the frangible disc shall be set to rupture at a nominal pressure equal to the test pressure. In addition, fusible elements conforming to 6.7.2.10.1 may also be used.

6.7.2.8.5　When the shell is fitted for pressure discharge, the inlet line shall be provided with a suitable pressure relief device set to operate at a pressure not higher than the MAWP of the shell, and a stop-valve shall be fitted as close to the shell as reasonably practicable.

6

6.7.2.9 **Setting of pressure relief devices**

6.7.2.9.1 It shall be noted that the pressure relief devices shall operate only in conditions of excessive rise in temperature, since the shell shall not be subject to undue fluctuations of pressure during normal conditions of transport (see 6.7.2.12.2).

6.7.2.9.2 The required pressure relief device shall be set to start to discharge at a nominal pressure of five sixths of the test pressure for shells having a test pressure of not more than 4.5 bar and 110% of two thirds of the test pressure for shells having a test pressure of more than 4.5 bar. After discharge, the device shall close at a pressure not more than 10% below the pressure at which the discharge starts. The device shall remain closed at all lower pressures. This requirement does not prevent the use of vacuum relief or combination pressure relief and vacuum relief devices.

6.7.2.10 **Fusible elements**

6.7.2.10.1 Fusible elements shall operate at a temperature between 100°C and 149°C on condition that the pressure in the shell at the fusing temperature will be not more than the test pressure. They shall be placed at the top of the shell with their inlets in the vapour space, and when used for transport safety purposes, they shall not be shielded from external heat. Fusible elements shall not be used on portable tanks with a test pressure which exceeds 2.65 bar unless specified by special provision TP36 in column 14 of the Dangerous Goods List of chapter 3.2. Fusible elements used on portable tanks intended for the transport of elevated-temperature substances shall be designed to operate at a temperature higher than the maximum temperature that will be experienced during transport and shall be to the satisfaction of the competent authority or its authorized body.

6.7.2.11 **Frangible discs**

6.7.2.11.1 Except as specified in 6.7.2.8.3, frangible discs shall be set to rupture at a nominal pressure equal to the test pressure throughout the design temperature range. Particular attention shall be given to the provisions of 6.7.2.5.1 and 6.7.2.8.3 if frangible discs are used.

6.7.2.11.2 Frangible discs shall be appropriate for the vacuum pressures which may be produced in the portable tank.

6.7.2.12 **Capacity of pressure relief devices**

6.7.2.12.1 The spring-loaded pressure relief device required by 6.7.2.8.1 shall have a minimum cross-sectional flow area equivalent to an orifice of 31.75 mm diameter. Vacuum relief devices, when used, shall have a cross-sectional flow area not less than 284 mm^2.

6.7.2.12.2 The combined delivery capacity of the pressure relief system (taking into account the reduction of the flow when the portable tank is fitted with frangible discs preceding spring-loaded pressure relief devices or when the spring-loaded pressure relief devices are provided with a device to prevent the passage of the flame), in conditions of complete fire engulfment of the portable tank shall be sufficient to limit the pressure in the shell to 20% above the start-to-discharge pressure of the pressure-limiting device. Emergency pressure relief devices may be used to achieve the full relief capacity prescribed. These devices may be fusible, spring-loaded or frangible disc components, or a combination of spring-loaded and frangible disc devices. The total required capacity of the relief devices may be determined using the formula in 6.7.2.12.2.1 or the table in 6.7.2.12.2.3.

6.7.2.12.2.1 To determine the total required capacity of the relief devices, which shall be regarded as being the sum of the individual capacities of all the contributing devices, the following formula shall be used:

$$Q = 12.4 \frac{FA^{0.82}}{LC} \sqrt{\frac{ZT}{M}}$$

where:

Q = minimum required rate of discharge in cubic metres of air per second (m^3/s) at standard conditions: 1 bar and 0°C (273 K);

F = a coefficient with the following value:

    for uninsulated shells, $F = 1$

    for insulated shells, $F = U(649 - t)/13.6$ but in no case is less than 0.25

    where:

        U = thermal conductance of the insulation, in kW·m^{-2}·K^{-1}, at 38°C;

        t = actual temperature of the substance during filling (in °C) (when this temperature is unknown, let $t = 15$°C);

    The value of F given above for insulated shells may be taken provided that the insulation is in conformance with 6.7.2.12.2.4;

A = total external surface area of shell in square metres;

Z = the gas compressibility factor in the accumulating condition (when this factor is unknown, let Z equal 1.0);

T = absolute temperature in kelvin (°C + 273) above the pressure relief devices in the accumulating condition;

L = the latent heat of vaporization of the liquid, in kJ/kg, in the accumulating condition;

M = molecular mass of the discharged gas;

C = a constant which is derived from one of the following formulae as a function of the ratio k of specific heats:

$$k = \frac{C_p}{C_v}$$

where:

C_p = specific heat at constant pressure; and

C_v = specific heat at constant volume.

When $k > 1$:

$$C = \sqrt{k \left(\frac{2}{k+1}\right)^{\frac{k+1}{k-1}}}$$

When $k = 1$ or k is unknown:

$$C = \frac{1}{\sqrt{e}} = 0.607$$

where e is the mathematical constant 2.7183.

C may also be taken from the following table:

k	C	k	C	k	C
1.00	0.607	1.26	0.660	1.52	0.704
1.02	0.611	1.28	0.664	1.54	0.707
1.04	0.615	1.30	0.667	1.56	0.71
1.06	0.620	1.32	0.671	1.58	0.713
1.08	0.624	1.34	0.674	1.60	0.716
1.10	0.628	1.36	0.678	1.62	0.719
1.12	0.633	1.38	0.681	1.64	0.722
1.14	0.637	1.40	0.685	1.66	0.725
1.16	0.641	1.42	0.688	1.68	0.728
1.18	0.645	1.44	0.691	1.70	0.731
1.20	0.649	1.46	0.695	2.0	0.77
1.22	0.652	1.48	0.698	2.2	0.793
1.24	0.656	1.50	0.701		

6.7.2.12.2.2 As an alternative to the formula above, shells designed for the transport of liquids may have their relief devices sized in accordance with the table in 6.7.2.12.2.3. This table assumes an insulation value of $F = 1$ and shall be adjusted accordingly when the shell is insulated. Other values used in determining this table are:

$M = 86.7$; $\quad T = 394$ K; $\quad L = 334.94$ kJ/kg; $\quad C = 0.607$; $\quad Z = 1$

6.7.2.12.2.3 Minimum required rate of discharge, Q, in cubic metres of air per second at 1 bar and 0°C (273 K):

A Exposed area (square metres)	Q (cubic metres of air per second)	A Exposed area (square metres)	Q (cubic metres of air per second)
2	0.230	14	1.132
3	0.320	16	1.263
4	0.405	18	1.391
5	0.487	20	1.517
6	0.565	22.5	1.670
7	0.641	25	1.821
8	0.715	27.5	1.969
9	0.788	30	2.115
10	0.859	32.5	2.258
12	0.998	35	2.400

6

A Exposed area (square metres)	Q (cubic metres of air per second)	A Exposed area (square metres)	Q (cubic metres of air per second)
37.5	2.539	62.5	3.860
40	2.677	65	3.987
42.5	2.814	67.5	4.112
45	2.949	70	4.236
47.5	3.082	75	4.483
50	3.215	80	4.726
52.5	3.346	85	4.967
55	3.476	90	5.206
57.5	3.605	95	5.442
60	3.733	100	5.676

6.7.2.12.2.4 Insulation systems, used for the purpose of reducing venting capacity, shall be approved by the competent authority or its authorized body. In all cases, insulation systems approved for this purpose shall:

(a) remain effective at all temperatures up to 649°C; and

(b) be jacketed with a material having a melting point of 700°C or greater.

6.7.2.13 **Marking of pressure relief devices**

6.7.2.13.1 Every pressure relief device shall be clearly and permanently marked with the following:

.1 the pressure (in bar or kPa) or temperature (in °C) at which it is set to discharge;

.2 the allowable tolerance at the discharge pressure, for spring-loaded devices;

.3 the reference temperature corresponding to the rated pressure, for frangible discs;

.4 the allowable temperature tolerance, for fusible elements;

.5 the rated flow capacity of the spring-loaded pressure relief devices, frangible discs or fusible elements in standard cubic metres of air per second (m^3/s); and

.6 the cross sectional flow areas of the spring-loaded pressure relief devices, frangible discs and fusible elements in mm^2.

When practicable, the following information shall also be shown:

.7 the manufacturer's name and relevant catalogue number.

6.7.2.13.2 The rated flow capacity marked on the spring-loaded pressure relief devices shall be determined according to ISO 4126-1:2004 and ISO 4126-7:2004.

6.7.2.14 **Connections to pressure relief devices**

6.7.2.14.1 Connections to pressure relief devices shall be of sufficient size to enable the required discharge to pass unrestricted to the safety device. No stop-valve shall be installed between the shell and the pressure relief devices except where duplicate devices are provided for maintenance or other reasons and the stop-valves serving the devices actually in use are locked open or the stop-valves are interlocked so that at least one of the duplicate devices is always in use. There shall be no obstruction in an opening leading to a vent or pressure relief device which might restrict or cut off the flow from the shell to that device. Vents or pipes from the pressure relief device outlets, when used, shall deliver the relieved vapour or liquid to the atmosphere in conditions of minimum back-pressure on the relieving devices.

6.7.2.15 **Siting of pressure relief devices**

6.7.2.15.1 Each pressure relief device inlet shall be situated on top of the shell in a position as near the longitudinal and transverse centre of the shell as reasonably practicable. All pressure relief device inlets shall, under maximum filling conditions, be situated in the vapour space of the shell and the devices shall be so arranged as to ensure the escaping vapour is discharged unrestrictedly. For flammable substances, the escaping vapour shall be directed away from the shell in such a manner that it cannot impinge upon the shell. Protective devices which deflect the flow of vapour are permissible provided the required relief-device capacity is not reduced.

6.7.2.15.2   Arrangements shall be made to prevent access to the pressure relief devices by unauthorized persons and to protect the devices from damage caused by the portable tank overturning.

6.7.2.16   **Gauging devices**

6.7.2.16.1   Glass level-gauges and gauges made of other fragile material, which are in direct communication with the contents of the tank, shall not be used.

6.7.2.17   **Portable tank supports, frameworks, lifting and tie-down attachments**

6.7.2.17.1   Portable tanks shall be designed and constructed with a support structure to provide a secure base during transport. The forces specified in 6.7.2.2.12 and the safety factor specified in 6.7.2.2.13 shall be considered in this aspect of the design. Skids, frameworks, cradles or other similar structures are acceptable.

6.7.2.17.2   The combined stresses caused by portable tank mountings (such as cradles, framework, etc.) and portable tank lifting and tie-down attachments shall not cause excessive stress in any portion of the shell. Permanent lifting and tie-down attachments shall be fitted to all portable tanks. Preferably they shall be fitted to the portable tank supports but may be secured to reinforcing plates located on the shell at the points of support.

6.7.2.17.3   In the design of supports and frameworks, the effects of environmental corrosion shall be taken into account.

6.7.2.17.4   Forklift pockets shall be capable of being closed off. The means of closing forklift pockets shall be a permanent part of the framework or permanently attached to the framework. Single-compartment portable tanks with a length less than 3.65 m need not have closed-off forklift pockets provided that:

.1   the shell, including all the fittings, is well protected from being hit by the forklift blades; and

.2   the distance between the centres of the forklift pockets is at least half of the maximum length of the portable tank.

6.7.2.17.5   When portable tanks are not protected during transport, according to 4.2.1.2, the shells and service equipment shall be protected against damage to the shell and service equipment resulting from lateral or longitudinal impact or overturning. External fittings shall be protected so as to preclude the release of the shell contents upon impact or overturning of the portable tank on its fittings. Examples of protection include:

.1   protection against lateral impact, which may consist of longitudinal bars protecting the shell on both sides at the level of the median line;

.2   protection of the portable tank against overturning, which may consist of reinforcement rings or bars fixed across the frame;

.3   protection against rear impact, which may consist of a bumper or frame;

.4   protection of the shell against damage from impact or overturning by use of an ISO frame in accordance with ISO 1496-3:1995.

6.7.2.18   **Design approval**

6.7.2.18.1   The competent authority or its authorized body shall issue a design approval certificate for any new design of a portable tank. This certificate shall attest that a portable tank has been surveyed by that authority, is suitable for its intended purpose and meets the provisions of this chapter and, where appropriate, the provisions for substances provided in chapter 4.2 and in the Dangerous Goods List in chapter 3.2. When a series of portable tanks are manufactured without change in the design, the certificate shall be valid for the entire series. The certificate shall refer to the prototype test report, the substances or group of substances allowed to be transported, the materials of construction of the shell and lining (when applicable) and an approval number. The approval number shall consist of the distinguishing sign or mark of the State in whose territory the approval was granted, i.e. the distinguishing sign for use in international traffic as prescribed by the Convention on Road Traffic, Vienna, 1968, and a registration number. Any alternative arrangements according to 6.7.1.2 shall be indicated on the certificate. A design approval may serve for the approval of smaller portable tanks made of materials of the same kind and thickness, by the same fabrication techniques and with identical supports, equivalent closures and other appurtenances.

6.7.2.18.2   The prototype test report for the design approval shall include at least the following:

.1   the results of the applicable framework test specified in ISO 1496-3:1995;

.2   the results of the initial inspection and test in 6.7.2.19.3; and

.3   the results of the impact test in 6.7.2.19.1, when applicable.

6.7.2.19   **Inspection and testing**

6.7.2.19.1   Portable tanks meeting the definition of *container* in the International Convention for Safe Containers (CSC), 1972, as amended, shall not be used unless they are successfully qualified by subjecting a representative

6

prototype of each design to the Dynamic, Longitudinal Impact Test prescribed in the Manual of Tests and Criteria, part IV, section 41. This provision only applies to portable tanks which are constructed according to a design approval certificate which has been issued on or after 1 January 2008.

6.7.2.19.2　The shell and items of equipment of each portable tank shall be inspected and tested before being put into service for the first time (initial inspection and test) and thereafter at not more than five-year intervals (5-year periodic inspection and test) with an intermediate periodic inspection and test (2.5-year periodic inspection and test) midway between the 5-year periodic inspections and tests. The 2.5-year periodic inspection and test may be performed within 3 months of the specified date. An exceptional inspection and test shall be performed regardless of the date of the last periodic inspection and test when necessary according to 6.7.2.19.7.

6.7.2.19.3　The initial inspection and test of a portable tank shall include a check of the design characteristics, an internal and external examination of the portable tank and its fittings with due regard to the substances to be transported, and a pressure test. Before the portable tank is placed into service, a leakproofness test and a test of the satisfactory operation of all service equipment shall also be performed. When the shell and its fittings have been pressure-tested separately, they shall be subjected together after assembly to a leakproofness test.

6.7.2.19.4　The 5-year periodic inspection and test shall include an internal and external examination and, as a general rule, a hydraulic pressure test. For tanks only used for the transport of solid substances other than toxic or corrosive substances, which do not liquefy during transport, the hydraulic pressure test may be replaced by a suitable pressure test at 1.5 times MAWP, subject to competent authority approval. Sheathing, thermal insulation and the like shall be removed only to the extent required for reliable appraisal of the condition of the portable tank. When the shell and equipment have been pressure-tested separately, they shall be subjected together after assembly to a leakproofness test.

6.7.2.19.4.1　The heating system shall be subject to inspection and tests including pressure tests on heating coils or ducts during the 5-year periodic inspection.

6.7.2.19.5　The intermediate 2.5-year periodic inspection and test shall at least include an internal and external examination of the portable tank and its fittings with due regard to the substances intended to be transported, a leakproofness test and a test of the satisfactory operation of all service equipment. Sheathing, thermal insulation and the like shall be removed only to the extent required for reliable appraisal of the condition of the portable tank. For portable tanks dedicated to the transport of a single substance, the 2.5-year internal examination may be waived or substituted by other test methods or inspection procedures specified by the competent authority or its authorized body.

6.7.2.19.6　A portable tank may not be filled and offered for transport after the date of expiry of the last 5-year or 2.5-year periodic inspection and test as required by 6.7.2.19.2. However, a portable tank filled prior to the date of expiry of the last periodic inspection and test may be transported for a period not to exceed three months beyond the date of expiry of the last periodic test or inspection. In addition, a portable tank may be transported after the date of expiry of the last periodic test and inspection:

.1　after emptying but before cleaning, for purposes of performing the next required test or inspection prior to refilling; and

.2　unless otherwise approved by the competent authority, for a period not to exceed six months beyond the date of expiry of the last periodic test or inspection, in order to allow the return of dangerous goods for proper disposal or recycling. Reference to this exemption shall be mentioned in the transport document.

6.7.2.19.7　The exceptional inspection and test is necessary when the portable tank shows evidence of damaged or corroded areas, or leakage, or other conditions that indicate a deficiency that could affect the integrity of the portable tank. The extent of the exceptional inspection and test shall depend on the amount of damage or deterioration of the portable tank. It shall include at least the 2.5-year periodic inspection and test according to 6.7.2.19.5.

6.7.2.19.8　The internal and external examinations shall ensure that:

△ .1　the shell is inspected for pitting, corrosion, or abrasions, dents, distortions, defects in welds or any other conditions, including leakage, that might render the portable tank unsafe for transport. The wall thickness shall be verified by appropriate measurement if this inspection indicates a reduction of wall thickness;

.2　the piping, valves, heating/cooling system, and gaskets are inspected for corroded areas, defects, or any other conditions, including leakage, that might render the portable tank unsafe for filling, discharge or transport;

.3　devices for tightening manhole covers are operative and there is no leakage at manhole covers or gaskets;

.4　missing or loose bolts or nuts on any flanged connection or blank flange are replaced or tightened;

.5　all emergency devices and valves are free from corrosion, distortion and any damage or defect that could prevent their normal operation. Remote closure devices and self-closing stop-valves shall be operated to demonstrate proper operation;

.6   linings, if any, are inspected in accordance with criteria outlined by the lining manufacturer;

△ .7   required marks on the portable tank are legible and in accordance with the applicable provisions; and

.8   the framework, supports and arrangements for lifting the portable tank are in a satisfactory condition.

6.7.2.19.9   The inspections and tests in 6.7.2.19.1, 6.7.2.19.3, 6.7.2.19.4, 6.7.2.19.5 and 6.7.2.19.7 shall be performed or witnessed by an expert approved by the competent authority or its authorized body. When the pressure test is a part of the inspection and test, the test pressure shall be the one indicated on the data plate of the portable tank. While under pressure, the portable tank shall be inspected for any leaks in the shell, piping or equipment.

6.7.2.19.10   In all cases when cutting, burning or welding operations on the shell have been effected, that work shall be to the approval of the competent authority or its authorized body, taking into account the pressure-vessel code used for the construction of the shell. A pressure test to the original test pressure shall be performed after the work is completed.

6.7.2.19.11   When evidence of any unsafe condition is discovered, the portable tank shall not be returned to service until it has been corrected and the test is repeated and passed.

6.7.2.20   Marking

6.7.2.20.1   Every portable tank shall be fitted with a corrosion-resistant metal plate permanently attached to the portable tank in a conspicuous place readily accessible for inspection. When for reasons of portable tank arrangements the plate cannot be permanently attached to the shell, the shell shall be marked with at least the information required by the pressure-vessel code. As a minimum, at least the following information shall be marked on the plate by stamping or by any other similar method:

(a)   Owner information

   (i)   Owner's registration number;

(b)   Manufacturing information

   (i)   Country of manufacture;

   (ii)   Year of manufacture;

   (iii)   Manufacturer's name or mark;

   (iv)   Manufacturer's serial number;

(c)   Approval information

   (i)   The United Nations packaging symbol:

   This symbol shall not be used for any purpose other than certifying that a packaging, a flexible bulk container, a portable tank or a MEGC complies with the relevant requirements in chapters 6.1, 6.2, 6.3, 6.5, 6.6, 6.7 or 6.9;

   (ii)   Approval country;

   (iii)   Authorized body for the design approval;

   (iv)   Design approval number;

   (v)   Letters "AA", if the design was approved under alternative arrangements (see 6.7.1.2);

   (vi)   Pressure-vessel code to which the shell is designed;

(d)   Pressures

   (i)   MAWP (in bar gauge or kPa gauge);[*]

   (ii)   Test pressure (in bar gauge or kPa gauge);[*]

   (iii)   Initial pressure test date (month and year);

   (iv)   Identification mark of the initial pressure test witness;

   (v)   External design pressure[†] (in bar gauge or kPa gauge);[*]

   (vi)   MAWP for heating/cooling system (in bar gauge or kPa gauge)[*] (when applicable);

(e)   Temperatures

   (i)   Design temperature range (in °C);[*]

(f)   Materials

   (i)   Shell material(s) and material standard reference(s);

   (ii)   Equivalent thickness in reference steel (in mm);[*] and

   (iii)   Lining material (when applicable);

---

[*] The unit used shall be indicated.

[†] See 6.7.2.2.10.

(g) Capacity

    (i) Tank water capacity at 20°C (in litres);[*]

        This indication is to be followed by the symbol "S" when the shell is divided by surge plates into sections of not more than 7,500 litres capacity;

    (ii) Water capacity of each compartment at 20°C (in litres)[*] (when applicable, for multi-compartment tanks).

        This indication is to be followed by the symbol "S" when the compartment is divided by surge plates into sections of not more than 7,500 litres capacity;

(h) Periodic inspections and tests

    (i) Type of the most recent periodic test (2.5-year, 5-year or exceptional);

    (ii) Date of the most recent periodic test (month and year);

    (iii) Test pressure (in bar gauge or kPa gauge)[*] of the most recent periodic test (if applicable);

    (iv) Identification mark of the authorized body who performed or witnessed the most recent test.

Figure 6.7.2.20.1 – *Example of a plate for marking*

Owner's registration number			
MANUFACTURING INFORMATION			
Country of manufacture			
Year of manufacture			
Manufacturer			
Manufacturer's serial number			
APPROVAL INFORMATION			
Approval country			
Authorized body for design approval			
Design approval number		"AA" *(if applicable)*	
Shell design code (pressure-vessel code)			
PRESSURES			
MAWP		bar *or* kPa	
Test pressure		bar *or* kPa	
Initial pressure test date:	*(mm/yyyy)*	Witness stamp:	
External design pressure		bar *or* kPa	
MAWP for heating/cooling system *(when applicable)*		bar *or* kPa	
TEMPERATURES			
Design temperature range		°C to °C	
MATERIALS			
Shell material(s) and material standard reference(s)			
Equivalent thickness in reference steel		mm	
Lining material *(when applicable)*			
CAPACITY			
Tank water capacity at 20°C		litres	"S" *(if applicable)*
Water capacity of compartment ___ at 20°C *(when applicable, for multi-compartment tanks)*		litres	"S" *(if applicable)*

[*] The unit used shall be indicated.

PERIODIC INSPECTIONS/TESTS							
Test type	Test date	Witness stamp and test pressure[a]		Test type	Test date	Witness stamp and test pressure[a]	
	(mm/yyyy)		bar *or* kPa		*(mm/yyyy)*		bar *or* kPa

[a] Test pressure if applicable.

6.7.2.20.2 The following information shall be durably marked either on the portable tank itself or on a metal plate firmly secured to the portable tank:

Name of the operator

Maximum permissible gross mass (MPGM) . . . . kg

Unladen (tare) mass . . . . kg

Portable tank instruction in accordance with 4.2.5.2.6.

6.7.2.20.3 If a portable tank is designed and approved for handling in open seas, the words "OFFSHORE PORTABLE TANK" shall be marked on the identification plate.

6.7.3 Provisions for the design, construction, inspection and testing of portable tanks intended for the transport of non-refrigerated liquefied gases of class 2

Note: These requirements also apply to portable tanks intended for the transport of chemicals under pressure (UN Nos. 3500, 3501, 3502, 3503, 3504 and 3505).

6.7.3.1 Definitions

For the purposes of this section:

Design pressure means the pressure to be used in calculations required by a recognized pressure-vessel code. The design pressure shall be not less than the highest of the following pressures:

.1   the maximum effective gauge pressure allowed in the shell during filling or discharge; or

.2   the sum of:

.1   the maximum effective gauge pressure to which the shell is designed, as defined in .2 of the MAWP definition (see below); and

.2   a head pressure determined on the basis of the static forces specified in 6.7.3.2.9, but not less than 0.35 bar;

Design reference temperature means the temperature at which the vapour pressure of the contents is determined for the purpose of calculating the MAWP. The design reference temperature shall be less than the critical temperature of the non-refrigerated liquefied gas or liquefied gas propellants of chemicals under pressure intended to be transported to ensure that the gas at all times is liquefied. This value for each portable tank type is as follows:

.1   shell with a diameter of 1.5 m or less: 65°C;

.2   shell with a diameter of more than 1.5 m:

.1   without insulation or sunshield: 60°C;

.2   with sunshield (see 6.7.3.2.12): 55°C; and

.3   with insulation (see 6.7.3.2.12): 50°C;

Design temperature range for the shell shall be −40°C to 50°C for non-refrigerated liquefied gases transported under ambient conditions. More severe design temperatures shall be considered for portable tanks subjected to severe climatic conditions;

Filling density means the average mass of non-refrigerated liquefied gas per litre of shell capacity (kg/L). The filling density is given in portable tank instruction T50 in 4.2.5.2.6;

Leakproofness test means a test using gas subjecting the shell and its service equipment to an effective internal pressure of not less than 25% of the MAWP;

6

Maximum allowable working pressure (MAWP) means a pressure that shall be not less than the highest of the following pressures measured at the top of the shell while in operating position, but in no case less than 7 bar:

.1 the maximum effective gauge pressure allowed in the shell during filling or discharge; or

.2 the maximum effective gauge pressure to which the shell is designed, which shall be:

.1 for a non-refrigerated liquefied gas listed in the portable tank instruction T50 in 4.2.5.2.6, the MAWP (in bar) given in portable tank instruction T50 for that gas;

.2 for other non-refrigerated liquefied gases, not less than the sum of:

– the absolute vapour pressure (in bar) of the non-refrigerated liquefied gas at the design reference temperature minus 1 bar; and

– the partial pressure (in bar) of air or other gases in the ullage space, being determined by the design reference temperature and the liquid phase expansion due to an increase of the mean bulk temperature of $t_r - t_f$ (t_f = filling temperature, usually 15°C; t_r = 50°C, maximum mean bulk temperature);

.3 for chemicals under pressure, the MAWP (in bar) given in T50 portable tank instruction for the liquefied gas portion of the propellants listed in T50 in 4.2.5.2.6.

Maximum permissible gross mass (MPGM) means the sum of the tare mass of the portable tank and the heaviest load authorized for transport;

Mild steel means a steel with a guaranteed minimum tensile strength of 360 N/mm^2 to 440 N/mm^2 and a guaranteed minimum elongation at fracture conforming to 6.7.3.3.3.3;

Portable tank means a multimodal tank having a capacity of more than 450 L used for the transport of non-refrigerated liquefied gases of class 2. The portable tank includes a shell fitted with service equipment and structural equipment necessary for the transport of gases. The portable tank shall be capable of being filled and discharged without the removal of its structural equipment. It shall possess stabilizing members external to the shell, and shall be capable of being lifted when full. It shall be designed primarily to be loaded onto a transport vehicle or ship and shall be equipped with skids, mountings or accessories to facilitate mechanical handling. Road tank-vehicles, rail tank-wagons, non-metallic tanks, intermediate bulk containers (IBCs), gas cylinders and large receptacles are not considered to fall within the definition for portable tanks;

Reference steel means a steel with a tensile strength of 370 N/mm^2 and an elongation at fracture of 27%;

Service equipment means measuring instruments and filling, discharge, venting, safety and insulating devices;

Shell means the part of the portable tank which retains the non-refrigerated liquefied gas intended for transport (tank proper), including openings and their closures, but does not include service equipment or external structural equipment;

Structural equipment means reinforcing, fastening, protective and stabilizing members external to the shell;

Test pressure means the maximum gauge pressure at the top of the shell during the pressure test.

6.7.3.2 General design and construction provisions

6.7.3.2.1 Shells shall be designed and constructed in accordance with the provisions of a pressure-vessel code recognized by the competent authority. Shells shall be made of steel suitable for forming. The materials shall, in principle, conform to national or international material standards. For welded shells, only a material whose weldability has been fully demonstrated shall be used. Welds shall be skilfully made and afford complete safety. When the manufacturing process or the materials make it necessary, the shells shall be suitably heat-treated to guarantee adequate toughness in the weld and in the heat-affected zones. In choosing the material, the design temperature range shall be taken into account with respect to risk of brittle fracture, to stress corrosion cracking and to resistance to impact. When fine-grain steel is used, the guaranteed value of the yield strength shall be not more than 460 N/mm^2 and the guaranteed value of the upper limit of the tensile strength shall be not more than 725 N/mm^2, according to the material specification. Portable tank materials shall be suitable for the external environment in which they may be transported.

6.7.3.2.2 Portable tank shells, fittings and pipework shall be constructed of materials which are:

.1 substantially immune to attack by the non-refrigerated liquefied gas(es) intended to be transported; or

.2 properly passivated or neutralized by chemical reaction.

6.7.3.2.3 Gaskets shall be made of materials compatible with the non-refrigerated liquefied gas(es) intended to be transported.

6.7.3.2.4 Contact between dissimilar metals which could result in damage by galvanic action shall be avoided.

6.7.3.2.5 The materials of the portable tank, including any devices, gaskets, and accessories, shall not adversely affect the non-refrigerated liquefied gas(es) intended for transport in the portable tank.

6.7.3.2.6   Portable tanks shall be designed and constructed with supports to provide a secure base during transport and with suitable lifting and tie-down attachments.

6.7.3.2.7   Portable tanks shall be designed to withstand, without loss of contents, at least the internal pressure due to the contents and the static, dynamic and thermal loads during normal conditions of handling and transport. The design shall demonstrate that the effects of fatigue, caused by repeated application of these loads through the expected life of the portable tank, have been taken into account.

6.7.3.2.7.1   For portable tanks that are intended for use as offshore tank-containers, the dynamic stresses imposed by handling in open seas shall be taken into account.

6.7.3.2.8   Shells shall be designed to withstand an external pressure of at least 0.4 bar gauge above the internal pressure without permanent deformation. When the shell is to be subjected to a significant vacuum before filling or during discharge, it shall be designed to withstand an external pressure of at least 0.9 bar gauge above the internal pressure and shall be proven at that pressure.

6.7.3.2.9   Portable tanks and their fastenings shall, under the maximum permissible load, be capable of absorbing the following separately applied static forces:

      .1   in the direction of travel: twice the MPGM multiplied by the acceleration due to gravity (*g*);[*]

      .2   horizontally at right angles to the direction of travel: the MPGM (when the direction of travel is not clearly determined, the forces shall be equal to twice the MPGM) multiplied by the acceleration due to gravity (*g*);[*]

      .3   vertically upwards: the MPGM multiplied by the acceleration due to gravity (*g*);[*] and

      .4   vertically downwards: twice the MPGM (total loading including the effect of gravity) multiplied by the acceleration due to gravity (*g*).[*]

6.7.3.2.10   Under each of the forces in 6.7.3.2.9, the safety factor to be observed shall be as follows:

      .1   for steels having a clearly defined yield point, a safety factor of 1.5 in relation to the guaranteed yield strength; or

      .2   for steels with no clearly defined yield point, a safety factor of 1.5 in relation to the guaranteed 0.2% proof strength and, for austenitic steels, the 1% proof strength.

6.7.3.2.11   The values of yield strength or proof strength shall be the values according to national or international material standards. When austenitic steels are used, the specified minimum values of yield strength and proof strength according to the material standards may be increased by up to 15% when these greater values are attested in the material inspection certificate. When no material standard exists for the steel in question, the value of yield strength or proof strength used shall be approved by the competent authority.

6.7.3.2.12   When the shells intended for the transport of non-refrigerated liquefied gases are equipped with thermal insulation, the thermal insulation system shall satisfy the following provisions:

      .1   It shall consist of a shield covering not less than the upper third but not more than the upper half of the surface of the shell and separated from the shell by an air space about 40 mm across; or

      .2   It shall consist of a complete cladding of adequate thickness of insulating materials, protected so as to prevent the ingress of moisture and damage under normal conditions of transport and so as to provide a thermal conductance of not more than 0.67 W/m·K;

      .3   When the protective covering is so closed as to be gas-tight, a device shall be provided to prevent any dangerous pressure from developing in the insulating layer in the event of inadequate gas-tightness of the shell or of its items of equipment;

      .4   The thermal insulation shall not inhibit access to the fittings and discharge devices.

6.7.3.2.13   Portable tanks intended for the transport of flammable non-refrigerated liquefied gases shall be capable of being electrically earthed.

6.7.3.3   Design criteria

6.7.3.3.1   Shells shall be of a circular cross-section.

6.7.3.3.2   Shells shall be designed and constructed to withstand a test pressure not less than 1.3 times the design pressure. The shell design shall take into account the minimum MAWP values provided in portable tank instruction T50 in 4.2.5.2.6 for each non-refrigerated liquefied gas intended for transport. Attention is drawn to the minimum shell thickness provisions for these shells specified in 6.7.3.4.

6.7.3.3.3   For steels exhibiting a clearly defined yield point or characterized by a guaranteed proof strength (0.2% proof strength, generally, or 1% proof strength for austenitic steels), the primary membrane stress σ (sigma) in the shell shall not exceed $0.75R_e$ or $0.50R_m$, whichever is lower, at the test pressure, where:

      R_e = yield strength in N/mm², or 0.2% proof strength or, for austenitic steels, 1% proof strength.

      R_m = minimum tensile strength in N/mm².

---

[*] For calculation purposes, $g = 9.81$ m/s².

6.7.3.3.3.1   The values of R_e and R_m to be used shall be the specified minimum values according to national or international material standards. When austenitic steels are used, these specified minimum values for R_e and R_m according to the material standards may be increased by up to 15% when these greater values are attested in the material inspection certificate. When no material standard exists for the steel in question, the values of R_e and R_m used shall be approved by the competent authority or its authorized body.

6.7.3.3.3.2   Steels which have a R_e/R_m ratio of more than 0.85 are not allowed for the construction of welded shells. The values of R_e and R_m to be used in determining this ratio shall be the values specified in the material inspection certificate.

6.7.3.3.3.3   Steels used in the construction of shells shall have an elongation at fracture, in %, of not less than $10,000/R_m$ with an absolute minimum of 16% for fine-grain steels and 20% for other steels.

6.7.3.3.3.4   For the purpose of determining actual values for materials, it shall be noted that for sheet metal, the axis of the tensile test specimen shall be at right angles (transversely) to the direction of rolling. The permanent elongation at fracture shall be measured on test specimens of rectangular cross-section in accordance with ISO 6892:1998 using a 50 mm gauge length.

6.7.3.4   Minimum shell thickness

6.7.3.4.1   The minimum shell thickness shall be the greater thickness based on:

.1   the minimum thickness determined in accordance with the provisions in 6.7.3.4; and

.2   the minimum thickness determined in accordance with the recognized pressure-vessel code, including the provisions in 6.7.3.3.

6.7.3.4.2   The cylindrical portions, ends (heads) and manhole covers of shells of not more than 1.80 m in diameter shall be not less than 5 mm thick in the reference steel or of equivalent thickness in the steel to be used. Shells of more than 1.80 m in diameter shall be not less than 6 mm thick in the reference steel or of equivalent thickness in the steel to be used.

6.7.3.4.3   The cylindrical portions, ends (heads) and manhole covers of all shells shall be not less than 4 mm thick regardless of the material of construction.

6.7.3.4.4   The equivalent thickness of a steel other than the thickness prescribed for the reference steel in 6.7.3.4.2 shall be determined using the following formula:

$$e_1 = \frac{21.4 \times e_0}{\sqrt[3]{R_{m1} \times A_1}}$$

where:

e_1 = required equivalent thickness (in mm) of the steel to be used;

e_0 = minimum thickness (in mm) of the reference steel specified in 6.7.3.4.2;

R_{m1} = guaranteed minimum tensile strength (in N/mm^2) of the steel to be used (see 6.7.3.3.3);

A_1 = guaranteed minimum elongation at fracture (in %) of the steel to be used according to national or international standards.

6.7.3.4.5   In no case shall the wall thickness be less than that prescribed in 6.7.3.4.1 to 6.7.3.4.3. All parts of the shell shall have a minimum thickness as determined by 6.7.3.4.1 to 6.7.3.4.3. This thickness shall be exclusive of any corrosion allowance.

6.7.3.4.6   When mild steel is used (see 6.7.3.1), calculation using the equation in 6.7.3.4.4 is not required.

6.7.3.4.7   There shall be no sudden change of plate thickness at the attachment of the ends (heads) to the cylindrical portion of the shell.

6.7.3.5   Service equipment

6.7.3.5.1   Service equipment shall be so arranged as to be protected against the risk of being wrenched off or damaged during handling and transport. When the connection between the frame and the shell allows relative movement between the sub-assemblies, the equipment shall be so fastened as to permit such movement without risk of damage to working parts. The external discharge fittings (pipe sockets, shut-off devices), the internal stop-valve and its seating shall be protected against the danger of being wrenched off by external forces (for example, by using shear sections). The filling and discharge devices (including flanges or threaded plugs) and any protective caps shall be capable of being secured against unintended opening.

6.7.3.5.1.1   For offshore tank-containers, where positioning of service equipment and the design and strength of protection for such equipment is concerned, the increased danger of impact damage when handling such tanks in open seas shall be taken into account.

6.7.3.5.2   All openings with a diameter of more than 1.5 mm in shells of portable tanks, except openings for pressure relief devices, inspection openings and closed bleed holes, shall be fitted with at least three mutually independent shut-off devices in series, the first being an internal stop-valve, excess flow valve or equivalent device, the second being an external stop-valve and the third being a blank flange or equivalent device.

6.7.3.5.2.1   When a portable tank is fitted with an excess flow valve, the excess flow valve shall be so fitted that its seating is inside the shell or inside a welded flange or, when fitted externally, its mountings shall be designed so that, in the event of impact, its effectiveness shall be maintained. The excess flow valves shall be selected and fitted so as to close automatically when the rated flow specified by the manufacturer is reached. Connections and accessories leading to or from such a valve shall have a capacity for a flow more than the rated flow of the excess flow valve.

6.7.3.5.3   For filling and discharge openings, the first shut-off device shall be an internal stop-valve and the second shall be a stop-valve placed in an accessible position on each discharge and filling pipe.

6.7.3.5.4   For filling and discharge bottom openings of portable tanks intended for the transport of flammable and/or toxic non-refrigerated liquefied gases or chemicals under pressure, the internal stop-valve shall be a quick-closing safety device which closes automatically in the event of unintended movement of the portable tank during filling or discharge or fire engulfment. Except for portable tanks having a capacity of not more than 1000 L, it shall be possible to operate this device by remote control.

6.7.3.5.5   In addition to filling, discharge and gas pressure equalizing orifices, shells may have openings in which gauges, thermometers and manometers can be fitted. Connections for such instruments shall be made by suitable welded nozzles or pockets and not be screwed connections through the shell.

6.7.3.5.6   All portable tanks shall be fitted with manholes or other inspection openings of suitable size to allow for internal inspection and adequate access for maintenance and repair of the interior.

6.7.3.5.7   External fittings shall be grouped together so far as reasonably practicable.

6.7.3.5.8   Each connection on a portable tank shall be clearly marked to indicate its function.

6.7.3.5.9   Each stop-valve or other means of closure shall be designed and constructed to a rated pressure not less than the MAWP of the shell, taking into account the temperatures expected during transport. All stop-valves with a screwed spindle shall close by a clockwise motion of the handwheel. For other stop-valves, the position (open and closed) and direction of closure shall be clearly indicated. All stop-valves shall be designed to prevent unintentional opening.

6.7.3.5.10   Piping shall be designed, constructed and installed so as to avoid the risk of damage due to thermal expansion and contraction, mechanical shock and vibration. All piping shall be of suitable metallic material. Welded pipe joints shall be used wherever possible.

6.7.3.5.11   Joints in copper tubing shall be brazed or have an equally strong metal union. The melting point of brazing materials shall be no lower than 525°C. The joints shall not decrease the strength of tubing, as may happen when cutting threads.

6.7.3.5.12   The burst pressure of all piping and pipe fittings shall be not less than the highest of four times the MAWP of the shell or four times the pressure to which it may be subjected in service by the action of a pump or other device (except pressure relief devices).

6.7.3.5.13   Ductile metals shall be used in the construction of valves and accessories.

6.7.3.6   **Bottom openings**

6.7.3.6.1   Certain non-refrigerated liquefied gases shall not be transported in portable tanks with bottom openings when portable tank instruction T50 in 4.2.5.2.6 indicates that bottom openings are not allowed. There shall be no openings below the liquid level of the shell when it is filled to its maximum permissible filling limit.

6.7.3.7   **Pressure relief devices**

6.7.3.7.1   Portable tanks shall be provided with one or more spring-loaded pressure relief devices. The pressure relief devices shall open automatically at a pressure not less than the MAWP and be fully open at a pressure equal to 110% of the MAWP. These devices shall, after discharge, close at a pressure not lower than 10% below the pressure at which discharge starts and shall remain closed at all lower pressures. The pressure relief devices shall be of a type that will resist dynamic forces, including liquid surge. Frangible discs not in series with a spring-loaded pressure relief device are not permitted.

6.7.3.7.2   Pressure relief devices shall be designed to prevent the entry of foreign matter, the leakage of gas and the development of any dangerous excess pressure.

6.7.3.7.3   Portable tanks intended for the transport of certain non-refrigerated liquefied gases identified in portable tank instruction T50 in 4.2.5.2.6 shall have a pressure relief device approved by the competent authority. Unless a portable tank in dedicated service is fitted with an approved relief device constructed of materials compatible with the load, such device shall comprise a frangible disc preceding a spring-loaded device. The space between the frangible disc and the device shall be provided with a pressure gauge or a suitable tell-tale indicator. This arrangement permits the detection of disc rupture, pinholing or leakage which could cause a malfunction of the pressure relief device. The frangible discs shall rupture at a nominal pressure 10% above the start-to-discharge pressure of the relief device.

6.7.3.7.4 In the case of multi-purpose portable tanks, the pressure relief devices shall open at a pressure indicated in 6.7.3.7.1 for the gas having the highest maximum allowable pressure of the gases allowed to be transported in the portable tank.

6.7.3.8 Capacity of relief devices

6.7.3.8.1 The combined delivery capacity of the relief devices shall be sufficient that, in the event of total fire engulfment, the pressure (including accumulation) inside the shell does not exceed 120% of the MAWP. Spring-loaded relief devices shall be used to achieve the full relief capacity prescribed. In the case of multi-purpose tanks, the combined delivery capacity of the pressure relief devices shall be taken for the gas which requires the highest delivery capacity of the gases allowed to be transported in portable tanks.

6.7.3.8.1.1 To determine the total required capacity of the relief devices, which shall be regarded as being the sum of the individual capacities of the several devices, the following formula[*] shall be used:

$$Q = 12.4 \frac{FA^{0.82}}{LC} \sqrt{\frac{ZT}{M}}$$

where:

Q = minimum required rate of discharge in cubic metres of air per second (m^3/s) at standard conditions: 1 bar and 0°C (273 K);

F = a coefficient with the following value:

for uninsulated shells, $F = 1$

for insulated shells, $F = U(649 - t)/13.6$ but in no case is less than 0.25

where:

U = thermal conductance of the insulation, in $kW \cdot m^{-2} \cdot K^{-1}$, at 38°C;

t = actual temperature of the non-refrigerated liquefied gas during filling (in °C) (when this temperature is unknown, let $t = 15°C$);

The value of F given above for insulated shells may be taken provided that the insulation is in conformance with 6.7.3.8.1.2;

A = total external surface area of shell in square metres;

Z = the gas compressibility factor in the accumulating condition (when this factor is unknown, let Z equal 1.0);

T = absolute temperature in kelvin (°C + 273) above the pressure relief devices in the accumulating condition;

L = the latent heat of vaporization of the liquid, in kJ/kg, in the accumulating condition;

M = molecular mass of the discharged gas;

C = a constant which is derived from one of the following formulae as a function of the ratio k of specific heats:

$$k = \frac{C_p}{C_v}$$

where:

C_p = specific heat at constant pressure; and

C_v = specific heat at constant volume.

When $k > 1$:

$$C = \sqrt{k \left(\frac{2}{k+1}\right)^{\frac{k+1}{k-1}}}$$

When $k = 1$ or k is unknown:

$$C = \frac{1}{\sqrt{e}} = 0.607$$

where e is the mathematical constant 2.7183.

---

[*] This formula applies only to non-refrigerated liquefied gases which have critical tempratures well above the temperature at the accumulating condition. For gases which have critical temperatures near or below the temperature at the accumulating condition, the calculation of the pressure-relief device delivery capacity shall consider further thermodynamic properties of the gas (see, e.g. CGA S-1.2-2003 *Pressure Relief Device Standards – Part 2 – Cargo and Portable Tanks for Compressed Gases*).

C may also be taken from the following table:

k	C	k	C	k	C
1.00	0.607	1.26	0.660	1.52	0.704
1.02	0.611	1.28	0.664	1.54	0.707
1.04	0.615	1.30	0.667	1.56	0.71
1.06	0.620	1.32	0.671	1.58	0.713
1.08	0.624	1.34	0.674	1.60	0.716
1.10	0.628	1.36	0.678	1.62	0.719
1.12	0.633	1.38	0.681	1.64	0.722
1.14	0.637	1.40	0.685	1.66	0.725
1.16	0.641	1.42	0.688	1.68	0.728
1.18	0.645	1.44	0.691	1.70	0.731
1.20	0.649	1.46	0.695	2.0	0.77
1.22	0.652	1.48	0.698	2.2	0.793
1.24	0.656	1.50	0.701		

6.7.3.8.1.2   Insulation systems, used for the purpose of reducing the venting capacity, shall be approved by the competent authority or its authorized body. In all cases, insulation systems approved for this purpose shall:

    .1   remain effective at all temperatures up to 649°C; and

    .2   be jacketed with a material having a melting point of 700°C or greater.

6.7.3.9   Marking of pressure relief devices

6.7.3.9.1   Every pressure relief device shall be clearly and permanently marked with the following:

    .1   the pressure (in bar or kPa) at which it is set to discharge;

    .2   the allowable tolerance at the discharge pressure, for spring-loaded devices;

    .3   the reference temperature corresponding to the rated pressure, for frangible discs;

    .4   the rated flow capacity of the device in standard cubic metres of air per second (m^3/s); and

    .5   the cross sectional flow areas of the spring-loaded pressure relief devices and frangible discs in mm^2.

When practicable, the following information shall also be shown:

    .6   the manufacturer's name and relevant catalogue number.

6.7.3.9.2   The rated flow capacity marked on the pressure relief devices shall be determined according to ISO 4126 1:2004 and ISO 4126-7:2004.

6.7.3.10   Connections to pressure relief devices

6.7.3.10.1   Connections to pressure relief devices shall be of sufficient size to enable the required discharge to pass unrestricted to the safety device. No stop-valve shall be installed between the shell and the pressure relief devices except when duplicate devices are provided for maintenance or other reasons and the stop-valves serving the devices actually in use are locked open or the stop-valves are interlocked so that at least one of the duplicate devices is always operable and capable of meeting the provisions of 6.7.3.8. There shall be no obstruction in an opening leading to a vent or pressure relief device which might restrict or cut off the flow from the shell to that device. Vents from the pressure relief devices, when used, shall deliver the relieved vapour or liquid to the atmosphere in conditions of minimum back-pressure on the relieving device.

6.7.3.11   Siting of pressure relief devices

6.7.3.11.1   Each pressure relief device inlet shall be situated on top of the shell in a position as near the longitudinal and transverse centre of the shell as reasonably practicable. All pressure relief device inlets shall, under maximum filling conditions, be situated in the vapour space of the shell and the devices shall be so arranged as to ensure that the escaping vapour is discharged unrestrictedly. For flammable non-refrigerated liquefied gases, the escaping vapour shall be directed away from the shell in such a manner that it cannot impinge upon the shell. Protective devices which deflect the flow of vapour are permissible provided the required relief-device capacity is not reduced.

6.7.3.11.2   Arrangements shall be made to prevent access to the pressure relief devices by unauthorized persons and to protect the devices from damage caused by the portable tank overturning.

6

6.7.3.12   Gauging devices

6.7.3.12.1   Unless a portable tank is intended to be filled by mass, it shall be equipped with one or more gauging devices. Glass level-gauges and gauges made of other fragile material, which are in direct communication with the contents of the shell, shall not be used.

6.7.3.13   Portable tank supports, frameworks, lifting and tie-down attachments

6.7.3.13.1   Portable tanks shall be designed and constructed with a support structure to provide a secure base during transport. The forces specified in 6.7.3.2.9 and the safety factor specified in 6.7.3.2.10 shall be considered in this aspect of the design. Skids, frameworks, cradles or other similar structures are acceptable.

6.7.3.13.2   The combined stresses caused by portable tank mountings (such as cradles, frameworks, etc.) and portable tank lifting and tie-down attachments shall not cause excessive stress in any portion of the shell. Permanent lifting and tie-down attachments shall be fitted to all portable tanks. Preferably they shall be fitted to the portable tank supports but may be secured to reinforcing plates located on the shell at the points of support.

6.7.3.13.3   In the design of supports and frameworks, the effects of environmental corrosion shall be taken into account.

6.7.3.13.4   Forklift pockets shall be capable of being closed off. The means of closing forklift pockets shall be a permanent part of the framework or permanently attached to the framework. Single-compartment portable tanks with a length less than 3.65 m need not have closed-off forklift pockets provided that:

    .1   the shell and all the fittings are well protected from being hit by the forklift blades; and

    .2   the distance between the centres of the forklift pockets is at least half of the maximum length of the portable tank.

6.7.3.13.5   When portable tanks are not protected during transport, according to 4.2.2.3, the shells and service equipment shall be protected against damage to the shell and service equipment resulting from lateral or longitudinal impact or overturning. External fittings shall be protected so as to preclude the release of the shell contents upon impact or overturning of the portable tank on its fittings. Examples of protection include:

    .1   protection against lateral impact, which may consist of longitudinal bars protecting the shell on both sides at the level of the median line;

    .2   protection of the portable tank against overturning, which may consist of reinforcement rings or bars fixed across the frame;

    .3   protection against rear impact, which may consist of a bumper or frame;

    .4   protection of the shell against damage from impact or overturning by use of an ISO frame in accordance with ISO 1496-3:1995.

6.7.3.14   Design approval

6.7.3.14.1   The competent authority or its authorized body shall issue a design approval certificate for any new design of a portable tank. This certificate shall attest that the portable tank has been surveyed by that authority, is suitable for its intended purpose and meets the provisions of this chapter and, when appropriate, the provisions for gases provided in portable tank instruction T50 in 4.2.5.2.6. When a series of portable tanks are manufactured without change in the design, the certificate shall be valid for the entire series. The certificate shall refer to the prototype test report, the gases allowed to be transported, the materials of construction of the shell and an approval number. The approval number shall consist of the distinguishing sign or mark of the State in whose territory the approval was granted, i.e. the distinguishing sign for use in international traffic, as prescribed by the Convention on Road Traffic, Vienna, 1968, and a registration number. Any alternative arrangements according to 6.7.1.2 shall be indicated on the certificate. A design approval may serve for the approval of smaller portable tanks made of materials of the same kind and thickness, by the same fabrication techniques and with identical supports, equivalent closures and other appurtenances.

6.7.3.14.2   The prototype test report for the design approval shall include at least the following:

    .1   the results of the applicable framework test specified in ISO 1496-3:1995;

    .2   the results of the initial inspection and test in 6.7.3.15.3; and

    .3   the results of the impact test in 6.7.3.15.1, when applicable.

6.7.3.15   Inspection and testing

6.7.3.15.1   Portable tanks meeting the definition of *container* in the International Convention for Safe Containers (CSC), 1972, as amended, shall not be used unless they are successfully qualified by subjecting a representative prototype of each design to the Dynamic, Longitudinal Impact Test prescribed in the Manual of Tests and Criteria, part IV, section 41. This provision only applies to portable tanks which are constructed according to a design approval certificate which has been issued on or after 1 January 2008.

6.7.3.15.2 The shell and items of equipment of each portable tank shall be inspected and tested before being put into service for the first time (initial inspection and test) and thereafter at not more than five-year intervals (5-year periodic inspection and test) with an intermediate periodic inspection and test (2.5-year periodic inspection and test) midway between the 5-year periodic inspections and tests. The 2.5-year periodic inspection and test may be performed within 3 months of the specified date. An exceptional inspection and test shall be performed regardless of the last periodic inspection and test when necessary according to 6.7.3.15.7.

6.7.3.15.3 The initial inspection and test of a portable tank shall include a check of the design characteristics, an internal and external examination of the portable tank and its fittings with due regard to the non-refrigerated liquefied gases to be transported, and a pressure test referring to the test pressures according to 6.7.3.3.2. The pressure test may be performed as a hydraulic test or by using another liquid or gas with the agreement of the competent authority or its authorized body. Before the portable tank is placed into service, a leakproofness test and a test of the satisfactory operation of all service equipment shall also be performed. When the shell and its fittings have been pressure-tested separately, they shall be subjected together after assembly to a leakproofness test. All welds subject to full stress level in the shell shall be inspected during the initial test by radiographic, ultrasonic, or another suitable non-destructive test method. This does not apply to the jacket.

6.7.3.15.4 The 5-year periodic inspection and test shall include an internal and external examination and, as a general rule, a hydraulic pressure test. Sheathing, thermal insulation and the like shall be removed only to the extent required for reliable appraisal of the condition of the portable tank. When the shell and equipment have been pressure-tested separately, they shall be subjected together after assembly to a leakproofness test.

6.7.3.15.5 The intermediate 2.5-year periodic inspection and test shall at least include an internal and external examination of the portable tank and its fittings with due regard to the non-refrigerated liquefied gases intended to be transported, a leakproofness test and a test of the satisfactory operation of all service equipment. Sheathing, thermal insulation and the like shall be removed only to the extent required for reliable appraisal of the condition of the portable tank. For portable tanks intended for the transport of a single non-refrigerated liquefied gas, the 2.5-year internal examination may be waived or substituted by other test methods or inspection procedures specified by the competent authority or its authorized body.

6.7.3.15.6 A portable tank may not be filled and offered for transport after the date of expiry of the last 5-year or 2.5-year periodic inspection and test as required by 6.7.3.15.2. However, a portable tank filled prior to the date of expiry of the last periodic inspection and test may be transported for a period not to exceed three months beyond the date of expiry of the last periodic test or inspection. In addition, a portable tank may be transported after the date of expiry of the last periodic test and inspection:

    .1 after emptying but before cleaning, for purposes of performing the next required test or inspection prior to refilling; and

    .2 unless otherwise approved by the competent authority, for a period not to exceed six months beyond the date of expiry of the last periodic test or inspection, in order to allow the return of dangerous goods for proper disposal or recycling. Reference to this exemption shall be mentioned in the transport document.

6.7.3.15.7 The exceptional inspection and test is necessary when the portable tank shows evidence of damaged or corroded areas, or leakage, or other conditions that indicate a deficiency that could affect the integrity of the portable tank. The extent of the exceptional inspection and test shall depend on the amount of damage or deterioration of the portable tank. It shall include at least the 2.5-year inspection and test according to 6.7.3.15.5.

6.7.3.15.8 The internal and external examinations shall ensure that:

    △ **.1** the shell is inspected for pitting, corrosion, or abrasions, dents, distortions, defects in welds or any other conditions, including leakage, that might render the portable tank unsafe for transport. The wall thickness shall be verified by appropriate measurement if this inspection indicates a reduction of wall thickness;

    .2 the piping, valves, and gaskets are inspected for corroded areas, defects, or any other conditions, including leakage, that might render the portable tank unsafe for filling, discharge or transport;

    .3 devices for tightening manhole covers are operative and there is no leakage at manhole covers or gaskets;

    .4 missing or loose bolts or nuts on any flanged connection or blank flange are replaced or tightened;

    .5 all emergency devices and valves are free from corrosion, distortion and any damage or defect that could prevent their normal operation. Remote closure devices and self-closing stop-valves shall be operated to demonstrate proper operation;

    △ **.6** required marks on the portable tank are legible and in accordance with the applicable provisions; and

    .7 the framework, the supports and the arrangements for lifting the portable tank are in satisfactory condition.

6.7.3.15.9 The inspections and tests in 6.7.3.15.1, 6.7.3.15.3, 6.7.3.15.4, 6.7.3.15.5 and 6.7.3.15.7 shall be performed or witnessed by an expert approved by the competent authority or its authorized body. When the pressure test is a part of the inspection and test, the test pressure shall be the one indicated on the data plate of the

6

portable tank. While under pressure, the portable tank shall be inspected for any leaks in the shell, piping or equipment.

6.7.3.15.10   In all cases when cutting, burning or welding operations on the shell have been effected, that work shall be to the approval of the competent authority or its authorized body, taking into account the pressure-vessel code used for the construction of the shell. A pressure test to the original test pressure shall be performed after the work is completed.

6.7.3.15.11   When evidence of any unsafe condition is discovered, the portable tank shall not be returned to service until it has been corrected and the pressure test is repeated and passed.

6.7.3.16   Marking

6.7.3.16.1   Every portable tank shall be fitted with a corrosion-resistant metal plate permanently attached to the portable tank in a conspicuous place readily accessible for inspection. When for reasons of portable tank arrangements the plate cannot be permanently attached to the shell, the shell shall be marked with at least the information required by the pressure-vessel code. As a minimum, at least the following information shall be marked on the plate by stamping or by any other similar method:

(a)   owner information
    (i)   owner's registration number;

(b)   manufacturing information
    (i)   country of manufacture;
    (ii)   year of manufacture;
    (iii)   manufacturer's name or mark;
    (iv)   manufacturer's serial number;

(c)   approval information
    (i)   the United Nations packaging symbol:

       This symbol shall not be used for any purpose other than certifying that a packaging, a flexible bulk container, a portable tank or a MEGC complies with the relevant requirements in chapters 6.1, 6.2, 6.3, 6.5, 6.6, 6.7 or 6.9;
    (ii)   approval country;
    (iii)   authorized body for the design approval;
    (iv)   design approval number;
    (v)   letters "AA", if the design was approved under alternative arrangements (see 6.7.1.2);
    (vi)   pressure-vessel code to which the shell is designed;

(d)   pressures
    (i)   MAWP (in bar gauge or kPa gauge);[*]
    (ii)   test pressure (in bar gauge or kPa gauge);[*]
    (iii)   initial pressure test date (month and year);
    (iv)   identification mark of the initial pressure test witness;
    (v)   external design pressure[†] (in bar gauge or kPa gauge);[*]

(e)   temperatures
    (i)   design temperature range (in °C);[*]
    (ii)   design reference temperature (in °C);[*]

(f)   materials
    (i)   shell material(s) and material standard reference(s);
    (ii)   equivalent thickness in reference steel (in mm);[*]

(g)   capacity
    (i)   tank water capacity at 20°C (in litres);[*]

(h)   periodic inspections and tests
    (i)   type of the most recent periodic test (2.5-year, 5-year or exceptional);
    (ii)   date of the most recent periodic test (month and year);
    (iii)   test pressure (in bar gauge or kPa gauge)[*] of the most recent periodic test (if applicable);
    (iv)   identification mark of the authorized body who performed or witnessed the most recent test.

---

[*] The unit used shall be indicated.

[†] See 6.7.3.2.8.

△

Figure 6.7.3.16.1 – *Example of a plate for marking*

Owner's registration number			
MANUFACTURING INFORMATION			
Country of manufacture			
Year of manufacture			
Manufacturer			
Manufacturer's serial number			
APPROVAL INFORMATION			
(un)	Approval country		
	Authorized body for design approval		
	Design approval number		"AA" *(if applicable)*
Shell design code (pressure-vessel code)			
PRESSURES			
MAWP			bar *or* kPa
Test pressure			bar *or* kPa
Initial pressure test date:	*(mm/yyyy)*	Witness stamp:	
External design pressure			bar *or* kPa
TEMPERATURES			
Design temperature range			°C to °C
Design reference temperature			°C
MATERIALS			
Shell material(s) and material standard reference(s)			
Equivalent thickness in reference steel			mm
CAPACITY			
Tank water capacity at 20°C			litres
PERIODIC INSPECTIONS/TESTS			

Test type	Test date	Witness stamp and test pressure[a]	Test type	Test date	Witness stamp and test pressure[a]
	(mm/yyyy)	bar *or* kPa		*(mm/yyyy)*	bar *or* kPa

[a] Test pressure if applicable.

6.7.3.16.2   The following information shall be durably marked either on the portable tank itself or on a metal plate firmly secured to the portable tank:

    Name of the operator

    Name of non-refrigerated liquefied gas(es) permitted for transport

    Maximum permissible load mass for each non-refrigerated liquefied gas permitted . . . . kg

    Maximum permissible gross mass (MPGM) . . . . kg

    Unladen (tare) mass . . . . kg

    Portable tank instruction in accordance with 4.2.5.2.6.

6.7.3.16.3   If a portable tank is designed and approved for handling in open seas, the words "OFFSHORE PORTABLE TANK" shall be marked on the identification plate.

6

6.7.4 Provisions for the design, construction, inspection and testing of portable tanks intended for the transport of refrigerated liquefied gases of class 2

6.7.4.1 Definitions

For the purposes of this section:

Holding time means the time that will elapse from the establishment of the initial filling condition until the pressure has risen due to heat influx to the lowest set pressure of the pressure-limiting device(s);

Jacket means the outer insulation cover or cladding, which may be part of the insulation system;

Leakproofness test means a test, using gas, subjecting the shell and its service equipment to an effective internal pressure not less than 90% of the MAWP;

Maximum allowable working pressure (MAWP) means the maximum effective gauge pressure permissible at the top of the shell of a filled portable tank in its operating position, including the highest effective pressure during filling and discharge;

Maximum permissible gross mass (MPGM) means the sum of the tare mass of the portable tank and the heaviest load authorized for transport;

Minimum design temperature means the temperature which is used for the design and construction of the shell, not higher than the lowest (coldest) temperature (service temperature) of the contents during normal conditions of filling, discharge and transport;

Portable tank means a thermally insulated multimodal tank having a capacity of more than 450 L fitted with service equipment and structural equipment necessary for the transport of refrigerated liquefied gases. The portable tank shall be capable of being filled and discharged without the removal of its structural equipment. It shall possess stabilizing members external to the tank, and shall be capable of being lifted when full. It shall be designed primarily to be loaded onto a transport vehicle or ship and shall be equipped with skids, mountings or accessories to facilitate mechanical handling. Road tank-vehicles, rail tank-wagons, non-metallic tanks, intermediate bulk containers (IBCs), gas cylinders and large receptacles are not considered to fall within the definition for portable tanks;

Reference steel means a steel with a tensile strength of 370 N/mm^2 and an elongation at fracture of 27%;

Service equipment means measuring instruments and filling, discharge, venting, safety, pressurizing, cooling and thermal insulation devices;

Shell means the part of the portable tank which retains the refrigerated liquefied gas intended for transport, including openings and their closures, but does not include service equipment or external structural equipment;

Structural equipment means the reinforcing, fastening, protective and stabilizing members external to the shell;

Tank means a construction which normally consists of either:

(a) a jacket and one or more inner shells where the space between the shell(s) and the jacket is exhausted of air (vacuum insulation) and may incorporate a thermal insulation system; or

(b) a jacket and an inner shell with an intermediate layer of solid thermally insulating material (such as solid foam);

Test pressure means the maximum gauge pressure at the top of the shell during the pressure test.

6.7.4.2 General design and construction provisions

6.7.4.2.1 Shells shall be designed and constructed in accordance with the provisions of a pressure-vessel code recognized by the competent authority. Shells and jackets shall be made of metallic materials suitable for forming. Jackets shall be made of steel. Non-metallic materials may be used for the attachments and supports between the shell and jacket, provided their material properties at the minimum design temperature are proven to be sufficient. The materials shall, in principle, conform to national or international material standards. For welded shells and jackets, only materials whose weldability has been fully demonstrated shall be used. Welds shall be skilfully made and afford complete safety. When the manufacturing process or the materials make it necessary, the shell shall be suitably heat-treated to guarantee adequate toughness in the weld and in the heat-affected zones. In choosing the material, the minimum design temperature shall be taken into account with respect to risk of brittle fracture, to hydrogen embrittlement, to stress corrosion cracking and to resistance to impact. When fine-grain steel is used, the guaranteed value of the yield strength shall be not more than 460 N/mm^2 and the guaranteed value of the upper limit of the tensile strength shall be not more than 725 N/mm^2, in accordance with the material specifications. Portable tank materials shall be suitable for the external environment in which they may be transported.

6.7.4.2.2 Any part of a portable tank, including fittings, gaskets and pipe-work, which can be expected normally to come into contact with the refrigerated liquefied gas transported shall be compatible with that refrigerated liquefied gas.

6.7.4.2.3 Contact between dissimilar metals which could result in damage by galvanic action shall be avoided.

6.7.4.2.4 The thermal insulation system shall include a complete covering of the shell(s) with effective insulating materials. External insulation shall be protected by a jacket so as to prevent the ingress of moisture and other damage under normal transport conditions.

6.7.4.2.5 When a jacket is so closed as to be gas-tight, a device shall be provided to prevent any dangerous pressure from developing in the insulation space.

6.7.4.2.6 Portable tanks intended for the transport of refrigerated liquefied gases having a boiling point below −182°C at atmospheric pressure shall not include materials which may react with oxygen or oxygen-enriched atmospheres in a dangerous manner when located in parts of the thermal insulation when there is a risk of contact with oxygen or with oxygen-enriched fluid.

6.7.4.2.7 Insulating materials shall not deteriorate unduly in service.

6.7.4.2.8 A reference holding time shall be determined for each refrigerated liquefied gas intended for transport in a portable tank.

6.7.4.2.8.1 The reference holding time shall be determined by a method recognized by the competent authority on the basis of the following:

.1 the effectiveness of the insulation system, determined in accordance with 6.7.4.2.8.2;

.2 the lowest set pressure of the pressure-limiting device(s);

.3 the initial filling conditions;

.4 an assumed ambient temperature of 30°C;

.5 the physical properties of the individual refrigerated liquefied gas intended to be transported.

6.7.4.2.8.2 The effectiveness of the insulation system (heat influx in watts) shall be determined by type testing the portable tank in accordance with a procedure recognized by the competent authority. This test shall consist of either:

.1 a constant-pressure test (for example at atmospheric pressure), when the loss of refrigerated liquefied gas is measured over a period of time; or

.2 a closed-system test, when the rise in pressure in the shell is measured over a period of time.

When performing the constant-pressure test, variations in atmospheric pressure shall be taken into account. When performing either test, corrections shall be made for any variation of the ambient temperature from the assumed ambient temperature reference value of 30°C.

Note: For the determination of the actual holding time before each journey, see 4.2.3.7.

6.7.4.2.9 The jacket of a vacuum-insulated double-wall tank shall have either an external design pressure not less than 100 kPa (1 bar) gauge pressure calculated in accordance with a recognized technical code or a calculated critical collapsing pressure of not less than 200 kPa (2 bar) gauge pressure. Internal and external reinforcements may be included in calculating the ability of the jacket to resist the external pressure.

6.7.4.2.10 Portable tanks shall be designed and constructed with supports to provide a secure base during transport and with suitable lifting and tie-down attachments.

6.7.4.2.11 Portable tanks shall be designed to withstand, without loss of contents, at least the internal pressure due to the contents and the static, dynamic and thermal loads during normal conditions of handling and transport. The design shall demonstrate that the effects of fatigue, caused by repeated application of these loads through the expected life of the portable tank, have been taken into account.

6.7.4.2.11.1 For tanks that are intended for use as offshore tank-containers, the dynamic stresses imposed by handling in open seas shall be taken into account.

6.7.4.2.12 Portable tanks and their fastenings under the maximum permissible load shall be capable of absorbing the following separately applied static forces:

.1 in the direction of travel: twice the MPGM multiplied by the acceleration due to gravity (*g*);[*]

.2 horizontally at right angles to the direction of travel: the MPGM (when the direction of travel is not clearly determined, the forces shall be equal to twice the MPGM) multiplied by the acceleration due to gravity (*g*);[*]

.3 vertically upwards: the MPGM multiplied by the acceleration due to gravity (*g*);[*] and

.4 vertically downwards: twice the MPGM (total loading including the effect of gravity) multiplied by the acceleration due to gravity (*g*).[*]

6

---

[*] For calculation purposes, $g = 9.81$ m/s^2.

6.7.4.2.13 Under each of the forces in 6.7.4.2.12, the safety factor to be observed shall be as follows:

.1 for materials having a clearly defined yield point, a safety factor of 1.5 in relation to the guaranteed yield strength; or

.2 for materials with no clearly defined yield point, a safety factor of 1.5 in relation to the guaranteed 0.2% proof strength or, for austenitic steels, the 1% proof strength.

6.7.4.2.14 The values of yield strength or proof strength shall be the values according to national or international material standards. When austenitic steels are used, the specified minimum values according to the material standards may be increased by up to 15% when these greater values are attested in the material inspection certificate. When no material standard exists for the metal in question, or when non-metallic materials are used, the values of yield strength or proof strength shall be approved by the competent authority.

6.7.4.2.15 Portable tanks intended for the transport of flammable refrigerated liquefied gases shall be capable of being electrically earthed.

6.7.4.3 Design criteria

6.7.4.3.1 Shells shall be of a circular cross-section.

6.7.4.3.2 Shells shall be designed and constructed to withstand a test pressure not less than 1.3 times the MAWP. For shells with vacuum insulation, the test pressure shall not be less than 1.3 times the sum of the MAWP and 100 kPa (1 bar). In no case shall the test pressure be less than 300 kPa (3 bar) gauge pressure. Attention is drawn to the minimum shell thickness provisions, specified in 6.7.4.4.2 to 6.7.4.4.7.

6.7.4.3.3 For metals exhibiting a clearly defined yield point or characterized by a guaranteed proof strength (0.2% proof strength, generally, or 1% proof strength for austenitic steels), the primary membrane stress σ (sigma) in the shell shall not exceed $0.75R_e$ or $0.50R_m$, whichever is lower, at the test pressure, where:

R_e = yield strength in N/mm^2, or 0.2% proof strength or, for austenitic steels, 1% proof strength;

R_m = minimum tensile strength in N/mm^2.

6.7.4.3.3.1 The values of R_e and R_m to be used shall be the specified minimum values according to national or international material standards. When austenitic steels are used, the specified minimum values for R_e and R_m according to the material standards may be increased by up to 15% when greater values are attested in the material inspection certificate. When no material standard exists for the metal in question, the values of R_e and R_m used shall be approved by the competent authority or its authorized body.

6.7.4.3.3.2 Steels which have a R_e/R_m ratio of more than 0.85 are not allowed for the construction of welded shells. The values of R_e and R_m to be used in determining this ratio shall be the values specified in the material inspection certificate.

6.7.4.3.3.3 Steels used in the construction of shells shall have an elongation at fracture, in %, of not less than $10,000/R_m$ with an absolute minimum of 16% for fine-grain steels and 20% for other steels. Aluminium and aluminium alloys used in the construction of shells shall have an elongation at fracture, in %, of not less than $10,000/6R_m$ with an absolute minimum of 12%.

6.7.4.3.3.4 For the purpose of determining actual values for materials, it shall be noted that for sheet metal, the axis of the tensile test specimen shall be at right angles (transversely) to the direction of rolling. The permanent elongation at fracture shall be measured on test specimens of rectangular cross-section in accordance with ISO 6892:1998 using a 50 mm gauge length.

6.7.4.4 Minimum shell thickness

6.7.4.4.1 The minimum shell thickness shall be the greater thickness based on:

.1 the minimum thickness determined in accordance with the provisions in 6.7.4.4.2 to 6.7.4.4.7; and

.2 the minimum thickness determined in accordance with the recognized pressure-vessel code, including the provisions in 6.7.4.3.

6.7.4.4.2 Shells of not more than 1.80 m in diameter shall be not less than 5 mm thick in the reference steel or of equivalent thickness in the metal to be used. Shells of more than 1.80 m in diameter shall be not less than 6 mm thick in the reference steel or of equivalent thickness in the metal to be used.

6.7.4.4.3 Shells of vacuum-insulated tanks of not more than 1.80 m in diameter shall be not less than 3 mm thick in the reference steel or of equivalent thickness in the metal to be used. Such shells of more than 1.80 m in diameter shall be not less than 4 mm thick in the reference steel or of equivalent thickness in the metal to be used.

6.7.4.4.4 For vacuum-insulated tanks, the aggregate thickness of the jacket and the shell shall correspond to the minimum thickness prescribed in 6.7.4.4.2, the thickness of the shell itself being not less than the minimum thickness prescribed in 6.7.4.4.3.

6.7.4.4.5 Shells shall be not less than 3 mm thick regardless of the material of construction.

6.7.4.4.6 The equivalent thickness of a metal other than the thickness prescribed for the reference steel in 6.7.4.4.2 and 6.7.4.4.3 shall be determined using the following equation:

$$e_1 = \frac{21.4 \times e_0}{\sqrt[3]{R_{m1} \times A_1}}$$

where:

e_1 = required equivalent thickness (in mm) of the steel to be used;

e_0 = minimum thickness (in mm) of the reference steel specified in 6.7.4.4.2 and 6.7.4.4.3;

R_{m1} = guaranteed minimum tensile strength (in N/mm^2) of the metal to be used (see 6.7.4.3.3);

A_1 = guaranteed minimum elongation at fracture (in %) of the metal to be used according to national or international standards.

6.7.4.4.7 In no case shall the wall thickness be less than that prescribed in 6.7.4.4.1 to 6.7.4.4.5. All parts of the shell shall have a minimum thickness as determined by 6.7.4.4.1 to 6.7.4.4.6. This thickness shall be exclusive of any corrosion allowance.

6.7.4.4.8 There shall be no sudden change of plate thickness at the attachment of the ends (heads) to the cylindrical portion of the shell.

6.7.4.5 Service equipment

6.7.4.5.1 Service equipment shall be so arranged as to be protected against the risk of being wrenched off or damaged during handling and transport. When the connection between the frame and the tank or the jacket and the shell allows relative movement, the equipment shall be so fastened as to permit such movement without risk of damage to working parts. The external discharge fittings (pipe sockets, shut-off devices), the stop-valve and its seating shall be protected against the danger of being wrenched off by external forces (for example, by using shear sections). The filling and discharge devices (including flanges or threaded plugs) and any protective caps shall be capable of being secured against unintended opening.

6.7.4.5.1.1 For offshore tank-containers, where positioning of service equipment and the design and strength of protection for such equipment is concerned, the increased danger of impact damage when handling such tanks in open seas shall be taken into account.

6.7.4.5.2 Each filling and discharge opening in portable tanks used for the transport of flammable refrigerated liquefied gases shall be fitted with at least three mutually independent shut-off devices in series, the first being a stop-valve situated as close as reasonably practicable to the jacket, the second being a stop-valve and the third being a blank flange or equivalent device. The shut-off device closest to the jacket shall be a quick-closing device, which closes automatically in the event of unintended movement of the portable tank during filling or discharge or fire engulfment. This device shall also be possible to operate by remote control.

6.7.4.5.3 Each filling and discharge opening in portable tanks used for the transport of non-flammable refrigerated liquefied gases shall be fitted with at least two mutually independent shut-off devices in series, the first being a stop-valve situated as close as reasonably practicable to the jacket, the second a blank flange or equivalent device.

6.7.4.5.4 For sections of piping which can be closed at both ends and where liquid product can be trapped, a method of automatic pressure relief shall be provided to prevent excess pressure build-up within the piping.

6.7.4.5.5 Vacuum-insulated tanks need not have an opening for inspection.

6.7.4.5.6 External fittings shall be grouped together so far as reasonably practicable.

6.7.4.5.7 Each connection on a portable tank shall be clearly marked to indicate its function.

6.7.4.5.8 Each stop-valve or other means of closure shall be designed and constructed to a rated pressure not less than the MAWP of the shell, taking into account the temperature expected during transport. All stop-valves with a screwed spindle shall be closed by a clockwise motion of the handwheel. In the case of other stop-valves, the position (open and closed) and direction of closure shall be clearly indicated. All stop-valves shall be designed to prevent unintentional opening.

6.7.4.5.9 When pressure-building units are used, the liquid and vapour connections to that unit shall be provided with a valve as close to the jacket as reasonably practicable to prevent the loss of contents in case of damage to the pressure-building unit.

6.7.4.5.10 Piping shall be designed, constructed and installed so as to avoid the risk of damage due to thermal expansion and contraction, mechanical shock and vibration. All piping shall be of a suitable material. To prevent leakage due to fire, only steel piping and welded joints shall be used between the jacket and the connection to the first closure of any outlet. The method of attaching the closure to this connection shall be to the satisfaction of the competent authority or its authorized body. Elsewhere, pipe joints shall be welded when necessary.

6.7.4.5.11 Joints in copper tubing shall be brazed or have an equally strong metal union. The melting point of brazing materials shall be no lower than 525°C. The joints shall not decrease the strength of the tubing, as may happen by cutting of threads.

6.7.4.5.12 The materials of construction of valves and accessories shall have satisfactory properties at the lowest operating temperature of the portable tank.

6.7.4.5.13 The burst pressure of all piping and pipe fittings shall be not less than the highest of four times the MAWP of the shell or four times the pressure to which it may be subjected in service by the action of a pump or other device (except pressure relief devices).

6.7.4.6 **Pressure relief devices**

6.7.4.6.1 Every shell shall be provided with not less than two independent spring-loaded pressure relief devices. The pressure relief devices shall open automatically at a pressure not less than the MAWP and be fully open at a pressure equal to 110% of the MAWP. These devices shall, after discharge, close at a pressure not lower than 10% below the pressure at which discharge starts and shall remain closed at all lower pressures. The pressure relief devices shall be of the type that will resist dynamic forces, including surge.

6.7.4.6.2 Shells for non-flammable refrigerated liquefied gases and hydrogen may in addition have frangible discs in parallel with the spring-loaded devices as specified in 6.7.4.7.2 and 6.7.4.7.3.

6.7.4.6.3 Pressure relief devices shall be designed to prevent the entry of foreign matter, the leakage of gas and the development of any dangerous excess pressure.

6.7.4.6.4 Pressure relief devices shall be approved by the competent authority or its authorized body.

6.7.4.7 **Capacity and setting of pressure relief devices**

6.7.4.7.1 In the case of the loss of vacuum in a vacuum-insulated tank or of loss of 20% of the insulation of a tank insulated with solid materials, the combined capacity of all pressure relief devices installed shall be sufficient so that the pressure (including accumulation) inside the shell does not exceed 120% of the MAWP.

6.7.4.7.2 For non-flammable refrigerated liquefied gases (except oxygen) and hydrogen, this capacity may be achieved by the use of frangible discs in parallel with the required safety relief devices. Frangible discs shall rupture at nominal pressure equal to the test pressure of the shell.

6.7.4.7.3 Under the circumstances described in 6.7.4.7.1 and 6.7.4.7.2 together with complete fire engulfment, the combined capacity of all pressure relief devices installed shall be sufficient to limit the pressure in the shell to the test pressure.

6.7.4.7.4 The required capacity of the relief devices shall be calculated in accordance with a well-established technical code recognized by the competent authority.[*]

6.7.4.8 **Marking of pressure relief devices**

6.7.4.8.1 Every pressure relief device shall be plainly and permanently marked with the following:

.1 the pressure (in bar or kPa) at which it is set to discharge;

.2 the allowable tolerance at the discharge pressure, for spring-loaded devices;

.3 the reference temperature corresponding to the rated pressure, for frangible discs;

.4 the rated flow capacity of the device in standard cubic metres of air per second (m^3/s); and

.5 the cross sectional flow areas of the spring-loaded pressure relief devices and frangible discs in mm^2.

When practicable, the following information shall also be shown:

.6 the manufacturer's name and relevant catalogue number.

6.7.4.8.2 The rated flow capacity marked on the pressure relief devices shall be determined according to ISO 4126-1:2004 and ISO 4126-7:2004.

---

[*] See, e.g. CGA S-1.2-2003 *Pressure Relief Device Standards – Part 2 – Cargo and Portable Tanks for Compressed Gases.*

6.7.4.9 **Connections to pressure relief devices**

6.7.4.9.1 Connections to pressure relief devices shall be of sufficient size to enable the required discharge to pass unrestricted to the safety device. No stop-valve shall be installed between the shell and the pressure relief devices except when duplicate devices are provided for maintenance or other reasons and the stop-valves serving the devices actually in use are locked open or the stop-valves are interlocked so that the provisions of 6.7.4.7 are always fulfilled. There shall be no obstruction in an opening leading to a vent or pressure relief device which might restrict or cut off the flow from the shell to that device. Pipework to vent the vapour or liquid from the outlet of the pressure relief devices, when used, shall deliver the relieved vapour or liquid to the atmosphere in conditions of minimum back-pressure on the relieving device.

6.7.4.10 **Siting of pressure relief devices**

6.7.4.10.1 Each pressure relief device inlet shall be situated on top of the shell in a position as near the longitudinal and transverse centre of the shell as reasonably practicable. All pressure relief device inlets shall, under maximum filling conditions, be situated in the vapour space of the shell and the devices shall be so arranged as to ensure that the escaping vapour is discharged unrestrictedly. For refrigerated liquefied gases, the escaping vapour shall be directed away from the tank and in such a manner that it cannot impinge upon the tank. Protective devices which deflect the flow of vapour are permissible provided the required relief-device capacity is not reduced.

6.7.4.10.2 Arrangements shall be made to prevent access to the devices by unauthorized persons and to protect the devices from damage caused by the portable tank overturning.

6.7.4.11 **Gauging devices**

6.7.4.11.1 Unless a portable tank is intended to be filled by mass, it shall be equipped with one or more gauging devices. Glass level-gauges and gauges made of other fragile material, which are in direct communication with the contents of the shell, shall not be used.

6.7.4.11.2 A connection for a vacuum gauge shall be provided in the jacket of a vacuum-insulated portable tank.

6.7.4.12 **Portable tank supports, frameworks, lifting and tie-down attachments**

6.7.4.12.1 Portable tanks shall be designed and constructed with a support structure to provide a secure base during transport. The forces specified in 6.7.4.2.12 and the safety factor specified in 6.7.4.2.13 shall be considered in this aspect of the design. Skids, frameworks, cradles or other similar structures are acceptable.

6.7.4.12.2 The combined stresses caused by portable tank mountings (such as cradles, frameworks, etc.) and portable tank lifting and tie-down attachments shall not cause excessive stress in any portion of the tank. Permanent lifting and tie-down attachments shall be fitted to all portable tanks. Preferably they shall be fitted to the portable tank supports but may be secured to reinforcing plates located on the tank at the points of support.

6.7.4.12.3 In the design of supports and frameworks, the effects of environmental corrosion shall be taken into account.

6.7.4.12.4 Forklift pockets shall be capable of being closed off. The means of closing forklift pockets shall be a permanent part of the framework or permanently attached to the framework. Single-compartment portable tanks with a length less than 3.65 m need not have closed-off forklift pockets provided that:

.1 the tank and all the fittings are well protected from being hit by the forklift blades; and

.2 the distance between the centres of the forklift pockets is at least half of the maximum length of the portable tank.

6.7.4.12.5 When portable tanks are not protected during transport, according to 4.2.3.3, the shells and service equipment shall be protected against damage to the shell and service equipment resulting from lateral or longitudinal impact or overturning. External fittings shall be protected so as to preclude the release of the shell contents upon impact or overturning of the portable tank on its fittings. Examples of protection include:

.1 protection against lateral impact, which may consist of longitudinal bars protecting the shell on both sides at the level of the median line;

.2 protection of the portable tank against overturning, which may consist of reinforcement rings or bars fixed across the frame;

.3 protection against rear impact, which may consist of a bumper or frame;

.4 protection of the shell against damage from impact or overturning by use of an ISO frame in accordance with ISO 1496-3:1995;

.5 protection of the portable tank from impact or overturning by a vacuum insulation jacket.

6

6.7.4.13   Design approval

6.7.4.13.1   The competent authority or its authorized body shall issue a design approval certificate for any new design of a portable tank. This certificate shall attest that a portable tank has been surveyed by that authority, is suitable for its intended purpose and meets the provisions of this chapter. When a series of portable tanks are manufactured without change in the design, the certificate shall be valid for the entire series. The certificate shall refer to the prototype test report, the refrigerated liquefied gases allowed to be transported, the materials of construction of the shell and jacket and an approval number. The approval number shall consist of the distinguishing sign or mark of the State in whose territory the approval was granted, i.e. the distinguishing sign for use in international traffic, as prescribed by the Convention on Road Traffic, Vienna, 1968, and a registration number. Any alternative arrangements according to 6.7.1.2 shall be indicated on the certificate. A design approval may serve for the approval of smaller portable tanks made of materials of the same kind and thickness, by the same fabrication techniques and with identical supports, equivalent closures and other appurtenances.

6.7.4.13.2   The prototype test report for the design approval shall include at least the following:

.1   the results of the applicable framework test specified in ISO 1496-3:1995;

.2   the results of the initial inspection and test in 6.7.4.14.3; and

.3   the results of the impact test in 6.7.4.14.1, when applicable.

6.7.4.14   Inspection and testing

6.7.4.14.1   Portable tanks meeting the definition of *container* in the International Convention for Safe Containers (CSC), 1972, as amended, shall not be used unless they are successfully qualified by subjecting a representative prototype of each design to the Dynamic, Longitudinal Impact Test prescribed in the Manual of Tests and Criteria, part IV, section 41. This provision only applies to portable tanks which are constructed according to a design approval certificate which has been issued on or after 1 January 2008.

6.7.4.14.2   The tank and items of equipment of each portable tank shall be inspected and tested before being put into service for the first time (initial inspection and test) and thereafter at not more than five-year intervals (5-year periodic inspection and test) with an intermediate periodic inspection and test (2.5-year periodic inspection and test) midway between the 5-year periodic inspections and tests. The 2.5-year periodic inspection and test may be performed within 3 months of the specified date. An exceptional inspection and test shall be performed regardless of the last periodic inspection and test when necessary according to 6.7.4.14.7.

6.7.4.14.3   The initial inspection and test of a portable tank shall include a check of the design characteristics, an internal and external examination of the portable tank shell and its fittings with due regard to the refrigerated liquefied gases to be transported, and a pressure test referring to the test pressures according to 6.7.4.3.2. The pressure test may be performed as a hydraulic test or by using another liquid or gas, with the agreement of the competent authority or its authorized body. Before the portable tank is placed into service, a leakproofness test and a test of the satisfactory operation of all service equipment shall also be performed. When the shell and its fittings have been pressure-tested separately, they shall be subjected together after assembly to a leakproofness test. All welds subject to full stress level shall be inspected during the initial test by radiographic, ultrasonic, or another suitable non-destructive test method. This does not apply to the jacket.

6.7.4.14.4   The 5-year and 2.5-year periodic inspections and tests shall include an external examination of the portable tank and its fittings with due regard to the refrigerated liquefied gases transported, a leakproofness test, a test of the satisfactory operation of all service equipment and a vacuum reading, when applicable. In the case of non-vacuum-insulated tanks, the jacket and insulation shall be removed during the 2.5-year and the 5-year periodic inspections and tests, but only to the extent necessary for a reliable appraisal.

6.7.4.14.5   [Reserved]

6.7.4.14.6   A portable tank may not be filled and offered for transport after the date of expiry of the last 5-year or 2.5-year periodic inspection and test as required by 6.7.4.14.2. However, a portable tank filled prior to the date of expiry of the last periodic inspection and test may be transported for a period not to exceed three months beyond the date of expiry of the last periodic test or inspection. In addition, a portable tank may be transported after the date of expiry of the last periodic test and inspection:

.1   after emptying but before cleaning, for purposes of performing the next required test or inspection prior to refilling; and

.2   unless otherwise approved by the competent authority, for a period not to exceed six months beyond the date of expiry of the last periodic test or inspection, in order to allow the return of dangerous goods for proper disposal or recycling. Reference to this exemption shall be mentioned in the transport document.

6.7.4.14.7   The exceptional inspection and test is necessary when the portable tank shows evidence of damaged or corroded areas, leakage, or any other conditions that indicate a deficiency that could affect the integrity of the portable tank. The extent of the exceptional inspection and test shall depend on the amount of damage or deterioration of the portable tank. It shall include at least the 2.5-year periodic inspection and test according to 6.7.4.14.4.

6.7.4.14.8 The internal examination during the initial inspection and test shall ensure that the shell is inspected for pitting, corrosion, or abrasions, dents, distortions, defects in welds or any other conditions that might render the portable tank unsafe for transport.

6.7.4.14.9 The external examination shall ensure that:

.1 the external piping, valves, pressurizing/cooling systems when applicable, and gaskets are inspected for corroded areas, defects, or any other conditions, including leakage, that might render the portable tank unsafe for filling, discharge or transport;

.2 there is no leakage at any manhole covers or gaskets;

.3 missing or loose bolts or nuts on any flanged connection or blank flange are replaced or tightened;

.4 all emergency devices and valves are free from corrosion, distortion and any damage or defect that could prevent their normal operation. Remote closure devices and self-closing stop-valves shall be operated to demonstrate proper operation;

△ .5 required marks on the portable tank are legible and in accordance with the applicable provisions; and

.6 the framework, the supports and the arrangements for lifting the portable tank are in satisfactory condition.

6.7.4.14.10 The inspections and tests in 6.7.4.14.1, 6.7.4.14.3, 6.7.4.14.4 and 6.7.4.14.7 shall be performed or witnessed by an expert approved by the competent authority or its authorized body. When the pressure test is a part of the inspection and test, the test pressure shall be the one indicated on the data plate of the portable tank. While under pressure, the portable tank shall be inspected for any leaks in the shell, piping or equipment.

6.7.4.14.11 In all cases when cutting, burning or welding operations on the shell of a portable tank have been effected, that work shall be to the approval of the competent authority or its authorized body, taking into account the pressure-vessel code used for the construction of the shell. A pressure test to the original test pressure shall be performed after the work is completed.

6.7.4.14.12 When evidence of any unsafe condition is discovered, the portable tank shall not be returned to service until it has been corrected and the test is repeated and passed.

6.7.4.15 Marking

6.7.4.15.1 Every portable tank shall be fitted with a corrosion-resistant metal plate permanently attached to the portable tank in a conspicuous place readily accessible for inspection. When for reasons of portable tank arrangements the plate cannot be permanently attached to the shell, the shell shall be marked with at least the information required by the pressure-vessel code. As a minimum, at least the following information shall be marked on the plate by stamping or by any other similar method:

(a) owner information
   (i) owner's registration number;

(b) manufacturing information
   (i) country of manufacture;
   (ii) year of manufacture;
   (iii) manufacturer's name or mark;
   (iv) manufacturer's serial number;

(c) approval information
   (i) the United Nations packaging symbol:

   This symbol shall not be used for any purpose other than certifying that a packaging, a flexible bulk container, a portable tank or a MEGC complies with the relevant requirements in chapters 6.1, 6.2, 6.3, 6.5, 6.6, 6.7 or 6.9;
   (ii) approval country;
   (iii) authorized body for the design approval;
   (iv) design approval number;
   (v) letters "AA", if the design was approved under alternative arrangements (see 6.7.1.2);
   (vi) pressure-vessel code to which the shell is designed;

(d) pressures
   (i) MAWP (in bar gauge or kPa gauge);[*]
   (ii) test pressure (in bar gauge or kPa gauge);[*]
   (iii) initial pressure test date (month and year);
   (iv) identification mark of the initial pressure test witness;

---

[*] The unit used shall be indicated.

    (e)   temperatures

         (i)   minimum design temperature (in °C);[*]

    (f)   materials

         (i)   shell material(s) and material standard reference(s);

         (ii) equivalent thickness in reference steel (in mm);[*]

    (g) capacity

         (i)   tank water capacity at 20°C (in litres);[*]

    (h) insulation

         (i)   either "Thermally insulated" or "Vacuum insulated" (as applicable);

         (ii) effectiveness of the insulation system (heat influx) (in Watts);[*]

    (i)   holding times – for each refrigerated liquefied gas permitted to be transported in the portable tank:

         (i)   name, in full, of the refrigerated liquefied gas;

         (ii) reference holding time (in days or hours);[*]

         (iii) initial pressure (in bar gauge or kPa gauge);[*]

         (iv) degree of filling (in kg);[*]

    (j)   periodic inspections and tests

         (i)   type of the most recent periodic test (2.5-year, 5-year or exceptional);

         (ii) date of the most recent periodic test (month and year);

         (iii) identification mark of the authorized body who performed or witnessed the most recent test.

---

[*] The unit used shall be indicated.

△   **Figure 6.7.4.15.1** – *Example of a plate for marking*

Owner's registration number			
MANUFACTURING INFORMATION			
Country of manufacture			
Year of manufacture			
Manufacturer			
Manufacturer's serial number			
APPROVAL INFORMATION			

(un) Approval country		
Authorized body for design approval		
Design approval number		"AA" *(if applicable)*

Shell design code (pressure-vessel code)		
PRESSURES		
MAWP		bar *or* kPa
Test pressure		bar *or* kPa

Initial pressure test date:	*(mm/yyyy)*	Witness stamp:	

TEMPERATURES		
Minimum design temperature		°C
MATERIALS		
Shell material(s) and material standard reference(s)		
Equivalent thickness in reference steel		mm
CAPACITY		
Tank water capacity at 20°C		litres
INSULATION		
"Thermally insulated" or "Vacuum insulated" *(as applicable)*		
Heat influx		Watts
HOLDING TIMES		

Refrigerated liquefied gas(es) permitted	Reference holding time	Initial pressure	Degree of filling
	days *or* hours	bar *or* kPa	kg

PERIODIC INSPECTIONS/TESTS

Test type	Test date	Witness stamp	Test type	Test date	Witness stamp
	(mm/yyyy)			*(mm/yyyy)*	

6

6.7.4.15.2 The following information shall be durably marked either on the portable tank itself or on a metal plate firmly secured to the portable tank:

> Name of the owner and the operator
>
> Name of the refrigerated liquefied gas being transported (and minimum mean bulk temperature)
>
> Maximum permissible gross mass (MPGM) . . . . kg
>
> Unladen (tare) mass . . . . kg
>
> Actual holding time for gas being transported . . . . days (or hours)
>
> Portable tank instruction in accordance with 4.2.5.2.6.

6.7.4.15.3 If a portable tank is designed and approved for handling in open seas, the words "OFFSHORE PORTABLE TANK" shall be marked on the identification plate.

6.7.5 Provisions for the design, construction, inspection and testing of multiple-element gas containers (MEGCs) intended for the transport of non-refrigerated gases

6.7.5.1 Definitions

For the purposes of this section:

Elements are cylinders, tubes or bundles of cylinders;

Leakproofness test means a test, using gas, subjecting the elements and the service equipment of the MEGC to an effective internal pressure of not less than 20% of the test pressure;

Manifold means an assembly of piping and valves connecting the filling and/or discharge openings of the elements;

Maximum permissible gross mass (MPGM) means the sum of the tare mass of the MEGC and the heaviest load authorized for transport;

Service equipment means measuring instruments and filling, discharge, venting and safety devices;

Structural equipment means the reinforcing, fastening, protective and stabilizing members external to the elements.

6.7.5.2 General design and construction provisions

6.7.5.2.1 The MEGC shall be capable of being filled and discharged without the removal of its structural equipment. It shall possess stabilizing members external to the elements to provide structural integrity for handling and transport. MEGCs shall be designed and constructed with supports to provide a secure base during transport and with lifting and tie-down attachments which are adequate for lifting the MEGC, including when loaded to its maximum permissible gross mass. The MEGC shall be designed to be loaded onto or into a vehicle or ship and shall be equipped with skids, mountings or accessories to facilitate mechanical handling.

6.7.5.2.2 MEGCs shall be designed, manufactured and equipped in such a way as to withstand all conditions to which they will be subjected during normal conditions of handling and transport. The design shall take into account the effects of dynamic loading and fatigue.

6.7.5.2.3 Elements of an MEGC shall be made of seamless steel and be constructed and tested according to chapter 6.2. All of the elements in an MEGC shall be of the same design type.

6.7.5.2.4 Elements of MEGCs, fittings and pipework shall be:

△ .1 compatible with the substances intended to be transported (for gases, see ISO 11114-1:2012 and ISO 11114-2:2013); or

.2 properly passivated or neutralized by chemical reaction.

6.7.5.2.5 Contact between dissimilar metals which could result in damage by galvanic action shall be avoided.

6.7.5.2.6 The materials of the MEGC, including any devices, gaskets, and accessories, shall not adversely affect the gases intended for transport in the MEGC.

6.7.5.2.7 MEGCs shall be designed to withstand, without loss of contents, at least the internal pressure due to the contents, and the static, dynamic and thermal loads during normal conditions of handling and transport. The design shall demonstrate that the effects of fatigue, caused by repeated application of these loads through the expected life of the multiple-element gas container, have been taken into account.

6.7.5.2.8 MEGCs and their fastenings shall, under the maximum permissible load, be capable of withstanding the following separately applied static forces:

.1 in the direction of travel: twice the MPGM multiplied by the acceleration due to gravity (*g*);[*]

.2 horizontally at right angles to the direction of travel: the MPGM (when the direction of travel is not clearly determined, the forces shall be equal to twice the MPGM) multiplied by the acceleration due to gravity (*g*);[*]

.3 vertically upwards: the MPGM multiplied by the acceleration due to gravity (*g*);[*] and

.4 vertically downwards: twice the MPGM (total loading including the effect of gravity) multiplied by the acceleration due to gravity (*g*).[*]

6.7.5.2.9 Under the forces defined above, the stress at the most severely stressed point of the elements shall not exceed the values given in either the relevant standards of 6.2.2.1 or, if the elements are not designed, constructed and tested according to those standards, in the technical code or standard recognized or approved by the competent authority of the country of use (see 6.2.3.1).

6.7.5.2.10 Under each of the forces in 6.7.5.2.8, the safety factor for the framework and fastenings to be observed shall be as follows:

.1 for steels having a clearly defined yield point, a safety factor of 1.5 in relation to the guaranteed yield strength; or

.2 for steels with no clearly defined yield point, a safety factor of 1.5 in relation to the guaranteed 0.2% proof strength and, for austenitic steels, the 1% proof strength.

6.7.5.2.11 MEGCs intended for the transport of flammable gases shall be capable of being electrically earthed.

6.7.5.2.12 The elements shall be secured in a manner that prevents undesired movement in relation to the structure and the concentration of harmful localized stresses.

6.7.5.3 Service equipment

6.7.5.3.1 Service equipment shall be configured or designed to prevent damage that could result in the release of the pressure receptacle contents during normal conditions of handling and transport. When the connection between the frame and the elements allows relative movement between the sub-assemblies, the equipment shall be so fastened as to permit such movement without damage to working parts. The manifolds, the discharge fittings (pipe sockets, shut-off devices), and the stop-valves shall be protected from being wrenched off by external forces. Manifold piping leading to shut-off valves shall be sufficiently flexible to protect the valves and the piping from shearing, or releasing the pressure receptacle contents. The filling and discharge devices (including flanges or threaded plugs) and any protective caps shall be capable of being secured against unintended opening.

6.7.5.3.2 Each element intended for the transport of gases of class 2.3 shall be fitted with a valve. The manifold for liquefied gases of class 2.3 shall be so designed that the elements can be filled separately and be kept isolated by a valve capable of being sealed. For the transport of gases of class 2.1, the elements shall be divided into groups of not more than 3000 litres each isolated by a valve.

6.7.5.3.3 For filling and discharge openings of the MEGC, two valves in series shall be placed in an accessible position on each discharge and filling pipe. One of the valves may be a non-return valve. The filling and discharge devices may be fitted to a manifold. For sections of piping which can be closed at both ends and where a liquid product can be trapped, a pressure relief valve shall be provided to prevent excessive pressure build-up. The main isolation valves on an MEGC shall be clearly marked to indicate their directions of closure. Each stop-valve or other means of closure shall be designed and constructed to withstand a pressure equal to or greater than 1.5 times the test pressure of the MEGC. All stop-valves with screwed spindles shall close by a clockwise motion of the handwheel. For other stop-valves, the positions (open and closed) and direction of closure shall be clearly indicated. All stop-valves shall be designed and positioned to prevent unintentional opening. Ductile metals shall be used in the construction of valves or accessories.

6.7.5.3.4 Piping shall be designed, constructed and installed so as to avoid damage due to expansion and contraction, mechanical shock and vibration. Joints in tubing shall be brazed or have an equally strong metal union. The melting point of brazing materials shall be no lower than 525°C. The rated pressure of the service equipment and of the manifold shall be not less than two thirds of the test pressure of the elements.

6.7.5.4 Pressure relief devices

6.7.5.4.1 The elements of MEGCs used for the transport of UN 1013 carbon dioxide and UN 1070 nitrous oxide shall be divided into groups of not more than 3000 litres each isolated by a valve. Each group shall be fitted with one

---

[*] For calculation purposes, $g = 9.81$ m/s^2.

or more pressure relief devices. If so required by the competent authority of the country of use, MEGCs for other gases shall be fitted with pressure relief devices as specified by that competent authority.

6.7.5.4.2   When pressure relief devices are fitted, every element or group of elements of an MEGC that can be isolated shall then be fitted with one or more pressure relief devices. Pressure relief devices shall be of a type that will resist dynamic forces, including liquid surge, and shall be designed to prevent the entry of foreign matter, the leakage of gas and the development of any dangerous excess pressure.

6.7.5.4.3   MEGCs used for the transport of certain non-refrigerated gases identified in instruction T50 in 4.2.5.2.6 may have a pressure relief device as required by the competent authority of the country of use. Unless an MEGC in dedicated service is fitted with an approved pressure relief device constructed of materials compatible with the load, such a device shall comprise a frangible disc preceding a spring-loaded device. The space between the frangible disc and the spring-loaded device may be equipped with a pressure gauge or a suitable tell-tale indicator. This arrangement permits the detection of disc rupture, pinholing or leakage which could cause a malfunction of the pressure relief device. The frangible disc shall rupture at a nominal pressure 10% above the start-to-discharge pressure of the spring-loaded device.

6.7.5.4.4   In the case of multi-purpose MEGCs used for the transport of low-pressure liquefied gases, the pressure relief devices shall open at a pressure as specified in 6.7.3.7.1 for the gas having the highest maximum allowable working pressure of the gases allowed to be transported in the MEGC.

6.7.5.5   Capacity of pressure relief devices

6.7.5.5.1   The combined delivery capacity of the pressure relief devices when fitted shall be sufficient that, in the event of complete fire engulfment of the MEGC, the pressure (including accumulation) inside the elements does not exceed 120% of the set pressure of the pressure relief device. The formula provided in CGA S-1.2-2003 *Pressure Relief Device Standards, Part 2, Cargo and Portable Tanks for Compressed Gases* shall be used to determine the minimum total flow capacity for the system of pressure relief devices. CGA S-1.1-2003 *Pressure Relief Device Standards, Part 1, Cylinders for Compressed Gases* may be used to determine the relief capacity of individual elements. Spring-loaded pressure relief devices may be used to achieve the full relief capacity prescribed in the case of low-pressure liquefied gases. In the case of multi-purpose MEGCs, the combined delivery capacity of the pressure relief devices shall be taken for the gas which requires the highest delivery capacity of the gases allowed to be transported in the MEGC.

6.7.5.5.2   To determine the total required capacity of the pressure relief devices installed on the elements for the transport of liquefied gases, the thermodynamic properties of the gas shall be considered (see, for example, CGA S-1.2-2003 *Pressure Relief Device Standards, Part 2, Cargo and Portable Tanks for Compressed Gases* for low-pressure liquefied gases and CGA S-1.1-2003 *Pressure Relief Device Standards, Part 1, Cylinders for Compressed Gases* for high-pressure liquefied gases).

6.7.5.6   Marking of pressure relief devices

6.7.5.6.1   Pressure relief devices shall be clearly and permanently marked with the following:

(a)   the manufacturer's name and relevant catalogue number;

(b)   the set pressure and/or the set temperature;

(c)   the date of the last test; and

(d)   the cross sectional flow areas of the spring-loaded pressure relief devices and frangible discs in mm^2.

6.7.5.6.2   The rated flow capacity marked on spring-loaded pressure relief devices for low-pressure liquefied gases shall be determined according to ISO 4126-1:2004 and ISO 4126-7:2004.

6.7.5.7   Connections to pressure relief devices

6.7.5.7.1   Connections to pressure relief devices shall be of sufficient size to enable the required discharge to pass unrestricted to the pressure relief device. No stop-valve shall be installed between the element and the pressure relief devices, except when duplicate devices are provided for maintenance or other reasons, and the stop-valves serving the devices actually in use are locked open, or the stop-valves are interlocked so that at least one of the duplicate devices is always operable and capable of meeting the requirements of 6.7.5.5. There shall be no obstruction in an opening leading to or leaving from a vent or pressure relief device which might restrict or cut off the flow from the element to that device. The opening through all piping and fittings shall have at least the same flow area as the inlet of the pressure relief device to which it is connected. The nominal size of the discharge piping shall be at least as large as that of the pressure relief device outlet. Vents from the pressure relief devices, when used, shall deliver the relieved vapour or liquid to the atmosphere in conditions of minimum back-pressure on the relieving device.

6.7.5.8 **Siting of pressure relief devices**

6.7.5.8.1 Each pressure relief device shall, under maximum filling conditions, be in communication with the vapour space of the elements for the transport of liquefied gases. The devices, when fitted, shall be so arranged as to ensure that the escaping vapour is discharged upwards and unrestrictedly so as to prevent any impingement of escaping gas or liquid upon the MEGC, its elements or personnel. For flammable, pyrophoric and oxidizing gases, the escaping gas shall be directed away from the element in such a manner that it cannot impinge upon the other elements. Heat-resistant protective devices which deflect the flow of gas are permissible provided the required pressure relief device capacity is not reduced.

6.7.5.8.2 Arrangements shall be made to prevent access to the pressure relief devices by unauthorized persons and to protect the devices from damage caused by the MEGC overturning.

6.7.5.9 **Gauging devices**

6.7.5.9.1 When an MEGC is intended to be filled by mass, it shall be equipped with one or more gauging devices. Level-gauges made of glass or other fragile material shall not be used.

6.7.5.10 **MEGC supports, frameworks, lifting and tie-down attachments**

6.7.5.10.1 MEGCs shall be designed and constructed with a support structure to provide a secure base during transport. The forces specified in 6.7.5.2.8 and the safety factor specified in 6.7.5.2.10 shall be considered in this aspect of the design. Skids, frameworks, cradles or other similar structures are acceptable.

6.7.5.10.2 The combined stresses caused by element mountings (e.g. cradles, frameworks, etc.) and MEGC lifting and tie-down attachments shall not cause excessive stress in any element. Permanent lifting and tie-down attachments shall be fitted to all MEGCs. In no case shall mountings or attachments be welded onto the elements.

6.7.5.10.3 In the design of supports and frameworks, the effects of environmental corrosion shall be taken into account.

6.7.5.10.4 When MEGCs are not protected during transport, according to 4.2.4.3, the elements and service equipment shall be protected against damage resulting from lateral or longitudinal impact or overturning. External fittings shall be protected so as to preclude the release of the elements' contents upon impact or overturning of the MEGC on its fittings. Particular attention shall be paid to the protection of the manifold. Examples of protection include:

.1   protection against lateral impact, which may consist of longitudinal bars;

.2   protection against overturning, which may consist of reinforcement rings or bars fixed across the frame;

.3   protection against rear impact, which may consist of a bumper or frame;

.4   protection of the elements and service equipment against damage from impact or overturning by use of an ISO frame in accordance with the relevant provisions of ISO 1496-3:1995.

6.7.5.11 **Design approval**

6.7.5.11.1 The competent authority or its authorized body shall issue a design approval certificate for any new design of an MEGC. This certificate shall attest that the MEGC has been surveyed by that authority, is suitable for its intended purpose and meets the requirements of this chapter, the applicable provisions for gases of chapter 4.1 and of packing instruction P200. When a series of MEGCs are manufactured without change in the design, the certificate shall be valid for the entire series. The certificate shall refer to the prototype test report, the materials of construction of the manifold, the standards to which the elements are made and an approval number. The approval number shall consist of the distinguishing sign or mark of the country granting the approval, i.e. the distinguishing sign for use in international traffic, as prescribed by the Convention on Road Traffic, Vienna, 1968, and a registration number. Any alternative arrangements according to 6.7.1.2 shall be indicated on the certificate. A design approval may serve for the approval of smaller MEGCs made of materials of the same type and thickness, by the same fabrication techniques and with identical supports, equivalent closures and other appurtenances.

6.7.5.11.2 The prototype test report for the design approval shall include at least the following:

.1   the results of the applicable framework test specified in ISO 1496-3:1995;

.2   the results of the initial inspection and test specified in 6.7.5.12.3;

.3   the results of the impact test specified in 6.7.5.12.1; and

.4   certification documents verifying that the cylinders and tubes comply with the applicable standards.

6

6.7.5.12   Inspection and testing

6.7.5.12.1   MEGCs meeting the definition of *container* in the International Convention for Safe Containers (CSC), 1972, as amended, shall not be used unless they are successfully qualified by subjecting a representative prototype of each design to the Dynamic, Longitudinal Impact Test prescribed in the Manual of Tests and Criteria, part IV, section 41. This provision only applies to MEGCs which are constructed according to a design approval certificate which has been issued on or after 1 January 2008.

6.7.5.12.2   The elements and items of equipment of each MEGC shall be inspected and tested before being put into service for the first time (initial inspection and test). Thereafter, MEGCs shall be inspected at no more than five-year intervals (5-year periodic inspection). An exceptional inspection and test shall be performed, regardless of the last periodic inspection and test, when necessary according to 6.7.5.12.5.

6.7.5.12.3   The initial inspection and test of an MEGC shall include a check of the design characteristics, an external examination of the MEGC and its fittings with due regard to the gases to be transported, and a pressure test performed at the test pressures according to packing instruction P200. The pressure test of the manifold may be performed as a hydraulic test or by using another liquid or gas with the agreement of the competent authority or its authorized body. Before the MEGC is placed into service, a leakproofness test and a test of the satisfactory operation of all service equipment shall also be performed. When the elements and their fittings have been pressure-tested separately, they shall be subjected together after assembly to a leakproofness test.

6.7.5.12.4   The 5-year periodic inspection and test shall include an external examination of the structure, the elements and the service equipment in accordance with 6.7.5.12.6. The elements and the piping shall be tested at the periodicity specified in packing instruction P200 and in accordance with the provisions described in 6.2.1.6. When the elements and equipment have been pressure-tested separately, they shall be subjected together after assembly to a leakproofness test.

6.7.5.12.5   An exceptional inspection and test is necessary when the MEGC shows evidence of damaged or corroded areas, leakage, or other conditions that indicate a deficiency that could affect the integrity of the MEGC. The extent of the exceptional inspection and test shall depend on the amount of damage or deterioration of the MEGC. It shall include at least the examinations required under 6.7.5.12.6.

6.7.5.12.6   The examinations shall ensure that:

.1   the elements are inspected externally for pitting, corrosion, abrasions, dents, distortions, defects in welds or any other conditions, including leakage, that might render the MEGC unsafe for transport;

.2   the piping, valves, and gaskets are inspected for corroded areas, defects, and other conditions, including leakage, that might render the MEGC unsafe for filling, discharge or transport;

.3   missing or loose bolts or nuts on any flanged connection or blank flange are replaced or tightened;

.4   all emergency devices and valves are free from corrosion, distortion and any damage or defect that could prevent their normal operation. Remote closure devices and self-closing stop-valves shall be operated to demonstrate proper operation;

△ .5   required marks on the MEGC are legible and in accordance with the applicable requirements; and

.6   the framework, the supports and the arrangements for lifting the MEGC are in satisfactory condition.

6.7.5.12.7   The inspections and tests in 6.7.5.12.1, 6.7.5.12.3, 6.7.5.12.4 and 6.7.5.12.5 shall be performed or witnessed by a body authorized by the competent authority. When the pressure test is a part of the inspection and test, the test pressure shall be the one indicated on the data plate of the MEGC. While under pressure, the MEGC shall be inspected for any leaks in the elements, piping or equipment.

6.7.5.12.8   When evidence of any unsafe condition is discovered, the MEGC shall not be returned to service until it has been corrected and the applicable tests and verifications are passed.

6.7.5.13   Marking

6.7.5.13.1   Every MEGC shall be fitted with a corrosion-resistant metal plate permanently attached to the MEGC in a conspicuous place readily accessible for inspection. The metal plate shall not be affixed to the elements. The elements shall be marked in accordance with chapter 6.2. As a minimum, at least the following information shall be marked on the plate by stamping or by any other similar method:

(a)   owner information

(i)   owner's registration number;

(b)   manufacturing information

(i)   country of manufacture;

(ii)   year of manufacture;

(iii)   manufacturer's name or mark;

(iv)   manufacturer's serial number;

(c)   approval information

(i)   the United Nations packaging symbol:

This symbol shall not be used for any purpose other than certifying that a packaging, a flexible bulk container, a portable tank or a MEGC complies with the relevant requirements in chapters 6.1, 6.2, 6.3, 6.5, 6.6, 6.7 or 6.9;

(ii)   approval country;

(iii)   authorized body for the design approval;

(iv)   design approval number;

(v)   letters "AA", if the design was approved under alternative arrangements (see 6.7.1.2);

(d)   pressures

(i)   test pressure (in bar gauge);[*]

(ii)   initial pressure test date (month and year);

(iii)   identification mark of the initial pressure test witness;

(e)   temperatures

(i)   design temperature range (in °C);[*]

(f)   elements/capacity

(i)   number of elements;

(ii)   total water capacity (in litres);[*]

(g)   periodic inspections and tests

(i)   type of the most recent periodic test (5-year or exceptional);

(ii)   date of the most recent periodic test (month and year);

(iii)   identification mark of the authorized body who performed or witnessed the most recent test.

---

[*] The unit used shall be indicated.

△   **Figure 6.7.5.13.1** *– Example of a plate for marking*

Owner's registration number			
MANUFACTURING INFORMATION			
Country of manufacture			
Year of manufacture			
Manufacturer			
Manufacturer's serial number			
APPROVAL INFORMATION			
ⓤⓝ Approval country			
Authorized body for design approval			
Design approval number		"AA" *(if applicable)*	
PRESSURES			
Test pressure		bar	
Initial pressure test date:	*(mm/yyyy)*	Witness stamp:	
TEMPERATURES			
Design temperature range		°C to °C	
ELEMENTS/CAPACITY			
Number of elements			
Total water capacity		litres	
PERIODIC INSPECTIONS/TESTS			

Test type	Test date	Witness stamp	Test type	Test date	Witness stamp
	(mm/yyyy)			*(mm/yyyy)*	

6.7.5.13.2   The following information shall be durably marked on a metal plate firmly secured to the MEGC:

        Name of the operator

        Maximum permissible load mass . . . . kg

        Working pressure at 15°C: . . . . bar gauge

        Maximum permissible gross mass (MPGM) . . . . kg

        Unladen (tare) mass . . . . kg

6

Chapter 6.8

Provisions for road tank vehicles

6.8.1   General

6.8.1.1   Tank support frameworks, fitting and tie-down attachments[*]

6.8.1.1.1   Road tank vehicles shall be designed and manufactured with supports to provide a secure base during transport and with suitable tie-down attachments. The tie-down attachments shall be located on the tank support or vehicle structure in such a manner that the suspension system is not left in free play.

6.8.1.1.2   Tanks shall be carried only on vehicles whose fastenings are capable, in conditions of maximum permissible loading of the tanks, of absorbing the forces specified in 6.7.2.2.12, 6.7.3.2.9 and 6.7.4.2.12.

6.8.2   Road tank vehicles for long international voyages for substances of classes 3 to 9

6.8.2.1   Design and construction

6.8.2.1.1   A road tank vehicle for long international voyages shall be fitted with a tank complying with the provisions of chapters 4.2 and 6.7 and shall comply with the relevant provisions for tank supports, frameworks, lifting and tie-down attachments,[*] except for the provisions for forklift pockets, and in addition comply with the provisions of 6.8.1.1.1.

6.8.2.2   Approval, testing and marking

6.8.2.2.1   For approval, testing and marking of the tank, see 6.7.2.

6.8.2.2.2   The tank supports and tie-down attachments[*] of vehicles for long international voyages shall be included in the visual external inspection provided for in 6.7.2.19.

6.8.2.2.3   The vehicle of a road tank vehicle shall be tested and inspected in accordance with the road transport provisions of the competent authority of the country in which the vehicle is operated.

6.8.3   Road tank vehicles for short international voyages

6.8.3.1   Road tank vehicles for substances of classes 3 to 9 (IMO type 4)

6.8.3.1.1   *General provisions*

6.8.3.1.1.1   An IMO type 4 tank shall comply with either:

    .1   the provisions of 6.8.2; or

    .2   the provisions of 6.8.3.1.2 and 6.8.3.1.3.

6.8.3.1.2   *Design and construction*

6.8.3.1.2.1   An IMO type 4 tank shall comply with the provisions of 6.7.2, with the exception of:

    .1   6.7.2.3.2; however, they shall have been subjected to a test pressure not less than that specified according to the appropriate tank instruction assigned to the substance;

---

[*] See also IMO Assembly resolution A.581(14) of 20 November 1985, Guidelines for securing arrangements for the transport of road vehicles on ro-ro ships.

  .2 6.7.2.4; however, the thickness of cylindrical portions and ends in reference steel shall be:

    .1 not more than 2 mm thinner than the thickness specified according to the appropriate tank instruction assigned to the substance;

    .2 subject to an absolute minimum thickness of 4 mm of reference steel; and

    .3 for other materials, subject to an absolute minimum thickness of 3 mm;

  .3 6.7.2.2.13; however, the safety factor shall be not less than 1.3;

  .4 6.7.2.2.1 to 6.7.2.2.7; however, the materials of construction shall comply with the provisions of the competent authority for road transport;

  .5 6.7.2.5.1; however, the protection of valves and accessories shall comply with the provisions of the competent authority for road transport;

  .6 6.7.2.5.3; however, IMO type 4 tanks shall be provided with manholes or other openings in the tank which comply with the provisions of the competent authority for road transport;

  .7 6.7.2.5.2 and 6.7.2.5.4; however, tank nozzles and external fittings shall comply with the provisions of the competent authority for road transport;

  .8 6.7.2.6; however, IMO type 4 tanks with bottom openings shall not be used for substances for which bottom openings are not permitted in the appropriate tank instruction assigned to the substance. In addition, existing openings and hand inspection holes shall be either closed by bolted flanges mounted both internally and externally, fitted with product-compatible gaskets, or by welding as specified in 6.7.2.6.1. The closing of openings and hand inspection holes shall be approved by the competent authority for sea transport;

  .9 6.7.2.7 to 6.7.2.15; however, IMO type 4 tanks shall be fitted with pressure relief devices of the type required according to the appropriate tank instruction assigned to the substance. The devices shall be acceptable to the competent authority for the road transport for the substances to be transported. The start-to-discharge pressure of the spring-loaded pressure relief devices shall in no case be less than the maximum allowable working pressure, nor greater than 25% above that pressure; and

  .10 6.7.2.17; however, tank supports on permanently attached IMO type 4 tanks shall comply with the provisions of the competent authority for road transport.

6.8.3.1.2.2 For IMO type 4 tanks, the maximum effective gauge pressure developed by the substances to be transported shall not exceed the maximum allowable working pressure of the tank.

6.8.3.1.3 *Approval, testing and marking*

6.8.3.1.3.1 IMO type 4 tanks shall be approved for road transport by the competent authority.

6.8.3.1.3.2 The competent authority for sea transport shall issue additionally, in respect of an IMO type 4 tank, a certificate attesting compliance with the relevant design, construction and equipment provisions of this subsection and the special provisions for certain substances, as applicable.

6.8.3.1.3.3 IMO type 4 tanks shall be periodically tested and inspected in accordance with the provisions of the competent authority for road transport.

6.8.3.1.3.4 An IMO type 4 tank shall be marked in accordance with 6.7.2.20. However, where the marking required by the competent authority for road transport is substantially in agreement with that of 6.7.2.20, it will be sufficient to endorse the metal plate attached to the IMO type 4 tank with "IMO 4".

6.8.3.1.3.5 IMO type 4 tanks which are not permanently attached to the chassis shall be marked "IMO type 4" in letters at least 32 mm high.

6.8.3.2 **Road tank vehicles for non-refrigerated liquefied gases of class 2 (IMO type 6)**

6.8.3.2.1 *General provisions*

6.8.3.2.1.1 An IMO type 6 tank shall comply with either:

  .1 the provisions of 6.7.3; or

  .2 the provisions of 6.8.3.2.2 and 6.8.3.2.3.

6.8.3.2.1.2 For an IMO type 6 tank, the design temperature range is defined in 6.7.3.1. The temperature to be taken is to be agreed by the competent authority for road transport.

6.8.3.2.2 *Design and construction*

6.8.3.2.2.1 An IMO type 6 tank shall comply with the provisions of 6.7.3, with the exception of:

  .1 the safety factor of 1.5 in 6.7.3.2.10; however, the safety factor shall not be less than 1.3;

.2   6.7.3.5.7;

.3   6.7.3.6.1, if bottom openings are approved by the competent authority for sea transport;

.4   6.7.3.7.1; however, the devices shall open at a pressure not less than the MAWP and be fully open at a pressure not exceeding the test pressure of the tank;

.5   6.7.3.8, if the delivery capacity of the pressure relief devices is approved by the competent authorities for sea and road transport;

.6   the location of the pressure relief device inlets in 6.7.3.11.1, which need not be in the longitudinal centre of the shell;

.7   the provisions for forklift pockets; and

.8   6.7.3.13.5.

6.8.3.2.2.2   If the landing legs of an IMO type 6 tank are to be used as support structure, the loads specified in 6.7.3.2.9 shall be taken into account in their design and method of attachment. Any bending stress induced in the shell as a result of this manner of support shall also be included in the design calculations.

6.8.3.2.2.3   Securing arrangements (tie-down attachments) shall be fitted to the tank support structure and the towing vehicle of an IMO type 6 tank. Semi-trailers unaccompanied by a towing vehicle shall be accepted for shipment only if the trailer supports and the securing arrangements and the position of stowage are agreed by the competent authority for sea transport, unless the approved Cargo Securing Manual includes this arrangement.

6.8.3.2.3   *Approval, testing and marking*

6.8.3.2.3.1   IMO type 6 tanks shall be approved for road transport by the competent authority for road transport.

6.8.3.2.3.2   The competent authority for sea transport shall issue additionally, in respect of an IMO type 6 tank, a certificate attesting compliance with the relevant design, construction and equipment provisions of this chapter and, where appropriate, the special provisions for the gases listed in the Dangerous Goods List. The certificate shall list the gases allowed to be transported.

6.8.3.2.3.3   An IMO type 6 tank shall be periodically tested and inspected in accordance with the provisions of the competent authority for road transport.

6.8.3.2.3.4   An IMO type 6 tank shall be marked in accordance with 6.7.3.16. However, where the marking required by the competent authority for road transport is substantially in agreement with that of 6.7.3.16.1, it will be sufficient to endorse the metal plate attached to the IMO type 6 tank with "IMO 6".

6.8.3.3   **Road tank vehicles for refrigerated liquefied gases of class 2 (IMO type 8)**

6.8.3.3.1   *General provisions*

6.8.3.3.1.1   An IMO type 8 tank shall comply with either:

.1   the provisions of 6.7.4; or

.2   the provisions of 6.8.3.3.2 and 6.8.3.3.3.

6.8.3.3.1.2   An IMO type 8 tank shall not be offered for transport by sea in a condition that would lead to venting during the voyage under normal conditions of transport.

6.8.3.3.2   *Design and construction*

6.8.3.3.2.1   An IMO type 8 tank shall comply with the provisions of 6.7.4, with the exception:

.1   that aluminium jackets may be used, with the approval of the competent authority for sea transport;

.2   that IMO type 8 tanks may have a shell thickness less than 3 mm, subject to the approval of the competent authority for sea transport;

.3   that for IMO type 8 tanks used for non-flammable refrigerated gases, one of the valves may be replaced by a frangible disc. The frangible disc shall rupture at a nominal pressure equal to the test pressure;

.4   of the provisions of 6.7.4.7.3 for the combined capacity of all pressure relief devices under complete fire-engulfment conditions;

.5   of the safety factor of 1.5 in 6.7.4.2.13; however, the safety factor shall not be less than 1.3;

.6   of 6.7.4.8; and

.7   of the provisions for forklift pockets.

6.8.3.3.2.2   If the landing legs of an IMO type 8 tank are to be used as support structure, the loads agreed as in 6.7.4.2.12 shall be taken into account in their design and method of attachment. Bending stress induced in the shell as a result of this manner of support shall be included in design calculations.

6

6.8.3.3.2.3   Securing arrangements (tie-down attachments) shall be fitted to the tank support structure and the towing vehicle of an IMO type 8 tank. Semi-trailers unaccompanied by a towing vehicle shall be accepted for shipment only if the trailer supports and the securing arrangements and the position of stowage are agreed by the competent authority for sea transport, unless the approved Cargo Securing Manual includes this arrangement.

6.8.3.3.3   *Approval, testing and marking*

6.8.3.3.3.1   IMO type 8 tanks shall be approved for road transport by the competent authority for road transport.

6.8.3.3.3.2   The competent authority for sea transport shall issue additionally, in respect of an IMO type 8 tank, a certificate attesting compliance with the relevant design, construction and equipment provisions of this subsection and, where appropriate, the special tank type provisions for the gases in the Dangerous Goods List. The certificate shall list the gases allowed to be transported.

6.8.3.3.3.3   IMO type 8 tanks shall be periodically tested and inspected in accordance with the provisions of the competent authority for road transport.

6.8.3.3.3.4   IMO type 8 tanks shall be marked in accordance with 6.7.4.15. However, where the marking required by the competent authority for road transport is substantially in agreement with that of 6.7.4.15.1, it will be sufficient to endorse the metal plate attached to the IMO type 8 tank with "IMO 8"; the reference to holding time may be omitted.

Chapter 6.9

Provisions for the design, construction, inspection and testing of bulk containers

Note: Sheeted bulk containers (BK1) shall not be used for sea transport, except as indicated in 4.3.3.

6.9.1 Definitions

For the purposes of this section:

Closed bulk container means a totally closed bulk container having a rigid roof, sidewalls, end walls and floor (including hopper-type bottoms), including bulk containers with an opening roof, or side or end wall that can be closed during transport. Closed bulk container may be equipped with openings to allow for the exchange of vapours and gases with air and which prevent, under normal conditions of transport, the release of solid contents as well as the penetration of rain and splash water.

Flexible bulk container means a flexible container with a capacity not exceeding 15 m^3 and includes liners and attached handling devices and service equipment.

Sheeted bulk container means an open-top bulk container with rigid bottom (including hopper-type bottom), side and end walls and a non-rigid covering.

6.9.2 Application and general provisions

6.9.2.1 Bulk containers and their service and structural equipment shall be designed and constructed to withstand, without loss of contents, the internal pressure of the contents and the stresses of normal handling and transport.

6.9.2.2 Where a discharge valve is fitted, it shall be capable of being made secure in the closed position and the whole discharge system shall be suitably protected from damage. Valves having lever closures shall be able to be secured against unintended opening and the open or closed position shall be readily apparent.

6.9.2.3 Code for designating types of bulk container

The following table indicates the codes to be used for designating types of bulk containers:

Types of bulk container	Code
Sheeted bulk container	BK1
Closed bulk container	BK2
Flexible bulk container	BK3

6.9.2.4 In order to take account of progress in science and technology, the use of alternative arrangements which offer at least equivalent safety as provided by the provisions of this chapter may be considered by the competent authority.

6.9.3 Provisions for the design, construction, inspection and testing of freight containers used as BK1 or BK2 bulk containers

6.9.3.1 Design and construction provisions

6.9.3.1.1 The general design and construction provisions in this section are deemed to be met if the bulk container complies with the requirements of ISO 1496-4:1991, *Series 1 freight containers – Specification and testing – Part 4: Non-pressurized containers for dry bulk*, and the container is siftproof.

6.9.3.1.2 Freight containers designed and tested in accordance with ISO 1496-1:1990, *Series 1 freight containers – Specification and testing – Part 1: General cargo containers for general purposes*, shall be equipped with operational equipment which is, including its connection to the freight container, designed to strengthen the end walls and to improve the longitudinal restraint as necessary to comply with the test requirements of ISO 1496-4:1991, as relevant.

6.9.3.1.3   Bulk containers shall be siftproof. Where a liner is used to make the container siftproof, it shall be made of a suitable material. The strength of the material used for, and the construction of, the liner shall be appropriate to the capacity of the container and its intended use. Joins and closures of the liner shall withstand pressures and impacts liable to occur under normal conditions of handling and transport. For ventilated bulk containers, any liner shall not impair the operation of ventilating devices.

6.9.3.1.4   The operational equipment of bulk containers designed to be emptied by tilting shall be capable of withstanding the total filling mass in the tilted orientation.

6.9.3.1.5   Any movable roof or side or end wall or roof section shall be fitted with locking devices with securing devices designed to show the locked state to an observer at ground level.

6.9.3.2   Service equipment

6.9.3.2.1   Filling and discharge devices shall be so constructed and arranged as to be protected against the risk of being wrenched off or damaged during transport and handling. The filling and discharge devices shall be capable of being secured against unintended opening. The open and closed position and direction of closure shall be clearly indicated.

6.9.3.2.2   Seals of openings shall be so arranged as to avoid any damage by the operation, filling and emptying of the bulk container.

6.9.3.2.3   Where ventilation is required, bulk containers shall be equipped with means of air exchange, either by natural convection, e.g. by openings, or active elements, e.g. fans. The ventilation shall be designed to prevent negative pressures in the container at all times. Ventilating elements of bulk containers for the transport of flammable substances or substances emitting flammable gases or vapours shall be designed so as not to be a source of ignition.

6.9.3.3   Inspection and testing

6.9.3.3.1   Freight containers used, maintained and qualified as bulk containers in accordance with the requirements of this section shall be tested and approved in accordance with the International Convention for Safe Containers (CSC), 1972, as amended.

6.9.3.3.2   Freight containers used and qualified as bulk containers shall be inspected periodically according to that Convention.

6.9.3.4   Marking

6.9.3.4.1   Freight containers used as bulk containers shall be marked with a Safety Approval Plate in accordance with the International Convention for Safe Containers.

6.9.4   Provisions for the design, construction and approval of BK1 or BK2 bulk containers other than freight containers

6.9.4.1   Bulk containers covered in this section include skips, offshore bulk containers, bulk bins, swap bodies, trough-shaped containers, roller containers, and load compartments of vehicles.

6.9.4.2   These bulk containers shall be designed and constructed so as to be strong enough to withstand the shocks and loadings normally encountered during transport, including, as applicable, transhipment between modes of transport.

6.9.4.3   Load compartments of vehicles shall comply with the requirements of, and be acceptable to, the competent authority responsible for land transport of the dangerous goods to be transported in bulk.

6.9.4.4   These bulk containers shall be approved by the competent authority and the approval shall include the code for designating types of bulk containers in accordance with 6.9.2.3 and the provisions for inspection and testing, as appropriate.

6.9.4.5   Where it is necessary to use a liner in order to retain the dangerous goods, it shall meet the provisions of 6.9.3.1.3.

6.9.4.6 The following statement shall be shown on the transport document:

"Bulk container BK(*x*) approved by the competent authority of ...".

Note: "(*x*)" shall be replaced with "1" or "2", as appropriate.

6.9.5 Requirements for the design, construction, inspection and testing of flexible bulk containers BK3

6.9.5.1 Design and construction requirements

6.9.5.1.1 Flexible bulk containers shall be sift-proof.

6.9.5.1.2 Flexible bulk containers shall be completely closed to prevent the release of contents.

6.9.5.1.3 Flexible bulk containers shall be waterproof.

6.9.5.1.4 Parts of the flexible bulk container which are in direct contact with dangerous goods:

(a) shall not be affected or significantly weakened by those dangerous goods;

(b) shall not cause a dangerous effect, e.g. catalysing a reaction or reacting with the dangerous goods; and

(c) shall not allow permeation of the dangerous goods that could constitute a danger under normal conditions of transport.

6.9.5.2 Service equipment and handling devices

6.9.5.2.1 Filling and discharge devices shall be so constructed as to be protected against damage during transport and handling. The filling and discharge devices shall be capable of being secured against unintended opening.

6.9.5.2.2 Slings of the flexible bulk container, if fitted, shall withstand pressure and dynamic forces which can appear in normal conditions of handling and transport.

6.9.5.2.3 The handling devices shall be strong enough to withstand repeated use.

6.9.5.3 Inspection and testing

6.9.5.3.1 Each flexible bulk container design type shall successfully pass the tests prescribed in this chapter before being used.

6.9.5.3.2 Tests shall also be repeated after each modification of design type which alters the design, material or manner of construction of a flexible bulk container.

6.9.5.3.3 Tests shall be carried out on flexible bulk containers prepared as for transport. Flexible bulk containers shall be filled to the maximum mass at which they may be used and the contents shall be evenly distributed. The substances to be transported in the flexible bulk container may be replaced by other substances except where this would invalidate the results of the tests. When another substance is used it shall have the same physical characteristics (mass, grain size, etc.) as the substance to be transported. It is permissible to use additives, such as bags of lead shot, to achieve the requisite total mass of the flexible bulk container, so long as they are placed so that the test results are not affected.

6.9.5.3.4 Flexible bulk containers shall be manufactured and tested under a quality assurance programme which satisfies the competent authority, in order to ensure that each manufactured flexible bulk container meets the requirements of this chapter.

6.9.5.3.5 *Drop test*

6.9.5.3.5.1 *Applicability*

For all types of flexible bulk containers, as a design type test.

6.9.5.3.5.2 *Preparation for testing*

The flexible bulk container shall be filled to its maximum permissible gross mass.

6.9.5.3.5.3 The flexible bulk container shall be dropped onto a target surface that is non-resilient and horizontal. The target surface shall be:

(a) integral and massive enough to be immovable;

(b) flat with a surface kept free from local defects capable of influencing the test results;

(c) rigid enough to be non-deformable under test conditions and not liable to become damaged by the tests; and

(d) sufficiently large to ensure that the test flexible bulk container falls entirely upon the surface.

Following the drop, the flexible bulk container shall be restored to the upright position for observation.

6.9.5.3.5.4 Drop height shall be:

Packing group III: 0.8 m

6.9.5.3.5.5 Criteria for passing the test:

(a) there shall be no loss of contents. A slight discharge, e.g. from closures or stitch holes, upon impact shall not be considered to be a failure of the flexible bulk container provided that no further leakage occurs after the container has been restored to the upright position;

(b) there shall be no damage which renders the flexible bulk container unsafe to be transported for salvage or for disposal.

6.9.5.3.6 *Top lift test*

6.9.5.3.6.1 *Applicability*

For all types of flexible bulk containers as a design type test.

6.9.5.3.6.2 *Preparation for testing*

Flexible bulk containers shall be filled to six times the maximum net mass, the load being evenly distributed.

6.9.5.3.6.3 A flexible bulk container shall be lifted in the manner for which it is designed until clear of the floor and maintained in that position for a period of five minutes.

6.9.5.3.6.4 Criteria for passing the test: there shall be no damage to the flexible bulk container or its lifting devices which renders the flexible bulk container unsafe for transport or handling, and no loss of contents.

6.9.5.3.7 *Topple test*

6.9.5.3.7.1 *Applicability*

For all types of flexible bulk containers as a design type test.

6.9.5.3.7.2 *Preparation for testing*

The flexible bulk container shall be filled to its maximum permissible gross mass.

6.9.5.3.7.3 A flexible bulk container shall be toppled onto any part of its top by lifting the side furthest from the drop edge upon a target surface that is non-resilient and horizontal. The target surface shall be:

(a) integral and massive enough to be immovable;

(b) flat with a surface kept free from local defects capable of influencing the test results;

(c) rigid enough to be non-deformable under test conditions and not liable to become damaged by the tests; and

(d) sufficiently large to ensure that the test flexible bulk container falls entirely upon the surface.

6.9.5.3.7.4 For all flexible bulk containers, the topple height is specified as follows:

Packing group III: 0.8 m

6.9.5.3.7.5 Criterion for passing the test: there shall be no loss of contents. A slight discharge, e.g. from closures or stitch holes, upon impact shall not be considered to be a failure of the flexible bulk container provided that no further leakage occurs.

6.9.5.3.8 *Righting test*

6.9.5.3.8.1 *Applicability*

For all types of flexible bulk containers designed to be lifted from the top or side, as a design type test.

6.9.5.3.8.2 *Preparation for testing*

The flexible bulk container shall be filled to not less than 95% of its capacity and to its maximum permissible gross mass.

6.9.5.3.8.3 The flexible bulk container, lying on its side, shall be lifted at a speed of at least 0.1 m/s to an upright position, clear of the floor, by no more than half of the lifting devices.

6.9.5.3.8.4 Criterion for passing the test: there shall be no damage to the flexible bulk container or its lifting devices which renders the flexible bulk container unsafe for transport or handling.

6.9.5.3.9 *Tear test*

6.9.5.3.9.1 *Applicability*

For all types of flexible bulk containers as a design type test.

6.9.5.3.9.2 *Preparation for testing*

The flexible bulk container shall be filled to its maximum permissible gross mass.

6.9.5.3.9.3 With the flexible bulk container placed on the ground, a 300 mm cut shall be made, completely penetrating all layers of the flexible bulk container on a wall of a wide face. The cut shall be made at a 45° angle to the principal axis of the flexible bulk container, halfway between the bottom surface and the top level of the contents. The flexible bulk container shall then be subjected to a uniformly distributed superimposed load equivalent to twice the maximum gross mass. The load must be applied for at least fifteen minutes. A flexible bulk container which is designed to be lifted from the top or the side shall, after removal of the superimposed load, be lifted clear of the floor and maintained in that position for a period of fifteen minutes.

6.9.5.3.9.4 Criterion for passing the test: the cut shall not propagate more than 25% of its original length.

6.9.5.3.10 *Stacking test*

6.9.5.3.10.1 *Applicability*

For all types of flexible bulk containers as a design type test.

6.9.5.3.10.2 *Preparation for testing*

The flexible bulk container shall be filled to its maximum permissible gross mass.

6.9.5.3.10.3 The flexible bulk container shall be subjected to a force applied to its top surface that is four times the design load-carrying capacity for 24 h.

6.9.5.3.10.4 Criterion for passing the test: there shall be no loss of contents during the test or after removal of the load.

6.9.5.4 **Test report**

6.9.5.4.1 A test report containing at least the following particulars shall be drawn up and shall be available to the users of the flexible bulk container:
1. name and address of the test facility;
2. name and address of applicant (where appropriate);
3. unique test report identification;
4. date of the test report;
5. manufacturer of the flexible bulk container;
6. description of the flexible bulk container design type (e.g. dimensions, materials, closures, thickness, etc.) and/or photograph(s);
7. maximum capacity/maximum permissible gross mass;
8. characteristics of test contents, e.g. particle size for solids;
9. test descriptions and results;
10. the test report shall be signed with the name and status of the signatory.

6.9.5.4.2 The test report shall contain statements that the flexible bulk container prepared as for transport was tested in accordance with the appropriate provisions of this chapter and that the use of other containment methods or components may render it invalid. A copy of the test report shall be available to the competent authority.

6.9.5.5 **Marking**

△ **6.9.5.5.1** Each flexible bulk container manufactured and intended for use according to these provisions shall bear marks that are durable, legible and placed in a location so as to be readily visible. Letters, numerals and symbols shall be at least 24 mm high and shall show:

(a) the United Nations packaging symbol:

This symbol shall not be used for any purpose other than certifying that a packaging, a flexible bulk container, a portable tank or a MEGC complies with the relevant requirements in chapters 6.1, 6.2, 6.3, 6.5, 6.6, 6.7 or 6.9;

(b) the code BK3;

(c) a capital letter designating the packing group(s) for which the design type has been approved: Z for packing group III only;

(d) the month and year (last two digits) of manufacture;

(e) the character(s) identifying the country authorizing the allocation of the mark; as indicated by the distinguishing sign for motor vehicles in international traffic;

(f) the name or symbol of the manufacturer and other identification of the flexible bulk container as specified by the competent authority;

(g) the stacking test load in kg;

(h) the maximum permissible gross mass in kg.

△ Marks shall be applied in the sequence shown in (a) to (h); each mark, required in these subparagraphs, shall be clearly separated, e.g. by a slash or space and presented in a way that ensures that all of the parts of the mark are easily identified.

6.9.5.5.2   Example of marking

    BK3/Z/11 09
RUS/NTT/MK-14-10
56000/14000

PART 7

PROVISIONS CONCERNING TRANSPORT OPERATIONS

Chapter 7.1

General stowage provisions

7.1.1 Introduction

This chapter contains the general provisions for the stowage of dangerous goods in all types of ships. Specific provisions applicable to, container ships, ro-ro ships, general cargo ships and barge carrying ships, are stipulated in chapters 7.4 to 7.7.

7.1.2 Definitions

△ **Note 1:** The term "magazine" is no longer used in the context of the IMDG Code. A magazine that is not a fixed part of the ship shall meet the provisions for a closed cargo transport unit for class 1 (see 7.1.2). A magazine that is a fixed part of the ship such as compartment, below deck area or hold shall meet the provisions of 7.6.2.4.

■ **Note 2:** Cargo holds cannot be interpreted as closed cargo transport units.

Clear of living quarters means that packages or cargo transport units shall be stowed a minimum distance of 3 m from accommodation, air intakes, machinery spaces and other enclosed work areas.

Closed cargo transport unit for class 1 means a unit which fully encloses the contents by permanent structures, can be secured to the ship's structure and is, except for division 1.4, structurally serviceable as defined in this section. Cargo transport units with fabric sides or tops are not closed cargo transport units. The floor of any closed cargo transport unit shall either be constructed of wood, close-boarded, or so arranged that goods are stowed on sparred gratings, wooden pallets or dunnage.

Combustible material means material which may or may not be dangerous goods but which is easily ignited and supports combustion. Examples of combustible materials include wood, paper, straw, vegetable fibres, products made from such materials, coal, lubricants, and oils. This definition does not apply to packaging material or dunnage.

Potential sources of ignition means, but is not limited to, open fires, machinery exhausts, galley uptakes, electrical outlets and electrical equipment including those on refrigerated or heated cargo transport units unless they are of certified safe type.[*]

Protected from sources of heat means that packages and cargo transport units shall be stowed at least 2.4 m from heated ship structures, where the surface temperature is liable to exceed 55°C. Examples of heated structures are steam pipes, heating coils, top or side walls of heated fuel and cargo tanks, and bulkheads of machinery spaces. In addition, packages not loaded inside a cargo transport unit and stowed on deck shall be shaded from direct sunlight. The surface of a cargo transport unit can heat rapidly when in direct sunlight in nearly windless conditions and the cargo may also become heated. Depending on the nature of the goods in the cargo transport unit and the planned voyage precautions shall be taken to ensure that exposure to direct sunlight is reduced.

Stowage means the proper placement of dangerous goods on board a ship in order to ensure safety and environmental protection during transport.

Stowage on deck means stowage on the weather deck. For open ro-ro cargo spaces see 7.5.2.6.

Stowage under deck means any stowage that is not on the weather deck. For hatchless containerships see 7.4.2.1.

Structurally serviceable for class 1 means the cargo transport unit shall not have major defects in its structural components, e.g. top and bottom rails, top and bottom end rails, door sill and header, floor cross-members, corner posts, and corner fittings in a freight container. Major defects are: dents or bends in the structural

---

[*] For cargo spaces, refer to SOLAS II-2/19.3.2 and for refrigerated or heated cargo transport units refer to Recommendations published by the International Electrotechnical Commission, in particular IEC 60079.

members greater than 19 mm in depth, regardless of length; cracks or breaks in structural members; more than one splice (e.g. a lapped splice) in top or bottom end rails or door headers; more than two splices in any one top or bottom side rail or any splice in a door sill or corner post; door hinges and hardware that are seized, twisted, broken, missing or otherwise inoperative; gaskets and seals that do not seal; or, for freight containers, any distortion of the overall configuration great enough to prevent proper alignment of handling equipment, mounting and securing on chassis or vehicle, or insertion into ship's cells. In addition, deterioration in any component of the cargo transport unit, regardless of the material of construction, such as rusted-out metal in sidewalls or disintegrated fibreglass, is unacceptable. Normal wear, however, including oxidation (rust), slight dents and scratches and other damage that does not affect serviceability or the weathertight integrity of the units, is acceptable.

7.1.3 Stowage categories

7.1.3.1 Stowage categories for class 1

Dangerous goods of class 1 other than division 1.4, compatibility group S, packed in limited quantities shall be stowed as indicated in column 16a of the Dangerous Goods List in accordance with one of the categories specified below.

Stowage category 01	Cargo ships (up to 12 passengers)	On deck in closed cargo transport unit or under deck
	Passenger ships	On deck in closed cargo transport unit or under deck
Stowage category 02	Cargo ships (up to 12 passengers)	On deck in closed cargo transport unit or under deck
	Passenger ships	On deck in closed cargo transport unit or under deck in closed cargo transport unit in accordance with 7.1.4.4.5
Stowage category 03	Cargo ships (up to 12 passengers)	On deck in closed cargo transport unit or under deck
	Passenger ships	Prohibited except if in accordance with 7.1.4.4.5
Stowage category 04	Cargo ships (up to 12 passengers)	On deck in closed cargo transport unit or under deck in closed cargo transport unit
	Passenger ships	Prohibited except if in accordance with 7.1.4.4.5
Stowage category 05	Cargo ships (up to 12 passengers)	On deck only in closed cargo transport unit
	Passenger ships	Prohibited except if in accordance with 7.1.4.4.5

7.1.3.2 Stowage categories for classes 2 to 9

Dangerous goods of classes 2 to 9 and division 1.4, compatibility group S, packed in limited quantities shall be stowed as indicated in column 16a of the Dangerous Goods List in accordance with one of the categories specified below:

Stowage category A

Cargo ships or passenger ships carrying a number of passengers limited to not more than 25 or to 1 passenger per 3 m of overall length, whichever is the greater number	ON DECK OR UNDER DECK
Other passenger ships in which the limiting number of passengers transported is exceeded	ON DECK OR UNDER DECK

Stowage category B

Cargo ships or passenger ships carrying a number of passengers limited to not more than 25 or to 1 passenger per 3 m of overall length, whichever is the greater number	ON DECK OR UNDER DECK
Other passenger ships in which the limiting number of passengers transported is exceeded	ON DECK ONLY

Stowage category C

| Cargo ships or passenger ships carrying a number of passengers limited to not more than 25 or to 1 passenger per 3 m of overall length, whichever is the greater number | **ON DECK ONLY** |
| Other passenger ships in which the limiting number of passengers transported is exceeded | **ON DECK ONLY** |

Stowage category D

| Cargo ships or passenger ships carrying a number of passengers limited to not more than 25 or to 1 passenger per 3 m of overall length, whichever is the greater number | **ON DECK ONLY** |
| Other passenger ships in which the limiting number of passengers transported is exceeded | **PROHIBITED** |

Stowage category E

| Cargo ships or passenger ships carrying a number of passengers limited to not more than 25 or to 1 passenger per 3 m of overall length, whichever is the greater number | **ON DECK OR UNDER DECK** |
| Other passenger ships in which the limiting number of passengers transported is exceeded | **PROHIBITED** |

7.1.4 Special stowage provisions

7.1.4.1 Stowage of empty uncleaned packagings, including IBCs and large packagings

Notwithstanding the stowage provisions given in the Dangerous Goods List, empty uncleaned packagings, including IBCs and large packagings, which shall be stowed *on deck only* when full may be stowed *on deck or under deck* in a mechanically ventilated cargo space. However, empty uncleaned pressure receptacles which carry a label of class 2.3 shall be stowed *on deck only* (see also 4.1.1.11) and waste aerosols shall only be stowed according to column 16a of the Dangerous Goods List.

7.1.4.2 Stowage of marine pollutants

Where stowage is permitted *on deck or under deck*, *under deck* stowage is preferred. Where stowage *on deck only* is required, preference shall be given to stowage on well-protected decks or to stowage inboard in sheltered areas of exposed decks.

7.1.4.3 Stowage of limited quantities and excepted quantities

For the stowage of limited quantities and excepted quantities see sections 3.4 and 3.5.

7.1.4.4 Stowage of goods of class 1

7.1.4.4.1 In cargo ships of 500 gross tons or over and passenger ships constructed before 1 September 1984 and in cargo ships of less than 500 gross tons constructed before 1 February 1992, goods of class 1 with the exception of division 1.4, compatibility group S, shall be stowed *on deck only*, unless otherwise approved by the Administration.

7.1.4.4.2 Goods of class 1 with the exception of division 1.4 shall be stowed not less than a horizontal distance of 12 m from living quarters, life-saving appliances and areas with public access.

7.1.4.4.3 Goods of class 1 with the exception of division 1.4 shall not be positioned closer to the ship's side than a distance equal to one eighth of the beam or 2.4 m, whichever is the lesser.

7.1.4.4.4 Goods of class 1 shall not be stowed within a horizontal distance of 6 m from potential sources of ignition.

7.1.4.4.5 *Stowage on passenger ships*

7.1.4.4.5.1 Goods in division 1.4, compatibility group S, may be transported in any amount on passenger ships. No other goods of class 1 may be transported on passenger ships except:

.1 goods in compatibility groups C, D and E and articles in compatibility group G, if the total net explosive mass does not exceed 10 kg per ship and if they are transported in closed cargo transport units *on deck or under deck*;

.2 articles in compatibility group B, if the total net explosive mass does not exceed 10 kg per ship and if they are transported *on deck only* in closed cargo transport units.

7.1.4.4.6 Alternative arrangements to those prescribed in chapter 7.1 for class 1 may be approved by the Administration.

7.1.4.5   Stowage of goods of class 7

7.1.4.5.1   The total activity in a single cargo space of a sea going vessel for transport of LSA material or SCO in Type IP 1, Type IP 2, Type IP 3 packaging or unpackaged shall not exceed the limits shown in the table hereunder.

**Conveyance activity limits for LSA material and SCO
in industrial packages or unpackaged**

Nature of material	Activity limit for a seagoing vessel
LSA I	No limit
LSA II and LSA III non-combustible solids	No limit
LSA II and LSA III combustible solids, and all liquids and gases	$100A_2$
SCO	$100A_2$

7.1.4.5.2   Provided that its average surface heat flux does not exceed 15 W/m^2 and that the immediately surrounding cargo is not in sacks or bags, a package or overpack may be transported or stored among packaged general cargo without any special stowage provisions except as may be specifically required by the competent authority in an applicable certificate of approval.

7.1.4.5.3   Loading of freight containers and accumulation of packages, overpacks and freight containers shall be controlled as follows:

    .1   Except under the condition of exclusive use, the total number of packages, overpacks and freight containers aboard a single conveyance shall be so limited that the total sum of the transport indexes aboard the conveyance does not exceed the values shown in the table hereunder. For consignments of LSA I material there shall be no limit on the sum of the transport indexes.

TI limits for freight containers and conveyances not under exclusive use

Type of freight container or conveyance	Limit on total sum of transport indexes in a freight container or aboard a conveyance

Freight container
   Small freight container
   Large freight container
	
	50
	50

Vehicle	50
Inland water-way vessel (barge)	50

Seagoing vessel[a]
△ 1 *Hold, compartment or defined deck area*
   Packages, overpacks, small freight containers
   Large freight containers (closed containers)
	
	50
	200

2 *Total vessel*
   Packages, overpacks, small freight containers
   Large freight containers (closed containers)
	
	200
	No limit

[a] Packages or overpacks transported in or on a vehicle which are in accordance with the provisions of 7.1.4.5.5 may be transported by vessels provided that they are not removed from the vehicle at any time while on board the ship.

    .2   Where a consignment is transported under exclusive use, there shall be no limit on the sum of the transport indexes aboard a single conveyance.

    .3   The radiation level under routine conditions of transport shall not exceed 2 mSv/h at any point on, and 0.1 mSv/h at 2 m from, the external surface of the conveyance, except for consignments transported under exclusive use by road or rail, for which the radiation limits around the vehicle are specified in 7.1.4.5.5.2 and 7.1.4.5.5.3.

    .4   The total sum of the criticality safety indexes in a freight container and aboard a conveyance shall not exceed the values shown in the table hereunder.

CSI limits for freight containers and conveyances containing fissile material

Type of freight container or conveyance	Limit on total sum of criticality safety indexes in a freight container or aboard a conveyance	
	Not under exclusive use	Under exclusive use
Freight container		
Small freight container	50	n.a.
Large freight container	50	100
Vehicle	50	100
Inland water-way vessel (barge)	50	100
Seagoing vessel[a]		
△ 1 *Hold, compartment or defined deck area*		
Packages, overpacks, small freight containers	50	100
Large freight containers (closed containers)	50	100
2 *Total vessel*		
Packages, overpacks, small freight containers	200[b]	200[c]
Large freight containers (closed containers)	No limit[b]	No limit[c]

[a] Packages or overpacks transported in or on a vehicle which are in accordance with the provisions of 7.1.4.5.5 may be transported by ships provided that they are not removed from the vehicle at any time while on board the ship. In that case, the entries under the heading "under exclusive use" apply.

[b] The consignment shall be so handled and stowed that the total sum of CSIs in any group does not exceed 50, and that each group is handled and stowed so as to maintain a spacing of at least 6 m from other groups.

[c] The consignment shall be so handled and stowed that the total sum of CSIs in any group does not exceed 100, and that each group is handled and stowed so as to maintain a spacing of at least 6 m from other groups. The intervening space between groups may be occupied by other cargo.

7.1.4.5.4 Any package or overpack having either a transport index greater than 10, or any consignment having a criticality safety index greater than 50, shall be transported only under exclusive use.

7.1.4.5.5 For consignments under exclusive use, the radiation level shall not exceed:

    .1   10 mSv/h at any point on the external surface of any package or overpack, and may only exceed 2 mSv/h provided that:

        .1   the vehicle is equipped with an enclosure which, during routine conditions of transport, prevents the access of unauthorized persons to the interior of the enclosure, and

        .2   provisions are made to secure the package or overpack so that its position within the vehicle enclosure remains fixed during routine conditions of transport, and

        .3   there is no loading or unloading during the shipment;

    .2   2 mSv/h at any point on the outer surfaces of the vehicle, including the upper and lower surfaces, or, in the case of an open vehicle, at any point on the vertical planes projected from the outer edges of the vehicle, on the upper surface of the load, and on the lower external surface of the vehicle; and

    .3   0.1 mSv/h at any point 2 m from the vertical planes represented by the outer lateral surfaces of the vehicle, or, if the load is transported in an open vehicle, at any point 2 m from the vertical planes projected from the outer edges of the vehicle.

7.1.4.5.6 In the case of road vehicles, no persons other than the driver and assistants shall be permitted in vehicles carrying packages, overpacks or freight containers bearing category II-YELLOW or III-YELLOW labels.

7.1.4.5.7 Packages or overpacks having a surface radiation level greater than 2 mSv/h, unless being transported in or on a vehicle under exclusive use in accordance with the table under 7.1.4.5.3, footnote (a), shall not be transported by ship except under special arrangement.

7.1.4.5.8 The transport of consignments by means of a special use ship which, by virtue of its design or by reason of its being chartered, is dedicated to the purpose of carrying radioactive material shall be excepted from the provisions specified in 7.1.4.5.3 provided that the following conditions are met:

    .1   a radiation protection programme for the shipment shall be approved by the Administration and, when requested, by the competent authority at each port of call;

    .2   stowage arrangements shall be predetermined for the whole voyage, including any consignments to be loaded at ports of call en route; and

    .3   the loading, transport and unloading of the consignments shall be supervised by persons qualified in the transport of radioactive material.

7

7.1.4.5.9 Any conveyance and equipment used regularly for the transport of radioactive material shall be periodically checked to determine the level of contamination. The frequency of such checks shall be related to the likelihood of contamination and the extent to which radioactive material is transported.

7.1.4.5.10 Except as provided in 7.1.4.5.11, any conveyance, or equipment or part thereof, which has become contaminated above the limits specified in 4.1.9.1.2 in the course of the transport of radioactive material, or which shows a radiation level in excess of 5 μSv/h at the surface, shall be decontaminated as soon as possible by a qualified person and shall not be re-used unless the following conditions are fulfilled:

.1 the non-fixed contamination shall not exceed the limits specified in 4.1.9.1.2;

.2 the radiation level resulting from the fixed contamination shall not exceed 5 μSv/h at the surface.

7.1.4.5.11 A freight container, tank, IBC or conveyance dedicated to the transport of unpackaged radioactive material under exclusive use shall be excepted from the provisions of 4.1.9.1.4 and 7.1.4.5.10 solely with regard to its internal surfaces and only for as long as it remains under that specific exclusive use.

7.1.4.5.12 Where a consignment is undeliverable, the consignment shall be placed in a safe location and the appropriate competent authority shall be informed as soon as possible and a request made for instructions on further action.

7.1.4.5.13 Radioactive material shall be segregated sufficiently from crew and passengers. The following values for dose shall be used for the purpose of calculating segregation distances or radiation levels:

.1 for crew in regularly occupied working areas, a dose of 5 mSv in a year;

.2 for passengers, in areas where the passengers have regular access, a dose of 1 mSv in a year, taking account of the exposures expected to be delivered by all other relevant sources and practices under control.

7.1.4.5.14 Category II-YELLOW or III-YELLOW packages or overpacks shall not be transported in spaces occupied by passengers, except those exclusively reserved for couriers specially authorized to accompany such packages or overpacks.

7.1.4.5.15 Any group of packages, overpacks and freight containers containing fissile material stored in transit in any one storage area shall be so limited that the total sum of the criticality safety indexes in the group does not exceed 50. Each group shall be stored so as to maintain a spacing of at least 6 m from other such groups.

7.1.4.5.16 Where the total sum of the criticality safety indexes on board a conveyance or in a freight container exceeds 50, as permitted in the table under 7.1.4.5.3.4, storage shall be such as to maintain a spacing of at least 6 m from other groups of packages, overpacks or freight containers containing fissile material or other conveyances carrying radioactive material.

7.1.4.5.17 Any departure from the provisions in 7.1.4.5.15 and 7.1.4.5.16 shall be approved by the Administration and, when requested, by the competent authority at each port of call.

7.1.4.5.18 The segregation requirements specified in 7.1.4.5.13 may be established in one of the following two ways:

– by following the segregation table for persons (table 7.1.4.5.18) in respect of living quarters or spaces regularly occupied by persons.

– by demonstration that, for the following indicated exposure times, the direct measurement of the radiation level in regularly occupied spaces and living quarters is less than:

for the crew:

0.0070 mSv/h up to 700 h in a year, or

0.0018 mSv/h up to 2750 h in a year; and

for the passengers:

0.0018 mSv/h up to 550 h in a year,

taking into account any relocation of cargo during the voyage. In all cases, the measurements of radiation level must be made and documented by a suitably qualified person.

7.1.4.6 Stowage of dangerous goods under temperature control

7.1.4.6.1 When stowage arrangements are made, it shall be borne in mind that it may become necessary to take the appropriate emergency action, such as jettisoning or flooding of the container with water, and the temperature needs to be monitored in accordance to 7.3.7. If, during transport, the control temperature is exceeded, an alerting procedure shall be initiated involving either repair of the refrigeration machinery or an increase in the cooling capacity (such as by adding liquid or solid refrigerants). If an adequate cooling capacity is not restored, emergency procedures shall be started.

Table 7.1.4.5.18 – CLASS 7 – Radioactive material
Segregation table for persons

Sum of transport indices (TI)	Segregation distance of radioactive material from passengers and crew				
	General cargo ship[1]		Ferry, etc.[2]	Offshore support vessel[3]
	Break bulk (m)	Containers (TEUs)[4]		
Up to 10	6	1	Stow at bow or stern furthest from living quarters and regularly occupied work areas	Stow at stern or at platform midpoint
More than 10 but not more than 20	8	1	as above	as above
More than 20 but not more than 50	13	2	as above	not applicable
More than 50 but not more than 100	18	3	as above	not applicable
More than 100 but not more than 200	26	4	as above	not applicable
More than 200 but not more than 400	36	6	as above	not applicable

[1] General cargo, break bulk or ro-ro containership of 150 m minimum length.
[2] Ferry or cross channel, coastal and inter-island ship of 100 m minimum length.
[3] Offshore support vessel of 50 m minimum length (in this case the practical maximum sum of TIs carried is 20).
[4] TEU means "20 ft Equivalent Unit" (this is equivalent to a standard freight container of 6 m nominal length).

7.1.5 Stowage codes

The stowage codes given in column 16a of the Dangerous Goods List are as specified below:

Stowage code	Description
SW1	Protected from sources of heat.
SW2	Clear of living quarters.
SW3	Shall be transported under temperature control.
SW4	Surface ventilation is required to assist in removing any residual solvent vapour.
SW5	If under deck, stow in a mechanically ventilated space.
SW6	When stowed under deck, mechanical ventilation shall be in accordance with SOLAS regulation II-2/19 (II-2/54) for flammable liquids with flashpoint below 23°C c.c.
SW7	As approved by the competent authorities of the countries involved in the shipment.
SW8	Ventilation may be required. The possible need to open hatches in case of fire to provide maximum ventilation and to apply water in an emergency, and the consequent risk to the stability of the ship through flooding of the cargo spaces, shall be considered before loading.
SW9	Provide a good through ventilation for bagged cargo. Double strip stowage is recommended. The illustration in 7.6.2.7.2.3 shows how this can be achieved. During the voyage regular temperature readings shall be taken at varying depths in the hold and recorded. If the temperature of the cargo exceeds the ambient temperature and continues to increase, ventilation shall be closed down.
SW10	Unless carried in closed cargo transport units, bales shall be properly covered by tarpaulins or the like. Cargo spaces shall be clean, dry and free from oil or grease. Ventilator cowls leading into the cargo space shall have sparking-preventing screens. All other openings, entrances and hatches leading to the cargo space shall be securely closed. During temporary interruption of loading, when the hatch remains uncovered, a fire-watch shall be kept. During loading or discharge, smoking in the vicinity shall be prohibited and fire-fighting appliances kept ready for immediate operation.

7

Stowage code	Description
SW11	Cargo transport units shall be shaded from direct sunlight. Packages in cargo transport units shall be stowed so as to allow for adequate air circulation throughout the cargo.
SW12	Taking account of any supplementary requirements specified in the transport documents.
SW13	Taking account of any supplementary requirements specified in the competent authority approval certificate(s).
SW14	Category A only if the special stowage provisions of 7.4.1.4 and 7.6.2.8.4 are complied with.
SW15	For metal drums, stowage category B.
SW16	For unit loads in open cargo transport units, stowage category B.
SW17	Category E, for closed cargo transport unit and pallet boxes only. Ventilation may be required. The possible need to open hatches in case of fire to provide maximum ventilation and to apply water in an emergency, and the consequent risk to the stability of the ship through flooding of the cargo space, shall be considered before loading.
SW18	Category A, when transported in accordance with P650.
SW19	For batteries transported in accordance with special provisions 376 or 377, category C, unless transported on a short international voyage.
SW20	For uranyl nitrate hexahydrate solution stowage, category D applies.
SW21	For uranium metal pyrophoric and thorium metal pyrophoric stowage, category D applies.
SW22	For AEROSOLS with a maximum capacity of 1 L: category A. For AEROSOLS with a capacity above 1 L: category B. For WASTE AEROSOLS: category C, clear of living quarters.
SW23	When transported in BK3 bulk container, see 7.6.2.12 and 7.7.3.9.
SW24	For special stowage provisions, see 7.4.1.3 and 7.6.2.7.2.
SW25	For special stowage provisions, see 7.6.2.7.3.
SW26	For special stowage provisions, see 7.4.1.4 and 7.6.2.11.1.1.
SW27	For special stowage provisions, see 7.6.2.7.2.1.
SW28	As approved by the competent authority of the country of origin.
SW29	For engines or machinery containing fuels with flashpoint equal or greater than 23°C, stowage Category A.

7.1.6   Handling codes

The handling codes given in column 16a of the Dangerous Goods List are as specified below:

Handling code	Description
H1	Keep as dry as reasonably practicable.
H2	Keep as cool as reasonably practicable.
H3	During transport, it should be stowed (or kept) in a cool ventilated place.
H4	If cleaning of cargo spaces has to be carried out at sea, the safety procedures followed and standard of equipment used shall be at least as effective as those employed as industry best practice in a port. Until such cleaning is undertaken, the cargo spaces in which the asbestos has been carried shall be closed and access to those spaces shall be prohibited.

Chapter 7.2

General segregation provisions

7.2.1 Introduction

This chapter contains the general provisions for the segregation of goods which are mutually incompatible.

Additional segregation provisions are given in:

- 7.3 Consigning operations concerning the packing and use of cargo transport units (CTUs) and related provisions;
- 7.4 Stowage and segregation on containerships;
- 7.5 Stowage and segregation on roll-on/roll-off ships;
- 7.6 Stowage and segregation on general cargo ships; and
- 7.7 Shipborne barges on barge-carrying ships.

7.2.2 Definitions

7.2.2.1 Segregation

Segregation is the process of separating two or more substances or articles which are considered mutually incompatible when their packing or stowage together may result in undue hazards in case of leakage or spillage, or any other accident.

However, as the extent of the hazard arising may vary, the segregation arrangements required may also vary as appropriate. Segregation is obtained by maintaining certain distances between incompatible dangerous goods or by requiring the presence of one or more steel bulkheads or decks between them, or a combination thereof. Intervening spaces between such dangerous goods may be filled with other cargo compatible with the dangerous substances or articles in question.

7.2.2.2 Segregation terms

The following segregation terms that are used throughout this Code are defined in other chapters of this part as they apply to packing cargo transport units and segregation on board different ship types:

- .1 "away from";
- .2 "separated from";
- .3 "separated by a complete compartment or hold from";
- .4 "separated longitudinally by an intervening complete compartment or hold from".

Segregation terms such as "away from class …" that are used in the Dangerous Goods List, "class …" is deemed to include:

- .1 all substances within "class …"; and
- .2 all substances for which a subsidiary risk label of "class …" is required.

7.2.3 Segregation provisions

7.2.3.1

To determine the segregation requirements between two or more dangerous goods, the segregation provisions, including the segregation table (7.2.4) and column 16b of the Dangerous Goods List shall be consulted, see also the annex to this chapter. In case of conflicting provisions, the provisions of column 16b of the Dangerous Goods List, always take precedence.

7.2.3.2

Whenever a segregation term applies (see 7.2.2.2), the goods are:

- .1 not permitted to be packed in the same outer packaging; and
- .2 not permitted to be transported in the same cargo transport unit except as provided in 7.2.6 and 7.3.4.

For "limited quantities" and "excepted quantities" see chapters 3.4 and 3.5.

7

7.2.3.3 Where the provisions of this Code indicate a single secondary hazard (one subsidiary risk label), the segregation provisions applicable to that hazard shall take precedence where they are more stringent than those of the primary hazard. The segregation provisions corresponding to a subsidiary risk of class 1 are those for class 1 division 1.3.

7.2.3.4 The segregation provisions for substances, materials or articles having more than two hazards (two or more subsidiary risk labels) are given in column 16b of the Dangerous Goods List.

For example:

In the Dangerous Goods List entry for BROMINE CHLORIDE, class 2.3, UN 2901, subsidiary risks 5.1 and 8, the following particular segregation is specified:

"segregation as for class 5.1, but "separated from" class 7".

7.2.4 Segregation table

The general provisions for segregation between the various classes of dangerous goods are shown in the "segregation table" given below.

Since the properties of substances, materials or articles within each class may vary greatly, the Dangerous Goods List shall always be consulted for particular provisions for segregation as, in the case of conflicting provisions, these take precedence over the general provisions.

Segregation shall also take account of a single subsidiary risk label.

CLASS		1.1 1.2 1.5	1.3 1.6	1.4	2.1	2.2	2.3	3	4.1	4.2	4.3	5.1	5.2	6.1	6.2	7	8	9
Explosives	1.1, 1.2, 1.5	*	*	*	4	2	2	4	4	4	4	4	4	2	4	2	4	X
Explosives	1.3, 1.6	*	*	*	4	2	2	4	3	3	4	4	4	2	4	2	2	X
Explosives	1.4	*	*	*	2	1	1	2	2	2	2	2	2	X	4	2	2	X
Flammable gases	2.1	4	4	2	X	X	X	2	1	2	2	2	2	X	4	2	1	X
Non-toxic, non-flammable gases	2.2	2	2	1	X	X	X	1	X	1	X	X	1	X	2	1	X	X
Toxic gases	2.3	2	2	1	X	X	X	2	X	2	X	X	2	X	2	1	X	X
Flammable liquids	3	4	4	2	2	1	2	X	X	2	2	2	2	X	3	2	X	X
Flammable solids (including self-reactive substances and solid desensitized explosives)	4.1	4	3	2	1	X	X	X	X	1	X	1	2	X	3	2	1	X
Substances liable to spontaneous combustion	4.2	4	3	2	2	1	2	2	1	X	1	2	2	1	3	2	1	X
Substances which, in contact with water, emit flammable gases	4.3	4	4	2	2	X	X	2	X	1	X	2	2	X	2	2	1	X
Oxidizing substances (agents)	5.1	4	4	2	2	X	X	2	1	2	2	X	2	1	3	1	2	X
Organic peroxides	5.2	4	4	2	2	1	2	2	2	2	2	2	X	1	3	2	2	X
Toxic substances	6.1	2	2	X	X	X	X	X	X	1	X	1	1	X	1	X	X	X
Infectious substances	6.2	4	4	4	4	2	2	3	3	3	2	3	3	1	X	3	3	X
Radioactive material	7	2	2	2	2	1	1	2	2	2	2	1	2	X	3	X	2	X
Corrosive substances	8	4	2	2	1	X	X	X	1	1	1	2	2	X	3	2	X	X
Miscellaneous dangerous substances and articles	9	X	X	X	X	X	X	X	X	X	X	X	X	X	X	X	X	X

The numbers and symbols in the table have the following meanings:

1 – "away from"

2 – "separated from"

3 – "separated by a complete compartment or hold from"

4 – "separated longitudinally by an intervening complete compartment or hold from"

X – the Dangerous Goods List has to be consulted to verify whether there are specific segregation provisions

* – see 7.2.7.1 of this chapter for the segregation provisions between class 1 substances or articles

7.2.5 Segregation groups

7.2.5.1 For the purpose of segregation, dangerous goods having certain similar chemical properties have been grouped together in segregation groups as listed in 7.2.5.2. The entries allocated to these segregation groups are listed in 3.1.4.4. Where in the Dangerous Goods List entry in column 16b a particular segregation requirement refers to a group of substances, such as "acids", the particular segregation requirement applies to the goods allocated to the respective segregation group.

7.2.5.2 Segregation groups referred to in the Dangerous Goods List:

    .1   acids

    .2   ammonium compounds

    .3   bromates

    .4   chlorates

    .5   chlorites

    .6   cyanides

    .7   heavy metals and their salts (including their organometallic compounds)

    .8   hypochlorites

    .9   lead and its compounds

    .10   liquid halogenated hydrocarbons

    .11   mercury and mercury compounds

    .12   nitrites and their mixtures

    .13   perchlorates

    .14   permanganates

    .15   powdered metals

    .16   peroxides

    .17   azides

    .18   alkalis.

7.2.5.3 It is recognized that not all substances, mixtures, solutions or preparations falling within a segregation group are listed in the IMDG Code by name. These are shipped under N.O.S. entries. Although these N.O.S. entries are not themselves listed in the segregation groups (see 3.1.4.4), the consignor shall decide whether inclusion under the segregation group is appropriate and, if so, shall mention that fact in the transport document (see 5.4.1.5.11).

7.2.5.4 The segregation groups in this Code do not cover substances which fall outside the classification criteria of this Code. It is recognized that some non-hazardous substances have similar chemical properties as substances listed in the segregation groups. A consignor or the person responsible for packing the goods into a cargo transport unit who does have knowledge of the chemical properties of such non-dangerous goods may decide to implement the segregation requirements of a related segregation group on a voluntary basis.

7.2.6 Special segregation provisions and exemptions

7.2.6.1 Notwithstanding 7.2.3.3 and 7.2.3.4, substances of the same class may be stowed together without regard to segregation required by secondary hazards (subsidiary risk label(s)), provided that the substances do not react dangerously with each other and cause:

    .1   combustion and/or evolution of considerable heat;

    .2   evolution of flammable, toxic or asphyxiant gases;

    .3   the formation of corrosive substances; or

    .4   the formation of unstable substances.

7.2.6.2 Where the Dangerous Goods List specifies that "segregation as for class ..." applies, the segregation provisions applicable to that class in 7.2.4 shall be applied. However, for the purposes of interpreting 7.2.6.1, which permits substances of the same class to be stowed together provided they do not react dangerously with each other, the segregation provisions of the class as represented by the primary hazard class in the Dangerous Goods List shall be applied.

For example:

UN 2965 – BORON TRIFLUORIDE DIMETHYL ETHERATE, class 4.3

△ The Dangerous Goods List entry specifies "segregation as for class 3, but "away from" classes 4.1 and 8".

For the purposes of establishing the segregation provisions applicable in 7.2.4, the class 3 column shall be consulted.

This substance may be stowed together with other class 4.3 substances where they do not react dangerously with each other, see 7.2.6.1.

7.2.6.3   No segregation needs to be applied:

.1   between dangerous goods of different classes which comprise the same substance but vary only in their water content, such as sodium sulphide in classes 4.2 and 8 or for class 7 if the difference is due to quantity only; and

.2   between dangerous goods which belong to a group of substances of different classes but for which scientific evidence exists that they do not react dangerously when in contact with each other. Substances within the same table shown below are compatible with one another.

Table 7.2.6.3.1

UN	Proper shipping name	Class	Subsidiary risk(s)	Packing group
2014	HYDROGEN PEROXIDE, AQUEOUS SOLUTION with not less than 20% but not more than 60% hydrogen peroxide (stabilized as necessary)	5.1	8	II
2984	HYDROGEN PEROXIDE, AQUEOUS SOLUTION with not less than 8% but less than 20% hydrogen peroxide (stabilized as necessary)	5.1		III
3105	ORGANIC PEROXIDE TYPE D, LIQUID (peroxyacetic acid, type D, stabilized)	5.2	8	
3107	ORGANIC PEROXIDE TYPE E, LIQUID (peroxyacetic acid, type E, stabilized)	5.2	8	
3109	ORGANIC PEROXIDE TYPE F, LIQUID (peroxyacetic acid, type F, stabilized)	5.2	8	
3149	HYDROGEN PEROXIDE AND PEROXYACETIC ACID, MIXTURE with acid(s), water and not more than 5% peroxyacetic acid, STABILIZED	5.1	8	II

Table 7.2.6.3.2

UN	Proper shipping name	Class	Subsidiary risk(s)	Packing group
1295	TRICHLOROSILANE	4.3	3/8	I
1818	SILICON TETRACHLORIDE	8	–	II
2189	DICHLOROSILANE	2.3	2.1/8	–

Table 7.2.6.3.3

UN	Proper shipping name	Class	Subsidiary risk(s)	Packing group
3391	ORGANOMETALLIC SUBSTANCE, SOLID, PYROPHORIC	4.2		I
3392	ORGANOMETALLIC SUBSTANCE, LIQUID, PYROPHORIC	4.2		I
3393	ORGANOMETALLIC SUBSTANCE, SOLID, PYROPHORIC, WATER-REACTIVE	4.2	4.3	I
3394	ORGANOMETALLIC SUBSTANCE, LIQUID, PYROPHORIC, WATER-REACTIVE	4.2	4.3	I
3395	ORGANOMETALLIC SUBSTANCE, SOLID, WATER-REACTIVE	4.3		I, II, III
3396	ORGANOMETALLIC SUBSTANCE, SOLID, WATER REACTIVE, FLAMMABLE	4.3	4.1	I, II, III

UN	Proper shipping name	Class	Subsidiary risk(s)	Packing group
3397	ORGANOMETALLIC SUBSTANCE, SOLID, WATER REACTIVE, SELF-HEATING	4.3	4.2	I, II, III
3398	ORGANOMETALLIC SUBSTANCE, LIQUID, WATER REACTIVE	4.3		I, II, III
3399	ORGANOMETALLIC SUBSTANCE, LIQUID, WATER REACTIVE, FLAMMABLE	4.3	3	I, II, III
3400	ORGANOMETALLIC SUBSTANCE, SOLID , SELF-HEATING	4.2		II, III

7.2.6.4   Notwithstanding the provisions of 7.2.5, substances of class 8, packing group II or III, that would otherwise be required to be segregated from one another due to the provisions pertaining to segregation groups as identified by an entry in column 16b of the Dangerous Goods List indicating "away from" or "separated from" "acids" or "away from" or "separated from" "alkalis", may be transported in the same cargo transport unit, whether in the same packaging or not, provided:

     .1   the substances comply with the provisions of 7.2.6.1;

     .2   the package does not contain more than 30 L for liquids or 30 kg for solids;

     .3   the transport document includes the statement required by 5.4.1.5.11.3; and

     .4   a copy of the test report that verifies that the substances do not react dangerously with each other shall be provided if requested by the competent authority.

7.2.7   Segregation of goods of class 1

7.2.7.1   Segregation between goods of class 1

7.2.7.1.1   Goods of class 1 may be stowed within the same compartment or hold, or closed cargo transport unit as indicated in 7.2.7.1.4. In other cases, they shall be stowed in separate compartments or holds, or closed cargo transport units.

7.2.7.1.2   When goods requiring different stowage arrangements are permitted by 7.2.7.1.4 to be transported in the same compartment or hold, or closed cargo transport unit, the appropriate stowage arrangement shall conform to the most stringent provisions for the entire load.

7.2.7.1.3   Where a mixed load of different divisions is transported within the same compartment or hold, or closed cargo transport unit, the entire load shall be treated as if belonging to the hazard division in the order 1.1 (most dangerous), 1.5, 1.2, 1.3, 1.6 and 1.4 (least dangerous) and the stowage arrangement shall conform to the most stringent provisions for the entire load.

7.2.7.1.4   *Permitted mixed stowage for goods of class 1*

Compatibility group	A	B	C	D	E	F	G	H	J	K	L	N	S
A	X												
B		X											X
C			X	X^6	X^6		X^1					X^4	X
D			X^6	X	X^6		X^1					X^4	X
E			X^6	X^6	X		X^1					X^4	X
F						X							X
G			X^1	X^1	X^1		X						X
H								X					X
J									X				X
K										X			X
L											X^2		
N			X^4	X^4	X^4							X^3	X^5
S		X	X	X	X	X	X	X	X	X		X^5	X

"X" indicates that goods of the corresponding compatibility groups may be stowed in the same compartment, hold, or closed cargo transport unit.

Notes

[1] Explosive articles in compatibility group G (other than fireworks and those requiring special stowage) may be stowed with explosive articles of compatibility groups C, D and E provided no explosive substances are transported in the same compartment or hold, or closed cargo transport unit.

[2] A consignment of one type in compatibility group L shall only be stowed with a consignment of the same type within compatibility group L.

[3] Different types of articles of Division 1.6, compatibility group N, may only be transported together when it is proven that there is no additional risk of sympathetic detonation between the articles. Otherwise they shall be treated as division 1.1.

[4] When articles of compatibility group N are transported with articles or substances of compatibility groups C, D or E, the goods of compatibility group N shall be treated as compatibility group D.

[5] When articles of compatibility group N are transported together with articles or substances of compatibility group S, the entire load shall be treated as compatibility group N.

[6] Any combination of articles in compatibility groups C, D and E shall be treated as compatibility group E. Any combination of substances in compatibility groups C and D shall be treated as the most appropriate compatibility group shown in 2.1.2.3, taking into account the predominant characteristics of the combined load. This overall classification code shall be displayed on any label or placard placed on a unit load or closed cargo transport unit as prescribed in 5.2.2.2.2.

7.2.7.1.5   Closed cargo transport units carrying different goods of class 1 do not require segregation from each other provided 7.2.7.1.4 authorizes the goods to be transported together. Where this is not permitted, closed cargo transport unit shall be "separated from" one another.

7.2.7.2   **Segregation from goods of other classes**

7.2.7.2.1   Notwithstanding the segregation provisions of this chapter, AMMONIUM NITRATE (UN 1942), AMMONIUM NITRATE FERTILIZERS (UN 2067), alkali metal nitrates (e.g. UN 1486) and alkaline earth metal nitrates (e.g. UN 1454) may be stowed together with blasting explosives (except EXPLOSIVE, BLASTING, TYPE C, UN 0083) provided the aggregate is treated as blasting explosives under class 1.

Note: Alkali metal nitrates include caesium nitrate (UN 1451), lithium nitrate (UN 2722), potassium nitrate (UN 1486), rubidium nitrate (UN 1477) and sodium nitrate (UN 1498). Alkaline earth metal nitrates include barium nitrate (UN 1446), beryllium nitrate (UN 2464), calcium nitrate (UN 1454), magnesium nitrate (UN 1474) and strontium nitrate (UN 1507).

7.2.8   Segregation codes

The segregation codes given in column 16b of the Dangerous Goods List are as specified below:

Segregation code	Description
SG1	For packages carrying a subsidiary risk label of class 1, segregation as for class 1, division 1.3.
SG2	Segregation as for class 1.2G.
SG3	Segregation as for class 1.3G.
SG4	Segregation as for class 2.1.
SG5	Segregation as for class 3.
SG6	Segregation as for class 5.1.
SG7	Stow "away from" class 3.
SG8	Stow "away from" class 4.1.
SG9	Stow "away from" class 4.3.
SG10	Stow "away from" class 5.1.
SG11	Stow "away from" class 6.2.
SG12	Stow "away from" class 7.
SG13	Stow "away from" class 8.
SG14	Stow "separated from" class 1 except for division 1.4S.
SG15	Stow "separated from" class 3.
SG16	Stow "separated from" class 4.1.
SG17	Stow "separated from" class 5.1.
SG18	Stow "separated from" class 6.2.
SG19	Stow "separated from" class 7.

7

Segregation code	Description
SG20	Stow "away from" acids.
SG21	Stow "away from" alkalis.
SG22	Stow "away from" ammonium salts.
SG23	Stow "away from" animal or vegetable oils.
SG24	Stow "away from" azides.
SG25	Stow "separated from" goods of classes 2.1 and 3.
SG26	In addition: from goods of classes 2.1 and 3 when stowed on deck of a containership a minimum distance of two container spaces athwartship shall be maintained, when stowed on ro-ro ships a distance of 6 m athwartship shall be maintained.
SG27	Stow "away from" explosives containing chlorates or perchlorates.
SG28	Stow "away from" ammonium compounds and explosives containing ammonium compounds or salts.
SG29	Segregation from foodstuffs as in 7.3.4.2.2, 7.6.3.1.2 or 7.7.3.7.
SG30	Stow "away from" heavy metals and their salts.
SG31	Stow "away from" lead and its compounds.
SG32	Stow "away from" liquid halogenated hydrocarbons.
SG33	Stow "away from" powdered metals.
SG34	When containing ammonium compounds, "away from" chlorates or perchlorates and explosives containing chlorates or perchlorates.
SG35	Stow "separated from" acids.
SG36	Stow "separated from" alkalis.
SG37	Stow "separated from" ammonia.
SG38	Stow "separated from" ammonium compounds.
SG39	Stow "separated from" ammonium compounds other than AMMONIUM PERSULPHATE (UN 1444).
SG40	Stow "separated from" ammonium compounds other than mixtures of ammonium persulphates and/or potassium persulphates and/or sodium persulphates.
SG41	Stow "separated from" animal or vegetable oil.
SG42	Stow "separated from" bromates.
SG43	Stow "separated from" bromine.
SG44	Stow "separated from" CARBON TETRACHLORIDE (UN 1846).
SG45	Stow "separated from" chlorates.
SG46	Stow "separated from" chlorine.
SG47	Stow "separated from" chlorites.
SG48	Stow "separated from" combustible material (particularly liquids). Combustible material does not include packing materials or dunnage.
SG49	Stow "separated from" cyanides.
SG50	Segregation from foodstuffs as in 7.3.4.2.1, 7.6.3.1.2 or 7.7.3.6.
SG51	Stow "separated from" hypochlorites.
SG52	Stow "separated from" iron oxide.
SG53	Stow "separated from" liquid organic substances.
SG54	Stow "separated from" mercury and mercury compounds.
SG55	Stow "separated from" mercury salts.
SG56	Stow "separated from" nitrites.
SG57	Stow "separated from" odour-absorbing cargoes.
SG58	Stow "separated from" perchlorates.
SG59	Stow "separated from" permanganates.

7

Segregation code	Description
SG60	Stow "separated from" peroxides.
SG61	Stow "separated from" powdered metals.
SG62	Stow "separated from" sulphur.
SG63	Stow "separated longitudinally by an intervening complete compartment or hold from" class 1.
SG64	[Reserved]
SG65	Stow "separated by a complete compartment or hold from" class 1 except for division 1.4.
SG66	[Reserved]
SG67	Stow "separated from" division 1.4 and "separated longitudinally by an intervening complete compartment of hold from" divisions 1.1, 1.2, 1.3, 1.5 and 1.6 except from explosives of compatibility group J.
SG68	If flashpoint 60°C c.c. or below, segregation as for class 3 but "away from" class 4.1.
SG69	For AEROSOLS with a maximum capacity of 1 L: segregation as for class 9. Stow "separated from" class 1 except for division 1.4. For AEROSOLS with a capacity above 1 L: segregation as for the appropriate subdivision of class 2. For WASTE AEROSOLS: segregation as for the appropriate subdivision of class 2.
SG70	For arsenic sulphides, "separated from" acids.
SG71	Within the appliance, to the extent that the dangerous goods are integral parts of the complete life-saving appliance, there is no need to apply the provisions on segregation of substances in chapter 7.2.
SG72	See 7.2.6.3.2.
SG73	[Reserved]
SG 74	Segregation as for 1.4G.
SG 75	Stow "separated from" strong acids.

7

Annex
Segregation flow chart

The use of this chart is not mandatory and is provided for information purposes only.

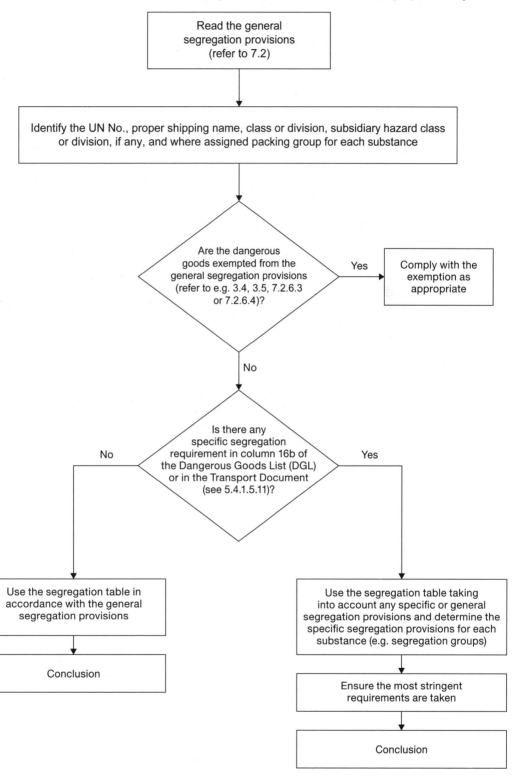

Examples

The following examples only illustrate the process of segregation. Subsequent additional provisions of this Code may apply (e.g. 7.3.4).

1   Segregation of 300 kg of celluloid, scrap (UN 2002) in one drum and 200 L of epibromohydrin (UN 2558) in one drum.

   .1   According to the Dangerous Goods List, UN 2002 is class 4.2, PG III, and UN 2558 is class 6.1, PG I and has a subsidiary risk of class 3.

   .2   Neither are exempted by 3.4, 3.5, 7.2.6.3 or 7.2.6.4.

   .3   There are no specific segregation requirements for these substances in column 16b of the Dangerous Goods List.

   .4   According to the segregation table given in 7.2.4 for classes 4.2 and 6.1, the intersecting box shows number 1, whereas for classes 4.2 and 3, the intersecting box shows a number 2. The value 2 is the more stringent, therefore the substances are required to be "separated from" one another.

2   Segregation of 50 kg of potassium perchlorate (UN 1489) in one drum and 50 kg of nickel cyanide (UN 1653) in one drum.

   .1   According to the Dangerous Goods List, UN 1489 is class 5.1, PG II and UN 1653 is class 6.1, PG II.

   .2   Neither are exempted by 3.4, 3.5, 7.2.6.3 or 7.2.6.4.

   .3   For UN 1489, column 16b of the Dangerous Goods List states: ""separated from" ammonium compounds and cyanides".

   .4   For UN 1653, column 16b of the Dangerous Goods List states: ""separated from" acids".

   .5   According to the segregation table given in 7.2.4 for classes 5.1 and 6.1, the intersecting box shows an "1".

   .6   According to the segregation groups in section 3.1.4, UN 1653 is listed in group 6 (cyanides).

   .7   Therefore, the substances are required to be "separated from" one another.

3   Segregation of 10 kg of acetone (UN 1090) in one box and 20 kg of ethyldichlorosilane (UN 1183) in another box.

   .1   According to the Dangerous Goods List, UN 1090 is class 3, PG II.

   .2   According to the Dangerous Goods List, UN 1183 is class 4.3, PG I and has subsidiary risks of classes 3 and 8.

   .3   Neither are exempted by 3.4, 3.5, 7.2.6.3 or 7.2.6.4.

   .4   UN 1090 has no specific segregation requirements in column 16b.

   .5   For UN 1183, column 16b of the Dangerous Goods List states: "segregation as for class 3 but "away from" classes 3, 4.1 and 8".

   .6   According to the segregation table given in 7.2.4, the intersecting box shows an "X" for classes 3 and 3, but as UN 1183 is required to be "away from" class 3, the substances are required to be "away from" one another.

4   Segregation of 10 kg of adhesives (UN 1133, PG III) in limited quantities and 40 kg of beryllium nitrate (UN 2464) in the same freight container.

   .1   According to the Dangerous Goods List, UN 1133 is class 3, PG III.

   .2   According to the Dangerous Goods List, UN 2464 is class 5.1, PG II and has a subsidiary risk of class 6.1.

   .3   According to section 3.4, UN 1133 in limited quantities is exempted from the segregation provisions of part 7.

   .4   Therefore, no segregation requirements shall apply.

Chapter 7.3

Consigning operations concerning the packing and use of cargo transport units (CTUs) and related provisions

7.3.1 Introduction

This chapter contains the provisions appropriate to those responsible for the consignment operations in the dangerous goods transport supply chain, including provisions relating to packing of dangerous goods into cargo transport units.

7.3.2 General provisions for cargo transport units

7.3.2.1 Packages containing dangerous goods shall only be loaded in cargo transport units that are strong enough to withstand the shocks and loadings normally encountered during transport, having regard to the conditions to be expected during the anticipated journey. The cargo transport unit shall be constructed in such a way as to prevent the loss of contents. Where appropriate, the cargo transport unit shall be fitted with devices to facilitate securing and handling of the dangerous goods. The cargo transport units shall be adequately maintained.

7.3.2.2 Unless otherwise specified, the applicable provisions of the International Convention for Safe Containers (CSC) 1972,[*] as amended, shall be followed for the use of any cargo transport unit which meets the definition of a "container" within the terms of that Convention.

7.3.2.3 The International Convention for Safe Containers does not apply to offshore containers that are handled in open seas. The design and testing of offshore containers shall take into account the dynamic lifting and impact forces that may occur when a container is handled in open seas in adverse weather and sea conditions. The requirement for such containers shall be determined by the approving competent authority. Such provisions should be based on MSC/Circ.860 Guidelines for the Approval of Offshore Containers handled in Open Seas. Such containers shall be clearly marked with the words "OFFSHORE CONTAINER" on the safety approval plate.

7.3.3 Packing of cargo transport units[†]

7.3.3.1 Prior to the use of a cargo transport unit it shall be checked to ensure that it is apparently fit for its intended purpose.[‡]

7.3.3.2 The interior and exterior of a cargo transport unit shall be inspected prior to loading to ensure that there is no damage that could affect its integrity or that of the packages to be loaded in it.

7.3.3.3 Packages shall be examined and any found to be damaged, leaking or sifting shall not be packed into a cargo transport unit. Care shall be taken to see that excessive water, snow, ice or foreign matter adhering to packages is removed before packing into a cargo transport unit. Whenever the handling provision "keep as dry as reasonably practicable" (H1) is assigned in column 16a of the Dangerous Goods List, the cargo transport unit including any contained goods, securing or packing materials shall be kept as dry as reasonably practicable.

7.3.3.4 Drums containing dangerous goods shall always be stowed in an upright position unless otherwise authorized by the competent authority.

7.3.3.5 Cargo transport units shall be loaded in accordance with 7.3.4, so that incompatible dangerous or other goods are segregated. Specific loading instructions such as orientation arrows, not to be double stacked, keep dry or temperature control requirements shall be met. Liquid dangerous goods shall be loaded below dry dangerous goods whenever possible.

---

[*] See IMO publication, sales number IC282E.

△ [†] See CTU Code.

[‡] For safety approval plates and maintenance and examination of containers see the International Convention for Safe Containers, 1972, as amended, annex I, regulations 1 and 2 (see 1.1.2.3).

7.3.3.6   Packages containing dangerous goods and unpackaged dangerous articles shall be secured by suitable means capable of restraining the goods (such as fastening straps, sliding slatboards, adjustable brackets) in the cargo transport unit in a manner that will prevent any movement during transport which would change the orientation of the packages or cause them to be damaged. When dangerous goods are transported with other goods (e.g. heavy machinery or crates), all goods shall be securely fixed or packed in the cargo transport units so as to prevent the release of dangerous goods. Movement of packages may also be prevented by filling any voids by the use of dunnage or by blocking and bracing. Where restraints such as banding or straps are used, these shall not be over-tightened to cause damage or deformation of the package or the securing points (such as D-rings) within the cargo transport unit. The packages shall be packed in such a way that there will be a minimum likelihood of damage to fittings during transport. Such fittings on packages shall be adequately protected. Where restraints such as banding or straps with integral container fittings are used, care should be taken to ensure that the Maximum Securing Load (*MSL*) of the fittings is not exceeded.

7.3.3.7   Packages shall not be stacked unless designed for that purpose. Where packages of different stacking designs are to be loaded together, consideration shall be given to their compatibility for stacking with each other. Where necessary, stacked packages shall be prevented from damaging the package below by the use of load bearing devices.

7.3.3.8   Cargo shall be entirely contained within the cargo transport unit without overhang or projections. Oversized machinery (such as tractors and vehicles) may overhang or project outside of the cargo transport unit provided that the dangerous goods integral to the machinery cannot leak or spill outside of the cargo transport unit.

7.3.3.9   During loading and unloading, packages containing dangerous goods shall be protected from being damaged. Particular attention shall be paid to the handling of packages during their preparation for transport, the type of cargo transport unit to be used for their carriage and to the method of loading or unloading, so that accidental damage is not caused through dragging or mishandling. Packages that appear to be leaking or damaged so that the contents may escape shall not be accepted for transport. If a package is found to be damaged so that the contents leak, the damaged package shall not be transported but moved to a safe place in accordance with instructions given by a competent authority or a designated responsible person who is familiar with the dangerous goods, the risks involved and the measures that should be taken in an emergency.

     Note 1: Additional operational requirements for the transport of packagings and IBCs are provided in the special packing provisions for packagings and IBCs (see chapter 4.1).

△ 7.3.3.10   When a dangerous goods consignment forms only part of the load of a cargo transport unit, it should, whenever possible, be packed adjacent to the doors with marks and labels visible, so as to be accessible in the event of an emergency or to facilitate inspection.

7.3.3.11   If the doors of a cargo transport unit are locked, the means of locking shall be such that, in cases of emergency, the doors can be opened without delay.

7.3.3.12   When venting is required, venting devices shall be kept clear and operable.

△ 7.3.3.13   Cargo transport units containing dangerous goods shall be marked and placarded according to chapter 5.3. Irrelevant marks, labels, placards, orange panels, signs and marine pollutant marks shall be removed, masked or otherwise obliterated before packing a cargo transport unit.

△ 7.3.3.14   Cargo transport units shall be packed so that the cargo is uniformly distributed consistent with the CTU Code.

7.3.3.15   If goods of class 1 are packed, the cargo transport unit shall comply with the definition in 7.1.2 for closed cargo transport unit for class 1.

7.3.3.16   If goods of class 7 are packed, the transport index and, if applicable, the criticality safety index, shall be limited according to 7.1.4.5.3.

7.3.3.17   Those responsible for the packing of dangerous goods into a cargo transport unit shall provide a "container/ vehicle packing certificate" (see 5.4.2). This document is not required for tanks.

7.3.3.18   Flexible bulk containers are not allowed to be transported in cargo transport units (see 4.3.4).

7.3.4   Segregation provisions within cargo transport units

7.3.4.1   Dangerous goods which have to be segregated from each other according to the provisions in chapter 7.2 shall not be transported in the same cargo transport unit with the exception of dangerous goods which shall be segregated "away from" each other which may be transported in the same cargo transport unit with the approval of the competent authority. In such cases an equivalent standard of safety shall be maintained.

7.3.4.2   Segregation in relation to foodstuffs

7.3.4.2.1   Dangerous goods having a primary or subsidiary risk of classes 2.3, 6.1, 6.2, 7 (with the exception of UN 2908, 2909, 2910 and 2911), 8 and dangerous goods having a reference to 7.3.4.2.1 in column 16b of the Dangerous Goods List shall not be transported together with foodstuffs (see 1.2.1) in the same cargo transport unit.

7.3.4.2.2   Notwithstanding the provisions in 7.3.4.2.1, the following dangerous goods may be transported with foodstuffs provided that they are not loaded within 3 m from foodstuffs:

    .1   dangerous goods of packing group III of classes 6.1 and 8;

    .2   dangerous goods of packing group II of class 8; and

    .3   any other dangerous goods of packing group III with a subsidiary risk of classes 6.1 or 8; and

    .4   dangerous goods having a reference to 7.3.4.2.2 in column 16b of the Dangerous Goods List.

7.3.5   Tracking and monitoring equipment

When security devices, beacons or other tracking or monitoring equipment are used, they shall be securely installed to the cargo transport unit and shall be of a certified safe type[*] for the dangerous goods that will be carried within the cargo transport unit.

7.3.6   Opening and unloading cargo transport units

7.3.6.1   Cargo transport units shall be approached with caution. Before opening the doors, the nature of the contents and the possibility that leakages may have caused an unsafe condition, concentration of toxic or flammable vapours, or an oxygen-enriched or oxygen-depleted atmosphere, shall be considered.

7.3.6.2   After a cargo transport unit carrying dangerous goods has been unpacked or unloaded, precautions shall be taken to ensure that there is no contamination likely to make the cargo transport unit dangerous.

7.3.6.3   After unpacking or unloading corrosive substances, particular attention shall be paid to cleaning, as residues may be highly corrosive to the metal structures.

7.3.6.4   When the cargo transport unit offers no further hazard, the dangerous goods placards and other marks related to dangerous goods shall be removed, masked or otherwise obliterated.

7.3.7   Cargo transport units under temperature control

7.3.7.1   Preamble

7.3.7.1.1   If the temperature of certain substances (such as organic peroxides and self-reactive substances) exceeds a value which is typical of the substance as packaged for transport, a self-accelerating decomposition, possibly of explosive violence, may result. To prevent such decomposition, it is necessary to control the temperature of such substances during transport. Other substances not requiring temperature control for safety reasons may be transported under controlled temperature conditions for commercial reasons.

7.3.7.1.2   The provisions for the temperature control of certain specified substances are based on the assumption that the temperature in the immediate surroundings of the cargo does not exceed 55°C during transport and attains this value for a relatively short time only during each period of 24 h.

7.3.7.1.3   If a substance which is not normally temperature controlled is transported under conditions where the temperature may exceed 55°C, it may require temperature control; in such cases, adequate measures shall be taken.

---

[*] Refer to the Recommendations published by the International Electrotechnical Commission, in particular, to publication IEC 60079.

7

7.3.7.2 General provisions

7.3.7.2.1 A self-accelerating decomposition temperature (SADT)[*] shall be determined in order to decide if a substance shall be subjected to temperature control during transport. The relationship between SADT, the control temperature and the emergency temperature is as follows:

Type of receptacle	SADT[†]	Control temperature	Emergency temperature
Single packagings and IBC	20°C or less over 20°C to 35°C over 35°C	20°C below SADT 15°C below SADT 10°C below SADT	10°C below SADT 10°C below SADT 5°C below SADT
Portable tanks	< 50°C	10°C below SADT	5°C below SADT

7.3.7.2.2 The substances for which a control temperature and an emergency temperature are indicated in 2.4.2.3.2.3 or 2.5.3.2.4 shall be transported under conditions of temperature control such that the temperature of the immediate surroundings of the cargo does not exceed the control temperature.

7.3.7.2.3 The actual transport temperature may be lower than the control temperature but shall be selected so as to avoid dangerous separation of phases.

7.3.7.2.4 Prior to the use of cargo transport unit, the refrigeration system shall be subjected to a thorough inspection and a test to ensure that all parts are functioning properly.

7.3.7.2.4.1 Refrigerant gas shall only be replaced in accordance with the manufacturer's operating instructions for the refrigeration system. Prior to filling replacement refrigerant gas, a certificate of analysis from the supplier shall be obtained and checked to confirm that the gas meets refrigeration system specifications. In addition, if concerns about the integrity of the supplier and/or the refrigerant gas supply chain give rise to suspicion of contamination of the gas, the replacement refrigerant gas shall be checked for possible contamination prior to use. If the refrigerant gas is found to be contaminated, it shall not be used, the cylinder shall be plainly marked "CONTAMINATED", the cylinder shall be sealed and sent for recycling or disposal, and notification shall be given to the refrigerant gas supplier and authorized distributor and competent authority(ies) of the countries to which the supplier and distributor reside, as appropriate. The date of last refrigerant replacement shall be included in the maintenance record of the refrigeration system.

Note: Contamination can be checked by using flame halide lamp tests, gas sniffer tube tests or gas chromatography. Replacement refrigerant gas cylinders may be marked with the test result and the date of testing.

7.3.7.2.5 When a cargo transport unit is to be filled with packages containing substances having different control temperatures, all packages shall be pre-cooled to avoid exceeding the lowest control temperature.

7.3.7.2.5.1 In the event that non-temperature-controlled substances are transported in the same cargo transport unit as temperature controlled substances, the package(s) containing substances that require refrigeration shall be stowed in such a way as to be readily accessible from the door(s) of the cargo transport unit.

7.3.7.2.5.2 If substances with different control temperatures are loaded in the cargo transport unit, the substances with the lowest control temperature shall be stowed in the most readily accessible position from the doors of the cargo transport unit.

7.3.7.2.5.3 The door(s) shall be capable of being opened readily in case of emergency so that the package(s) can be removed. The carrier shall be informed about the location of the different substances within the unit. The cargo shall be secured to prevent packages from falling when the door(s) is (are) opened. The packages shall be securely stowed so as to allow for adequate air circulation throughout the cargo.

7.3.7.2.6 The master shall be provided with operating instructions for the refrigeration system, procedures to be followed in the event of loss of control and instructions for regular monitoring of operating temperatures. Spare parts shall be carried for the systems described in 7.3.7.3.2.3 and 7.3.7.3.2.4, 7.3.7.3.2.5 so that they are available for emergency use should the refrigeration system malfunction during transport.

7.3.7.2.7 In cases where it may not be possible to carry specific substances according to the general provisions, full details of the proposed method of shipment shall be submitted to the competent authority concerned for approval.

---

[*] The self-accelerating decomposition temperature (SADT) shall be determined in accordance with the Manual of Tests and Criteria. Test methods for determining flammability are given in part III, 32.4 of the Manual of Tests and Criteria. Because organic peroxides may react vigorously when heated, it is recommended to determine their flashpoint using small sample sizes such as described in ISO 3679.

[†] Refer to the Recommendations published by the International Electrotechnical Commission, in particular, to publication IEC 60079.

7.3.7.3   Methods of temperature control

7.3.7.3.1   The suitability of a particular means of temperature control for transport depends on a number of factors. Among those to be considered are:

.1   the control temperature(s) of the substance(s) to be transported;

.2   the difference between the control temperature and the anticipated ambient temperature conditions;

.3   the effectiveness of the thermal insulation of the cargo transport unit. The overall heat transfer coefficient shall not be more than 0.4 W/(m²·K) for cargo transport units and 0.6 W/(m²·K) for tanks; and

.4   the duration of the voyage.

7.3.7.3.2   Suitable methods for preventing the control temperature being exceeded are, in order of increasing capability:

.1   thermal insulation, provided that the initial temperature of the substance is sufficiently below the control temperature;

.2   thermal insulation with a cooling method, provided that:
–   an adequate quantity of non-flammable coolant (such as liquid nitrogen or solid carbon dioxide), allowing a reasonable margin for delay, is carried;
–   liquid oxygen or air is not used as a coolant;
–   there is uniform cooling effect even when most of the coolant has been consumed; and
–   the need to ventilate the cargo transport unit before entering is clearly indicated by a warning on the door(s) (see 5.5.3);

.3   single mechanical refrigeration, provided that the unit is thermally insulated and, for substances with a flashpoint lower than the sum of the emergency temperature plus 5°C, explosion proof electrical fittings are used within the cooling compartment to prevent ignition of flammable vapours from the substances;

.4   combined mechanical refrigeration system and cooling method, provided that:
–   the two systems are independent of one another; and
–   the provisions of 7.3.7.3.2.2 and 7.3.7.3.2.3 are met;

.5   dual mechanical refrigeration system, provided that:
–   apart from the integral power supply unit, the two systems are independent of one another;
–   each system alone is capable of maintaining adequate temperature control; and
–   for substances with a flashpoint lower than the sum of the emergency temperature plus 5°C, explosion proof electrical fittings are used within the coolant compartment to prevent ignition of flammable vapours from the substances.

7.3.7.3.3   The refrigeration equipment and its controls shall be readily and safely accessible and all electrical connections weatherproof. Inside the cargo transport unit, the temperature shall be measured continuously. The measurement shall be taken in the air space of the unit, using two measuring devices independent of each other. The type and place of the measuring devices shall be selected so that their results are representative of the actual temperature in the cargo. At least one of the two measurements shall be recorded in such a manner that temperature changes are easily detectable.

7.3.7.3.4   If substances are transported with a control temperature less than +25°C, the cargo transport unit shall be equipped with a visible and audible alarm effectively set at no higher than the control temperature. The alarms shall work independently from the power supply of the refrigeration system.

7.3.7.3.5   If an electrical supply is necessary for the cargo transport unit to operate the refrigeration or heating equipment, it shall be ensured that the correct connecting plugs are fitted. For under deck stowage, plugs shall, as a minimum, be of an IP 55 enclosure in accordance with IEC Publication 60529,[*] with the specification for electrical equipment of temperature class T4 and explosion group IIB. However, when stowed on deck, these plugs shall be of an IP 56 enclosure in accordance with IEC Publication 60529.[*]

7.3.7.4   Special provisions for self-reactive substances (class 4.1) and organic peroxides (class 5.2)

7.3.7.4.1   For self-reactive substances (class 4.1) identified by UN Nos. 3231 and 3232 and organic peroxides (class 5.2) identified by UN Nos. 3111 and 3112, one of the following methods of temperature control described in 7.3.7.3.2 shall be used:

.1   the methods referred to under 7.3.7.3.2.4 or 7.3.7.3.2.5; or

.2   the method referred to under 7.3.7.3.2.3 when the maximum ambient temperature to be expected during transport is at least 10°C below the control temperature.

---

[*] Reference is made to the Recommendations published by the International Electrotechnical Commission (IEC) and, in particular, to publication 60529 *Classification of Degrees of Protection provided by Enclosures*.

7.3.7.4.2 For self-reactive substances (class 4.1) identified by UN Nos. 3233 to 3240 and organic peroxides (class 5.2) identified by UN Nos. 3113 to 3120, one of the following methods shall be used:

.1 the methods referred to under 7.3.7.3.2.4 or 7.3.7.3.2.5;

.2 the method referred to under 7.3.7.3.2.3 when the maximum ambient temperature to be expected during transport does not exceed the control temperature by more than 10°C; or

.3 for short international voyages only (see 1.2.1), the methods referred to under 7.3.7.3.2.1 and 7.3.7.3.2.2 when the maximum ambient temperature to be expected during transport is at least 10°C below the control temperature.

7.3.7.5 **Special provisions applicable to the transport of substances stabilized by temperature control (other than self-reactive substances and organic peroxides)**

△ **7.3.7.5.1** These provisions apply to the transport of substances for which:

.1 The proper shipping name as indicated in column 2 of the Dangerous Goods List of chapter 3.2 or according to 3.1.2.6 contains the word "STABILIZED"; and

.2 The SADT or the SAPT[*] determined for the substance (with or without chemical stabilization) as offered for transport is:

.1 50°C or less for packagings and IBCs; or

.2 45°C or less for portable tanks.

△ **7.3.7.5.2** The provisions in 7.3.7.2.1 to 7.3.7.2.3 and 7.3.7.3 apply to substances meeting criteria .1 and .2 in 7.3.7.5.1, except that the term "SADT" as used in these paragraphs is understood to include also "SAPT" when the substance concerned reacts by polymerization.

7.3.7.5.3 The actual transport temperature may be lower than the control temperature (see 7.3.7.2.1) but shall be selected so as to avoid dangerous separation of phases.

⊗

△ **7.3.7.5.4** If a substance the proper shipping name of which contains the word "STABILIZED" and which is not normally required to be transported under temperature control is transported under conditions where the temperature may exceed 55°C, it may require temperature control.

7.3.7.6 **Special provisions for flammable gases or liquids having a flashpoint less than 23°C c.c. transported under temperature control**

7.3.7.6.1 When flammable gases or liquids having a flashpoint less than 23°C c.c. are packed or loaded in a cargo transport unit equipped with a refrigerating or heating system, the cooling or heating equipment shall comply with 7.3.7.3.

7.3.7.6.2 When flammable liquids having a flashpoint less than 23°C c.c. and not requiring temperature control for safety reasons are transported under temperature control conditions for commercial reasons, explosion proof electrical fittings are required except when the substances are pre-cooled to and transported at a control temperature of at least 10°C below the flashpoint. In case of failure of a non-explosion proof refrigerating system, the system shall be disconnected from the power supply. It shall not be reconnected if the temperature has risen to a temperature less than 10°C below the flashpoint.

7.3.7.6.3 When flammable gases not requiring temperature control for safety reasons are transported under temperature control conditions for commercial reasons, explosion proof electrical fittings are required.

7.3.7.7 **Special provisions for vehicles transported on ships**

Insulated, refrigerated and mechanically refrigerated vehicles shall conform to the provisions of 7.3.7.3 and 7.3.7.4 or 7.3.7.5 as appropriate. In addition, the refrigerating appliance of a mechanically refrigerated vehicle shall be capable of operating independently of the engine used to propel the vehicle.

7.3.7.8 **Approval**

The competent authority may approve that less stringent means of temperature control may be used or that artificial refrigeration may be dispensed with under conditions of transport such as short international voyages or low ambient temperatures.

---

[*] The self-accelerating polymerization temperature (SAPT) shall be determined in accordance with the Manual of Tests and Criteria. The SADT tests in Section 28, Series H as appropriate may be equally applied to determine a self-accelerating polymerization temperature.

7.3.8 Loading of cargo transport units on board ships

Before loading, cargo transport units used for the transport of dangerous goods shall be examined for external signs of damage, leakage or sifting of contents. Any cargo transport unit found to be damaged, leaking or sifting shall not be loaded on to a ship until repairs have been effected or damaged packages have been removed.

7

Chapter 7.4

Stowage and segregation on containerships

Note: To facilitate familiarization with these requirements and to support training of relevant personnel, illustrations applicable to the segregation requirements on containerships are given in MSC.1/Circ.1440.

7.4.1 Introduction

7.4.1.1 The provisions of this chapter apply to the stowage and segregation of containers which meet the definition of a container within the term of the International Convention for Safe Containers (CSC) 1972, as amended, which are transported on deck and in the cargo holds of container ships or on deck and in the cargo holds of other types of ships provided that these stowage positions are properly fitted to give a permanent stowage of containers during transport.

7.4.1.2 For ships carrying containers in conventional cargo spaces not properly fitted for the permanent stowage of containers the provisions of chapter 7.6 apply.

7.4.1.3 For stowage of FISHMEAL, UNSTABILIZED (UN 1374), FISHMEAL, STABILIZED (UN 2216) and KRILL MEAL (UN 3497) in containers, the provisions of 7.6.2.7.2.2 also apply.

7.4.1.4 For stowage of AMMONIUM NITRATE (UN 1942), AMMONIUM NITRATE BASED FERTILIZER (UN 2067 AND 2071) in containers, the applicable provisions of 7.6.2.8.4 and 7.6.2.11.1 also apply.

7.4.2 Stowage requirements

7.4.2.1 **Provisions for hatchless containerships**

Dangerous goods shall only be transported in or vertically above hatchless container holds if:

.1 the dangerous goods are permitted for under deck stowage as specified in the Dangerous Goods List; and

.2 the hatchless container hold is in full compliance with the provisions of regulation II-2/19 of SOLAS, as amended, or regulation II-2/54 of SOLAS, as amended by the resolutions indicated in II-2/1.2.1, as applicable.

7.4.2.2 **Provisions for ships with partially weathertight hatchway covers**

7.4.2.2.1 *Provisions for partially weathertight hatchway covers with effective gutterbars**

7.4.2.2.1.1 Partially weathertight hatchway covers fitted with *effective gutterbars** can be regarded as "resistant to fire and liquid" for the purpose of stowage and segregation of containers containing dangerous goods on containerships fitted with such hatchway covers. Additionally segregation requirements shall be in accordance with the requirements in paragraph 7.4.3.2.

7.4.2.2.1.2 When "not in the same vertical line unless separated by a deck" is required, containers containing dangerous goods shall not be stowed in any tier directly above a *clear gap** unless the cargo hold complies with the relevant requirements for the class and flashpoint of the dangerous goods in regulation II-2/19 of SOLAS 74, as amended, or regulation II-2/54 of SOLAS, as amended by resolutions indicated in II-2/1.2.1, as applicable. Additionally, containers containing incompatible dangerous goods shall not be stowed within the relevant *sensitive vertical lines** under deck.

---

* For definitions and details see MSC/Circ.1087 found in the IMDG Code Supplement.

7.4.2.2.2 *Provisions for partially weathertight hatchway covers without effective gutterbars**

7.4.2.2.2.1 Where hatchway covers are *not fitted with effective gutterbars*, containers containing dangerous goods shall not be stowed on such hatchway covers, unless the cargo hold complies with the relevant requirements for the class and flashpoint of the dangerous goods in regulation II-2/19 of SOLAS 74, as amended, or regulation II-2/54 of SOLAS, as amended by the resolutions indicated in II-2/1.2.1, as applicable.

7.4.2.2.2.2 Where hatchway covers are not fitted with *effective gutterbars,** the following applies where stowage "not in the same vertical line" is required in 7.4.3.3.

7.4.2.2.2.3 When containers containing dangerous goods are stowed on deck, containers containing incompatible dangerous goods shall not be stowed within the relevant *sensitive vertical lines** of any *clear gap** on either side of the hatchway cover below deck.

7.4.2.2.2.4 When containers containing dangerous goods are stowed below deck within the relevant sensitive vertical lines of a clear gap, containers with incompatible dangerous goods shall not be stowed on the hatches above the hold.*

7.4.2.3 **Provisions for containers with flammable gases and highly flammable liquids**

7.4.2.3.1 In cargo ships of 500 gross tons or over and passenger ships constructed before 1 September 1984, and in cargo ships of less than 500 gross tons constructed before 1 February 1992, containers with flammable gases or with flammable liquids having a flashpoint of less than 23°C c.c, shall be stowed on deck only, unless otherwise approved by the Administration.

7.4.2.3.2 A container with flammable gases or with flammable liquids having a flashpoint of less than 23°C c.c transported on deck shall be stowed at least 2.4 m from any potential source of ignition.

7.4.2.3.3 A container under temperature control that is not of a certified safe type shall not be stowed under deck together with containers containing flammable gases or with liquids having a flashpoint of less than 23°C c.c.

7.4.2.4 **Ventilation provisions**

7.4.2.4.1 In cargo ships of 500 gross tons or over and passenger ships constructed before 1 September 1984, and in cargo ships of less than 500 gross tons constructed before 1 February 1992, containers with the following dangerous goods may be stowed under deck only if the cargo space is equipped with mechanical ventilation and if under deck stowage is permitted in the Dangerous Goods List:

– dangerous goods of class 2.1;

– dangerous goods of class 3 with a flashpoint of less than 23°C c.c.;

– dangerous goods of class 4.3;

– dangerous goods of class 6.1 with a subsidiary risk of class 3;

– dangerous goods of class 8 with a subsidiary risk of class 3; and

– dangerous goods to which a specific stowage requirement requiring mechanical ventilation in column 16a of the Dangerous Goods List is assigned.

Otherwise containers shall be stowed on deck only.

7.4.2.4.2 The capacity of the mechanical ventilation (number of air changes per hour) shall be to the satisfaction of the Administration.

7.4.3 Segregation requirements

7.4.3.1 **Definitions and application**

7.4.3.1.1 Container space means a distance of not less than 6 m fore and aft or not less than 2.4 m athwartships.

7.4.3.1.2 The provisions for segregation between containers onboard containerships with closed cargo holds and onboard hatchless containerships are given in the tables in 7.4.3.2 and 7.4.3.3 respectively.

---

* For definitions and details see MSC/Circ.1087 found in the IMDG Code Supplement.

7

7.4.3.2

Table of segregation of containers on board containerships with closed cargo holds

Segregation requirement	Direction	Vertical — Closed versus closed	Vertical — Closed versus open	Vertical — Open versus open	Horizontal Closed versus closed — On deck	Closed versus closed — Under deck	Closed versus open — On deck	Closed versus open — Under deck	Open versus open — On deck	Open versus open — Under deck
"Away from" .1	Fore and aft	One on top of the other permitted	Open on top of closed permitted — Otherwise as for "open versus open"	Not in the same vertical line unless segregated by a deck	No restriction	No restriction	No restriction	No restriction	One container space	One container space or one bulkhead
	Athwartships				No restriction	No restriction	No restriction	No restriction	One container space	One container space
"Separated from" .2	Fore and aft	Not in the same vertical line unless segregated by a deck	As for "open versus open"	(as above)	One container space	One container space or one bulkhead	One container space	One container space or one bulkhead	One container space	One bulkhead
	Athwartships				One container space	One container space	One container space	Two container spaces	Two container spaces	One bulkhead
"Separated by a complete compartment or hold from" .3	Fore and aft	Prohibited	Prohibited	Prohibited	One container space	One bulkhead	One container space	One bulkhead	Two container spaces	Two bulkheads
	Athwartships				Two container spaces	One bulkhead	Two container spaces	One bulkhead	Three container spaces	Two bulkheads
"Separated longitudinally by an intervening complete compartment or hold from" .4*	Fore and aft	Prohibited	Prohibited	Prohibited	Minimum horizontal distance of 24 m	One bulkhead and minimum horizontal distance of 24 m*	Minimum horizontal distance of 24 m	Two bulkheads	Minimum horizontal distance of 24 m	Two bulkheads
	Athwartships				Prohibited	Prohibited	Prohibited	Prohibited	Prohibited	Prohibited

* Containers not less than 6 m from intervening bulkhead.

Note: All bulkheads and decks shall be resistant to fire and liquids.

7.4.3.3   Table of segregation of containers on board hatchless containerships

Vertical

Segregation requirement	Closed versus closed	Closed versus open	Open versus open
"Away from" .1	One on top of the other permitted	Open on top of closed permitted otherwise as for "open versus open"	Not in the same vertical line
"Separated from" .2	Not in the same vertical line	As for "open versus open"	Not in the same vertical line
"Separated by a complete compartment or hold from" .3	Prohibited	Prohibited	Prohibited
"Separated longitudinally by an intervening complete compartment or hold from" .4	Prohibited	Prohibited	Prohibited

Horizontal

Segregation requirement		Closed versus closed – On deck	Closed versus closed – Under deck	Closed versus open – On deck	Closed versus open – Under deck	Open versus open – On deck	Open versus open – Under deck
"Away from" .1	Fore and aft	No restriction	No restriction	No restriction	No restriction	One container space	One container space or one bulkhead
	Athwartships	No restriction	No restriction	No restriction	No restriction	One container space	One container space
"Separated from" .2	Fore and aft	One container space	One container space or one bulkhead	One container space	One container space or one bulkhead	One container space and not in or above same hold	One bulkhead
	Athwartships	One container space	One container space	Two container spaces	Two container spaces	Two container spaces and not in or above same hold	One bulkhead
"Separated by a complete compartment or hold from" .3	Fore and aft	One container space and not in or above same hold	One bulkhead	One container space and not in or above same hold	One bulkhead	Two container spaces and not in or above same hold	Two bulkheads
	Athwartships	Two container spaces and not in or above same hold	One bulkhead	Two container spaces and not in or above same hold	One bulkhead	Three container spaces and not in or above same hold	Two bulkheads
"Separated longitudinally by an intervening complete compartment or hold from" .4	Fore and aft	Minimum horizontal distance of 24 m and not in or above same hold	One bulkhead and minimum horizontal distance of 24 m*	Minimum horizontal distance of 24 m and not in or above same hold	Two bulkheads	Minimum horizontal distance of 24 m and not in or above same hold	Two bulkheads
	Athwartships	Prohibited	Prohibited	Prohibited	Prohibited	Prohibited	Prohibited

* Containers not less than 6 m from intervening bulkhead.

Note: All bulkheads and decks shall be resistant to fire and liquids.

7

Chapter 7.5

Stowage and segregation on ro-ro ships

Note: To facilitate familiarization with these requirements and to support training of relevant personnel, illustrations applicable to the segregation requirements on ro-ro ships are given in MSC.1/Circ.1440.

7.5.1 Introduction

7.5.1.1 The provisions of this chapter apply to the stowage and segregation of cargo transport units which are transported in ro-ro cargo spaces.

7.5.1.2 For ro-ro ships which incorporate stowage positions which are properly fitted to give a permanent stowage of containers during transport, the provisions of chapter 7.4 apply for containers carried in these spaces.

7.5.1.3 For ro-ro ships which incorporate conventional cargo spaces, the provisions of chapter 7.6 apply in these spaces.

7.5.1.4 In case more than one container is loaded on the same chassis in a ro-ro cargo space, the segregation of chapter 7.4 applies between the containers.

7.5.2 Stowage provisions

7.5.2.1 Loading and unloading operations on each ro-ro cargo space shall take place under the supervision of either a working party consisting of officers and other crew members or responsible persons appointed by the master.

7.5.2.2 During the voyage, access to such spaces by passengers and other unauthorized persons shall only be permitted when such persons are accompanied by an authorized crew member.

7.5.2.3 All doors leading directly to these spaces shall be securely closed during the voyage and notices or signs prohibiting entrance to such spaces shall be conspicuously displayed.

7.5.2.4 The transport of dangerous goods shall be prohibited in any ro-ro cargo space in which the foregoing provisions cannot be met.

7.5.2.5 Closing arrangements for the openings between ro-ro cargo spaces and machinery and accommodation spaces shall be such as to avoid the possibility of dangerous vapours and liquids entering such spaces. Such openings shall normally be kept securely closed when dangerous cargo is on board, except to permit access by authorized persons or for emergency use.

7.5.2.6 Dangerous goods required to be carried on deck only shall not be carried in closed ro-ro cargo spaces, but may be carried in open ro-ro cargo spaces when authorized by the Administration.

7.5.2.7 Flammable gases or liquids having a flashpoint of less than 23°C c.c. shall not be stowed in a closed ro-ro cargo space or special category space on a passenger ship unless:

- the design, construction and equipment of the space comply with the provisions of regulation II-2/19 of SOLAS, as amended, or regulation II-2/54 of SOLAS, as amended by the resolutions indicated in II-2/1.2.1, as applicable, and the ventilation system is operated to maintain at least six air changes per hour; or

- the ventilation system of the space is operated to maintain at least ten air changes per hour and non-certified safe electrical systems in the space are capable of being isolated by means other than removal of fuses in the event of failure of the ventilation system or any other circumstance likely to cause accumulation of flammable vapours.

Otherwise stowage is restricted to *on deck only*.

7.5.2.8 Cargo transport units with flammable gases or liquids having a flashpoint of less than 23°C c.c. and transported on deck shall be stowed at least 3 m from any potential sources of ignition.

7.5.2.9 Mechanically operated refrigeration or heating equipment fitted to any cargo transport unit shall not be operated during the voyage when stowed in a closed ro-ro cargo space or a special category space on a passenger ship.

7.5.2.10 Electrically operated refrigeration or heating equipment fitted to any cargo transport unit stowed in a closed ro-ro cargo space or special category space on a passenger ship shall not be operated when flammable gases or liquids having a flashpoint of less than 23°C c.c. are present in the cargo transport unit or in the same space, unless:

–   the design, construction and equipment of the space comply with the provisions of regulation II-2/19 of SOLAS, as amended, or regulation II-2/54 of SOLAS, as amended by the resolutions indicated in II-2/1.2.1, as applicable; or

–   the ventilation system of the space is operated to maintain at least ten air changes per hour and all electrical systems in the space are capable of being isolated by means other than removal of fuses in the event of ventilation failure or other circumstance likely to cause accumulation of flammable vapours;

–   and, in either case, the refrigeration or heating equipment of the cargo transport unit shall comply with paragraph 7.3.7.6.

7.5.2.11 In ships the keel of which was laid before 1 September 1984 and for which regulation II-2/20 of SOLAS, as amended, or regulations II 2/37 and 38 of SOLAS, as amended by the resolutions indicated in II-2/1.2.1, are not applicable to a closed ro-ro cargo space, mechanical ventilation shall be provided to the satisfaction of the Administration. The ventilation fans shall be operating at all times when vehicles are in such spaces.

7.5.2.12 If continuous ventilation is impracticable in a closed ro-ro cargo space other than a special category space on a passenger ship, ventilation fans shall be operated daily for a limited period, as weather permits. In any case, prior to discharge, the fans shall be operated for a reasonable period. The ro-ro cargo space shall be proved gas-free at the end of the period. When the ventilation is not continuous, electrical systems which are not certified safe shall be isolated.

7.5.2.13 The master of a ship carrying dangerous goods in ro-ro cargo spaces shall ensure that, during loading and unloading operations and during the voyage, regular inspections of these spaces are made by an authorized crew member or responsible person in order to achieve early detection of any hazard.

7.5.3 Segregation provisions

7.5.3.1 The provisions for segregation between cargo transport units onboard ro-ro ships are given in the table in 7.5.3.2.

7.5.3.2 Table of segregation of cargo transport units on board ro-ro ships

Segregation requirement		Horizontal					
		Closed versus closed		Closed versus open		Open versus open	
		On deck	Under deck	On deck	Under deck	On deck	Under deck
"Away from" .1	Fore and aft	No restriction	No restriction	No restriction	No restriction	At least 3 m	At least 3 m
	Athwartships	No restriction	No restriction	No restriction	No restriction	At least 3 m	At least 3 m
"Separated from" .2	Fore and aft	At least 6 m	At least 6 m or *one* bulkhead	At least 6 m	At least 6 m or *one* bulkhead	At least 6 m	At least 12 m or *one* bulkhead
	Athwartships	At least 3 m	At least 3 m or *one* bulkhead	At least 3 m	At least 6 m or *one* bulkhead	At least 6 m	At least 12 m or *one* bulkhead
"Separated by a complete compartment or hold from" .3	Fore and aft	At least 12 m	At least 24 m + deck	At least 24 m	At least 24 m + deck	At least 36 m	*Two* decks or *two* bulkheads
	Athwartships	At least 12 m	At least 24 m + deck	At least 24 m	At least 24 m + deck	Prohibited	Prohibited
"Separated longitudinally by an intervening complete compartment or hold from" .4	Fore and aft	At least 36 m	*Two* bulkheads or at least 36 m + *two* decks	At least 36 m	At least 48 m including *two* bulkheads	At least 48 m	Prohibited
	Athwartships	Prohibited	Prohibited	Prohibited	Prohibited	Prohibited	Prohibited

Note: All bulkheads and decks shall be resistant to fire and liquid.

7

Chapter 7.6

Stowage and segregation on general cargo ships

7.6.1 Introduction

7.6.1.1 The provisions of this chapter apply to the stowage and segregation of dangerous goods stowed in the conventional way on board general cargo ships. They apply also to containers which are transported in conventional cargo spaces, including cargo spaces on the weather deck, not properly fitted to give a permanent stowage of the containers during transport.

7.6.1.2 For ships carrying containers in stowage positions which are properly fitted for the permanent stowage of containers the provisions of chapter 7.4 apply.

7.6.2 Stowage and handling provisions

7.6.2.1 Provisions for all classes

7.6.2.1.1 The minimum stacking height for testing packagings intended to contain dangerous goods in accordance with chapter 6.1 is 3 m. For IBCs and large packagings, the stacking test load shall be determined in accordance with 6.5.6.6.4 and 6.6.5.3.3.4 respectively.

7.6.2.1.2 Drums containing dangerous goods shall always be stowed in an upright position unless otherwise authorized by the competent authority.

7.6.2.1.3 The stowage of dangerous goods shall be so arranged as to ensure clear walkways and access to all facilities necessary for the safe working of the ship. When dangerous goods are stowed on deck, hydrants, sounding pipes and the like and access thereto shall be kept free and clear of such goods.

7.6.2.1.4 Fibreboard packagings, paper bags and other packages susceptible to water damage shall be stowed *under deck* or, if they are stowed on deck, they shall be so protected that at no time are they exposed to weather or to seawater.

7.6.2.1.5 Portable tanks shall not be overstowed by other cargo unless they are designed for that purpose or unless they are protected to the satisfaction of the competent authority.

7.6.2.1.6 Cargo spaces and decks shall be clean and dry as relevant to the hazards of the dangerous goods to be carried. In order to reduce the risk of ignition, the space shall be free of dust from other cargoes, such as grain or coal dust.

7.6.2.1.7 Packages and cargo transport units found to be damaged, leaking or sifting shall not be loaded on a general cargo ship. Care shall be taken to ensure that excessive water, snow, ice or foreign matter adhering to packages and cargo transport units shall be removed before loading.

7.6.2.1.8 Packages and cargo transport units and any other goods shall be adequately braced and secured for the voyage.[*] Packages shall be loaded in such a way that there will be a minimum likelihood of damage to them and to any fittings during transport. Fittings on packages or portable tanks shall be adequately protected.

7.6.2.2 Provisions for flammable gases and highly flammable liquids

7.6.2.2.1 In cargo ships of 500 gross tons or over and passenger ships constructed before 1 September 1984, and in cargo ships of less than 500 gross tons constructed before 1 February 1992, flammable gases or flammable liquids having a flashpoint of less than 23°C c.c, shall be stowed on deck only, unless otherwise approved by the Administration.

7.6.2.2.2 Flammable gases or liquids having a flashpoint less than 23°C c.c. transported on deck shall be stowed at least 3 m from any potential source of ignition.

---

[*] Refer to regulation VII/5 of SOLAS, as amended.

7.6.2.3 **Ventilation provisions**

7.6.2.3.1 In cargo ships of 500 gross tons or over and passenger ships constructed before 1 September 1984, and in cargo ships of less than 500 gross tons constructed before 1 February 1992, the following dangerous goods, may be stowed *under deck* only if the cargo space is equipped with mechanical ventilation and if under deck stowage is permitted in the Dangerous Goods List:

– dangerous goods of class 2.1;

– dangerous goods of class 3 with a flashpoint of less than 23°C c.c.;

– dangerous goods of class 4.3;

– dangerous goods of class 6.1 with a subsidiary risk of class 3;

– dangerous goods of class 8 with a subsidiary risk of class 3, and

– dangerous goods to which a specific stowage requirement requiring mechanical ventilation in column 16a of the Dangerous Goods List is assigned.

Otherwise containers shall be stowed on deck only.

7.6.2.3.2 The capacity of the mechanical ventilation (number of air changes per hour) shall be to the satisfaction of the Administration.

7.6.2.4 **Provisions for class 1**

7.6.2.4.1 All compartments or holds and cargo transport units shall be locked or suitably secured in order to prevent unauthorized access. The means of locking and securing shall be such that, in the case of emergency, access can be gained without delay.

7.6.2.4.2 Loading and unloading procedures and equipment used should be of such a nature that sparks are not produced, in particular where the floors of the cargo compartment are not constructed of close-boarded wood. All cargo handlers should be briefed by the shipper or receiver of the potential risks and necessary precautions, prior to commencing the handling of explosives. In the event of the contents of packages being affected by water whilst on board, immediate advice shall be sought from the shipper; pending this advice, handling of the packages shall be avoided.

7.6.2.4.3 *Segregation on deck*

When goods in different compatibility groups are transported on deck, they shall be stowed not less than 6 m apart unless their mixed stowage is allowed according to 7.2.7.

7.6.2.4.4 *Segregation in single hold ships*

In a single hold ship, dangerous goods of class 1 shall be segregated in accordance with 7.2.7 except that:

.1 Goods in Division 1.1 or 1.2 of compatibility group B may be stowed in the same hold as substances of compatibility group D provided:

– the net explosives mass of goods of compatibility group B does not exceed 50 kg; and

– such goods are stowed in a closed cargo transport unit which is stowed at least 6 m from the substances of compatibility group D.

.2 Goods in Division 1.4 of compatibility group B may be stowed in the same hold as substances of compatibility group D provided they are separated either by a distance of at least 6 m or by a steel division.

7.6.2.4.5 In the event that a package containing goods of class 1 is found to be suffering from breakage or leakage expert advice should be obtained for its safe handling and disposal.

7.6.2.5 **Provisions for class 2**

7.6.2.5.1 When pressure receptacles are stowed in a vertical position they shall be stowed in a block, cribbed or boxed-in with suitable sound lumber and the box or crib dunnaged to provide clearance from a steel deck. Pressure receptacles in a box or crib shall be braced to prevent any movement. The box or crib (gas rack) shall be securely chocked and lashed to prevent movement in any direction.

7.6.2.5.2 Pressure receptacles stowed on deck shall be protected from sources of heat.

7.6.2.6 **Provisions for class 3**

7.6.2.6.1 Class 3 substances with a flashpoint of less than 23°C c.c. packaged in jerricans, plastics (3H1, 3H2), drums, plastics (1H1,1H2), plastics receptacles in a plastic drum (6HH1, 6HH2) and Plastic Intermediate Bulk Containers (IBCs 31H1 and 31H2), shall be stowed *on deck only* unless packed in a closed cargo transport unit.

7

7.6.2.6.2   Packages loaded on deck shall be protected from sources of heat.

7.6.2.7   **Provisions for classes 4.1, 4.2 and 4.3**

7.6.2.7.1   Packages stowed on deck shall be protected from sources of heat.

7.6.2.7.2   Stowage provisions for FISHMEAL, UNSTABILIZED (UN 1374), FISHMEAL, STABILIZED (UN 2216, class 9) and KRILL MEAL (UN 3497)

7.6.2.7.2.1   For loose packagings:

.1   Temperature readings shall be taken 3 times a day during the voyage and recorded.

.2   If the temperature of the cargo exceeds 55°C and continues to increase, ventilation to the hold shall be restricted. If self-heating continues, then carbon dioxide or inert gas shall be introduced. The ship shall be equipped with facilities for introducing carbon dioxide or inert gas into the holds.

.3   The cargo shall be stowed protected from sources of heat.

.4   For UN 1374 and 3497, where loose bags are being carried, double strip stowage is recommended, provided there is good surface and through ventilation. The diagram in 7.6.2.7.2.3 shows how this can be achieved. For UN 2216, where loose bags are being carried, no special ventilation is required for block stowage of bagged cargo.

7.6.2.7.2.2   For containers:

.1   After packing, the doors and other openings shall be sealed to prevent the penetration of air into the unit.

.2   Temperature readings in the hold shall be taken once a day early in the morning during the voyage and recorded.

.3   If the temperature of the hold rises excessively above ambient and continues to increase, the possible need to apply copious quantities of water in an emergency and the consequent risk to the stability of the ship shall be considered.

.4   The cargo shall be stowed protected from sources of heat.

7.6.2.7.2.3

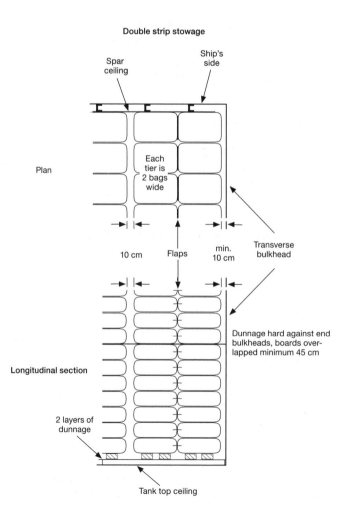

7.6.2.7.3 *Stowage provisions for SEED CAKE (UN 1386)*

7.6.2.7.3.1 Stowage provisions for SEED CAKE, containing vegetable oil (a) mechanically expelled seeds, containing more than 10% oil or more than 20% oil and moisture combined:

.1 through and surface ventilation is required;

.2 if the voyage exceeds 5 days, the ship shall be equipped with facilities for introducing carbon dioxide or inert gas into the cargo spaces;

.3 bags shall always be stowed in double strip, as shown in 7.6.2.7.2.3 of this Code for fishmeal, unstabilized; and

.4 regular temperature readings shall be taken at varying depths in the cargo space and recorded. If the temperature of the cargo exceeds 55°C and continues to increase, ventilation to the cargo spaces shall be restricted. If self-heating continues, then carbon dioxide or inert gas shall be introduced.

7.6.2.7.3.2 Stowage provisions for SEED CAKE, containing vegetable oil (b) solvent extractions and expelled seeds containing not more than 10% of oil and, when the amount of moisture is higher than 10%, not more than 20% of oil and moisture combined:

.1 surface ventilation is required to assist in removing any residual solvent vapour;

.2 if bags are stowed without provision for ventilation to circulate throughout the stow and the voyage exceeds 5 days, regular temperature readings shall be taken at varying depths in the hold and recorded; and

.3 if the voyage exceeds 5 days, the vessel shall be equipped with facilities for introducing carbon dioxide or inert gas into the cargo spaces.

7.6.2.8 **Provisions for class 5.1**

7.6.2.8.1 Cargo spaces shall be cleaned before oxidizing substances are loaded into them. All combustible materials which are not necessary for the stowage of such cargoes shall be removed from the hold.

7.6.2.8.2 As far as reasonably practicable, non-combustible securing and protecting materials and only a minimum of clean dry wooden dunnage shall be used.

7.6.2.8.3 Precautions shall be taken to avoid the penetration of oxidizing substances into other cargo spaces, bilges, etc., which may contain combustible material.

7.6.2.8.4 UN 1942 AMMONIUM NITRATE and UN 2067 AMMONIUM NITRATE BASED FERTILIZER may be stowed under deck in a clean cargo space capable of being opened up in an emergency. The possible need to open hatches in case of fire to provide maximum ventilation and to apply water in an emergency and the consequent risk to the stability of the ship through flooding of cargo space shall be considered before loading.

7.6.2.8.5 After discharge, cargo spaces used for the transport of oxidizing substances shall be inspected for contamination. A space that has been contaminated shall be properly cleaned and examined before being used for other cargoes.

7.6.2.9 **Provisions for self-reactive substances of class 4.1 and for class 5.2**

7.6.2.9.1 Packages shall be stowed protected from sources of heat.

7.6.2.9.2 When stowage arrangements are made, it shall be borne in mind that it may become appropriate to jettison a package or packages of this cargo.

7.6.2.10 **Provisions for classes 6.1 and 8**

7.6.2.10.1 After discharge, spaces used for the transport of substances of this class shall be inspected for contamination. A space which has been contaminated shall be properly cleaned and examined before being used for other cargoes.

7.6.2.10.2 Substances of class 8 shall be kept as dry as reasonably practicable, since in the presence of moisture they may be corrosive to most metals and some also react violently with water.

7.6.2.11 **Stowage of goods of class 9**

7.6.2.11.1 *Stowage provisions for AMMONIUM NITRATE BASED FERTILIZER, UN 2071*

7.6.2.11.1.1 AMMONIUM NITRATE BASED FERTILIZER, UN 2071 shall be stowed in a clean cargo space capable of being opened up in an emergency. In the case of bagged fertilizer or fertilizer in containers or in bulk containers, it is sufficient if, in the case of an emergency, the cargo is accessible through free approaches (hatch entries), and mechanical ventilation enables the master to exhaust any gases or fumes resulting from decomposition. The possible need to open hatches in case of fire to provide maximum ventilation and to apply water in an emergency, and the consequent risk to the stability of the ship through flooding of the cargo space, shall be considered before loading.

7.6.2.11.1.2 If suppression of decomposition should prove impracticable (such as in bad weather), there would not necessarily be immediate danger to the structure of the ship. However, the residue left after decomposition may have only half the mass of the original cargo; this loss of mass may also affect the stability of the ship and shall be considered before loading.

7.6.2.11.1.3 AMMONIUM NITRATE BASED FERTILIZER, UN 2071 shall be stowed out of direct contact with a metal engine-room bulkhead. In the case of bagged material, this may be done, for example, by using wooden boards to provide an air space between the bulkhead and the cargo. This requirement need not apply to short international voyages.

7.6.2.11.1.4 In the case of ships not fitted with smoke-detecting or other suitable devices, arrangements shall be made during the voyage to inspect cargo spaces containing these fertilizers at intervals not exceeding 4 h (such as to sniff at the ventilators serving them) to ensure early detection of decomposition should that occur.

7.6.2.11.2 *Stowage provisions for FISHMEAL, STABILIZED (UN 2216, class 9)*

7.6.2.11.2.1 For stowage provisions for FISHMEAL, STABILIZED (UN 2216, class 9), see 7.6.2.7.2.

7.6.2.12 **Stowage of dangerous goods in flexible bulk containers**

7.6.2.12.1 The stowage of dangerous goods in flexible bulk containers is not permitted on deck.

7.6.2.12.2 Flexible bulk containers shall be stowed in such a way that there are no void spaces between flexible bulk containers in the hold. If the flexible bulk containers do not completely fill the hold, adequate measures shall be taken to avoid shifting of cargo.

7.6.2.12.3 The maximum permissible stacking height of flexible bulk containers shall never exceed three high.

7.6.2.12.4 When flexible bulk containers are fitted with venting devices, the stowage of the flexible bulk containers shall not impede their function.

7.6.3   Segregation provisions

7.6.3.1 **Segregation from foodstuffs**

7.6.3.1.1 For the purpose of this subsection, the terms "away from", "separated from" and "separated by a complete compartment or hold from" are defined in 7.6.3.2.

7.6.3.1.2 Dangerous goods having a primary or subsidiary risk of classes 2.3, 6.1, 7 (with the exception of UN 2908, 2909, 2910 and 2911), 8 and dangerous goods having a reference to 7.6.3.1.2 in column 16b of the Dangerous Goods List stowed in a conventional way shall be "separated from" foodstuffs stowed in a conventional way. If either dangerous goods or foodstuffs are in a closed cargo transport unit, dangerous goods shall be stowed "away from" foodstuffs. If both dangerous goods and foodstuffs are in different closed cargo transport units, no segregation requirements shall apply.

7.6.3.1.3 Dangerous goods of class 6.2 stowed in a conventional way shall be "separated by a complete compartment or hold from" foodstuffs stowed in a conventional way. If either dangerous goods or foodstuffs are in a closed cargo transport unit, dangerous goods shall be stowed "separated from" foodstuffs.

7.6.3.2   Segregation of packages containing dangerous goods and stowed in the conventional way

Definitions of the segregation terms

Away from:

Effectively segregated so that the incompatible goods cannot interact dangerously in the event of an accident but may be transported in the same compartment or hold or *on deck*, provided a minimum horizontal separation of **3 m, projected vertically, is obtained.**

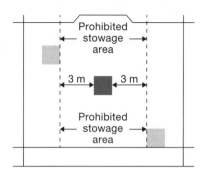

Separated from:

In different compartments or holds when stowed *under deck*. Provided the intervening deck is resistant to fire and liquid, a vertical separation, i.e. in different compartments, may be accepted as equivalent to this segregation. For *on deck* stowage, this segregation means a separation by a distance of **at least 6 m horizontally.**

Separated by a complete compartment or hold from:

Either a vertical or a horizontal separation. If the intervening decks are not resistant to fire and liquid, then only a longitudinal separation, i.e. by an intervening complete compartment or hold, is acceptable. For *on deck* stowage, this segregation means a separation by a distance of **at least 12 m horizontally**. The same distance has to be applied if one package is stowed on deck, and the other one in an upper compartment.

Note: One of the two decks must be resistant to fire and to liquid

Separated longitudinally by an intervening complete compartment or hold from:

Vertical separation alone does not meet this requirement. Between a package *under deck* and one on deck, a minimum distance of 24 m, including a complete compartment, must be maintained longitudinally. For *on deck* stowage, this segregation means a separation by a distance of **at least 24 m longitudinally.**

Legend

Reference package. . . . . ▪

Package containing incompatible goods. . . . . ▪

Deck resistant to fire and liquid . . . . ⊢——⊣

Note: Vertical lines represent transverse watertight bulkheads between cargo spaces.

7

7.6.3.3 **Segregation of dangerous goods stowed in the conventional way from those transported in cargo transport units**

7.6.3.3.1 Dangerous goods stowed in the conventional way shall be segregated from goods transported in open cargo transport units in accordance with 7.6.3.2.

7.6.3.3.2 Dangerous goods stowed in the conventional way shall be segregated from goods transported in closed cargo transport units in accordance with 7.6.3.2 except that:

.1 where "away from" is required, no segregation between the packages and the closed cargo transport units is required; and

.2 where "separated from" is required, the segregation between the packages and the closed cargo transport units may be as for "away from" as defined in 7.6.3.2.

7.6.3.4 **Segregation of dangerous goods in cargo transport units stowed in conventional cargo spaces**

7.6.3.4.1 Dangerous goods in different closed cargo transport units (closed freight containers) stowed in holds and compartments not properly fitted to give a permanent stowage of the containers during transport shall be segregated from each other in accordance with 7.6.3.2 except that:

.1 where "away from" is required, no segregation between the closed cargo transport units is required; and

.2 where "separated from" is required, the segregation between the closed cargo transport units may be as for "away from" as defined in 7.6.3.2.

7.6.3.5 **Segregation between bulk materials possessing chemical hazards and dangerous goods in packaged form**

7.6.3.5.1 Unless otherwise required in this Code or in the IMSBC Code, segregation between bulk materials possessing chemical hazards and dangerous goods in packaged form shall be in accordance with the following table.

7.6.3.5.2 *Segregation table*

Bulk materials (classified as dangerous goods)	CLASS	Dangerous goods in packaged form														
		1.1 1.2 1.5	1.3 1.6	1.4	2.1	2.2 2.3	3	4.1	4.2	4.3	5.1	5.2	6.1	6.2	7	8	9
Flammable solids	4.1	4	3	2	2	2	2	X	1	X	1	2	X	3	2	1	X
Substances liable to spontaneous combustion	4.2	4	3	2	2	2	2	1	X	1	2	2	1	3	2	1	X
Substances which, in contact with water, emit flammable gases	4.3	4	4	2	2	X	2	X	1	X	2	2	X	2	2	1	X
Oxidizing substances (agents)	5.1	4	4	2	2	X	2	1	2	2	X	2	1	3	1	2	X
Toxic substances	6.1	2	2	X	X	X	X	X	1	X	1	1	X	1	X	X	X
Radioactive material	7	2	2	2	2	2	2	2	2	2	1	2	X	3	X	2	X
Corrosive substance	8	4	2	2	1	X	1	1	1	1	2	2	X	3	2	X	X
Miscellaneous dangerous substances and articles	9	X	X	X	X	X	X	X	X	X	X	X	X	X	X	X	X
Materials hazardous only in bulk (MHB)		X	X	X	X	X	X	X	X	X	X	X	X	3	X	X	X

Numbers and symbols relate to the following terms, as defined in this chapter:

1 – "away from"

2 – "separated from"

3 – "separated by a complete compartment or hold from"

4 – "separated longitudinally by an intervening complete compartment or hold from"

X – the segregation, if any, is shown in the Dangerous Goods List in this Code or the individual entries in the IMSBC Code

7.6.3.5.3   *Definitions of the segregation terms*

Away from:
Effectively segregated so that incompatible materials cannot interact dangerously in the event of an accident but may be transported in the same compartment or hold or *on deck* provided a minimum horizontal separation of 3 m, projected vertically, is provided.

Separated from:
In different holds when stowed *under deck*. Provided an intervening deck is resistant to fire and liquid, a vertical separation, i.e. in different compartments, may be accepted as equivalent to this segregation.

Separated by a complete compartment or hold from:
Either a vertical or a horizontal separation. If the decks are not resistant to fire and liquid, then only a longitudinal separation, i.e. by an intervening complete compartment, is acceptable.

Separated longitudinally by an intervening complete compartment or hold from:
Vertical separation alone does not meet this requirement.

Legend

Reference bulk material . . . .

Package containing incompatible goods . . . .

Deck resistant to fire and liquid . . . .

Note: Vertical lines represent transverse watertight bulkheads between cargo spaces.

Chapter 7.7

Shipborne barges on barge-carrying ships

7.7.1 Introduction

7.7.1.1 The provisions of this chapter are applicable to shipborne barges which contain packaged dangerous goods or solid bulk materials possessing chemical hazards while aboard barge-carrying ships.

7.7.1.2 Barges used for the shipborne transport of packaged dangerous goods or solid bulk materials possessing chemical hazards shall be of proper design and adequate strength to resist the stresses imposed by the conditions of the services in which they are employed and they shall be adequately maintained. Shipborne barges shall be approved in accordance with provisions for certification of a recognized classification society, or any organization approved by and acting on behalf of the competent authority of the countries concerned.

7.7.2 Definitions

7.7.2.1 *Loading*, for the purpose of this chapter, means the placement of cargo into a shipborne barge.

7.7.2.2 *Stowage*, for the purposes of this chapter, means the placement of a shipborne barge aboard the barge-carrying ship.

7.7.3 Barge loading

7.7.3.1 Packages shall be examined and any found to be damaged, leaking or sifting shall not be loaded into a shipborne barge. Care shall be taken to ensure that excessive water, snow, ice or foreign matter adhering to packages shall be removed before loading into a shipborne barge.

7.7.3.2 Packages containing dangerous goods, cargo transport units and any other goods within a shipborne barge shall be adequately braced and secured for the voyage. Packages shall be loaded in such a way that there will be a minimum likelihood of damage to them and to any fittings during transport. Fittings on packages or portable tanks shall be adequately protected.

7.7.3.3 Certain dry dangerous goods may be transported in bulk in shipborne barges; this is indicated by the Code "BK2" in column 13 of the Dangerous Goods List. Where such solid bulk materials possessing chemical hazards are transported in shipborne barges, it shall be ensured that at all times the cargo is evenly distributed, properly trimmed and secured.

7.7.3.4 Shipborne barges into which packaged dangerous goods or solid bulk materials possessing chemical hazards are to be loaded shall be examined visually for hull or hatch cover damage which could impair watertight integrity. If there is evidence of such damage, the shipborne barge may not be used for the transport of packaged dangerous goods or solid bulk materials possessing chemical hazards and shall not be loaded.

7.7.3.5 Dangerous goods which have to be segregated from each other according to the provisions in chapter 7.2 shall not be transported in the same barge with the exception of dangerous goods which shall be segregated "away from" each other which may be transported in the same barge with the approval of the competent authority. In such cases an equivalent standard of safety shall be maintained.

7.7.3.6 Dangerous goods having a primary or subsidiary risk of classes 2.3, 6.1, 6.2, 7 (with the exception of UN 2908, 2909, 2910 and 2911), 8 and dangerous goods having a reference to 7.7.3.6 in column 16b of the Dangerous Goods List shall not be transported together with foodstuffs (see 1.2.1) in the same barge.

7.7.3.7 Notwithstanding the provisions in 7.7.3.6, the following dangerous goods may be transported with foodstuffs in the same barge provided that they are not loaded within 3 m from foodstuffs:

.1 dangerous goods of packing group III of classes 6.1 and 8;

.2 dangerous goods of packing group II of class 8;

.3 any other dangerous goods of packing group III with a subsidiary risk of classes 6.1 or 8; and

.4 dangerous goods having a reference to 7.7.3.7 in column 16b of the Dangerous Goods List.

7.7.3.8   Shipborne barges containing a residue of a dangerous cargo or shipborne barges loaded with empty packagings still containing a residue of a dangerous substance shall comply with the same provisions as barges loaded with the substance itself.

7.7.3.9   Stowage of dangerous goods in flexible bulk containers

7.7.3.9.1   Flexible bulk containers shall be stowed in the barge in such a way that there are no void spaces between the flexible bulk containers in the barge. If the flexible bulk containers do not completely fill the barge, adequate measures shall be taken to avoid shifting of cargo.

7.7.3.9.2   The maximum permissible height of the stack of the flexible bulk containers shall never exceed three high.

7.7.3.9.3   When flexible bulk containers are fitted with venting devices, the stowage of the flexible bulk containers in their barge shall not impede their function.

7.7.4   Stowage of shipborne barges

7.7.4.1   Stowage of shipborne barges carrying packaged dangerous goods or solid bulk materials possessing chemical hazards aboard barge-carrying ships shall be as required for the substance in chapter 7.1 and in column 16a of the Dangerous Goods List. When a shipborne barge is loaded with more than one substance, and the stowage locations differ for the substances (i.e. some substances require *on deck* stowage while other substances require *under deck* stowage), the shipborne barge containing these substances shall be stowed on deck.

7.7.4.2   Provision shall be made to ensure that shipborne barges stowed under deck and loaded with cargoes requiring ventilation because of their dangerous nature are ventilated to the extent necessary.

7.7.4.3   Where it is required that a dangerous good shall be protected from sources of heat, this provision shall be applied to the shipborne barge as a whole, unless suitable alternative measures are provided.

7.7.4.4   When packaged dangerous goods or solid bulk materials possessing chemical hazards are loaded in shipborne barges aboard barge-carrying ships having the capability of providing fixed fire-fighting systems or fire-detection systems to individual barges, care shall be taken to ensure that these systems are attached to the shipborne barge and operating properly.

7.7.4.5   When packaged dangerous goods or solid bulk materials possessing chemical hazards are loaded in shipborne barges aboard barge-carrying ships having fixed fire-fighting systems or fire-detection systems installed in individual barge holds, care shall be taken to ensure that the ventilation closures on the shipborne barges are open, to permit the fire fighting medium to enter the barges in case of fire.

7.7.4.6   When ventilation ducts are provided to individual shipborne barges, the ventilation fans shall be secured when fire-fighting medium is introduced into the hold to permit the medium to enter the shipborne barges.

7.7.5   Segregation between barges on board barge-carrying ships

7.7.5.1   For barge-carrying ships which incorporate other cargo spaces or any other method of stowage, the appropriate chapter shall apply to the relevant cargo space.

7.7.5.2   When a shipborne barge is loaded with two or more substances with different provisions for segregation, the most stringent segregation applicable shall be applied.

7.7.5.3   "Away from" and "separated from" require no segregation between shipborne barges.

7.7.5.4   "Separated by a complete compartment or hold from" means, for barge-carrying ships with vertical holds, that separate holds are required. On barge-carrying ships having horizontal barge levels, separate barge levels are required and the barges shall not be in the same vertical line.

7.7.5.5   "Separated longitudinally by an intervening complete compartment or hold from" means, for barge-carrying ships with vertical holds, that separation by an intervening hold or engine room is required. On barge-carrying ships having horizontal barge levels, separate barge levels and a longitudinal separation by at least two intervening barge spaces is required.

7

Chapter 7.8

Special requirements in the event of an incident and fire precautions involving dangerous goods

Note: The provisions of this chapter are not mandatory.

7.8.1 General

7.8.1.1 In the event of an incident involving dangerous goods, detailed recommendations are contained in *The EmS Guide: Emergency Response Procedures for Ships Carrying Dangerous Goods.*

7.8.1.2 In the event of personnel exposure during an incident involving dangerous goods, detailed recommendations are contained in *Medical First Aid Guide for Use in Accidents Involving Dangerous Goods (MFAG).*

7.8.1.3 In the event that a package containing dangerous goods is found to be suffering from breakage or leakage while the ship is in port, the port authorities should be informed and appropriate procedures should be followed.

7.8.2 General provisions in the event of incidents

7.8.2.1 Recommendations on emergency action may differ depending on whether or not the goods are stowed on deck or under deck or whether a substance is gaseous, liquid or solid. When dealing with incidents involving flammable gases, or flammable liquids with a flashpoint of 60°C closed-cup (c.c.) or below, all sources of ignition (such as naked lights, unprotected light bulbs, electric handtools) should be avoided.

7.8.2.2 In general, the recommendation is to wash spillages on deck overboard with copious quantities of water and, where there is likely to be a dangerous reaction with water, from as far away as practicable. Disposal of spilt dangerous goods overboard is a matter for judgement by the master, bearing in mind that the safety of the crew has priority over pollution of the sea. If it is safe to do so, spillages and leakages of substances, articles and materials identified in this Code as MARINE POLLUTANT should be collected for safe disposal. Inert absorbent material should be used for liquids.

7.8.2.3 Toxic, corrosive and/or flammable vapours in under deck cargo spaces should, where possible, be dispersed before undertaking any emergency action. Where a mechanical ventilation system is used, care will be necessary to ensure that flammable vapours are not ignited.

7.8.2.4 If there is any reason to suspect leakage of these substances, entry into a hold or cargo space should not be permitted until the master or responsible officer has taken all safety considerations into account and is satisfied that it is safe to do so.

7.8.2.5 Emergency entry into the hold under other circumstances should only be undertaken by trained crew wearing self-contained breathing apparatus and other protective clothing.

7.3.2.6 A careful inspection for structural damage should be carried out after dealing with spillages of substances corrosive to steel and cryogenic liquids.

7.8.3 Special provisions for incidents involving infectious substances

7.8.3.1 If any person responsible for the transport or opening of packages containing infectious substances becomes aware of damage to or leakage from such packages, he should:

    .1 avoid handling the package or keep handling to a minimum;

    .2 inspect adjacent packages for contamination and put aside any that have been contaminated;

    .3 inform the appropriate public health authority or veterinary authority, and provide information on any other countries of transit where persons may have been exposed to danger; and

    .4 notify the consignor and/or the consignee.

7.8.3.2 Decontamination

A cargo transport unit, a bulk container or a cargo space of a ship, which has been used to transport infectious substances, shall be inspected for release of the substance before re-use. If infectious substances were released during transport, the cargo transport unit, the bulk container or the cargo space of a ship shall be decontaminated before it is re-used. Decontamination may be achieved by any means which effectively inactivates the infectious substance released.

7.8.4 Special provisions for incidents involving radioactive material

7.8.4.1 If it is evident that a package is damaged or leaking, or if it is suspected that the package may have leaked or been damaged, access to the package should be restricted and a qualified person should, as soon as possible, assess the extent of contamination and the resultant radiation level of the package. The scope of the assessment should include the package, the conveyance, the adjacent loading and unloading areas, and, if necessary, all other material which has been transported in the conveyance. When necessary, additional steps for the protection of persons, property and the environment, in accordance with provisions established by the relevant competent authority, should be taken to overcome and minimize the consequences of such leakage or damage.

7.8.4.2 Packages damaged or leaking radioactive contents in excess of allowable limits for normal conditions of transport may be removed to an acceptable interim location under supervision, but should not be forwarded until repaired or reconditioned and decontaminated.

7.8.4.3 In the event of accidents or incidents during the transport of radioactive material, emergency provisions, as established by relevant national and/or international organizations, should be observed to protect persons, property and the environment. Appropriate guidelines for such provisions are contained in the International Atomic Energy Agency's document *Planning and Preparing for Emergency Response to Transport Accidents involving Radioactive Material*, Safety Standard Series No. TS-G-1.2 (ST-3), IAEA, Vienna (2002).

7.8.4.4 Attention is drawn to the latest versions of both *The EmS Guide: Emergency Response Procedures for Ships Carrying Dangerous Goods* and the *Medical First Aid Guide for Use in Accidents Involving Dangerous Goods (MFAG)*.

7.8.4.5 Emergency response procedures should take into account the formation of other dangerous substances that may result from the reaction between the contents of a consignment and the environment in the event of an accident.

7.8.4.6 In the event of a package containing radioactive material suffering from breakage or leakage while the ship is in port, the port authorities should be informed and advice obtained from them or from the competent authority.[*] Procedures have been drawn up in many countries for summoning radiological assistance in any such emergency.

7.8.5 General fire precautions

7.8.5.1 The prevention of fire in a cargo of dangerous goods is achieved by practising good seamanship, observing in particular the following precautions:

.1 keep combustible material away from ignition sources;

.2 protect a flammable substance by adequate packing;

.3 reject damaged or leaking packages;

.4 stow packages protected from accidental damage or heating;

.5 segregate packages from substances liable to start or spread fire;

.6 where appropriate and practicable, stow dangerous goods in an accessible position so that packages in the vicinity of a fire may be protected;

.7 enforce prohibition of smoking in dangerous areas and display clearly recognizable "NO SMOKING" notices or signs; and

.8 the dangers from short-circuits, earth leakages or sparking will be apparent. Lighting and power cables and fittings should be maintained in good condition. Cables or equipment found to be unsafe should be disconnected. Where a bulkhead is required to be suitable for segregation purposes, cables and conduit penetrations of the decks and bulkheads should be sealed against the passage of gas and vapours.

---

[*] Reference is made to chapter 7.9 and the IAEA list of national competent authorities responsible for approvals and authorizations in respect of the transport of radioactive material. The list is updated annually.

When stowing dangerous goods on deck, the position and design of auxiliary machinery, electrical equipment and cable runs should be considered in order to avoid sources of ignition.

7.8.5.2 Fire precautions applying to individual classes, and where necessary to individual substances, are recommended in 7.8.2 and 7.8.6 to 7.8.9 and in the Dangerous Goods List.

7.8.6 Special fire precautions for class 1

7.8.6.1.1 The greatest risk in the handling and transport of goods of class 1 is that of fire from a source external to the goods, and it is vital that any fire should be detected and extinguished before it can reach such goods. Consequently, it is essential that fire precautions, fire-fighting measures and equipment are of a high standard and ready for immediate application and use.

7.8.6.1.2 Compartments containing goods of class 1 and adjacent cargo spaces should be provided with a fire-detection system. If such spaces are not protected by a fixed fire-extinguishing system, they should be accessible for fire-fighting operations.

7.8.6.1.3 No repair work should be carried out in a compartment containing goods of class 1. Special care should be exercised in carrying out repairs in any adjacent space. No welding, burning, cutting, or riveting operations involving the use of fire, flame, spark, or arc-producing equipment should be carried out in any space other than machinery spaces and workshops where fire-extinguishing arrangements are available, except in any emergency and, if in port, with prior authorization of the port authority.

7.8.7 Special fire precautions for class 2

7.8.7.1 Effective ventilation should be provided to remove any leakage of gas from within the cargo space or spaces, bearing in mind that some gases are heavier than air and may accumulate in dangerous concentrations in the lower part of the ship.

7.8.7.2 Measures should be taken to prevent leaking gases from penetrating into any other part of the ship.

7.8.7.3.1 If there is any reason to suspect leakage of a gas, entry into cargo spaces or other enclosed spaces should not be permitted until the master or responsible officer has taken all safety considerations into account and is satisfied that it is safe to do so. Emergency entry under other circumstances should only be undertaken by trained crew wearing self-contained breathing apparatus, and protective clothing when recommended, and always under the supervision of a responsible officer.

7.8.7.3.2 Leakage from pressure receptacles containing flammable gases may give rise to explosive mixtures with air. Such mixtures, if ignited, may result in explosion and fire.

7.8.8 Special fire precautions for class 3

7.8.8.1 Flammable liquids give off flammable vapours which, especially in an enclosed space, form explosive mixtures with air. Such vapours, if ignited, may cause a "flashback" to the place in which the substances are stowed. Due regard should be paid to the provision of adequate ventilation to prevent accumulation of vapours.

7.8.9 Special fire precautions and fire fighting for class 7

7.8.9.1 The radioactive contents of Excepted, Industrial, and Type A packages are so restricted that, in the event of an accident and damage to the package, there is a high probability that any material released, or shielding efficiency lost, would not give rise to such radiological hazard as to hamper fire-fighting or rescue operations.

7.8.9.2 Type B(U) packages, Type B(M) packages and Type C packages are designed to be strong enough to withstand severe fire without significant loss of contents or dangerous loss of radiation shielding.

△ Chapter 7.9

Exemptions, approvals and certificates

7.9.1 Exemptions

Note 1 The provisions of this section do not apply to exemptions mentioned in chapters 1 to 7.8 of this Code and to approvals (including permits, authorizations or agreements) and certificates which are referred to in chapters 1 to 7.8 of this Code. For the said approvals and certificates, see 7.9.2.

Note 2 The provisions of this section do not apply to class 7. For consignments of radioactive material for which conformity with any provision of this Code applicable to class 7 is impracticable, refer to 1.5.4.

7.9.1.1 Where this Code requires that a particular provision for the transport of dangerous goods shall be complied with, a competent authority or competent authorities (port State of departure, port State of arrival or flag State) may authorize any other provision by exemption if satisfied that such provision is at least as effective and safe as that required by this Code. Acceptance of an exemption authorized under this section by a competent authority not party to it is subject to the discretion of that competent authority. Accordingly, prior to any shipment covered by the exemption, the recipient of the exemption shall notify other competent authorities concerned.

7.9.1.2 Competent authority or competent authorities which have taken the initiative with respect to the exemption:

.1 shall send a copy of such exemption to the International Maritime Organization which shall bring it to the attention of the Contracting Parties to SOLAS and/or MARPOL, as appropriate, and

.2 if appropriate, take action to amend the IMDG Code to include the provisions covered by the exemption.

7.9.1.3 The period of validity of the exemption shall be not more than five years from the date of authorization. An exemption that is not covered under 7.9.1.2.2 may be renewed in accordance with the provisions of this section.

7.9.1.4 A copy of the exemption shall accompany each consignment when offered to the carrier for transport under the terms of the exemption. A copy of the exemption or an electronic copy thereof shall be maintained on board each ship transporting dangerous goods in accordance with the exemption, as appropriate.

7.9.2 Approvals (including permits, authorizations or agreements) and certificates

7.9.2.1 Approvals, including permits, authorizations or agreements, and certificates referred to in chapters 1 to 7.8 of this Code and issued by the competent authority (authorities when the Code requires a multilateral approval) or a body authorized by that competent authority (e.g. approvals for alternative packaging in 4.1.3.7, approval for segregation as in 7.3.4.1 or certificates for portable tanks in 6.7.2.18.1) shall be recognized, as appropriate:

.1 by other contracting parties to SOLAS if they comply with the requirements of the International Convention for the Safety of Life at Sea (SOLAS), 1974, as amended; and/or

.2 by other contracting parties to MARPOL if they comply with the requirements of the International Convention for the Prevention of Pollution from Ships, 1973, as modified by the Protocol of 1978 relating thereto (MARPOL, Annex III), as amended.

7.9.3 Contact information for the main designated national competent authorities

Contact information for the main designated national competent authorities concerned is given in this paragraph.[*] Corrections to these addresses should be sent to the Organization.[†]

---

[*] Reference is made to MSC.1/Circ.1517, as may be amended, which provides a more comprehensive listing of contact information for competent authorities and bodies.

[†] International Maritime Organization
4 Albert Embankment
London SE1 7SR
United Kingdom
Email: info@imo.org
Fax: +44 20 7587 3120

7

Country	Contact information for the main designated national competent authority

ALGERIA	Ministère des Transports
	Direction de la Marine marchande et des Ports
	1 Chemin Ibn Badis El Mouiz (ex Poirson)
	El Biar – Alger
	ALGERIE
	Telephone: +213 219 29881
	    +213 219 20931
	Telefax: +213 219 23046
	    +213 219 29894
	Email: benyelles@ministere-transports.gov.dz

AMERICAN SAMOA	Silila Patane Harbour Master Port Administration Pagopago American Samoa AMERICAN SAMOA 96799
ANGOLA	National Director Marine Safety, Shipping and Ports National Directorate of Merchant Marine and Ports Rua Rainha Ginga 74, 4 Andar Luanda ANGOLA Telephone: +244 2 39 0034 +244 2 39 7984 Fax: +244 2 31 037 Mobile: +244 9243 9336 Email: ispscode_angola@snet.co.ao
ARGENTINA	Prefectura Naval Argentina (Argentine Coast Guard) Dirección de protección ambiental Departamento de protección ambiental y mercancías peligrosas Division mercancías y residuos peligrosos Avda. Eduardo Madero 235 4° piso, Oficina 4.36 y 4.37 Buenos Aires (C1106ACC) REPÚBLICA ARGENTINA Telephone: +54 11 4318 7669 Fax: +54 11 4318 7474 Email: dpma-mp@prefecturanaval.gov.ar
AUSTRALIA	Manager – Ship Inspection and Registration Ship Safety Division Australian Maritime Safety Authority GPO Box 2181 Canberra ACT 2601 AUSTRALIA Telephone: +61 2 6279 5048 Fax: +61 2 6279 5058 Email: psc@amsa.gov.au Website: www.amsa.gov.au
AUSTRIA	Federal Ministry for Transport, Innovation and Technology Transport of Dangerous Goods and Safe Containers Radetzkystraße 2 A-1030 Wien AUSTRIA Telephone: +43 1 71162 65 5771 Fax: +43 1 71162 65 5725 Email: st6@bmvit.gv.at Website: www.bmvit.gv.at

7

Country	Contact information for the main designated national competent authority
BAHAMAS	Bahamas Maritime Authority 120 Old Broad Street London, EC2N 1AR UNITED KINGDOM Telephone: +44 20 7562 1300 Fax: +44 20 7614 0650 Email: tech@bahamasmaritime.com Website: www.bahamasmaritime.com
BANGLADESH	Department of Shipping 141-143, Motijheel Commercial Area BIWTA Bhaban (8th Floor) Dhaka-1000 Bangladesh Telephone: +880 2 9555128 Fax: +880 2 7168363 Email: dosdgdbd@bttb.net.bd
BARBADOS	Director of Maritime Affairs Ministry of Tourism and International Transport 2nd Floor, Carlisle House Hincks Street Bridgetown St. Michael BARBADOS Telephone: +1 246 426 2710/3342 Fax: +1 246 426 7882 Email: ctech@sunbeach.net
BELGIUM	*Antwerp office* Federale Overheidsdienst Mobiliteit en Vervoer Directoraat-generaal Maritiem Vervoer Scheepvaartcontrole Posthoflei 3 B-2000 Antwerpen (Berchem) BELGIUM Telephone: +32 3 229 0030 Fax: +32 3 229 0031 Email: HAZMAT.MAR@mobilit.fgov.be *Ostend office* Federale Overheidsdienst Mobiliteit en Vervoer Directoraat-generaal Maritiem Vervoer Scheepvaartcontrole Natiënkaai 5 B-8400 Oostende BELGIUM Telephone: +32 59 56 1450 Fax: +32 59 56 1474 Email: HAZMAT.MAR@mobilit.fgov.be

BELIZE	Ports Commissioner/Harbour Master
	120 Corner North Front and Pickstock Street
	Belize City
	BELIZE
	Telephone: +501 223 0752
	   +501 223 0762
	   +501 223 0743
	Fax: +501 223 0433
	Website: www.portauthority.bz

Country	Contact information for the main designated national competent authority
BRAZIL	Diretoria de Portos e Costas (DPC-20) Rua Teófilo Otoni No. 04 Centro Rio de Janeiro CEP 20090-070 BRAZIL Telephone: +55 21 2104 5203 Fax: +55 21 2104 5202 Email: secom@dpc.mar.mil.br

BULGARIA	*Head office*
	Captain Petar Petrov, Director
	Directorate "Quality Management"
	Bulgarian Maritime Administration
	9 Dyakon Ignatii Str.
	Sofia 1000
	REPUBLIC OF BULGARIA
	Telephone: +359 2 93 00 910
	   +359 2 93 00 912
	Fax: +359 2 93 00 920
	Email: bma@marad.bg
	   petrov@marad.bg
	
	Regional offices
	Harbour-Master
	Directorate
	"Maritime Administration" – Bourgas
	3 Kniaz Alexander Batemberg Str.
	Bourgas 8000
	REPUBLIC OF BULGARIA
	Telephone: +359 56 875 775
	Fax: +359 56 840 064
	Email: hm_bs@marad.bg
	
	Harbour-Master
	Directorate
	"Maritime Administration" – Varna
	5 Primorski Bvd
	Varna 9000
	REPUBLIC OF BULGARIA
	Telephone: +359 52 684 922
	Fax: +359 52 602 378
	Email: hm_vn@marad.bg

BURUNDI	Minister Ministère des Transports, Postes et Télécommunications B.P. 2000 Bujumbura BURUNDI Telephone: +257 219 324 Fax: +257 217 773

7

Country	Contact information for the main designated national competent authority
CABO VERDE	The Director General Ministry of Infrastructure and Transport St. Vicente CABO VERDE Telephone: +238 2 328 199 +238 2 585 4643 Email: dgmp@cvtelecom.cv

CANADA	The Chairman
	Marine Technical Review Board
	Contact: Director, Operations and Environmental Programs
	Marine Safety, Transport Canada
	Tower C, Place de Ville
	330 Sparks Street, 10th Floor
	Ottawa, Ontario
	K1A 0N5
	CANADA
	Telephone: +1 613 991 3132
	   +1 613 991 3143
	   +1 613 991 3139
	   +1 613 991 3140
	Fax: +1 613 993 8196
	
	Packaging approvals
	Director, Regulatory Affairs
	Transport Dangerous Goods Directorate
	Tower C, Place de Ville
	330 Sparks Street, 9th Floor
	Ottawa, Ontario
	K1A 0N5
	CANADA
	Telephone: +1 613 998 0519
	   +1 613 990 1163
	   +1 613 993 5266
	Fax: +1 613 993 5925

CHILE	Dirección General del Territorio Marítimo y de Marina Mercante
	Dirección de Seguridad y Operaciones Marítimas
	Servicio de Inspecciones Marítimas
	División Prevención de Riesgos y Cargas Peligrosas
	Subida Cementerio No. 300
	Valparaíso
	CHILE
	Telephone: +56 32 220 8699
	   +56 32 220 8654
	   +56 32 220 8692
	Email: cargaspeligrosas@directemar.cl

CHINA	Maritime Safety Administration People's Republic of China 11 Jianguomen Nei Avenue Beijing 100736 CHINA Telephone: +86 10 6529 2588 +86 10 6529 2218 Fax: +86 10 6529 2245 Telex: 222258 CMSAR CN

Country	Contact information for the main designated national competent authority
COMOROS	Ministère d'État Ministère du développement des infrastructures des postes et des télécommunications et des transports internationaux Moroni UNION DES COMORES Telephone: +269 744 287 +269 735 794 Fax: +269 734 241 +269 834 241 Mobile: +269 340 248 Email: houmedms@yahoo.fr
CROATIA	Ministry of Maritime Affairs, Transport and Infrastructure Marine Safety Directorate MRCC Rijeka Senjsko pristanište 3 51000 Rijeka REPUBLIC OF CROATIA Telephone: +385 51 195 +385 51 312 301 Fax: +385 51 312 254 Email: mrcc@pomorstvo.hr *Testing and certification of packagings* Cargo Superintendence and Testing Services Adriainspekt Ciottina 17/b 51000 Rijeka REPUBLIC OF CROATIA Telephone: +385 51 356 080 Fax: +385 51 356 090 Email: ai@adriainspekt.hr Website: www.adriainspekt.hr *Classification society for CSC containers (including IMO tanks)* Croatian Register of Shipping Marasovićeva 67 21000 Split REPUBLIC OF CROATIA Telephone: +385 21 408 180 Fax: +385 51 358 159 Email: constr@crs.hr
CUBA	Ministerio del Transporte Dirección de Seguridad e Inspección Marítima Boyeros y Tulipán Plaza Ciudad de la Habana CUBA Telephone: +537 881 6607 +537 881 9498 Fax: +537 881 1514 Email: dsim@mitrans.transnet.cu
CYPRUS	Department of Merchant Shipping Ministry of Communications and Works Kylinis Street Mesa Geitonia CY-4007 Lemesos P.O. Box 56193 CY-3305 Lemesos CYPRUS Telephone: +357 5 848 100 Fax: +357 5 848 200 Telex: 2004 MERSHIP CY Email: dms@cytanet.com.cy

7

Country	Contact information for the main designated national competent authority
CZECH REPUBLIC	*Implementation* Ministry of Transport of the Czech Republic Navigation Department Nábr. L. Svobody 12 110 15 Praha 1 CZECH REPUBLIC Telephone: +420 225 131 151 Fax: +420 225 131 110 Email: sekretariat.230@mdcr.cz Cesky urad pro zkouseni zbrani a streliva (Czech office for weapon and ammunition testing) Jilmova 759/12 130 00 Praha 3 CZECH REPUBLIC Telephone: +420 284 081 831 Email: info@cuzzs.cz rockai@cuzzs.cz *Examination, testing and assessing functional sustainability of packages or materials used for packaging of dangerous goods* IMET, s. r. o. Kamýcká 234 160 00 Praha 6 - Sedlec CZECH REPUBLIC Telephone: +420 220 922 085 +420 603 552 565 Fax: +420 220 921 676 Email: imet@imet.cz *Classification of dangerous goods of class 1 (explosives)* *(interim authorization expiring on 20 November 2010)* Ceskoslovensky Lloyd, spol.s. r.o. (Czechoslovak 184) Vinohradska 184 130 00 Praha 3 Vinohrady CZECH REPUBLIC Telephone: +420 777 767 +420 777 706 Email: info@cslloyd.cz
DEMOCRATIC PEOPLE'S REPUBLIC OF KOREA (THE)	Maritime Administration of the Democratic People's Republic of Korea Ryonhwa-2 Dong Central District P.O.Box 416 Pyongyang DEMOCRATIC PEOPLE'S REPUBLIC OF KOREA Telephone: +850 2 18111 ext. 8059 Fax: +850 3 381 4410 Email: mab@silibank.com

7

Country	Contact information for the main designated national competent authority
DENMARK	Danish Maritime Authority Carl Jacobsens Vei 31 DK-2500 Valby DENMARK Telephone: +45 72 19 60 00 Fax: +45 72 19 60 01 Email: SFS@dma.dk *Packing, testing and certification* Emballage og Transportinstituttet (E.T.I.) Dansk Teknologisk Institut Gregersensvej 2630 Tåstrup DENMARK Packagings in conformity with the IMDG Code will be marked "DK Eti"
DJIBOUTI	Director of Maritime Affairs Ministère de l'equipement et des transports P.O. Box 59 Djibouti DJIBOUTI Telephone: +253 357 913 Fax: +253 351 538 +253 931 +253 355 879
ECUADOR	Dirección General de la Marine Mercante y del Litoral P.O. Box 7412 Guayaquil ECUADOR Telephone: +593 4 526 760 Fax: +593 4 324 246 Telex: 04 3325 DIGMER ED
EQUATORIAL GUINEA	The Director General (Maritime Affairs) Ministerio de Transportes, Tecnologia, Correos y Telecomunicaciones Malabo REPUBLICA DE GUINEA ECUATORIAL Telephone: +240 275 406 Fax: +240 092 618
ERITREA	Director General Department of Maritime Transport Ministry of Transport and Communications ERITREA Telephone: +291 1 121 317 +291 1 189 156 +291 1 185 251 Fax: +291 1 184 690 +291 1 186 541 Email: motcrez@eol.com.er

Country	Contact information for the main designated national competent authority
ESTONIA	Estonian Maritime Administration Maritime Safety Division Valge 4 EST-11413 Tallinn ESTONIA Telephone: +372 6205 700 +372 6205 715 Fax: +372 6205 706 Email: mot@vta.ee
ETHIOPIA	Maritime Affairs Authority P.O. Box 1B61 Addis Ababa ETHIOPIA Telephone: +251 11 550 36 83 +251 11 550 36 38 Fax: +251 11 550 39 60 Mobile: +251 91 151 39 73 Email: maritime@ethione.et
FAROES (THE)	Sjóvinnustýrið Faroese Maritime Authority Inni á Støð, P. O. Box 26 FO-375 Miðvágur, Faroe Islands Telephone: +298 355 600 Fax: +298 355 601 Email: fma@fma.fo
FIJI	The Director of Maritime Safety Fiji Islands Maritime Safety Administration GPO Box 326 Suva FIJI Telephone: +679 331 5266 Fax: +679 330 3251 Email: fimsa@connect.com.fj
FINLAND	Transport Safety Agency Trafi P.O. Box 320 FI-00101 Helsinki FINLAND Telephone: +358 29 534 5000 Fax: +358 29 534 5095 Email: kirjaamo@trafi.fi *Packaging and certification institute* Safety Technology Authority (TUKES) P.O. Box 123 FI-00181 Helsinki FINLAND Telephone: +358 96 1671 Fax: +358 96 1674 66 Email: kirjaamo@tukes.fi

7

Country	Contact information for the main designated national competent authority

FRANCE	Ministère de l'Environnement, de l'Énergie et de la Mer (MEEM) DGPR – Mission Transport de Matières Dangereuses (MTMD)
	Tour Séquoia
	92055 Paris La Défense Cedex
	FRANCE
	Telephone: +33 1 40 81 14 96
	Fax: +33 1 40 81 10 65
	Email: pierre.dufour@developpement-durable.gouv.fr
	
	Organizations authorized for packagings, large packagings and intermediate bulk containers (IBCs) (*)
	1 Association des Contrôleurs Indépendants (ACI)
	   22, rue de l'Est
	   92100 Boulogne-Billancourt
	   FRANCE
	
	2 APAVE
	   191, rue de Vaugirard
	   75738 Paris Cedex 15
	   FRANCE
	
	3 Association pour la Sécurité des Appareils à Pression (ASAP)
	   Continental Square – BP 16757
	   95727 Roissy-Charles de Gaulle Cedex
	   FRANCE
	
	4 Bureau de Vérifications Techniques (BVT)
	   ZAC de la Cerisaie - 31, rue de Montjean
	   94266 Fresnes Cedex
	   FRANCE
	
	5 Bureau Veritas
	   67-71, rue du Château
	   92200 Neuilly-sur-Seine
	   FRANCE
	
	6 Centre Français de l'Emballage Agréé (CeFEA)
	   5, rue Janssen
	   75019 Paris
	   FRANCE
	
	7 Laboratoire d'Études et de Recherches des Emballages Métalliques (LEREM)
	   Marches de l'Oise – 100, rue Louis-Blanc
	   60160 Montataire
	   FRANCE
	
	8 Laboratoire National de métrologie et d'Essais (LNE)
	   1, rue Gaston-Boissier
	   75724 Paris Cedex 15
	   FRANCE
	Organizations authorized for pressure receptacles
	1 Association des Contrôleurs Indépendants (ACI)
	   (For contact details see above)
	2 APAVE
	   (For contact details see above)
	3 Association pour la Sécurité des Appareils à Pression (ASAP)
	   (For contact details see above)
	4 Bureau Veritas
	   (For contact details see above)
	Organizations authorized for tanks and multiple-element gas containers (MEGCs)*
	1 Association des Contrôleurs Indépendants (ACI)
	   (For contact details see above)
	2 APAVE
	   (For contact details see above)
	3 Bureau Veritas
	   (For contact details see above)

* Contact competent authority for further details of areas of authorization.

Country	Contact information for the main designated national competent authority

GAMBIA (ISLAMIC REPUBLIC OF)	The Director General
	Gambia Port Authority
	P.O. Box 617
	Banjul
	THE GAMBIA
	Telephone: +220 4 227 270
	    +220 4 227 260
	    +220 4 227 266
	Fax: +220 4 227 268

GEORGIA	Maritime Transport Agency 23 Ninoshvili str., 6000 Batumi GEORGIA Telephone: +995 422 274925 Fax: +995 422 273929 Email: info@mta.gov.ge Website: www.mta.gov.ge State Ships' Registry and Flag State Implementation Department: fsi@mta.gov.ge Seafarers' Department: stcw@mta.gov.ge Maritime Search and Rescue Centre: mrcc@mta.gov.ge

GERMANY	Federal Ministry of Transport and Digital Infrastructure
	Division G 24 – Transport of Dangerous Goods
	Robert-Schuman-Platz 1
	53175 Bonn
	GERMANY
	Telephone: +49 228 300-0 or 300-extension
	    +49 228 300 2551
	Fax: +49 228 300 807 2551
	Email: ref-g24@bmvi.bund.de
	
	Packing, Testing and Certification Institute:
	Federal Institute for Materials Research and Testing
	(Bundesanstalt für Materialforschung und -prüfung (BAM))
	Unter den Eichen 87
	D-12205 Berlin
	GERMANY
	Telephone: +49 30 8104 0 or extension
	    +49 30 8104 1310
	    +49 30 8104 3407
	Fax: +49 30 8104 1227
	Email: ingo.doering@bam.de
	
	Packagings, IBCs, and multimodal tank-containers in conformity with the IMDG Code will be marked as specified in section 6 of annex I to the Code (references are to amendment 29). The markings in accordance with 6.2(f) will be "D/BAM".

GHANA	The Director General Ghana Maritime Authority P.M.B. 34, Ministries Post Office Ministries – Accra GHANA Telephone: +233 21 662 122 +233 21 684 392 Fax: +233 21 677 702 Email: info@ghanamaritime.org

Country	Contact information for the main designated national competent authority
GREECE	Ministry of Mercantile Marine Safety of Navigation Division International Relations Department 150 Gr. Lambraki Av. 185 18 Piraeus GREECE Telephone: +301 4191188 Fax: +301 4128150 Telex: +212022, 212239 YEN GR Email: dan@yen.gr
GUINEA BISSAU	The Minister Ministry of Transport & Communication Av. 3 de Agosto, Bissau GUINEA BISSAU Telephone: +245 212 583 +245 211 308
GUYANA	Guyana Maritime Authority/Administration Ministry of Public Works and Communications Building Top Floor Fort Street Kingston Georgetown REPUBLIC OF GUYANA Telephone: +592 226 3356 +592 225 7330 +592 226 7842 Fax: +592 226 9581 Email: MARAD@networksgy.com
ICELAND	Iceland Maritime Administration Verturvör 2 IS-202 Kópavogur ICELAND Telephone: +354 560 0000 Fax: +354 560 0060 Email: skrifstofa@vh.is Directorate of Shipping Hringbraut 121 P.O. Box 7200 127 Reykjavik ICELAND Telephone: +354 1 25844 Fax: +354 1 29835 Telex: 2307 ISINFO
INDIA	The Directorate General of Shipping Jahz Bhawan Walchand Hirachand Marg Bombay 400 001 INDIA Telephone: +91 22 263651 Telex: +DEGESHIP 2813-BOMBAY *Packaging, Testing and Certification Institute* Indian Institute of Packaging Bombay Madras Calcutta INDIA

Country	Contact information for the main designated national competent authority
INDONESIA	Director of Marine Safety Directorate-General of Sea Communication (Department Perhubungan) Jl. Medan Merdeka Barat No. 8 Jakarta Pusat INDONESIA Telephone: +62 381 3269 Fax: +62 384 0788
IRAN (ISLAMIC REPUBLIC OF)	Ports and Maritime Organization PMO. No.1. Shahidi St., Haghani Exp'way, Vanak Sq. Tehran ISLAMIC REPUBLIC OF IRAN Postal Code: 1518663111 Telephone: +98 2184932081 +98 2184932082 Email: info@pmo.ir
IRELAND	The Chief Surveyor Marine Survey Office Department of Transport Leeson Lane Dublin 2 IRELAND Telephone: +353 1 604 14 20 Fax: +353 1 604 14 08 Email: mso@transport.ie
ISRAEL	Shipping and Ports Inspectorate Itzhak Rabin Government Complex Building 2 Pal-Yam 15a Haifa 31999 ISRAEL Telephone: +972 4 8632080 Fax: +972 4 8632118 Email: techni@mot.gov.il
ITALY	Coast Guard Headquarters Via dell'Arte, 16 00100 Roma ITALY Telephone: +39 0659084652 +39 0659084267 Fax: +39 0659084630 Email: segreteria.reparto6@mit.gov.it

7

Country	Contact information for the main designated national competent authority

JAMAICA	The Maritime Authority of Jamaica
	4th Floor, Dyoll Building
	40 Knutsford Boulevard
	Kingston 5
	JAMAICA, W.I.
	Telephone: +1 876 929 2201
	                     +1 876 754 7260
	                     +1 876 754 7265
	Telex: +1 876 7256
	Email: maj@jamaicaships.com
	Website: www.jamaicaships.com
	
	Testing and certifying authority
	The Bureau of Standards
	6 Winchester Road
	P.O. Box 113
	Kingston
	JAMAICA
	Telephone: +1 809 92 63140 7
	Telex: 2291 STANBUR Jamaica
	Cable: STANBUREAU

JAPAN	Inspection and Measurement Division Maritime Bureau Ministry of Land, Infrastructure and Transport 2-1-3 Kasumigaseki, Chiyoda-ku Tokyo JAPAN Telephone: +81 3 5253 8639 Fax: +81 3 5253 1644 Email: MRB_KSK@mlit.go.jp *Packaging, Testing and Certification Institute* Nippon Hakuyohin Kentei Kyokai (HK) (The Ship Equipment Inspection Society of Japan) 3-32, Kioi-Cho, Chiyoda-ku Tokyo JAPAN Telephone: +81 3 3261 6611 Fax: +81 3 3261 6979 Packagings, IBCs and large packagings in conformity with the IMDG Code will be marked "J", "J/JG" or "J/HK"

KENYA	Director General
	Kenya Maritime Authority
	P.O. Box 95076 (80104)
	Mombasa
	KENYA
	Telephone: +254 041 2318398
	                     +254 041 2318399
	Fax: +254 041 2318397
	Email: nkarigithu@yahoo.co.uk
	                     info@maritimeauthority.co.ke
	                     karigithu@ikenya.com
	
	Ministry of Transport & Communications
	P.O. Box 52692
	Nairobi
	KENYA
	Telephone: +254 020 2729200
	Fax: +254 020 2724553
	Email: motc@insightkenya.com
	                     peterthuo_2004@yahoo.com

7

Country	Contact information for the main designated national competent authority
LATVIA	Maritime Administration of Latvia Maritime Safety Department Trijadibas iela, 5 LV-1048 Riga LATVIA Telephone: +371 670 62 177 +371 670 62 142 Fax: +371 678 60 083 Email: zane.paulovska@lja.lv lja@lja.lv Website: www.lja.lv *Classification Societies* American Bureau of Shipping Bureau Veritas Det Norske Veritas Lloyd's Register of Shipping Russian Maritime Register of Shipping
LIBERIA	Commissioner/Administration Bureau of Maritime Affairs P.O. Box 10-9042 1000 Monrovia 10 Monrovia LIBERIA Telephone: +231 227 744/37747/510 201 Fax: +231 226 069 Email: maritime@liberia.net *Testing and certification* American Bureau of Shipping Bureau Veritas China Classification Society Det Norske Veritas Germanischer Lloyd Korean Register of Shipping Lloyd's Register of Shipping Nippon Kaiji Kyokai Polski Rejestr Statkow Registro Italiano Navale Russian Maritime Register of Shipping
LITHUANIA	*Implementation* Ministry of Transport and Communications Water Transport Department Gedimino Av. 17 01505 Vilnius LITHUANIA Telephone: +370 5 239 3986 Fax: +370 5 212 4335 Email: d.krivickiene@transp.lt *Inspection* Lithuanian Maritime Safety Administration J. Janonio Str. 24 92251 Klaipeda LITHUANIA Telephone: +370 46 469 662 Fax: +370 46 469 600 Email: alvydas.nikolajus@msa.lt

Country	Contact information for the main designated national competent authority
MADAGASCAR	Director Agence Portuaire Maritime et Fluviale (APMF) P.O. Box 581 Antananarivo – 101 MADAGASCAR Telephone: +261 20 242 5701 Telephone/Fax: +261 20 222 5860 Mobile: +261 320 229 259 Email: spapmf.dt@mttpat.gov.mg

MALAWI	Director of Marine Services
	Marine Department
	Ministry of Transport & Civil Aviation
	Private Bag A81
	Capital City Lilongwe
	MALAWI
	Telephone: +265 1 755 546
	                 +265 1 752 666
	                 +265 1 753 531 (direct line)
	Fax: +265 1 750 157
	                 +265 1 758 894
	Email: marinedepartment@malawi.net
	                 marinesafety@africa-online.net

MALAYSIA	Director Marine Department Peninsular Malaysia P.O. Box 12 42009 Port Kelang Selangor MALAYSIA Telex: MA 39748 Director Marine Department, Sabah P.O. Box 5 87007 Labuan Sabah MALAYSIA Director Marine Department, Sarawak P.O. Box 530 93619 Kuching Sarawak MALAYSIA
MARSHALL ISLANDS	Office of the Maritime Administrator Technical Services Republic of the Marshall Islands 11495 Commerce Park Drive Reston, Virginia 20191-1506 USA Telephone: +1 703 620 4880 Fax: +1 703 476 8522 Email: technical@register-iri.com

7

Country	Contact information for the main designated national competent authority

MAURITIUS	Director of Shipping
	Ministry of Land Transport, Shipping and Public Safety
	New Government Centre, 4 Floor
	Port Louis
	MAURITIUS
	Telephone: +230 201 2115
	Mobile: +230 774 0764
	Fax: +230 211 7699
	    +230 216 1612
	    +230 201 3417
	Email: pseebaluck@mail.gov.mu

MEXICO	*Stowage, segregation, labelling and documentation of goods* Coordinación General de Puertos y Marina Mercante Secretaría de Comunicación y Transportes Boulevard Adolfo López Mateos No. 1990 Col. Los Alpes Tlacopac, Del. Álvaro Obregón, C.P. 01010 Distrito Federal MEXICO Telephone: +52 55 5723 9300 Email: coordgral.cgpmm@sct.gob.mx Coordinador General: Ruiz de Teresa Guillermo Raúl *Receipt and processing of notifications in the event* *of a package falling overboard* Secretaría de Marina Eje 2 Oriente, Tramo Heroica Escuela Naval Militar No. 861 Colonia Los Cipreses, C.P. 04830 Distrito Federal MEXICO Telephone: +52 55 5624 6500 (extension 6388) Email: ayjemg@semar.gob.mx Jefe del Estado Mayor General de la Armada de México: Vicealmirante C.G. DEM Joaquín Zetina Angulo *Laboratory testing of packagings containing dangerous goods* Sociedad Mexicana de Normalización y Certificación S.C. (NORMEX) Avenida San Antonio No. 256, Piso 7 Colonia Ampliación Nápoles, C.P. 03849 Distrito Federal MEXICO Telephone: +52 55 5598 3036 Fax: +52 55 5598 5899 Email: normex@normex.com.mx Directora Ejecutiva y de Normalización: I.Q. Olga Arce León
MONTENEGRO	Ministry of Interior and Public Administration of the Republic of Montenegro Department for Contingency Plans and Civil Security REPUBLIC OF MONTENEGRO Telephone: +382 81 241 590 Fax: +382 81 246 779 Email: mup.emergency@cg.yu

MOROCCO	Direction de la Marine Marchande et des Pêches Maritimes
	Boulevard El Hansali
	Casablanca
	MOROCCO
	Telephone: +1 212 2 278 092
	    +1 212 2 221 931
	Telex: 24613 MARIMAR M
	    22824

Country	Contact information for the main designated national competent authority
MOZAMBIQUE	General Director National Maritime Authority (INAMAR) Av. Marquês do Pombal No. 297 P.O. Box 4317 Maputo MOZAMBIQUE Telephone: +258 21 320 552 Fax: +258 21 324 007 Mobile: +258 82 153 0280 Email: inamar@tvcabo.co.mz *Testing and certification of packaging, intermediate bulk containers and large packaging* Instituto Nacional de Normalização e Qualidade (INNOQ) Av. 25 de Setembro No. 1179, 2nd Floor Maputo MOZAMBIQUE Telephone: +258 21 303 822/3 Fax: +258 21 304 206 Mobile: +258 823 228 840 Email: innoq@emilmoz.com

NAMIBIA	Director of Maritime Affairs
	Ministry of Works, Transport and Communications
	Private Bag 13341
	6719 Bell Street
	Snyman Circle, Windhoek
	NAMIBIA
	Telephone: +264 61 208 8025/6
	    Direct line: +264 61 208 8111
	Fax: +264 61 240 024
	    +264 61 224 060
	Mobile: +264 811 220 599
	Email: mmnangolo@mwtc.gov.na

NETHERLANDS	Ministry of Infrastructure and the Environment P.O. Box 20901 2500 EX The Hague NETHERLANDS Telephone: +31 70 456 0000 Email: dangerousgoods@minienm.nl *For competent authority approvals under the IMDG Code:* Ministry of Infrastructure and the Environment Human Environment and Transport Inspectorate P.O. Box 90653 2509 LR The Hague NETHERLANDS Telephone: +31 88 489 0000 Fax: +31 70 456 2413 Email: via www.ivw.nl/english/contact

NETHERLANDS ANTILLES	Directorate of Shipping and Maritime Affairs
	Seru Mahuma z/n
	Curaçao
	NETHERLANDS ANTILLES (NETHERLANDS)
	Telephone: +599 9 839 3700
	    +599 9 839 3701
	Fax: +599 9 868 9964
	Email: sina@onenet.an
	    expertise@dsmz.org
	    management@dsmz.org

7

Country	Contact information for the main designated national competent authority
NEW ZEALAND	Maritime New Zealand Level 10 1 Grey Street Wellington PO Box 25620 Wellington 6146 NEW ZEALAND Telephone: +64 4 473 0111 Fax: +64 4 494 1263 Email: enquiries@maritimenz.govt.nz Website: www.maritimenz.govt.nz The authorized organizations which have delegated authority from the Director of Maritime New Zealand for the approval, inspection and testing of all portable tanks, tank containers and freight containers are: American Bureau of Shipping Bureau Veritas Det Norske Veritas Germanischer Lloyd Lloyd's Register of Shipping

NIGERIA	Nigerian Maritime Administration and Safety Agency (NIMASA)
	Marine House
	4 Burma Road, Apapa
	PMB 12861, GPO
	Marina Lagos
	NIGERIA
	Telephone: +234 587 2214
	    +234 580 4800
	    +234 580 4809
	Fax: +234 587 1329
	Telex: 23891 NAMARING
	Website: www.nimasa.gov.ng

NORWAY	Norwegian Maritime Authority PO Box 2222 N-5509 Haugesund NORWAY Telephone: +47 5274 5000 Fax: +47 5274 5001 Email: post@sdir.no *Certification of packaging and IBCs* DNV GL AS Veritasveien 1 N-1322 Høvik NORWAY Telephone: +47 67 57 99 00 Email: moano378@dnvgl.com *Certification of CSC containers* DNG GL AS Veritasveien 1 N-1322 Høvik NORWAY Telephone: +47 67 57 99 00 Fax: +47 67 57 99 11 Email: moano374@dnvgl.com

7

Country	Contact information for the main designated national competent authority
NORWAY *(continued)*	Lloyd's Register EMEA P.O. Box 36 M-1300 Sandvika NORWAY Telephone: +47 23 28 22 00 Email: oslo@lr.org *Certification of portable tanks to the IMDG Code* DNV GL AS Veritasveien 1 N-1322 Høvik NORWAY Telephone: +47 67 57 99 00 Fax: +47 67 57 99 11 Email: moano374@gnvgl.com

PAKISTAN	Mercantile Marine Department
	70/4 Timber Hard
	N.M. Reclamation
	Keamari, Post Box No. 4534
	Karachi 75620
	PAKISTAN
	Telephone: +92 21 2851306
	    +92 21 2851307
	Fax: +92 21 4547472 (24 h)
	    +92 21 4547897
	Telex: 29822 DGPS PK (24 h)

PANAMA	Autoridad Marítima de Panamá Edificio 5534 Diablo Heights P.O. Box 0816 01548 Panamá PANAMA Telephone: +507 501 5000 Fax: +507 501 5007 Email: ampadmon@amp.gob.pa Website: www.amp.gob.pa
PAPUA NEW GUINEA	First Assistant Secretary Department of Transport Division of Marine P.O. Box 457 Konedobu PAPUA NEW GUINEA Telephone: +675 211866 Telex: 22203

Country	Contact information for the main designated national competent authority
PERU	Dirección General de Capitanías y Guardacostas (DICAPI) Jirón Constitución No.150 Callao PERU Telephone: +51 12099300 Anexo: 6757/6792 Email: jefemercanciaspeligrosas@dicapi.mil.pe Dirección General de Capitanías y Guardacostas Comandancia de Operaciones Guardacostas Constitución 150 Callao PERU Telephone: +51 1 4291547 +51 1 4200766 +51 1 4202020 Fax: +51 1 4291547 Email: pemcc@dicapi.mil.pe comoperguard@dicapi.mil.pe Dirección General de Capitanías y Guardacostas Costera Paita Paita PERU Telephone: +51 1 73 211670 Fax: +51 1 73 211670 Email: costera.paita@dicapi.mil.pe MMSI: 007600121 Radio Call Sign: OBY2 Lenguaje entendido: Español/ingles Dirección General de Capitanías y Guardacostas Costera Callao Constitución 150 Callao PERU Telephone: +51 1 4299798 +51 1 4200177 Fax: +51 1 4299798 Email: costera.callao@dicapi.mil.pe MMSI: 007600125 Radio Call Sign: OB3 Lenguaje entendido: Español/ingles Telephone: +51 1 6136868 anexo 6671 +51 1 6136868 anexo 6752 Fax: +51 1 6136856 +51 1 4121913 Email: dicaasuntos@dicapi.mil.pe

7

Country	Contact information for the main designated national competent authority
PHILIPPINES	Philippine Ports Authority Port of Manila Safety Staff P.O. Box 193 Port Area Manila 2803 PHILIPPINES Telephone: +63 2473441 to 49
POLAND	Ministry of Transport, Construction and Maritime Economy Department of Sea Transport and Shipping Safety 00-928 Warsaw ul. Chałubińskiego 4/6 POLAND Telephone: +48 22 630 1639 Fax: +48 22 630 1497 *Packaging, Testing and Certification Institute* Centralny Ośrodek Badawczo-Rozwojowy Opakowań ul Konstancińska 11 02-942 Warszawa POLAND Telephone: +48 22 42 2011 Fax: +48 22 42 2303 Email: info@cobro.org.pl Packagings in conformity with the IMDG Code will be marked "PL" *Classification societies* For CSC Containers Polski Rejestr Statków (Polish Register of Shipping) Al.Gen.J.Hallera 126 80-416 Gdańsk POLAND Telephone: +48 58 751 1100 +48 58 751 1204 Fax: +48 58 346 0392 Email: mailbox@prs.pl
PORTUGAL	Direcção-Geral de Navegação e dos Transportes Marítimos Praça Luis de Camões, 22 – 2° Dto 1200 Lisboa PORTUGAL Telephone: +351 1 373821 Fax: +351 1 373826 Telex: 16753 SEMM PO
REPUBLIC OF KOREA	Marine Industry and Technology Division Marine Safety Bureau Ministry of Ocean and Fisheries (MOF) Government Complex Sejong, 5-Dong, 94, Dasom 2-Ro, Sejong-City, 339-012, REPUBLIC OF KOREA Telephone: +82 44 200 5836 Fax: +82 44 200 5849

7

Country	Contact information for the main designated national competent authority
RUSSIAN FEDERATION[*]	Department of State Policy for Maritime and River Transport Ministry of Transport of the Russian Federation Rozhdestvenka Street, 1, bldg. 1 Moscow 109012 RUSSIAN FEDERATION Telephone: +7 499 495 05 50 Fax: +7 499 495 00 00 (ext. 0559) Email: rusma@mintrans.ru *Classification society has been designated as competent inspector agency for the approval, acceptance and all consequential activities connected with IMO Type tanks, CSC containers, Intermediate Bulk Containers (IBCs) and packaging to be registered in the Russian Federation:* Russian Maritime Register of Shipping Dvortsovaya Naberezhnaya, 8 Saint-Petersburg 191186 Russian Federation Telephone: +7 812 380 20 72 Fax: +7 812 314 10 87 Email: pobox@rs-class.org

SAINT KITTS AND NEVIS	Department of Maritime Affairs
	Director of Maritime Affairs
	Ministry of Transport
	P.O. Box 186
	Needsmust
	ST. KITTS, W.I.
	Telephone: +869 466 7032
	    +869 4664846
	Fax: +869 465 0604
	    +869 465 9475
	Email: Maritimeaffairs@yahoo.com
	
	St. Kitts and Nevis
	International Registrar of Shipping and Seamen
	West Wing, York House
	48-50 Western Road
	Romford RM1 3LP
	UNITED KINGDOM
	Telephone: +44 1708 380 400
	Fax: +44 1708 380 401
	Email: mail@stkittsregistry.net

SAO TOME AND PRINCIPE	The Minister Ministry of Public Works, Infrastructure & Land Planning C.P. 171 SAO TOME AND PRINCIPE Telephone: +239 223 203 +239 226 368 Fax: +239 222 824
SAUDI ARABIA	Port Authority Saudi Arabia Civil Defence Riyadh SAUDI ARABIA Telephone: +966 1 464 9477

[*] Except for governmental explosives.

7

Country	Contact information for the main designated national competent authority
SEYCHELLES	Director General Seychelles Maritime Safety Administration P.O. Box 912 Victoria, Mahe Seychelles Telephone: +248 224 866 Telefax: +248 224 829 Email: dg@msa.sc
SIERRA LEONE	The Executive Director Sierra Leone Maritime Administration Maritime House Government Wharf Ferry Terminal P.O. Box 313 Freetown SIERRA LEONE Telephone: +232 22 221 211 Fax: +232 22 221 215 Email: slma@sierratel.sl slmaoffice@yahoo.com
SINGAPORE	Maritime and Port Authority of Singapore Shipping Division 21st Storey PSA Building 460 Alexandra Road SINGAPORE 119963 Telephone: +65 375 1931 +65 375 6223 +65 375 1600 Fax: +65 375 6231 Email: shipping@mpa.gov.sg
SLOVENIA	Ministry of Infrastructure and Spatial Planning Slovenian Maritime Administration Ukmarjev trg 2 6000 Koper SLOVENIA Telephone: +386 566 32 100 +386 566 32 106 Fax: +386 566 32 102 Email: ursp.box@gov.si

Country	Contact information for the main designated national competent authority
SOUTH AFRICA	South African Maritime Safety Authority P.O. Box 13186 Hatfield 0028 Pretoria SOUTH AFRICA Telephone: +27 12 342 3049 Fax: +27 12 342 3160 South African Maritime Safety Authority Hatfield Gardens, Block E (Ground Floor) Corner Arcadia and Grosvenor Street Hatfield 0083 Pretoria SOUTH AFRICA *Head Office Administration* Chief Director Chief Directorate – Shipping Department of Transport Private Bag X193 0001 Pretoria SOUTH AFRICA Telephone: +27 12 290 2904 Fax: +27 12 323 7009 *Durban, East London, Port Elizabeth and Richards Bay* Chief Ship Surveyor Eastern Zone Department of Transport Marine Division Private Bag X54309 Durban SOUTH AFRICA Telephone: +27 12 3071501 Fax: +27 23 3064983 *Cape Town, Saldanha Bay and Mossel Bay* Chief Ship Surveyor Western Zone Department of Transport Marine Division Private Bag X7025 8012 Roggebaai SOUTH AFRICA Telephone: +2721 216 170 Fax: +2721 419 0730

SPAIN	Dirección General de la Marina Mercante
	Subdirección General de Seguridad Marítima y Contaminación
	c/Ruiz de Alarcón, 1
	28071 Madrid
	SPAIN
	Telephone: +34 91 597 92 69
	  +34 91 597 92 70
	Fax: +34 91 597 92 87
	Email: mercancias.peligrosas@fomento.es
	  pmreal@fomento.es
	
	Subdirección General de Calidad y Seguridad Industrial
	Ministerio de Industria, Turismo y Comercio
	c/Paseo de la Castellana, 160
	28071 Madrid
	SPAIN
	Telephone: +34 91 349 43 03
	Fax: +34 91 349 43 00

7

Country	Contact information for the main designated national competent authority
SUDAN	Director Maritime Administration Directorate Ministry of Transport Port Sudan P.O. Box 531 SUDAN Telephone: +249 311 825 660 +249 012 361 766 Fax: +249 311 831 276 +249 183 774 215 Email: smaco22@yahoo.com/info@smacosd.com
SWEDEN	Swedish Transport Agency Civil Aviation and Maritime Department Box 653 SE-601 78 Norrköping SWEDEN Telephone: +46 771 503 503 Fax: +46 11 239 934 Email: sjofart@transportstyrelsen.se Website: www.transportstyrelsen.se SP, Technical Research Institute of Sweden Box 857 SE-501 15 Borås SWEDEN Telephone: +46 10 516 5000 Fax: +46 33 135 520 Email: info@sp.se Website: www.sp.se
SWITZERLAND	Office suisse de la navigation maritime Elisabethenstrasse 33 4010 Basel SWITZERLAND Telephone: +41 61 270 91 20 Fax: +41 61 270 91 29 Email: dv-ssa@eda.admin.ch
TANZANIA (UNITED REPUBLIC OF)	Director General Surface & Marine Transport Regulatory Authority (SUMATRA) P.O. Box 3093 Dar es Salaam UNITED REPUBLIC OF TANZANIA Telephone: +255 22 213 5081 Mobile: +255 744 781 865 Fax: +255 22 211 6697 Email: dg@sumatra.or.tz Ministry of Infrastructure Development P.O. Box 9144 Dar es Salaam UNITED REPUBLIC OF TANZANIA Telephone: +255 22 212 2268 Fax: +255 22 211 2751 +255 22 212 2079 Mobile: +254 748 7404 +254 748 5404 Email: brufunjo@yahoo.com

7

Country	Contact information for the main designated national competent authority
THAILAND	Ministry of Transport and Communications Ratchadamnoen-Nok Avenue Bangkok 10100 THAILAND Telephone: +66 2 281 3422 Fax: +66 2 280 1714 Telex: 70000 MINOCOM TH
TUNISIA	Ministère du Transport Direction Générale de la Marine Marchande Avenue 7 novembre (près de l'aéroport) 2035 Tunis B.P. 179 Tunis Cedex TUNISIA Telephone: +216 71 806 362 Fax: +216 71 806 413
TURKEY	Ministry of Transport, Maritime Affairs and Communications Directorate General for Regulation of Dangerous Goods and Combined Transport GMK Bulvari No: 128/A Maltepe 06570 Ankara TURKEY Telephone: +90 312 2032291 Fax: +90 312 2315189 Email: dangerousgoods@udhb.gov.tr *Testing, inspection and certification* Turkish standard institution Necatibey Cad. No:112 06100 Bakanliklar Ankara TURKEY Telephone: +90 312 416 62 00 Telefax: +90 312 416 66 10 Email: bilgi@tse.org Türk Loydu Foundation Tersaneler Caddesi 26, 34944 Tuzla Istanbul TURKEY Telephone: +90 216 581 37 00 Telefax: +90 216 581 38 00 Email: info@turkloydu.org
UNITED ARAB EMIRATES	National Transport Authority Marine Affairs Department P.O. Box 900 Abu Dhabi UNITED ARAB EMIRATES Telephone: +971 2 4182 124 Fax: +971 2 4491 500 Email: marine@nta.gov.ae
UNITED KINGDOM	Maritime and Coastguard Agency Bay 2/21 Spring Place 105 Commercial Road Southampton SO15 1EG UNITED KINGDOM Telephone: +44 23 8032 9100 Fax: +44 23 8032 9204 Email: dangerous.goods@mcga.gov.uk

7

Country	Contact information for the main designated national competent authority
UNITED STATES	US Department of Transportation Pipeline and Hazardous Materials Safety Administration Office of International Standards East Building/PHH-70 1200 New Jersey Ave, S.E. Washington, D.C. 20590 USA Telephone: +1 202 366 0656 Fax: +1 202 366 5713 Email: infocntr@dot.gov Website: hazmat.dot.gov United States Coast Guard Hazardous Materials Standards Division (CG-5223) 2100 Second Street, S.W. Washington, D.C. 20593-7126 USA Telephone: +1 202 372 1420 +1 202 372 1426 Fax: +1 202 372 1926
URUGUAY	Perfectura Nacional Naval Direccion Registral y de Marina Mercante Edificio Aduana 1er. Piso CP 11.000 Montevideo URUGUAY Telephone: +5982 9157913 +5982 9164914 Fax: +5982 9164914 Email: dirme01@armada.mil.uy dirme_secretario@armada.mil.uy delea@armada.mil.uy
VANUATU	Deputy Commissioner of Maritime Affairs c/o Vanuatu Maritime Services Limited 39 Broadway, Suite 2020 New York, New York 10006 USA Telephone: +212 425 9600 Fax: +212 425 9652 Email: email@vanuatuships.com Website: www.vanuatuships.com
VENEZUELA (BOLIVARIAN REPUBLIC OF)	Instituto Nacional de los Espacios Acuáticos Avenida Orinoco entre calles Perijá y Mucuchies Edificio INEA, Piso 6, Las Mercedes Caracas 1060 BOLIVARIAN REPUBLIC OF VENEZUELA Telephone: +58 212 909 1430 +58 212 909 1450 +58 212 909 1587 Fax: +58 212 909 1461 +58 212 909 1573 Email: asuntos_internacionales@inea.gob.ve Website: www.inea.gob.ve

7

Country	Contact information for the main designated national competent authority
VIET NAM	Shipping and Maritime Services Department Viet Nam Maritime Administration 8 Pham Hung Street Ha Noi VIET NAM Telephone: +84 4 3768 3065 Fax: +84 4 3768 3058 Email: dichvuvantai@vinamarine.gov.vn Website: www.vinamarine.gov.vn

YEMEN	Executive Chairman
	Maritime Affairs Authority
	P.O. Box 19395
	Sana'a
	REPUBLIC OF YEMEN
	Telephone: +967 1 414 412
	    +967 1 419 914
	    +967 1 423 005
	Fax: +967 1 414 645
	Email: MAA-Headoffice@y.net.ye
	Website: www.MAA.gov.ye

ZAMBIA	Department of Maritime & Inland Waterways
	Ministry of Communications & Transport
	P.O. Box 50346
	Fairley Road
	Lusaka
	ZAMBIA
	Telephone: +260 1 250 716
	    +260 1 251 444
	    +260 1 251 022
	Fax: +260 1 253 165
	    +260 1 251 795
	Email: dmiw@zamtel.zm

Associate Member HONG KONG, CHINA	The Director of Marine Marine Department GPO Box 4155 HONG KONG, CHINA Telephone: +852 2852 3085 Fax: +852 2815 8596 Email: pfdg@mardep.gov.hk

7

Notes

Notes

Notes

Notes

Notes

Notes